TROUBLESHOOTING ELECTRIC MOTORS

AMERICAN TECHNICAL PUBLISHERS, INC
HOMEWOOD, ILLINOIS 60430

Glen A. Mazur
Thomas E. Proctor

1 2 3 4 5 6 7 8 9 - 93 - 9 8 7 6 5 4 3 2 1

Printed in the United States of America

ISBN 0-8269-1762-3

CONTENTS

chapter 1

SINGLE-PHASE MOTORS

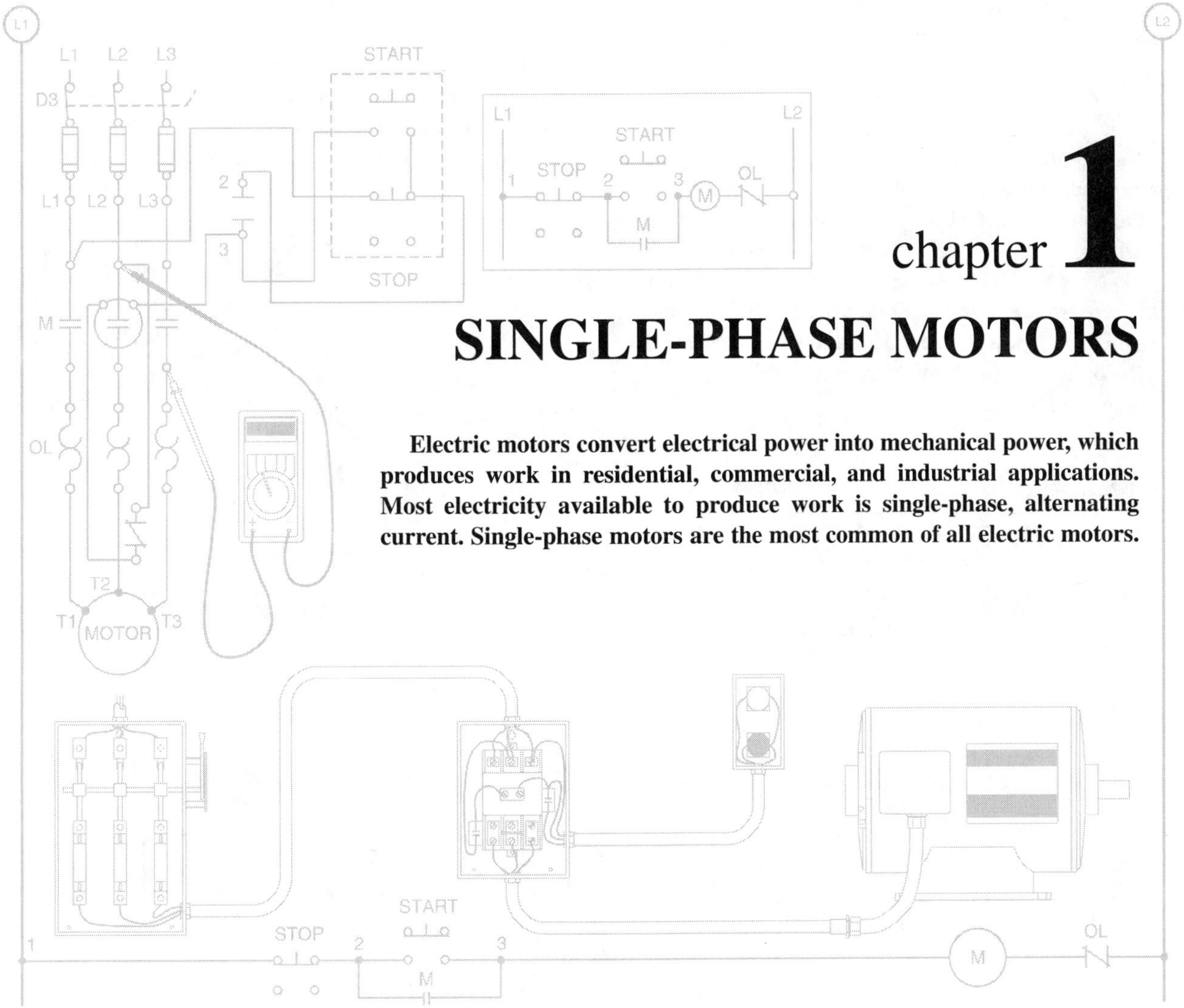

Electric motors convert electrical power into mechanical power, which produces work in residential, commercial, and industrial applications. Most electricity available to produce work is single-phase, alternating current. Single-phase motors are the most common of all electric motors.

SINGLE-PHASE MOTORS

Alternating current (AC) power is the standard power generated and distributed to consumers of electricity. *Alternating current* is current that reverses its direction of flow twice per cycle. See Figure 1-1. Alternating current is usually generated and distributed as three-phase (3ϕ) power. *Three-phase power* is a combination of three alternating currents (phases A, B, and C) in a circuit with their voltages displaced 120° or one-third of a cycle. The three currents are common because they are produced by the same generator.

For almost all dwellings and many small businesses, single-phase (1ϕ) power is delivered from the 3ϕ distribution system. *Single-phase power* is one of the three alternating currents in a circuit. The amount of potential power available is equal to the voltage times the current in a single-phase circuit.

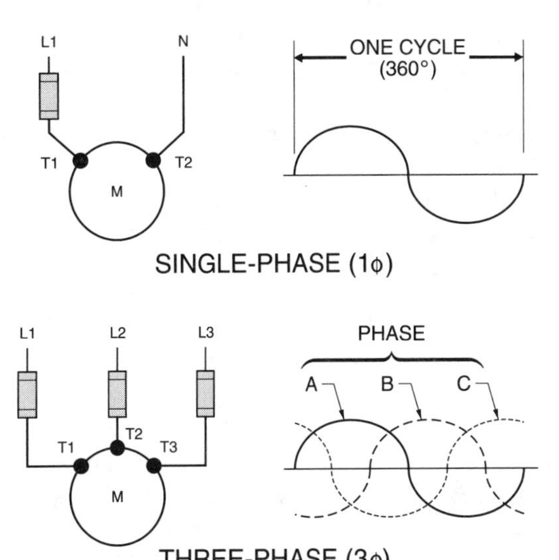

Figure 1-1. Alternating current (AC) is single-phase (1ϕ) or three-phase (3ϕ).

More 1ϕ, AC motors are used for residential applications than any other type of motor. Single-phase, AC, motor-driven appliances and devices in a typical dwelling include furnaces, air conditioners, refrigerators, washing machines, dryers, ovens, microwave ovens, clocks, and cooling fans for computers, stereos, etc.

Single-phase motors, like all motors, have two main parts, the rotor and the stator. See Figure 1-2. A *rotor* is the rotating part of an AC motor. The rotor rotates the motor shaft and delivers the work. Motors deliver work by converting electrical power to mechanical power. A *stator* is the stationary part of an AC motor to which the power lines are directly connected. The stator produces a rotating magnetic field.

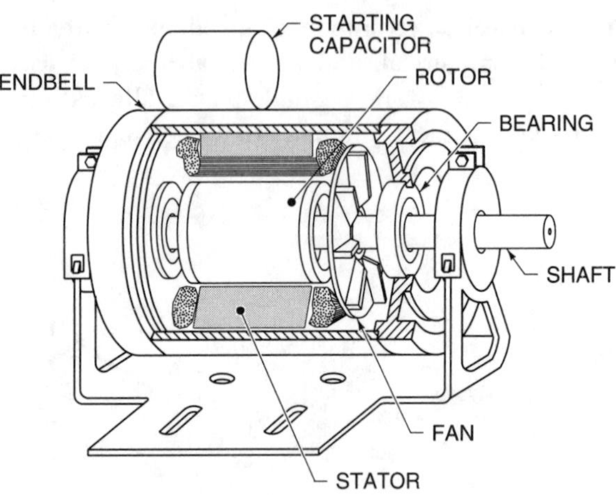

Figure 1-2. The stationary part of a single-phase motor is the stator. The rotating part is the rotor.

Motors also have endbells, bearings, and a fan connected to the motor shaft. A 1ϕ motor must also have a part to start the motor. Single-phase motors will not rotate without some way of first starting the motor. The method used to start a 1ϕ motor gives the motor its name. Single-phase motors named for their starting methods are the:

- Shaded-pole motor
- Split-phase motor
- Capacitor-start motor
- Capacitor-run motor
- Capacitor start-and-run motor

A relationship exists between the stator and rotor of a 1ϕ motor. See Figure 1-3. When electrical power is applied to the stator, a magnetic field is produced by the stator windings. The magnetic field induces a voltage into the rotor bars. This induced voltage causes current to flow in each rotor bar. The current flow produces a magnetic field in the rotor. The magnetic field produces poles on the rotor, which are opposite polarity to the stator poles.

Polarity is the particular state of an object, either positive or negative, which refers to the two electrical poles, north and south. Because unlike poles attract, a horizontal force is produced between the stator and rotor poles.

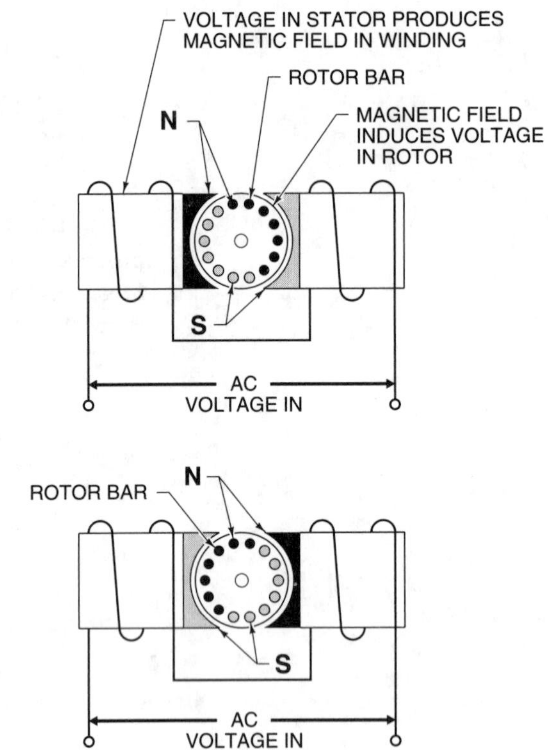

Figure 1-3. The stator is connected to the supply voltage and produces a magnetic field around the rotor.

The magnetic field alternates back and forth with a change in the direction of current because the motor is connected to alternating current. Even though the magnetic field is alternating, no rotating magnetic field is produced. As no rotating magnetic field is produced, the motor will probably not start, even with the produced horizontal force. No vertical force is produced without a rotating magnetic field. Even if it were to start, the motor may not start in the right direction. A motor can start in either direction, depending on the position of the rotor when power is first applied. The direction of rotation for which a motor is wired is based upon its application.

The position of the rotor can affect the direction of rotation of a motor. A starting method is required to start a 1ϕ motor. Without a starting method, the rotor can start in either direction. See Figure 1-4.

STATOR
ROTOR
WINDING
N
N
S
S
AC
VOLTAGE IN

CLOCKWISE START

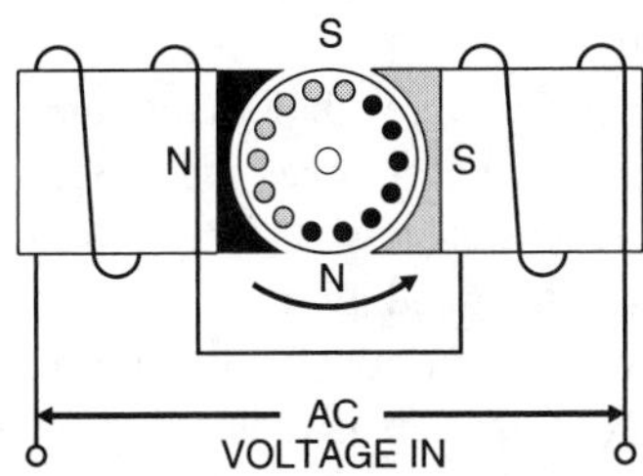

COUNTERCLOCKWISE START

Figure 1-4. Without a starting method, the rotor can start in either direction.

If the north pole of the rotor is nearest the top of the south pole of the stator, the motor rotates in the clockwise direction. If the north pole of the rotor is nearest the bottom of the south pole of the stator, the motor rotates in the counterclockwise direction.

Regardless of the position the rotor is in when power is applied, the rotor may still not rotate. The stator field only alternates back and forth and does so at such a rapid rate (60 times per second for standard 60 cycle AC) that the rotor's magnetic field may simply lock in step with the stator's alternating magnetic field and not rotate.

Locked in step is the lack of rotation when the stator's field and the rotor's field are parallel to one another. Rotation is not possible because the magnetic repulsion between the two fields is equal for both directions of rotation. The force rotating the motor clockwise is equal to the force rotating the motor counterclockwise. If the rotor is given a spin in one direction or the other, it will continue to rotate in the direction of the spin. The rotor will then quickly accelerate until it reaches a speed slightly less than the rated synchronous speed of the motor.

Synchronous speed is the theoretical speed of a motor based on the motor's number of poles and the line frequency. *Line frequency* is the number of cycles of supplied voltage per second. The speed of a motor is measured in revolutions per minute (rpm). All motors, except synchronous motors, turn at speeds less than the synchronous speed. This operating (actual) speed is listed on the motor's nameplate. For example, a motor with a nameplate-listed speed of 1725 rpm has a synchronous speed of 1800 rpm.

Slip is the difference between the synchronous speed and actual speed of a motor. Slip is measured in percentages. For example, the slip of a 1725 rpm motor (1800 rpm synchronous speed) is approximately 4% (1800 rpm − 1725 rpm = 75 rpm / 1800 rpm = .041 = 4%).

One way to start a 1ϕ motor without spinning the rotor is to make the stator's magnetic field rotate instead of just alternate. There are many different methods used to produce this rotating magnetic field in the stator. The method used gives the 1ϕ motor its name.

Shaded-Pole Motor

The simplest method used to start a 1ϕ motor is by shading the stator poles. A *shaded-pole motor* is an AC motor that uses a shaded stator pole for starting. See Figure 1-5.

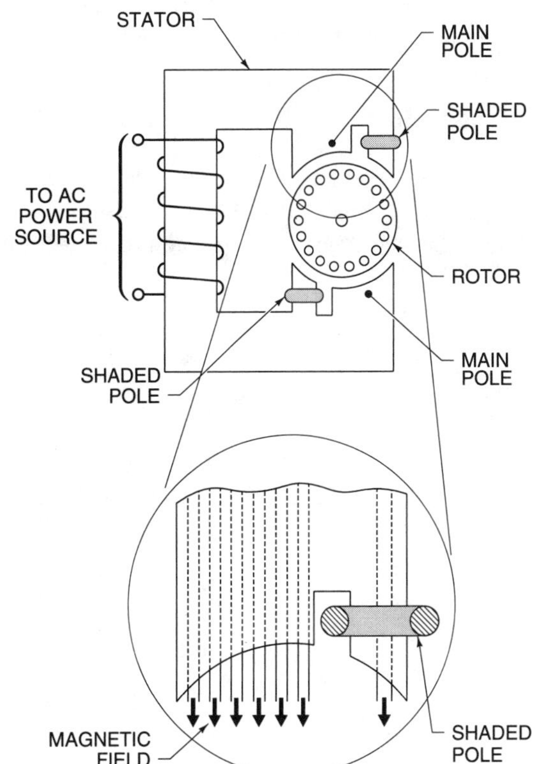

Figure 1-5. A 1ϕ motor can start in a given direction by shading the stator poles.

Shading the poles is accomplished by applying a short-circuited wire on one side of each stator pole. The shaded pole is usually a solid, single turn of copper wire placed around a portion of the main pole laminations.

The function of the shaded pole is to delay the magnetic flux in the area of the pole that is shaded. Shading causes the magnetic flux at the pole area to be about 90° apart from the magnetic flux of the main stator pole. Since 360° equal the distance of the two poles, the shading pole is offset by one-fourth the distance of the main pole. As a result of the offset field, the rotor moves from the main pole toward the shaded pole. This movement determines the starting direction of the motor.

Although the shaded pole produces a rotation effect on the rotor, it produces low starting torque. For this reason, shaded-pole motors are used primarily in applications requiring very small loads to be driven. *Torque* is the force that produces rotation in a motor. Motor torque is measured in pound-feet (lb-ft). *Note:* Ft-lb is used with energy or work. See Figure 1-6.

Shaded-pole motors are commonly 1/20 HP or less and have low starting torque. The most common application of shaded-pole motors is for use as the cooling fan in small appliances, such as computers and stereos. The only load the motor must turn in such applications is the fan blade.

Split-Phase Motor

A *split-phase motor* is an AC motor that can run on one or more phases. A 1ϕ motor can also be made self-starting by adding a second stator winding. See Figure 1-7. The main winding is the running winding. The auxiliary winding is the starting winding. The two windings are placed in the stator slots and spaced 90° apart.

The running winding is always made of larger wire with a greater number of turns. When the motor is first connected to power, the inductive reactance of the running winding is higher, and the resistance is lower than the starting winding. *Inductive reactance* is the opposition to the flow of alternating current in a circuit due to inductance. The starting winding is made of relatively small wire with less turns. When the motor is first connected to power, the inductive reactance of the starting winding is lower, and the resistance is higher than the running winding.

When power is first applied, both the running winding and the starting winding are energized. Because of their different inductive reactances, the running winding current lags the starting winding current. This produces a phase difference between the starting and running windings. A 90° phase difference is required to produce maximum starting torque, but is commonly much less. However, since the two windings are out of phase, a rotating magnetic field is developed.

The rotating magnetic field starts the rotor turning. With the running and starting windings out of phase, the current changes in magnitude and direction as the magnetic field moves around the stator. This movement forces the rotor to rotate with the rotating magnetic field.

To minimize energy loss and prevent heat build-up in the starting winding once the motor is started, a centrifugal switch is used to remove the starting winding

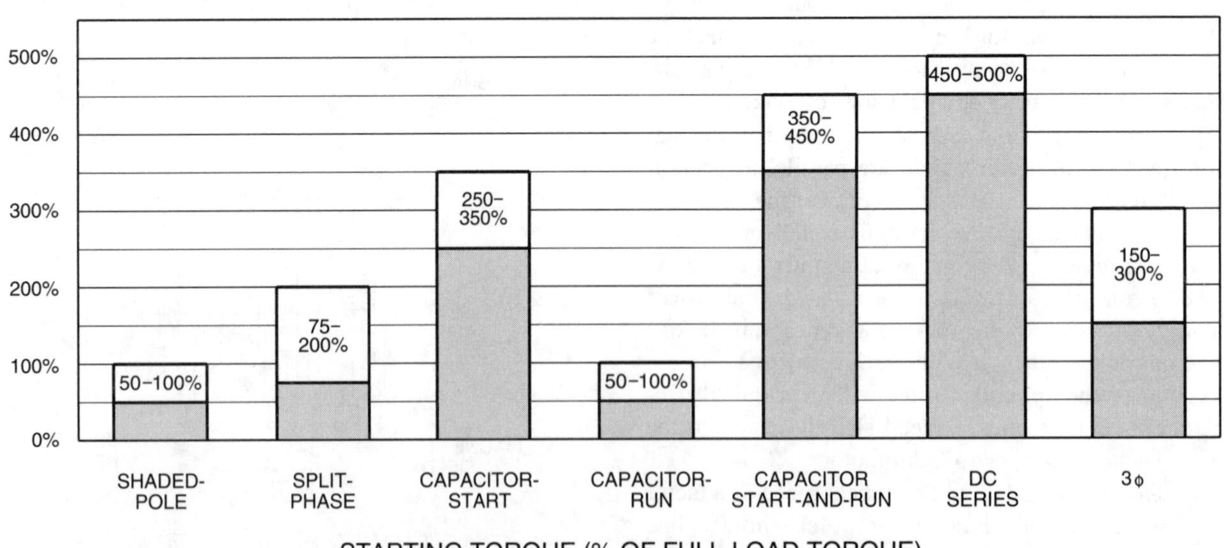

Figure 1-6. Torque is the force that produces rotation in a motor.

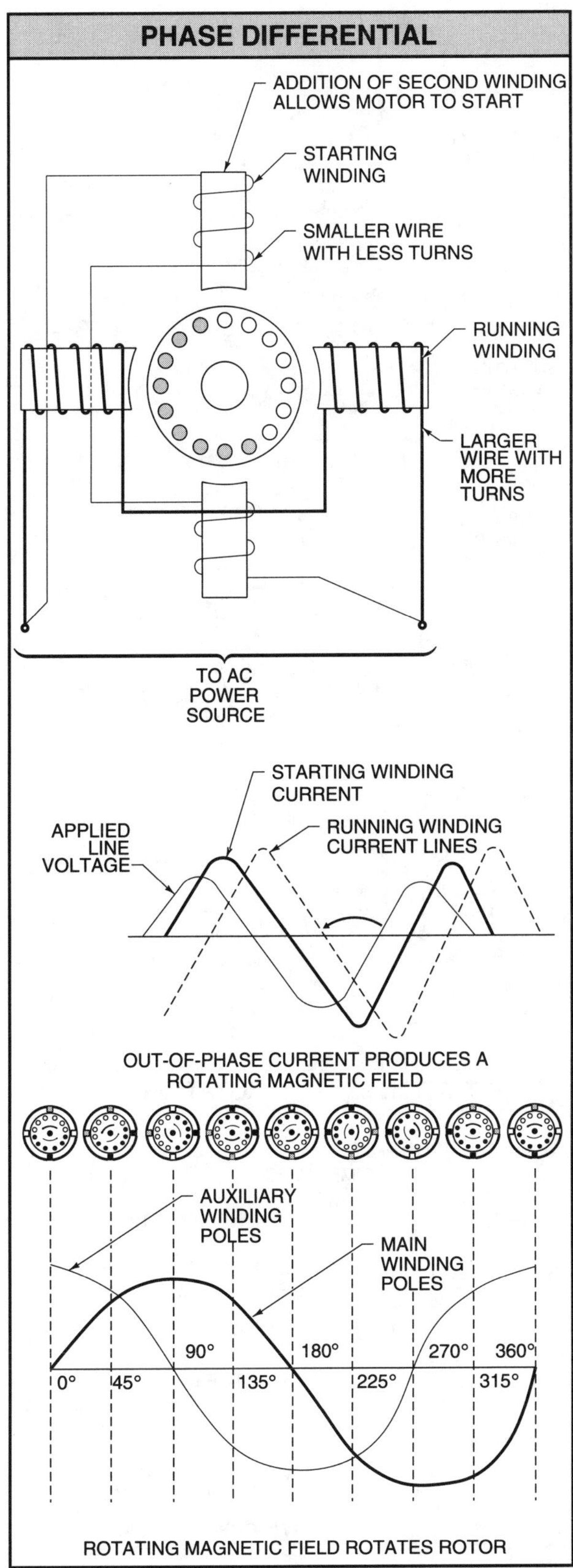

Figure 1-7. A split-phase motor starts because of the phase differential.

when the motor reaches a set speed. A *centrifugal switch* is a switch that opens to disconnect the starting winding when the rotor reaches a certain preset speed and reconnects the starting winding when the speed falls below a preset value. In most motors, the centrifugal switch is located inside the enclosure on the shaft. See Figure 1-8.

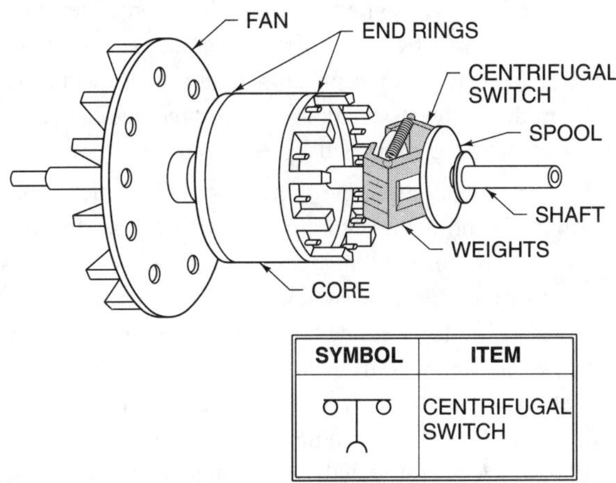

SYMBOL	ITEM
	CENTRIFUGAL SWITCH

Figure 1-8. A centrifugal switch automatically disconnects the starting winding as a split-phase motor accelerates.

As the motor shaft rotates and the speed of the motor accelerates, the switch is activated by centrifugal force. *Centrifugal force* is the force that moves rotating bodies away from the center of rotation. For some motors, the centrifugal switch is often located outside the enclosure for easier repair. For example, switches for motors used on washers and dryers are located outside the enclosure.

The centrifugal switch is connected in line (series) with the starting winding. *Series* is the end-to-end connection of components in the circuit that provides only one path for current flow. The centrifugal switch is used to automatically de-energize the starting winding at a set speed. The set speed is usually about 60% to 80% of the running speed. After the starting winding is removed, the motor continues to operate on the running winding only.

When the motor is first connected to power, the starting winding produces a high starting torque. As the motor accelerates, the effect of this torque is reduced and then eliminated when the centrifugal switch opens. As the motor accelerates, the torque of the running winding keeps the motor running, once the starting winding is removed.

The split-phase motor is one of the oldest and most common motor types. It is used in such applications as fans, business machines, machine tools, and centrifugal pumps, wherever starting is easy. The split-phase motor is generally available in sizes ranging from 1/30 HP to 1/2 HP.

Thermal Protection. In addition to a centrifugal switch, many motors also contain a thermal switch. A *thermal switch* is a switch that operates its contacts when a preset temperature is reached. This internal switch is used to protect the motor windings from burnout. See Figure 1-9.

The thermal switch is activated by high temperatures. It automatically removes both the starting and running windings from the power source. A higher-than-normal temperature can be caused by lack of proper ventilation, too high of a motor load, high ambient temperature, or a mechanical problem that prevents rotation. *Ambient temperature* is the temperature of the air around a piece of equipment.

In normal operation, the thermal switch is in a closed position. As more current than normal is allowed to pass through the motor windings, the switch begins to heat. At a preset temperature, the switch opens. This automatically removes the motor windings from power. When the motor windings are removed from power, they begin to cool. The thermal switch closes as it cools, and the motor is automatically restarted. If the problem that caused the original overheating is not corrected, the thermal switch constantly recycles the motor ON and OFF.

Reversing. To reverse the direction of rotation of a split-phase motor, the connections of either the starting or the running windings are reversed. If both the starting and the running windings are reversed, the motor will not change direction of rotation. Reversing the starting winding is the industrial standard for reversing the direction of rotation of a 1ϕ motor.

Dual Voltage. Many 1ϕ motors can be connected for either of two voltages. The purpose in making motors for two voltages is to enable the same motor to be used with two different power line voltages. Usually the dual-voltage rating of 1ϕ motors is 115/230 V. Other voltage ratings are 120/240 V and 110/220 V. The nameplate of the motor should always be checked for proper voltage ratings.

When there is a choice of which voltage to use for a dual-voltage motor, the higher voltage is preferred. The motor develops the same amount of power for either voltage. However, as the voltage is doubled (115 V to 230 V), the current is reduced by half. With half the current, the ampacity of conductors is reduced and the installation is more cost-efficient. *Ampacity* is the amount of current for which a conductor or device is rated.

In a typical dual-voltage motor, the running winding is split into two sections. See Figure 1-10. The two sections may be connected in series or in parallel. The series connection is used for high voltage. The parallel connection is used for low voltage. *Parallel* is the side-by-

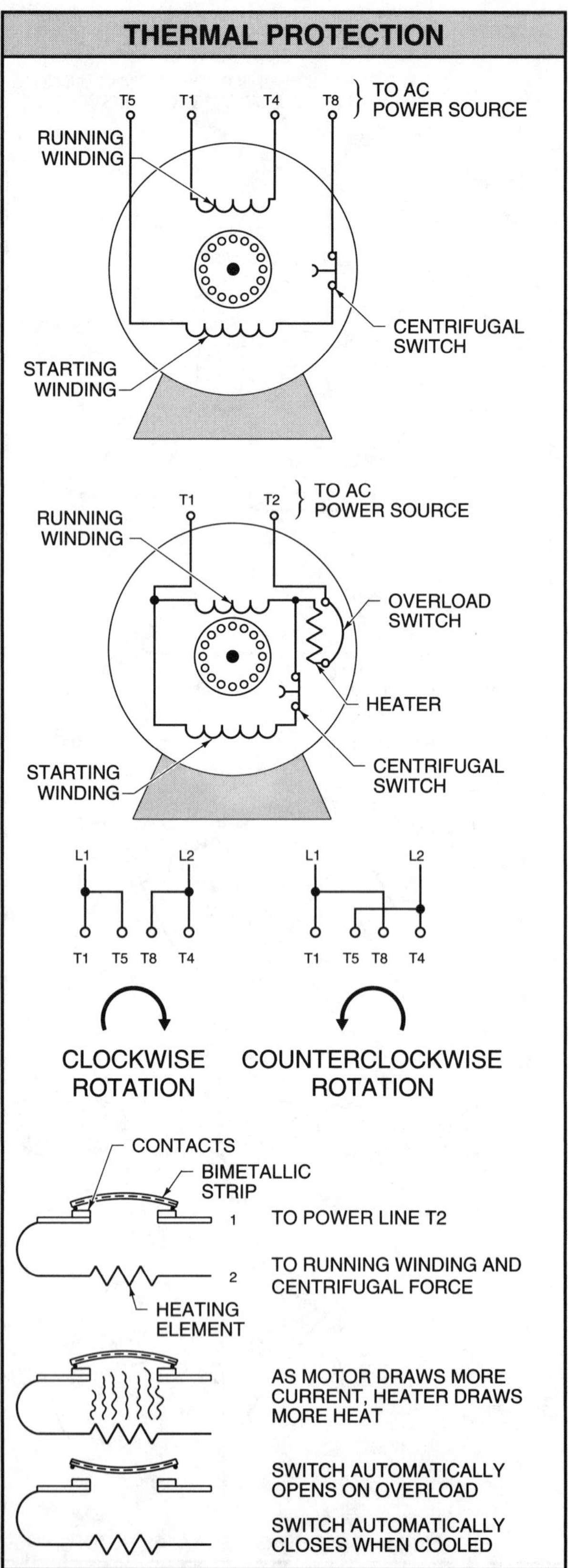

Figure 1-9. A thermal switch protects the split-phase motor from overheating by removing the windings from power.

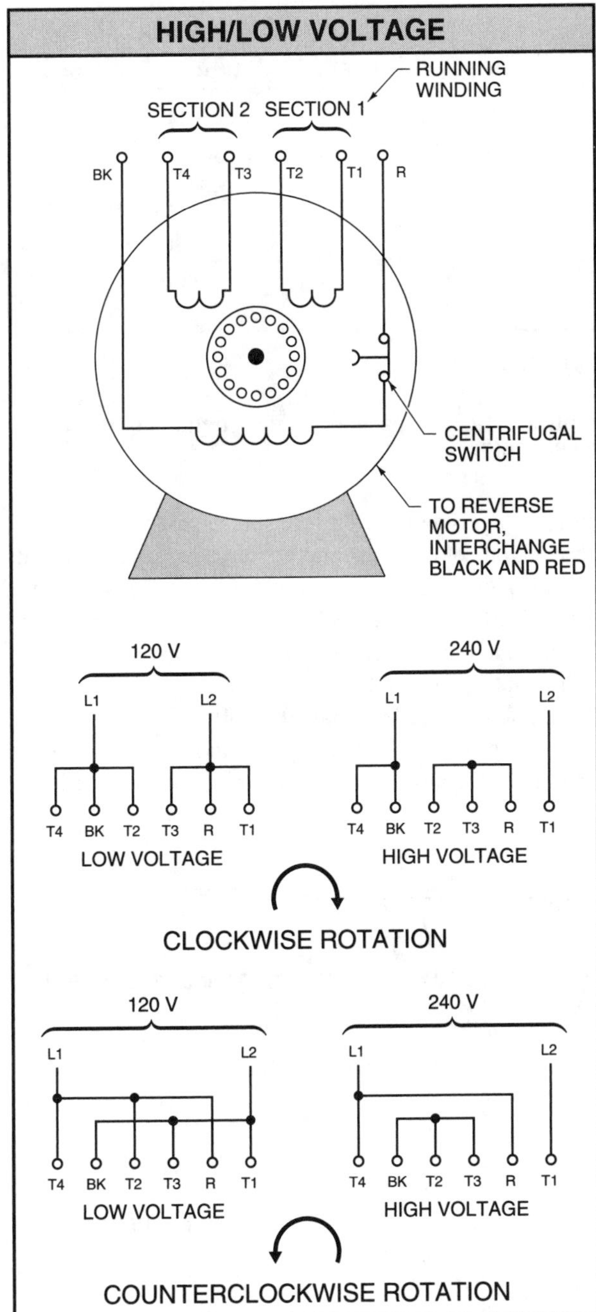

Figure 1-10. The running winding is split into two sections for a dual-voltage motor.

side connection of components that provides more than one path for current to flow. The starting winding is connected across one of the running winding sections. Electrically, all windings receive the same voltage when wired for low- or high-voltage operation.

Two Speed. The speed at which a split-phase motor runs is determined by the number of poles in the motor and the frequency of the supply voltage. *Frequency* is the number of complete electric cycles per second. Since the frequency is almost always fixed, the speed of a split-phase motor is usually changed by changing the number of poles. To change frequency requires a frequency drive unit.

A split-phase motor can be constructed several ways to have different numbers of poles. One method is to build the motor with two running windings and one starting winding. A second method is to build the motor with two running windings and two starting windings. A third method reconnects the motor poles so that the resulting number of poles are either half or twice the number of the original motor poles. This consequent pole-connection method does not require any additional poles.

In a typical two-speed, split-phase motor, two running windings and one starting winding are used to develop two separate speeds. As the number of poles is increased, the speed of the motor is decreased. As the number of poles is decreased, the speed of the motor is increased. See Figure 1-11.

A two-speed, split-phase motor is commonly wound to run on either six or eight poles. When the motor is connected to six poles, the synchronous speed is 1200 rpm, and the actual speed is about 1152 rpm. When the motor is connected to eight poles, the synchronous speed is 900 rpm and the actual speed is about 864 rpm. A double-contact centrifugal switch is used in the circuit. The motor starts on the high-speed running winding, regardless of which speed is selected by the starting switch. However, when the starting switch is set for low speed, the centrifugal switch disconnects the high-speed running winding and connects the low-speed running winding after the motor has reached a set speed.

The number of poles may be changed, providing two or three different possible speeds. Two-speed motors are the most common. However, three-speed motors are often used for washing machines and fans.

Capacitor Motors

A *capacitor motor* is a 1ϕ motor with a capacitor connected in series with the stator windings to produce phase displacement in the starting winding. A *capacitor* is a device that stores an electric charge. It introduces capacitance into an AC circuit. See Figure 1-12.

A capacitor motor is similar in design to a split-phase motor. Both of these motors have a starting and running winding, but the capacitor motor has a capacitor connected in series with the starting winding. The capacitor is added to provide a higher starting torque at lower starting

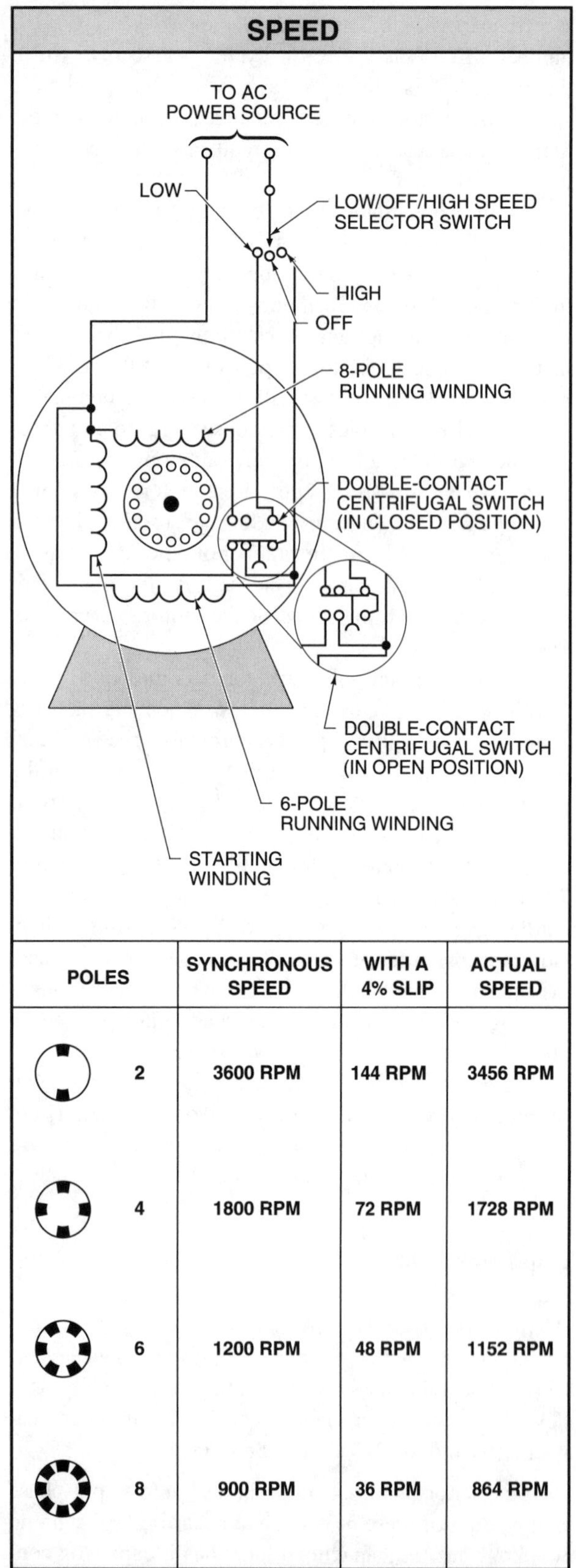

POLES	SYNCHRONOUS SPEED	WITH A 4% SLIP	ACTUAL SPEED
2	3600 RPM	144 RPM	3456 RPM
4	1800 RPM	72 RPM	1728 RPM
6	1200 RPM	48 RPM	1152 RPM
8	900 RPM	36 RPM	864 RPM

Figure 1-11. A split-phase motor can be made to run at different speeds by adding additional running windings.

TYPICAL CAPACITOR VALUES

Motor Horsepower	Capacitor Value*
1/8	70–90
1/6	90–110
1/4	110–150
1/3	150–190
1/2	190–260
3/4	260–370
1	370–440

* microfarads
(.001 = 1 microfarad)

Figure 1-12. A capacitor is a device that stores an electrical charge.

current than is delivered by the split-phase motor. Typical applications of capacitor motors include refrigerators, air conditioners, air compressors, and some power tools. These loads are harder to start and require more starting torque than the split-phase motor produces.

In a split-phase motor, the starting winding current lags the applied voltage by about 20° to 50°. The main winding current lags the applied voltage by about 50°. This phase shift gives the motor its starting torque. See Figure 1-13.

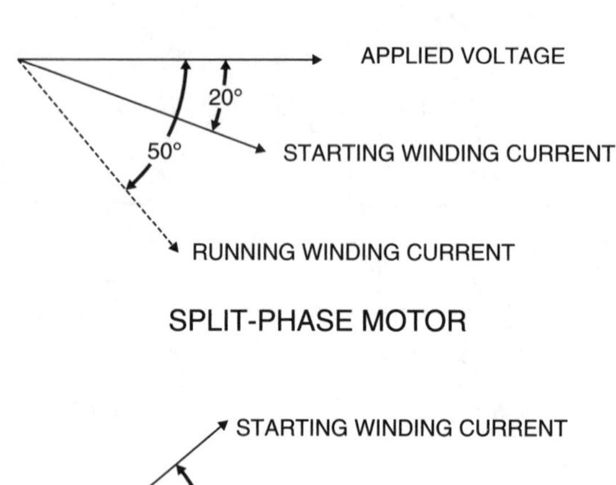

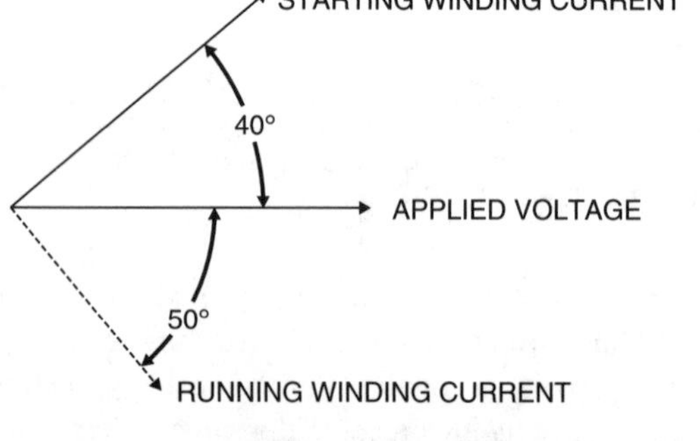

Figure 1-13. The starting and running windings of a capacitor motor are approximately 90° out of phase, giving the motor much more starting torque.

In a capacitor motor, the capacitor causes the starting winding current to lead the applied voltage by about 40°. Since the starting and running windings are about 90° out of phase, the motor's operating characteristics are improved. A higher starting torque is produced, and the motor has a better power factor with a lower current draw. Three types of capacitor motors are the capacitor-start motor, capacitor-run motor, and the capacitor start-and-run motor.

Capacitor-Start Motor. The capacitor-start motor is the most common type of capacitor motor. With the capacitor in the circuit, the capacitor-start motor develops considerably more locked rotor torque per ampere than the split-phase motor. *Locked rotor torque* is the torque a motor produces when the rotor is stationary and full power is applied to the motor. See Figure 1-14.

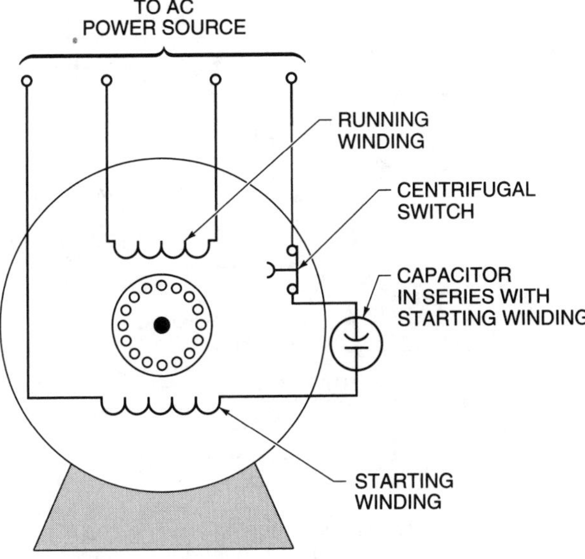

Figure 1-14. The capacitor-start motor is the most common type of capacitor motor.

The capacitor-start motor develops more starting torque than the split-phase motor. However, because the capacitor and starting windings are removed when the motor comes up to speed, both motor types are the same when running. For this reason, the capacitor-start motor is also known as a capacitor-start induction run motor.

In a typical capacitor-start motor, the capacitor is connected in series with the starting winding. The capacitor is connected only during starting. The capacitor and starting winding are both disconnected from the power by the centrifugal switch at a set speed. Capacitor-start motors are typically used to drive power tools, pumps, and small machines.

Capacitor-Run Motor. The capacitor-run motor leaves the starting winding and capacitor in the circuit at all times. The starting winding is not removed as the motor speed increases because there is no centrifugal switch. The capacitor-run motor has a lower full-load speed than the capacitor-start motor because the capacitor remains in the circuit at all times. See Figure 1-15.

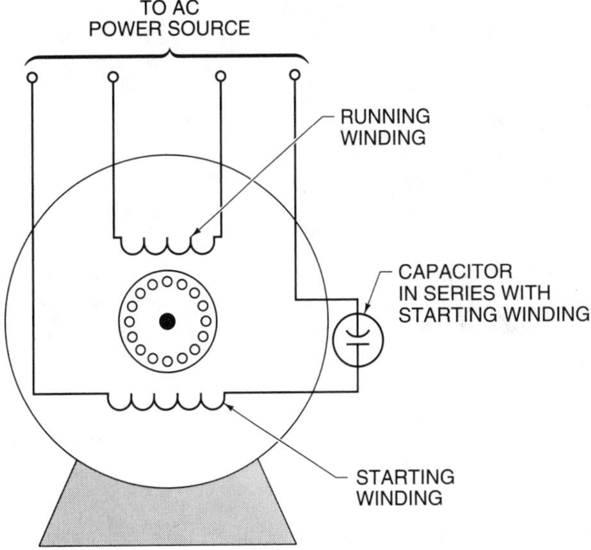

Figure 1-15. In a capacitor-run motor, the capacitor is not removed while the motor is running.

The advantage of leaving the capacitor in the circuit is that the motor has more running torque than the capacitor-start motor or split-phase motor. This allows the capacitor-run motor to be used for loads that require a higher running torque. For example, capacitor-run motors are typically used to drive shaft-mounted fans and blowers ranging in size from 1⁄16 HP to 1⁄3 HP.

Capacitor Start-and-Run Motor. The capacitor start-and-run motor uses two capacitors. It starts with one value capacitor in series with the starting winding and runs with a different value capacitor in series with the running winding. This motor is also known as a dual-capacitor motor. See Figure 1-16.

The capacitor start-and-run motor has the same starting torque as the capacitor-start motor. However, the capacitor-start motor has more running torque than the capacitor-start motor or capacitor-run motor.

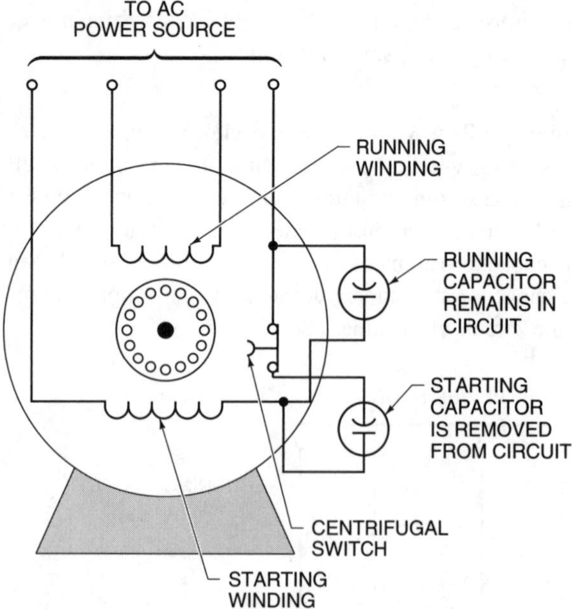

Figure 1-16. In a capacitor start-and-run motor, the starting capacitor is removed when the motor reaches speed, but remains in the circuit.

This is because the capacitance is better matched for starting and running.

In a typical two-capacitor motor, one capacitor is used for starting the motor and the other capacitor remains in the circuit while the motor is running. A larger-value capacitor is used for starting and a smaller-value capacitor is used for running. Capacitor start-and-run motors are typically used to run refrigerators and air compressors.

Dual Voltage. As with a split-phase motor, a capacitor motor can also be designed for dual-voltage operation. See Figure 1-17. Typical voltage levels are 110/220 V, 115/230 V, and 120/240 V. The dual-voltage capacitor motor usually has two main windings and one starting winding. As with the split-phase motor, the motor coils are connected in series for the higher voltage and in parallel for the lower voltage.

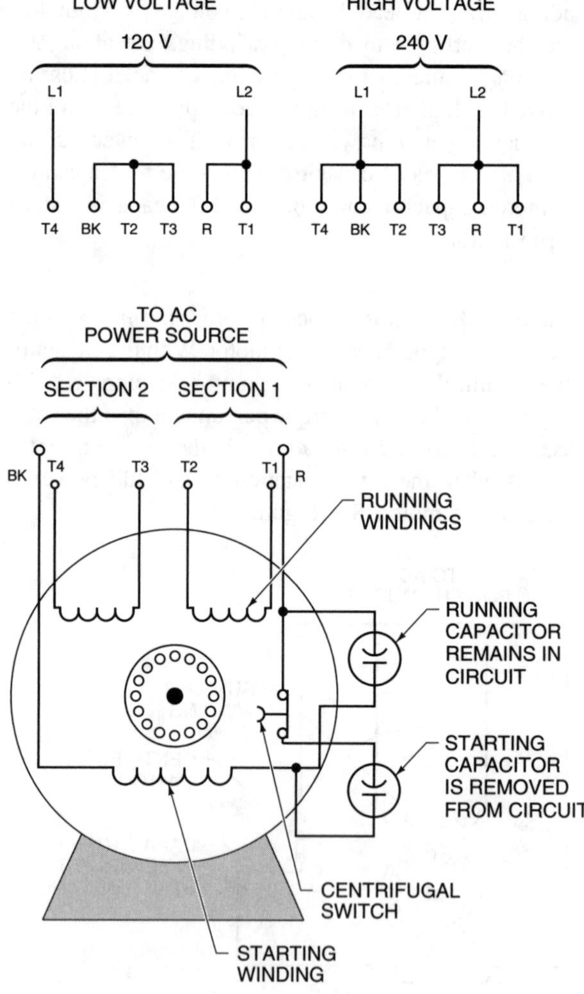

Figure 1-17. By splitting the running winding, the capacitor motor can be used with two different voltages.

In a typical dual-voltage capacitor motor, two main running windings allow two different voltages to be used to run the motor. One capacitor is used to start the motor and a second capacitor remains in the circuit while the motor is running.

chapter 1

SINGLE-PHASE MOTORS

APPLICATIONS

Application — Bleeder Resistors

A centrifugal switch removes the capacitor from the circuit after the motor accelerates in a capacitor-start motor. In normal applications, the charged capacitor slowly discharges as the motor runs. In rapid cycling applications, the capacitor is added back to the circuit before it is discharged. The charged capacitor causes arcing and welding on the contacts of the centrifugal switch. In rapid cycling applications, a bleeder resistor is connected across the terminals of the starting capacitor to bleed off the electric charge that is stored in the capacitor. See Capacitor-Start Motor.

The value of the resistor must be low enough to bleed the stored charge, but high enough not to interfere with starting the motor. Most bleeder resistors are between 12,000 Ω and 20,000 Ω, and are rated at 2 W. If a motor manufacturer does not specify a value, a 15,000 Ω resistor is used. If the motor application requires fast cycling, a 12,000 Ω resistor is used. See Resistor Color Codes.

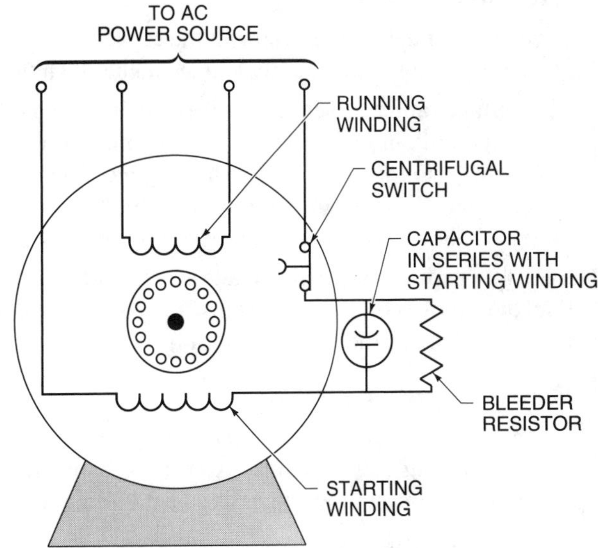

CAPACITOR-START MOTOR

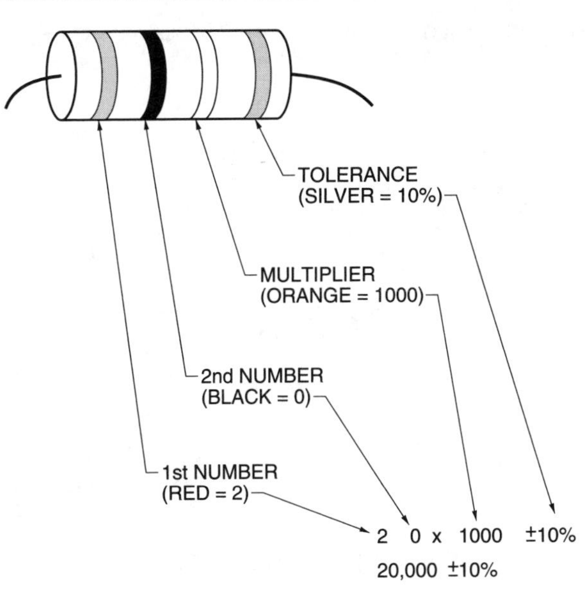

RESISTOR COLOR CODES

RESISTOR COLOR CODES

Color	Number		Multiplier	Tolerance (%)
	1st	2nd		
Black (BK)	0	0	1	0
Brown (BR)	1	1	10	—
Red (R)	2	2	100	—
Orange (O)	3	3	1000	—
Yellow (Y)	4	4	10,000	—
Green (G)	5	5	100,000	—
Blue (BL)	6	6	1,000,000	—
Violet (V)	7	7	10,000,000	—
Gray (GY)	8	8	100,000,000	—
White (W)	9	9	1,000,000,000	—
Gold (Au)	—	—	0.1	5
Silver (Ag)	—	—	0.01	10
None	—	—	0	20

Application — Motor Capacitor Failure

Single-phase motor capacitors fail because of excessive temperature, excessive voltage, excessive duty cycles, internal corrosion, or an open fuse. If a capacitor is suspected to be defective, a substitute capacitor is placed in the circuit to check the motor. The original capacitor is defective if motor operation improves.

Excessive Temperature

Capacitors normally operate in ambient temperatures up to 80°C (176°F). A capacitor's life is shortened at high temperatures. Operating at low temperatures does not harm a capacitor. The capacitance of a capacitor decreases at temperatures below 0°C.

Excessive Voltage

Excessive voltage causes arcing in the capacitor that leads to permanent damage. Excessive voltage is applied by connecting a motor to a supply voltage higher than the capacitor voltage rating, or by a faulty centrifugal switch.

The voltage rating of a capacitor is typically listed on the capacitor. The capacitor voltage rating must be equal to or greater than the supply voltage applied to the motor. **Caution:** Never replace a capacitor with one that has a lower voltage rating than the original. Never use a capacitor with a voltage rating higher than +10% of the original. Using a capacitor with too high or too low of a voltage rating increases the amperage and wattage drawn by the motor. This increase can burn out the motor windings. See Capacitor Ratings in Appendix.

Faulty centrifugal-switch contacts chatter before opening. The voltage on the capacitor is several times higher than the supply voltage when centrifugal-switch contacts chatter. The high voltage is induced by the collapsing magnetic field of the starting winding.

Excessive Duty Cycle

A capacitor is damaged by normal voltage if the motor is started many times or if the load applied to the motor requires a long starting time. A starting capacitor is normally in a circuit for less than 3 seconds. Extra acceleration time causes excessive heat buildup in the capacitor, which reduces capacitor life.

Internal Corrosion

A capacitor with an open seal allows moisture absorption. Moisture absorption leads to corrosion that destroys the film inside the capacitor.

Open Fuse

Many capacitors have an internal fuse that opens when excessive voltage or current is applied to the capacitor. This internal fuse is also opened by improper servicing of the motor. A capacitor with an open internal fuse shows a resistance reading of infinity when checked with an ohmmeter.

Caution: Never discharge a capacitor by creating a short circuit across the terminals with a screwdriver. Creating a short circuit with a screwdriver discharges the capacitor, and may blow the fuse. To safely discharge a capacitor, place a 20,000 Ω, 2 W resistor across the terminals for 5 seconds. The resistor safely discharges the capacitor without blowing the fuse. See Capacitor Discharging.

WARNING: A GOOD CAPACITOR CAN HOLD A CHARGE FOR A LONG PERIOD OF TIME.

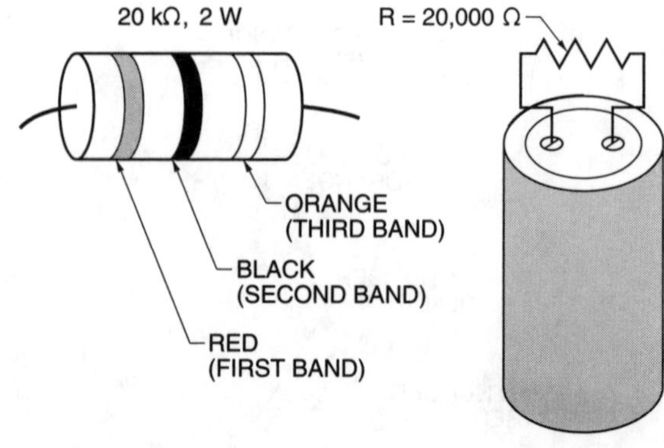

CAPACITOR DISCHARGING

Application — Capacitor Connection

A capacitor is replaced with a capacitor of the same rating when the capacitor fails. If a capacitor of the same rating is not available, capacitors with different ratings are connected together to obtain the required rating. Capacitors are connected in series, parallel, or series/parallel. The connected capacitors are used to test motor operation. The connected capacitors are only used until a replacement is available.

Capacitors Connected in Series

Starting capacitors have voltage ratings of 110–125 V and 220–250 V. Running capacitors have voltage ratings of 370 V and 440 V. Capacitors with different voltage ratings are not used together. The applied voltage for capacitors connected in series is divided over each capacitor. The applied voltage is divided evenly between two capacitors of the same value. For example, two 110 V capacitors connected in series have 110 V across them when connected to a 220 V power source. See Capacitors Connected in Series.

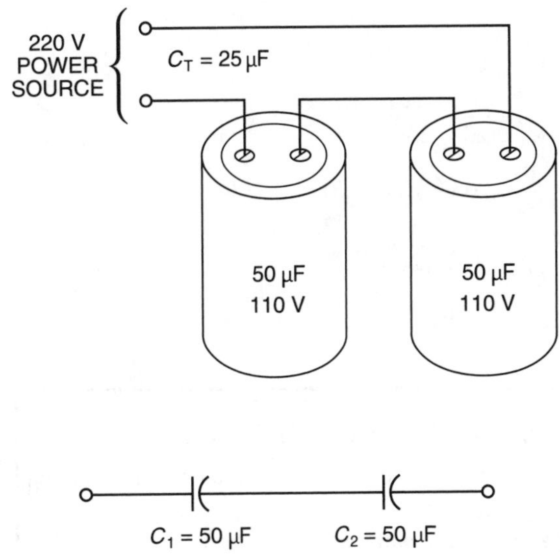

CAPACITORS CONNECTED IN SERIES

The total capacitance of two capacitors connected in series is less than the lowest-value capacitor. To find total capacitance of two capacitors connected in series, apply the formula:

$$C_T = \frac{C_1 \times C_2}{C_1 + C_2}$$

where

C_T = total capacitance (in µF)
C_1 = capacitance of capacitor 1 (in µF)
C_2 = capacitance of capacitor 2 (in µF)

Example: Finding Total Capacitance — Capacitors Connected in Series

Two 50 µF capacitors are connected in series. Find the total capacitance.

$$C_T = \frac{C_1 \times C_2}{C_1 + C_2}$$

$$C_T = \frac{50 \times 50}{50 + 50}$$

$$C_T = \frac{2500}{100}$$

C_T = **25 µF**

To find the total capacitance of three or more capacitors connected in series, apply the formula:

$$\frac{1}{C_T} = \frac{1}{C_1} + \frac{1}{C_2} + \ldots$$

Example: Finding Total Capacitance — Three Capacitors Connected in Series

Capacitors of 20 μF, 25 μF, and 100 μF are connected in series. Find the total capacitance.

$$\frac{1}{C_T} = \frac{1}{C_1} + \frac{1}{C_2} + \ldots$$

$$\frac{1}{C_T} = \frac{1}{20} + \frac{1}{25} + \frac{1}{100}$$

$$\frac{1}{C_T} = .05 + .04 + .01$$

$$\frac{1}{C_T} = .1$$

$$C_T = \mathbf{10\ \mu F}$$

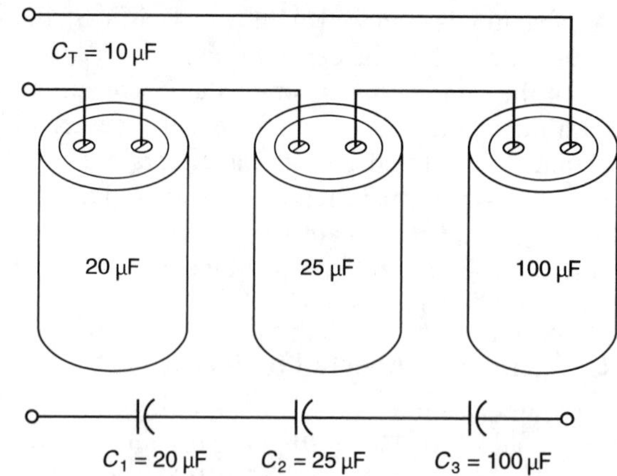

THREE CAPACITORS CONNECTED IN SERIES

Capacitors Connected in Parallel

Capacitors connected in parallel have the same voltage across them. The voltage rating of each capacitor is the same as or greater than the supply voltage applied to the motor. For example, two 220 V capacitors connected in parallel have 220 V across them when connected to a 220 V power source. See Capacitors Connected in Parallel.

The equivalent capacitance of capacitors connected in parallel is equal to the sum of the individual capacitors. To find total capacitance of capacitors connected in parallel, apply the formula:

$$C_T = C_1 + C_2 + \ldots$$

Example: Finding Total Capacitance — Capacitors Connected in Parallel

Two 100 μF capacitors are connected in parallel. Find the total capacitance.

$$C_T = C_1 + C_2 + \ldots$$

$$C_T = 100 + 100$$

$$C_T = \mathbf{200\ \mu F}$$

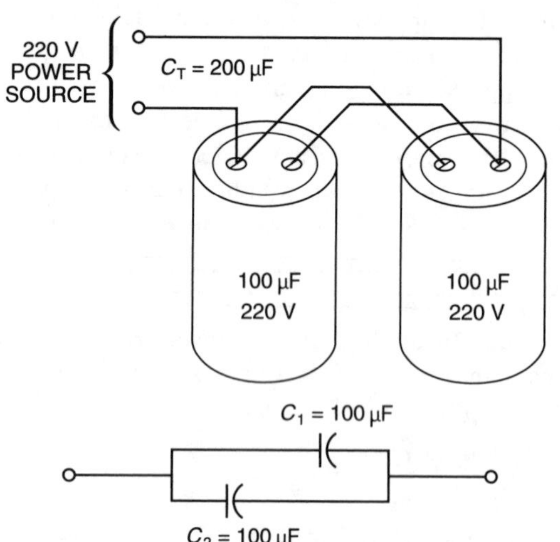

CAPACITORS CONNECTED IN PARALLEL

Capacitors Connected in Series/Parallel

To determine the total capacitance of capacitors connected in series/parallel, apply the procedure:

1. Calculate the capacitance of each parallel branch.
2. Calculate the capacitance of each series branch. See Capacitors Connected in Series/Parallel.

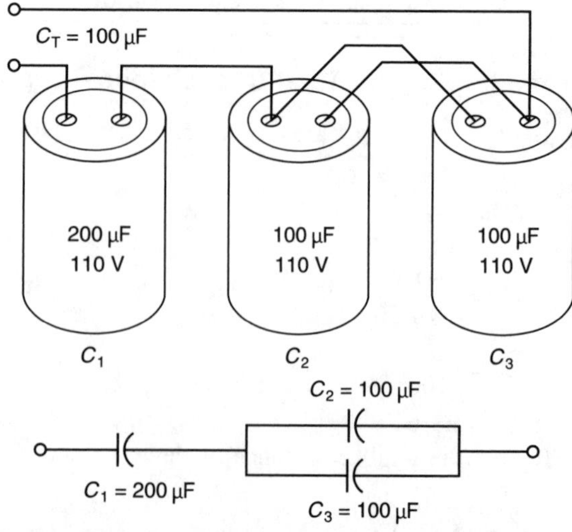

CAPACITORS CONNECTED IN SERIES/PARALLEL

20020834

Example: Finding Total Capacitance — Capacitors Connected in Series/Parallel

Two 100 μF capacitors are connected in parallel with a 200 μF capacitor connected in series. Find the total capacitance.

1. Calculate the capacitance of the parallel branch.

$C_T = C_1 + C_2$

$C_T = 100 + 100$

$C_T = \mathbf{200\ \mu F}$

2. Calculate the capacitance of the series combination.

$$C_T = \frac{C_1 \times C_2}{C_1 + C_2}$$

$$C_T = \frac{200 \times 200}{200 + 200}$$

$$C_T = \frac{40{,}000}{400}$$

$$C_T = \mathbf{100\ \mu F}$$

Capacitor Connection Methods

The three methods of connecting a capacitor to a motor circuit are the quick-connect, screw, and solder methods. The capacitor connection method varies based on the manufacturer. See Capacitor Connection Methods.

Capacitor terminals are plugged into receptacles on the wire leads in the quick-connect method. The quick-connect method provides fast capacitor changing. The disadvantage is that capacitors have different types and sizes of terminals that can cause loose electric connections. Loose electric connections produce heat at the connection and early capacitor failure.

Capacitor terminals are secured by using screws in the screw method. The screw method provides tight electric connections. The disadvantage is that overtightening the leads cracks the capacitor seal. A cracked capacitor seal leads to corrosion and early capacitor failure.

Capacitor terminals are soldered to the wire leads in the solder method. The solder method provides tight electric connections. The disadvantage is that solder connections are time-consuming to replace.

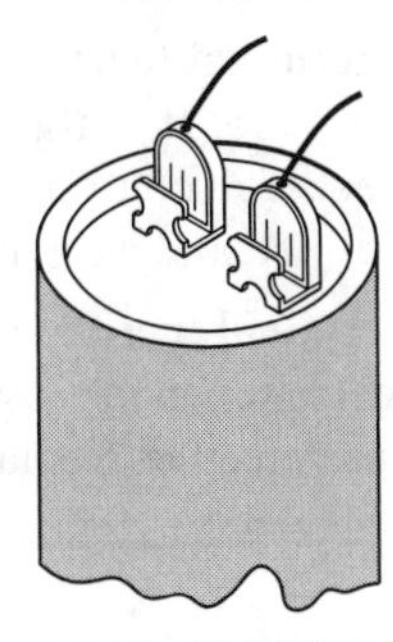

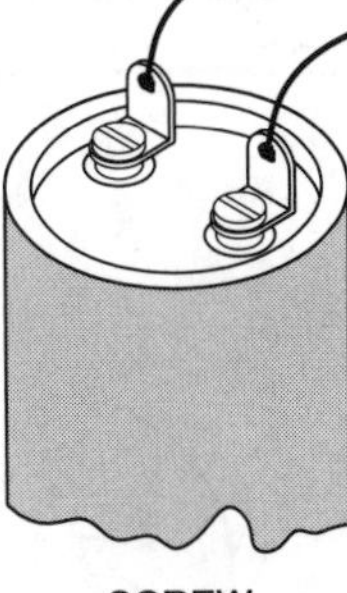

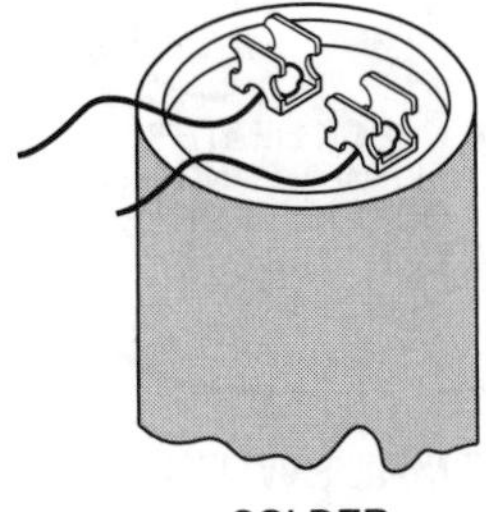

CAPACITOR CONNECTION METHODS

Application — Thermal Switch Testing

A thermal switch removes the starting and running motor windings from the circuit at a preset temperature. The switch removes the windings by opening contacts connected in series with the motor windings. When the windings cool, the contacts close. A motor does not operate or operates without thermal protection when the thermal switch is not operating properly. To test a thermal switch, apply the procedure:

1. Remove the motor from the power lines and let cool.
2. Remove the end of the motor that includes the thermal switch.
3. Remove one of the leads running from the thermal switch to the motor windings.

4. In a motor containing a two-terminal thermal switch, check for continuity (very low resistance) using an ohmmeter. Set the ohmmeter on the lowest resistance scale and check across the switch contacts. If a high-resistance reading is obtained, the contacts are open and the switch is defective. See Two-Terminal Thermal Switch.

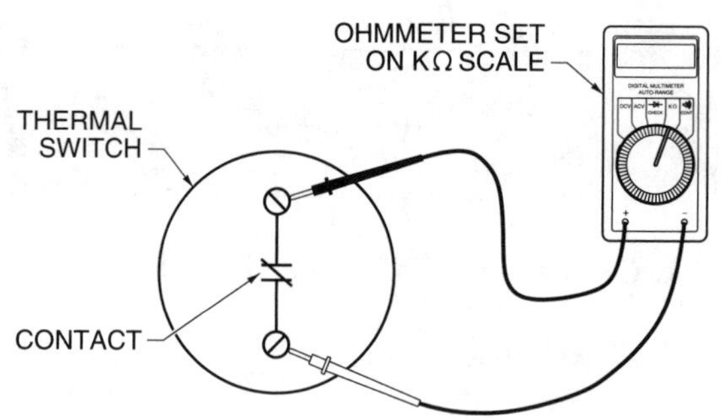

TWO-TERMINAL THERMAL SWITCH

In a motor containing a three-terminal thermal switch, check for continuity across the switch contacts using an ohmmeter set on the lowest scale. If a high-resistance reading is obtained, the contacts are open and the switch is defective. Also, check for continuity across the heater element. If a high-resistance reading is obtained, the heater element is open and defective. See Three-Terminal Thermal Switch.

In a motor containing a four-terminal thermal switch, check for continuity across the switch contacts and the heater element using an ohmmeter set on the lowest scale. If a high-resistance reading is obtained, the contacts or the heater element is open and defective. Replace the defective component. See Four-Terminal Thermal Switch.

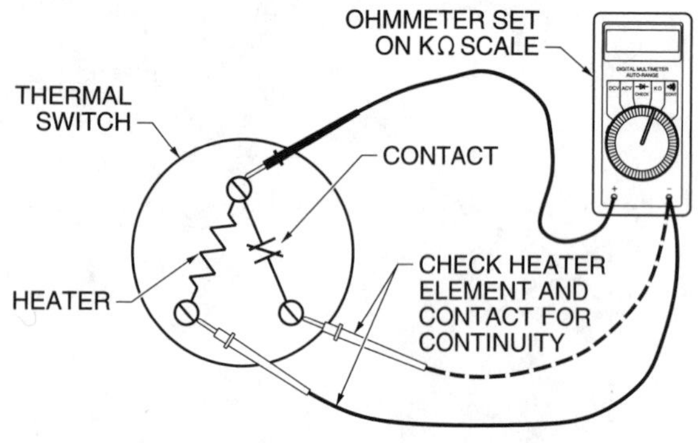

THREE-TERMINAL THERMAL SWITCH

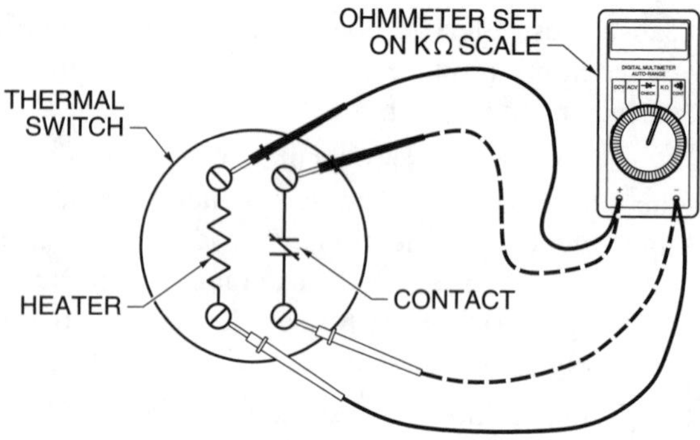

FOUR-TERMINAL THERMAL SWITCH

Application — Single-Phase AC Motor Terminal Designations

Manufacturers use different terminal and wire designations for 1ϕ motors. Most 1ϕ motors and their auxiliary devices, such as capacitors, starting switches, and thermal protection, placed in operation over the past few years use standard letters, numbers, and colors.

- Capacitor— J1, J2, J3, J4, etc.
- Supply line— L1, L2, L3, L4, etc.
- Stator— T1, T2, T3, T4, etc.
- Thermal protection device— P1, P2, P3, P4, etc.

The colored wires used in single-phase motors are assigned specific colors:

- T1— Blue
- T5— Black
- T2— White
- T8— Red
- T3— Orange
- P1— No color assigned
- T4— Yellow
- P2— Brown

Single-Voltage Designations

On single-voltage, 1ϕ motors, T1 and T4 are assigned to the running winding, and T5 and T8 are assigned to the starting winding (if present). See Single-Voltage Motor.

Dual-Voltage Designations

On dual-voltage motors in which the running winding is divided into two parts, one-half of the winding is designated T1 and T2, and the other half is designated T3 and T4. One-half of the starting winding is designated T5 and T6, and the other half is designated T7 and T8 (if used). If only two wires are used for the starting winding, they are designated T5 and T8. See Dual-Voltage Motor.

Some manufacturers mix numbers and colors. Typically, the running winding is designated T1, T2, etc., and the starting winding is designated with a color. Red and black are commonly used to designate starting windings. See Single-Phase Motor.

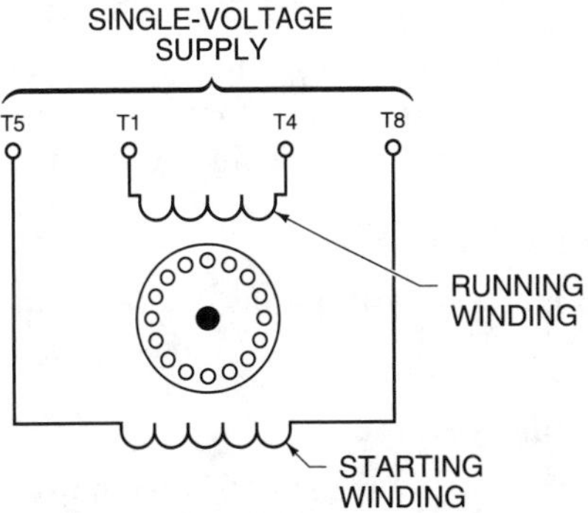

SINGLE-VOLTAGE MOTOR

DUAL-VOLTAGE
SUPPLY
T5 T6 T1
T2 T3
T4 T7 T8
RUNNING
WINDINGS
STARTING
WINDINGS

DUAL-VOLTAGE MOTOR

Application — Motor Winding Lead Termination

Motor winding leads are terminated outside a motor or in a terminal box on a motor. Motors with winding leads terminated outside the motor are used in machines that include the motor as part of other equipment. Applications include central air conditioners, furnaces, and portable equipment. The advantage is that the motor is connected to other devices through a terminal strip. The terminal strip includes other wiring, such as the control circuit. See Motor Winding Lead Termination.

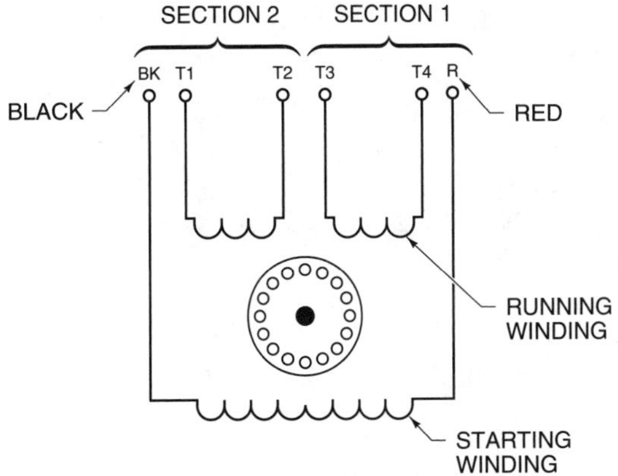

SINGLE-PHASE MOTOR

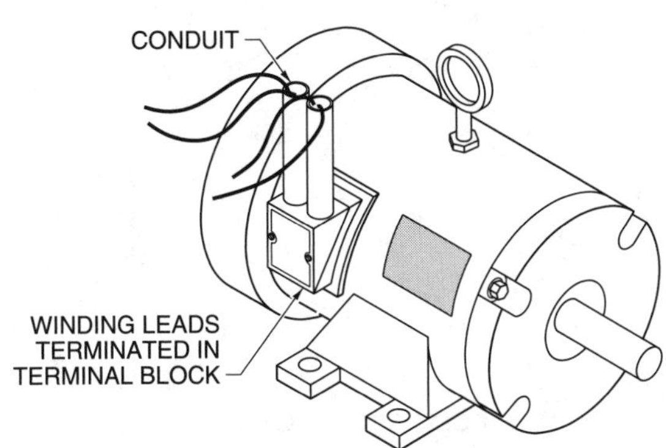

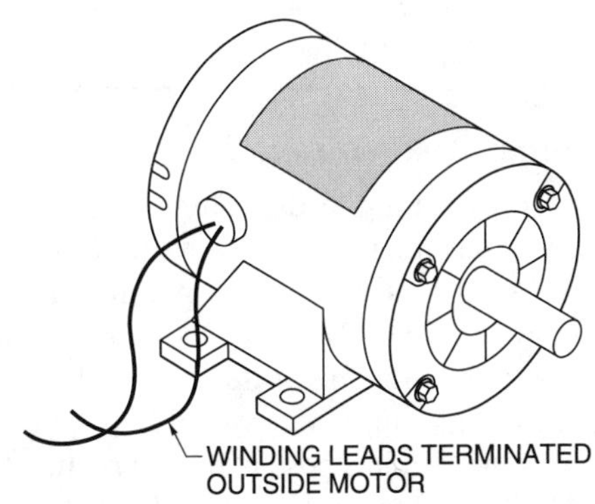

MOTOR WINDING LEAD TERMINATION

Motors with winding leads terminated inside a terminal box mounted on the motor are the most common. The power lines are brought to the motor through conduit or cable connected to the terminal box. Wiring methods inside a terminal box include direct wire, terminal post, and terminal post with links.

Direct Wire

The motor winding leads are connected to the power lines using wire connectors (nuts) in the direct wire method. The wires are then pushed inside the terminal box. See Direct Wire Method.

Terminal Post

The terminal post method is the most common terminal box wiring method. The ends of the motor winding leads and power lines have terminal bolt or spade lugs. The ends of motor winding leads that require periodic changing have spade lugs. The terminal bolt lugs are connected to terminal posts. The terminal bolt lugs are placed under the bolt on the terminal post and tightened. The spade lugs are connected to spade posts. The spade lugs are designed to be easily connected to the spade post, which permits easy motor direction changes. See Terminal Post Method.

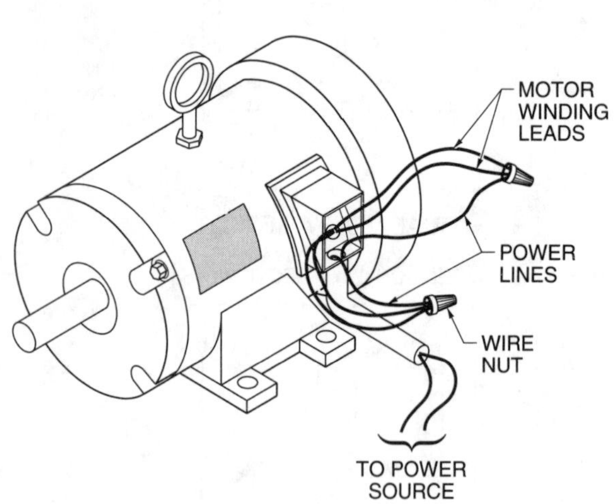

DIRECT WIRE METHOD

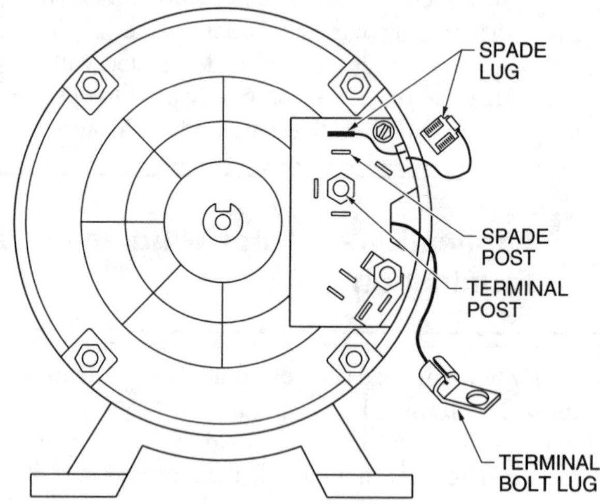

TERMINAL POST METHOD

Terminal Post with Links

The motor winding leads from the motor are connected to terminal posts inside the terminal box. The terminal posts are evenly spaced to allow connection of pre-drilled links. The links are used as jumpers to change motor direction. The links are added by removing the terminal bolt, placing the link over the terminal post, and reconnecting the terminal bolt. See Terminal Post with Links Method.

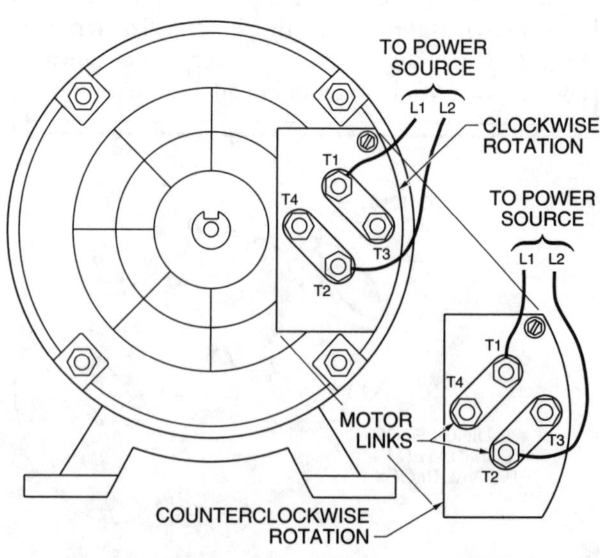

TERMINAL POST WITH LINKS METHOD

Application — Reversing Single-Phase Motors

A 1ϕ motor is reversed by interchanging motor leads and/or the incoming power lines. The motor leads and power lines are interchanged at the motor starter. To determine the wiring arrangement of a 1ϕ motor for forward and reverse directions, apply the procedure:

1. Determine the number of power lines that must be switched. All hot power lines must be switched. A *hot power line (ungrounded power line)* is any power line that is not grounded. See Power Line Switching Requirements.

2. Determine the required voltage. A motor nameplate lists the voltage of the motor. If the motor is a dual-voltage motor, select the higher available voltage. Connecting a motor to the higher voltage reduces the current drawn in the power lines. See Voltage Selection.

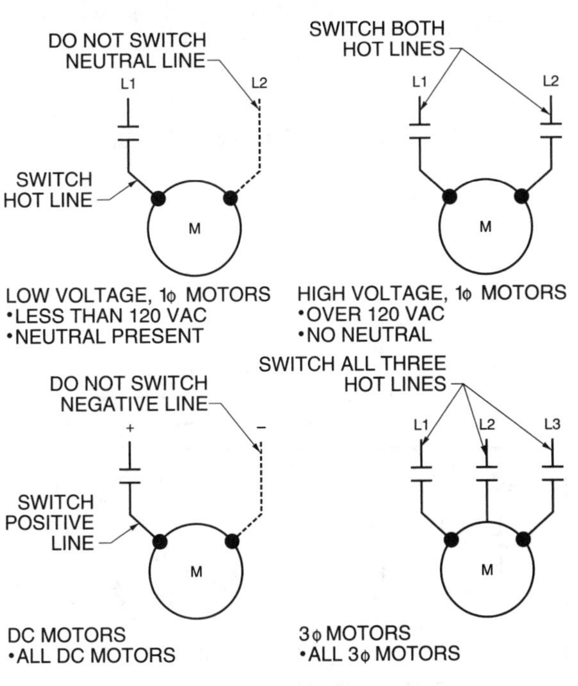

POWER LINE SWITCHING REQUIREMENTS

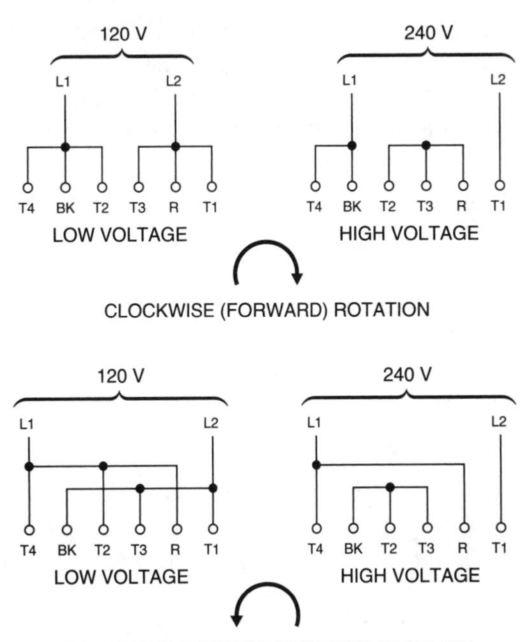

VOLTAGE SELECTION

3. Use the information provided on the motor wiring diagram to record the connections that must be made to operate the motor in the forward and reverse directions. Record the conductors that must be interchanged in the forward direction. Interchange their position in the reverse direction. For 1ϕ motors, the starting winding leads are the conductors that are interchanged.

A. Show the motor terminals that are connected to the conductors that are interchanged. Do not include any power lines.

B. Add the power lines. Do not show them connected to the lines that are interchanged. See Motor Connections.

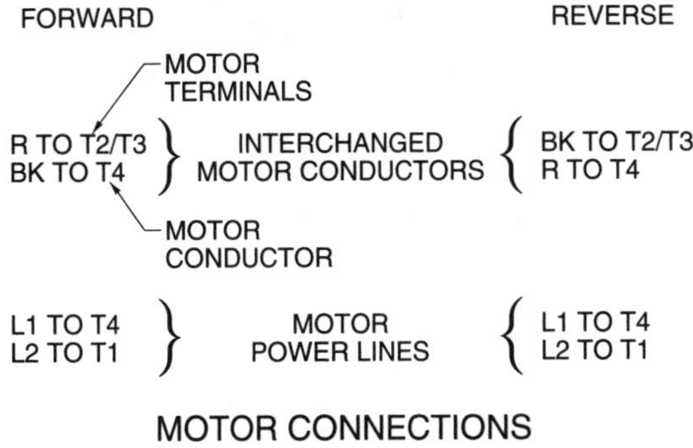

MOTOR CONNECTIONS

4. **Remove common connections that are not hot power lines.** Remove any common connections that are not power lines and remain connected in both the forward and reverse directions. Connect the common conductors at the motor and select the name of the lowest number for the common name. See Common Connection Removal.
5. **Connect the power line that is not switched.** If a power line is not a hot power line, connect it directly to the motor. If both power lines are hot, do not connect them directly to the motor.
6. **Determine the contacts.** A set of electric contacts is required for each place the word "to" appears in the connections. See Motor Contacts.
7. **Draw the wiring diagram.** Connect all lines that are the same. List the name of the common line only on the forward contacts. See Motor Control Wiring Diagram.

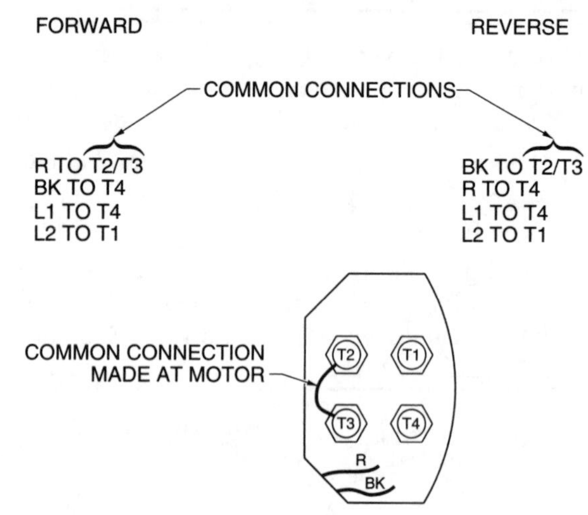

COMMON CONNECTION REMOVAL

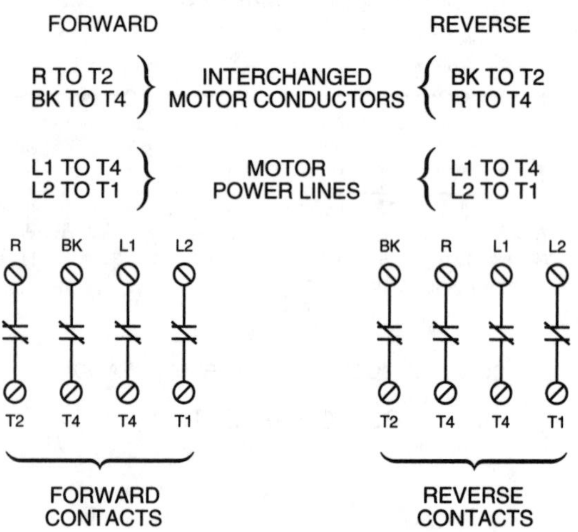

MOTOR CONTACTS

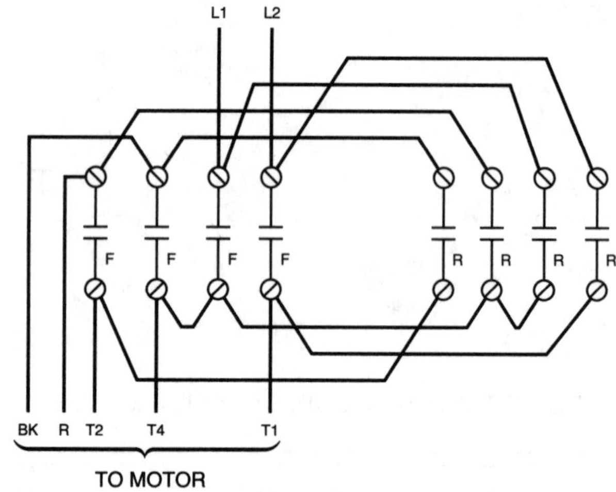

MOTOR CONTROL WIRING DIAGRAM

Name ______________________ Date ____________

chapter **1**

ACTIVITIES

SINGLE-PHASE MOTORS

Activity 1-1. Bleeder Resistor Values

List the value of each resistor using Resistor Color Codes on page 11.

______ **1.** red, black, orange, silver

______ **2.** brown, gray, orange, silver

______ **3.** brown, green, orange, silver

______ **4.** brown, white, orange, silver

______ **5.** brown, yellow, orange, silver

______ **6.** brown, blue, orange, silver

______ **7.** brown, red, orange, silver

______ **8.** brown, violet, orange, silver

______ **9.** brown, brown, orange, silver

______ **10.** brown, orange, orange, silver

______ **11.** orange, blue, orange, silver

______ **12.** red, brown, green, silver

Activity 1-2. Bleeder Resistor Color Codes

State the color code for each resistor value.

______ ______ ______ **1.** 9500 Ω

______ ______ ______ **2.** 850 Ω

______ ______ ______ **3.** 1500 Ω

______ ______ ______ **4.** 900 Ω

______ ______ ______ **5.** 7200 Ω

______ ______ ______ **6.** 80 Ω

______ ______ ______ **7.** 4600 Ω

______ ______ ______ **8.** 50,000 Ω

______ ______ ______ **9.** 140,000 Ω

______ ______ ______ **10.** 1,100,000 Ω

______ ______ ______ **11.** 670,000 Ω

______ ______ ______ **12.** 300 Ω

______ ______ ______ **13.** 20,000 Ω

______ ______ ______ **14.** 33 Ω

______ ______ ______ **15.** 100,000 Ω

Activity 1-3. Motor Capacitor Failure

State the specifications for a new capacitor that can replace the original.

_________ **1.** The maximum operating temperature of the replacement capacitor is _________°F.

_________ **2.** The minimum operating temperature of the replacement capacitor without decreasing the capacitance rating is _________°F.

_________ **3.** The maximum time the replacement capacitor can be connected to power without damaging the capacitor is _________ seconds.

_________ **4.** The minimum voltage rating of the power supply that the replacement capacitor can be connected to is _________ VAC.

_________ **5.** If the motor manufacturer specifies that a replacement capacitor must be within +10% or −10% of the original for proper motor operation, the maximum rating of the replacement capacitor is _________ μF.

_________ **6.** The minimum rating of the replacement capacitor is _________ μF.

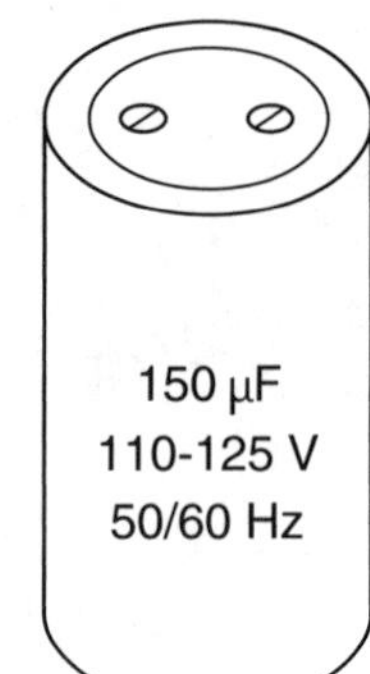

Activity 1-4. Total Capacitance

Determine the maximum voltage and the total capacitance that can be applied.

1. _______ V

2. _______ μF

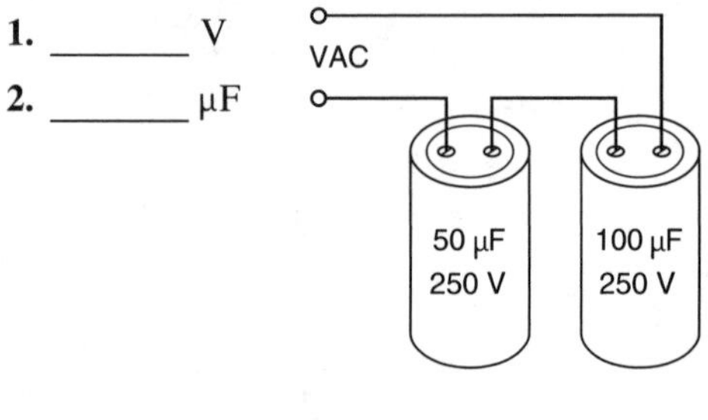

3. _______ V

4. _______ μF

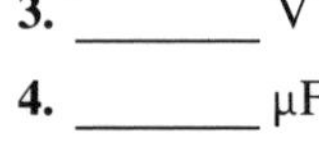

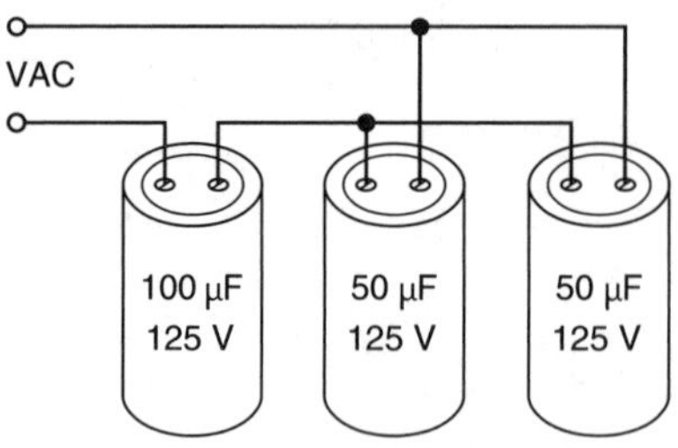

5. _______ V

6. _______ μF

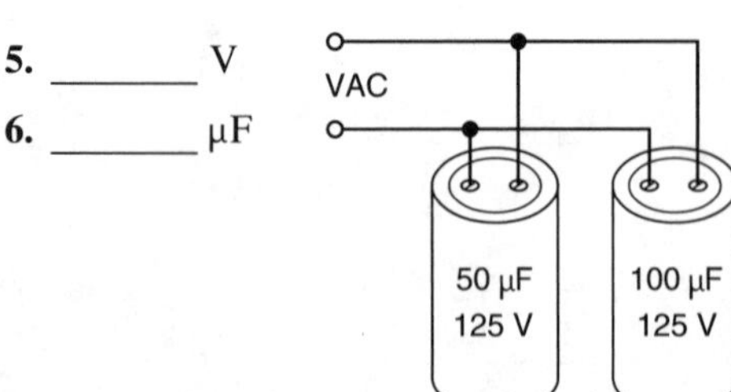

7. _______ V

8. _______ μF

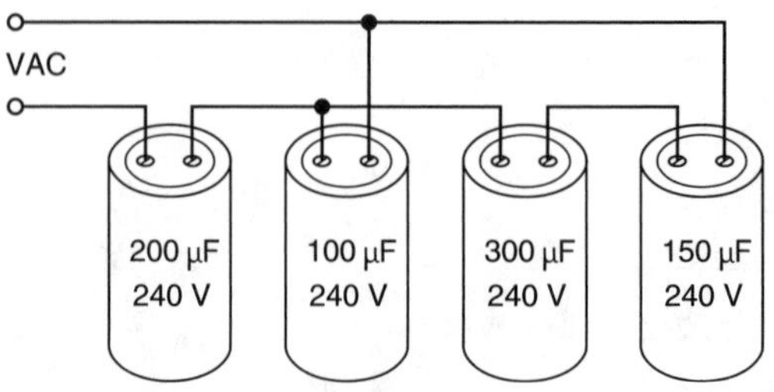

Activity 1-5. Capacitor Voltage

Determine the voltage across each capacitor.

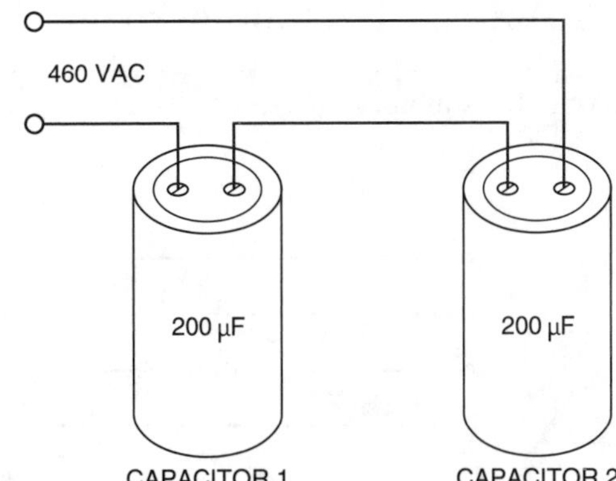

__________ **1.** Voltage across Capacitor 1 is ________ V.

__________ **2.** Voltage across Capacitor 2 is ________ V.

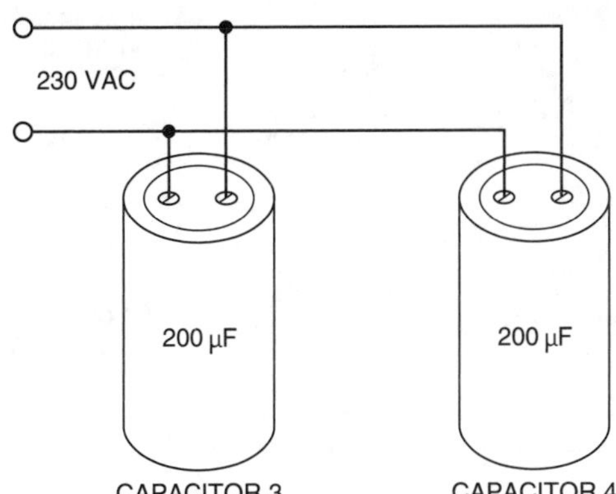

__________ **3.** Voltage across Capacitor 3 is ________ V.

__________ **4.** Voltage across Capacitor 4 is ________ V.

Activity 1-6. Thermal Switch Testing

__________ **1.** The correct setting of Meter 1 to test the thermal switch is ________.

__________ **2.** If good, Meter 1 reading is very ________.

__________ **3.** The correct setting of Meter 2 to test the thermal switch is ________.

__________ **4.** If good, Meter 2 reading is very ________.

5. Connect Meter 1 to test the thermal switching contact. Connect Meter 2 to test the thermal switch-heating element.

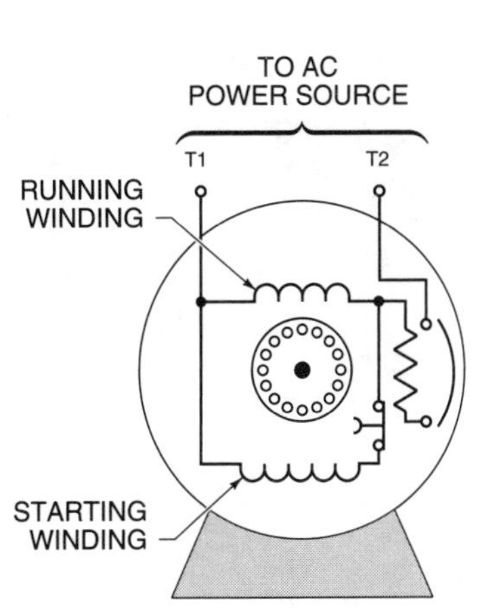

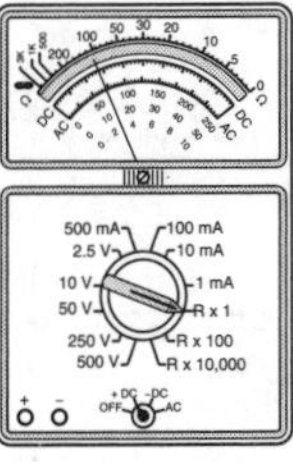
METER 1

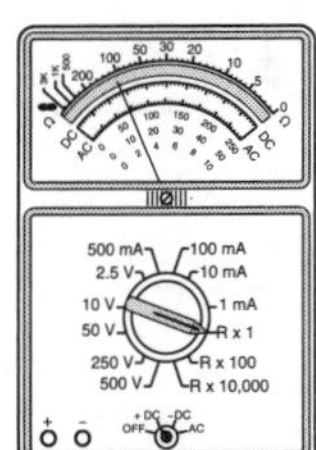
METER 2

Activity 1-7. Single-Phase, AC Motor Terminal Designations

1. Mark each motor lead using the correct color designation.

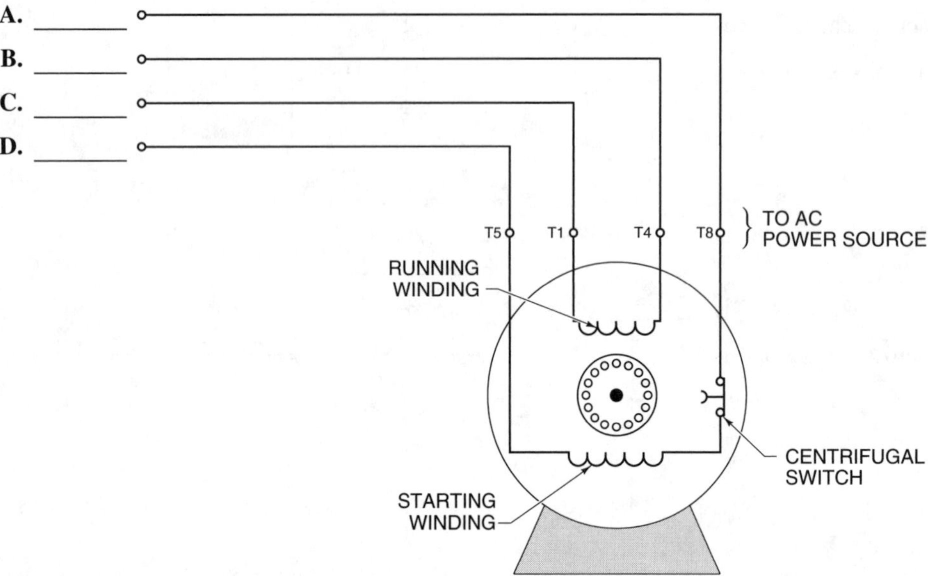

2. Mark each motor lead using the correct letter/number terminal designation.

A. _______ 2
B. _______
C. _______ 1
D. _______ 2
E. _______ 1
F. _______ 2
G. _______
H. _______
I. _______
J. _______ 3

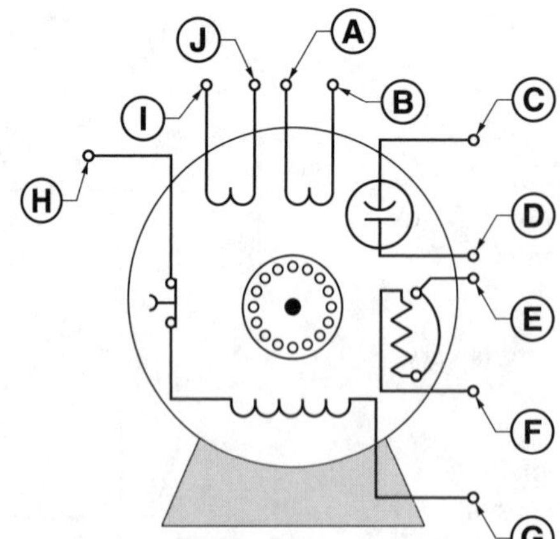

Activity 1-8. Motor Winding Lead Termination

Answer the questions using Wire Nut Specifications and Conductor Cross Section.

_____ **1.** The minimum conductor cross-section size that an O-1 wire nut can secure is _____ mm^2.

_____ **2.** The maximum conductor cross-section size that an O-1 wire nut can secure is _____ mm^2.

_____ **3.** The minimum conductor cross-section size that a Y-1 wire nut can secure is _____ mm^2.

_____ **4.** The maximum conductor cross-section size that a Y-1 wire nut can secure is _____ mm^2.

_____ **5.** The minimum conductor cross-section size that an R-l wire nut can secure is _____ mm^2.

_____ **6.** The maximum conductor cross-section size that an R-l wire nut can secure is _____ mm^2.

_____ **7.** Can four #14 conductors be joined with one Y-1 wire nut?

_____ **8.** Can two #12 and two #14 conductors be joined with one R-1 wire nut?

_____ **9.** Can five #18 conductors be joined with one R-1 wire nut?

_____ **10.** Can one #12 and three #16 conductors be joined with one Y-1 wire nut?

_____ **11.** Can two #16 and three #14 conductors be joined with one Y-1 wire nut?

_____ **12.** Can two #22 and three #16 conductors be joined with one O-1 wire nut?

_____ **13.** The smallest wire nut that can join two #14 conductors is a(n) _____.

_____ **14.** The smallest wire nut that can join one #18 and two #16 conductors is a(n) _____.

_____ **15.** The smallest wire nut that can join one #12 and two #14 conductors is a(n) _____.

_____ **16.** Can an R-1 wire nut join two #8 conductors?

_____ **17.** Can an O-1 wire nut join two #20 conductors?

_____ **18.** The conductor cross section of one #10 and two #8 conductors is _____ mm^2.

_____ **19.** The conductor cross section of two #22 and three #16 conductors is _____ mm^2.

_____ **20.** The conductor cross section of three #20 and three #18 conductors is _____ mm^2.

WIRE NUT SPECIFICATIONS

Number	Temp Rating	Wire Combination Range
O-1	105°C	Joins #22 through #14 AWG Minimum 3 #22 Maximum 3 #16 and 1 #18
Y-1	105°C	Joins #18 through #12 AWG Minimum 1 #14 and 1 #18 Maximum 2 #14 and 3 #16
R-1	105°C	Joins #18 through #10 AWG Minimum 1 #12 and 2 #18 Maximum 2 #10 and 1 #12

CONDUCTOR CROSS SECTION

AWG #	Cross Section (in mm^2)
22	.324
20	.519
18	.823
16	1.31
14	2.08
12	3.31
10	5.261
8	8.37
6	13.3
4	21.15

Activity 1-9. Reversing Single-Phase Motors

Connect the motor for forward and reverse directions.

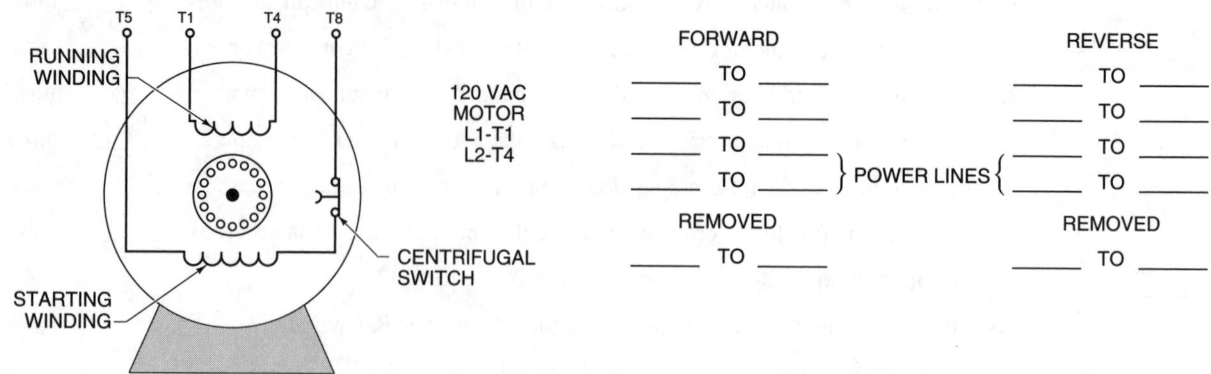

120 VAC
L1 L2

F F F

R R R

F F F

R R R

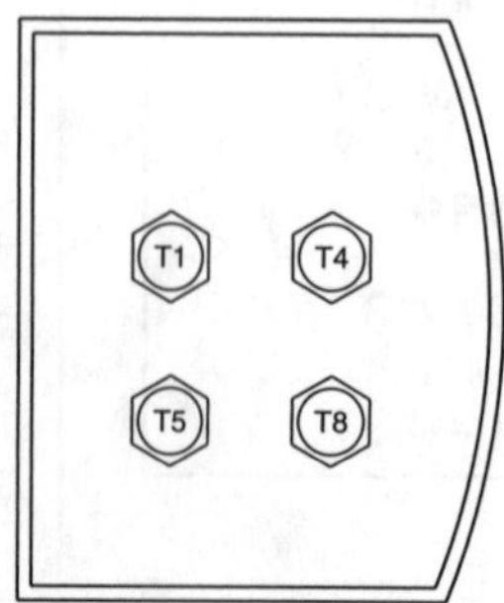

◯ Activity 1-10. Reversing Dual-Voltage, Single-Phase Motors

Connect the motor for forward and reverse directions using low voltage.

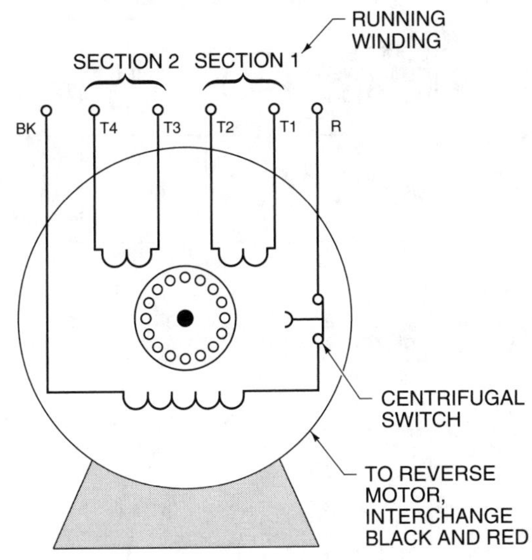

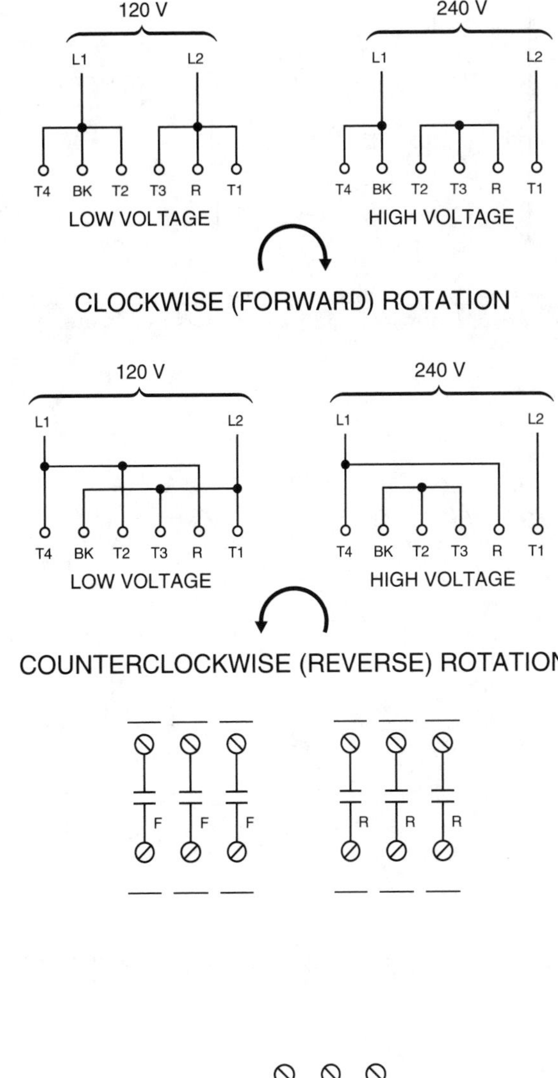

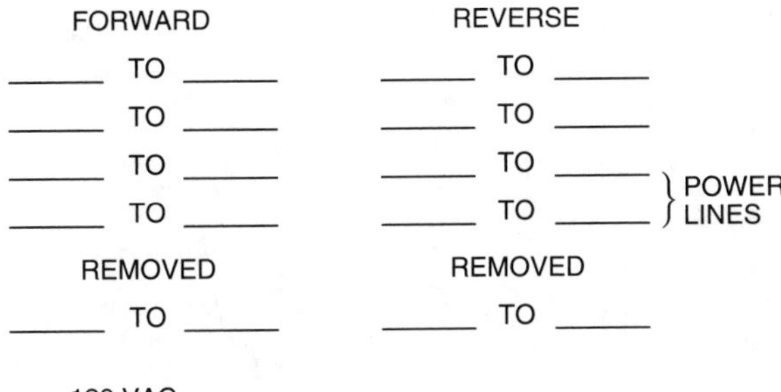

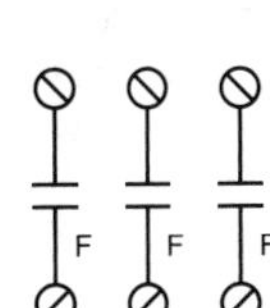

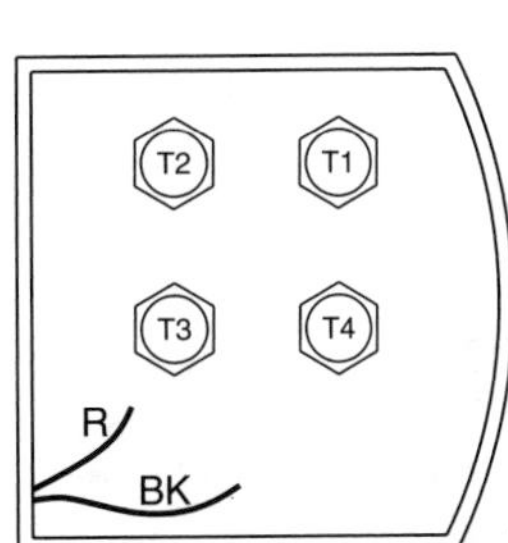

Activity 1-11. Wiring Split-Phase Motors

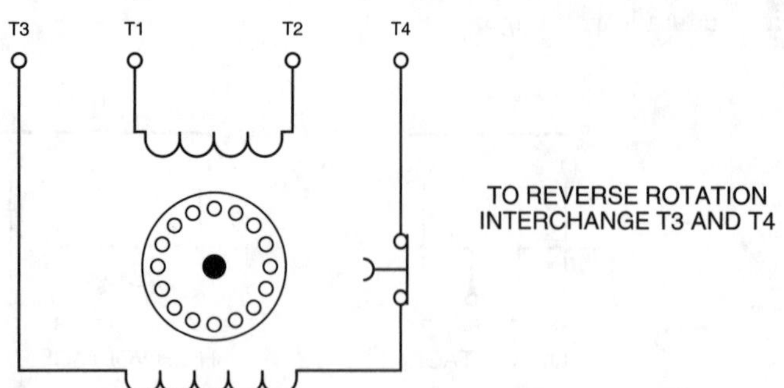

ROTATION	L1	L2
COUNTER-CLOCKWISE ROTATION	T1-T4	T2-T3
CLOCKWISE ROTATION	T1-T3	T2-T4

1. Connect the motor and power leads inside the terminal box for counterclockwise rotation.

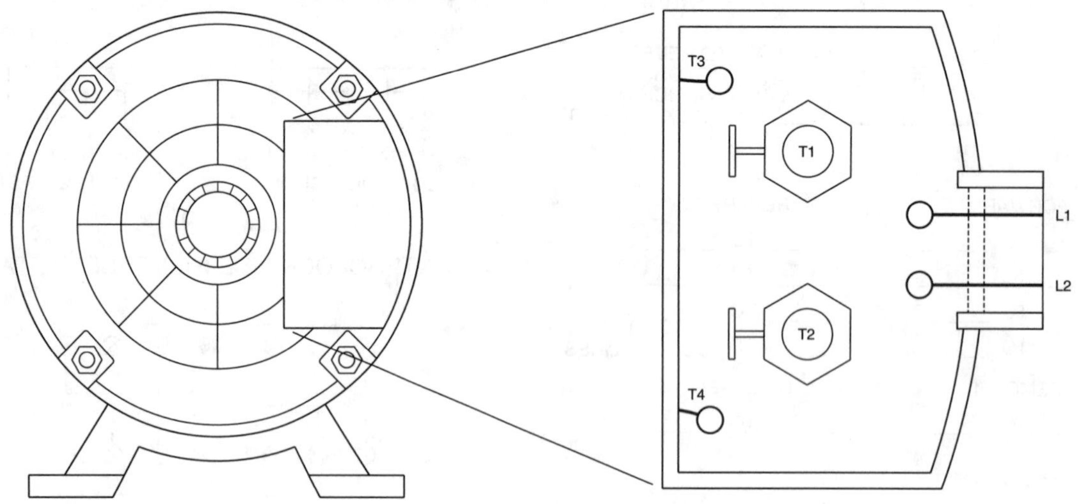

2. Connect the motor and power leads inside the terminal box for clockwise rotation.

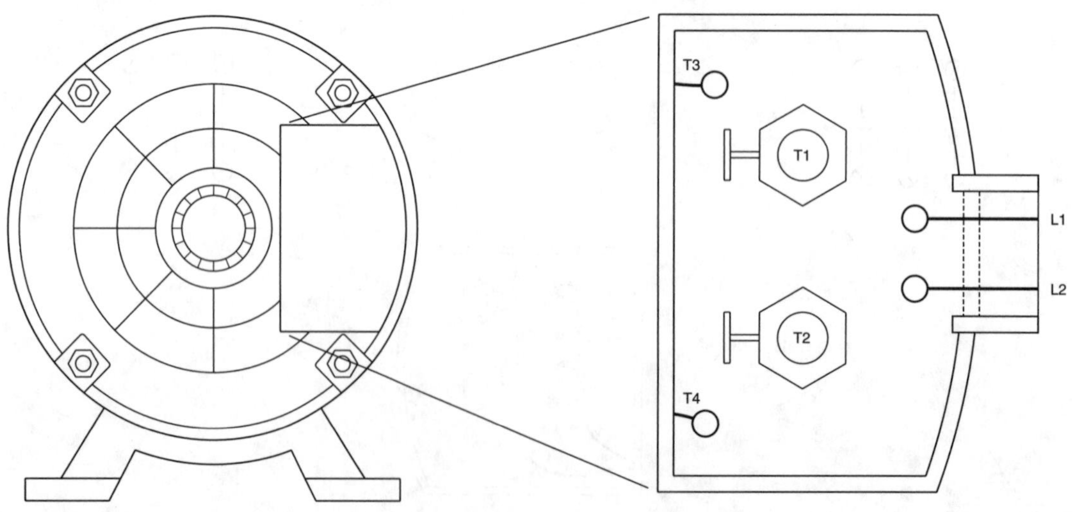

◯ Activity 1-12. Wiring Dual-Voltage Motors

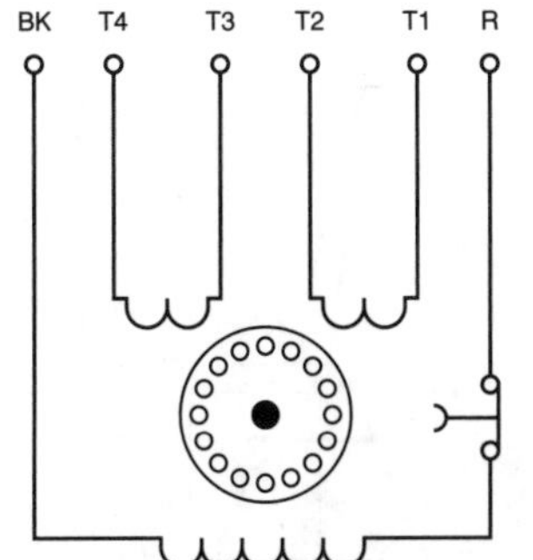

TO REVERSE ROTATION INTERCHANGE BLACK AND RED LEADS

		L1	L2	JOIN
HIGH NAMEPLATE VOLTAGE	CCW	T4-R	T1	T3-T2-BK
	CW	T4-BK	T1	T2-T3-R
LOW NAMEPLATE VOLTAGE	CCW	T4-T2-R	T1-T3-BK	———
	CW	T4-T2-BK	T3-T1-R	———

1. Connect the motor and power leads inside the terminal box for counterclockwise rotation at 115 V.

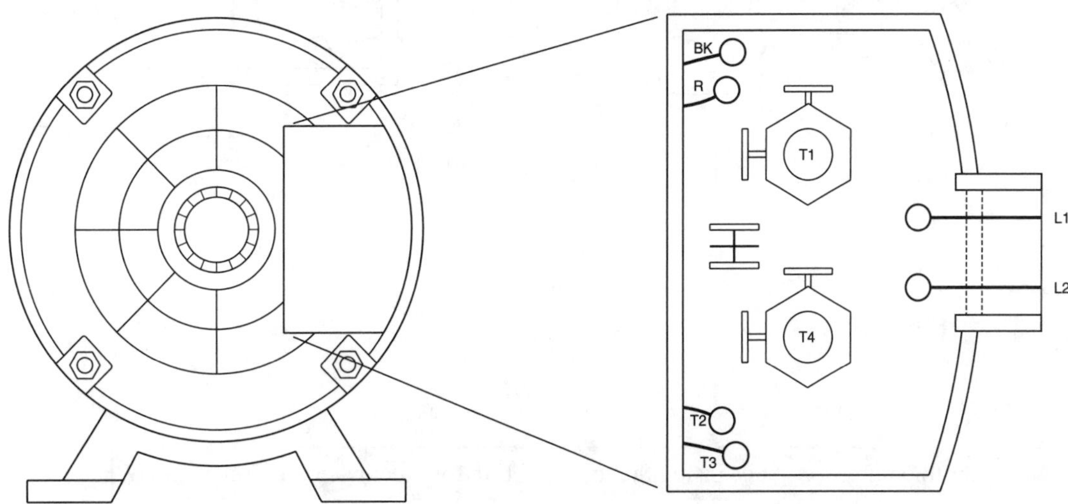

2. Connect the motor and power leads inside the terminal box for clockwise rotation at 115 V.

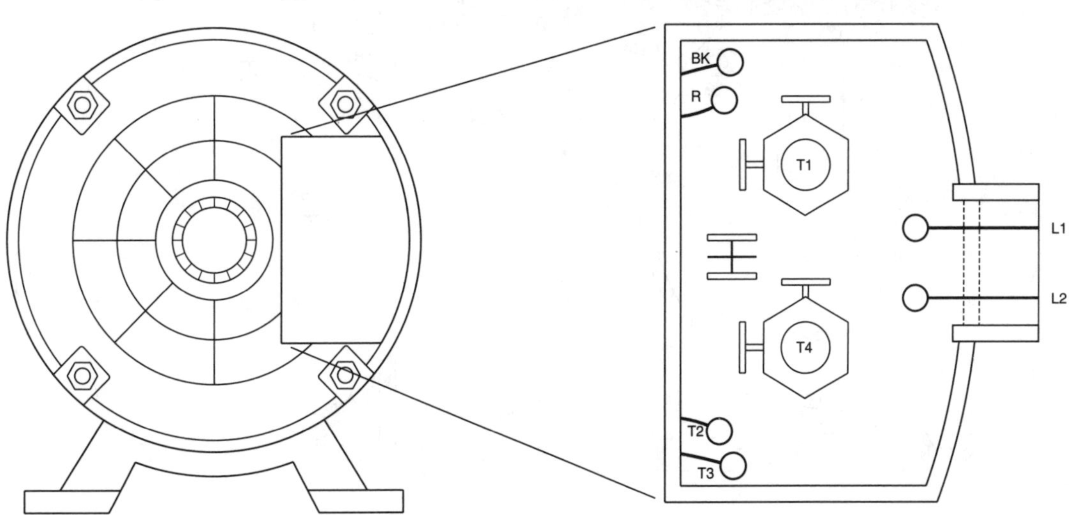

3. Connect the motor and power leads inside the terminal box for counterclockwise rotation at 230 V.

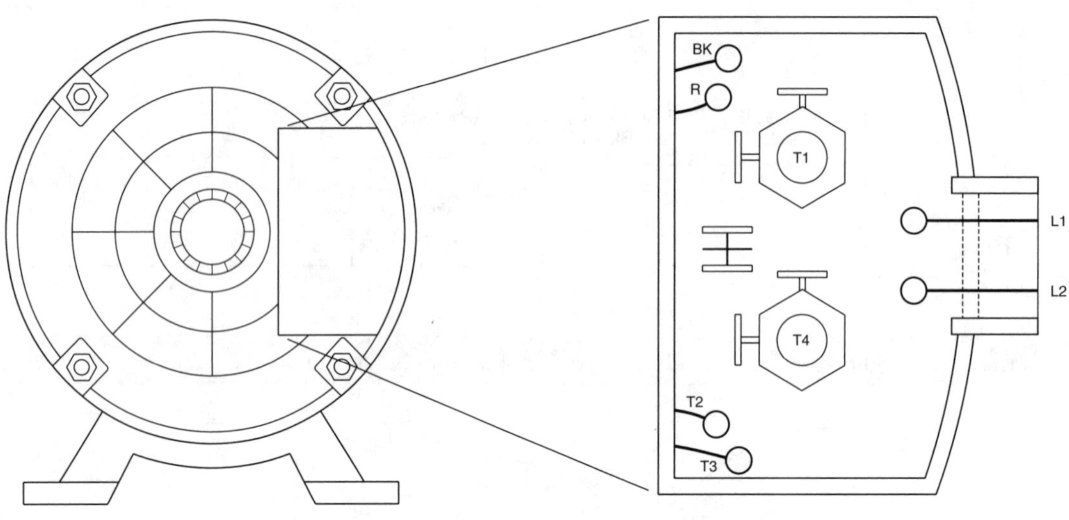

4. Connect the motor and power leads inside the terminal box for clockwise rotation at 230 V.

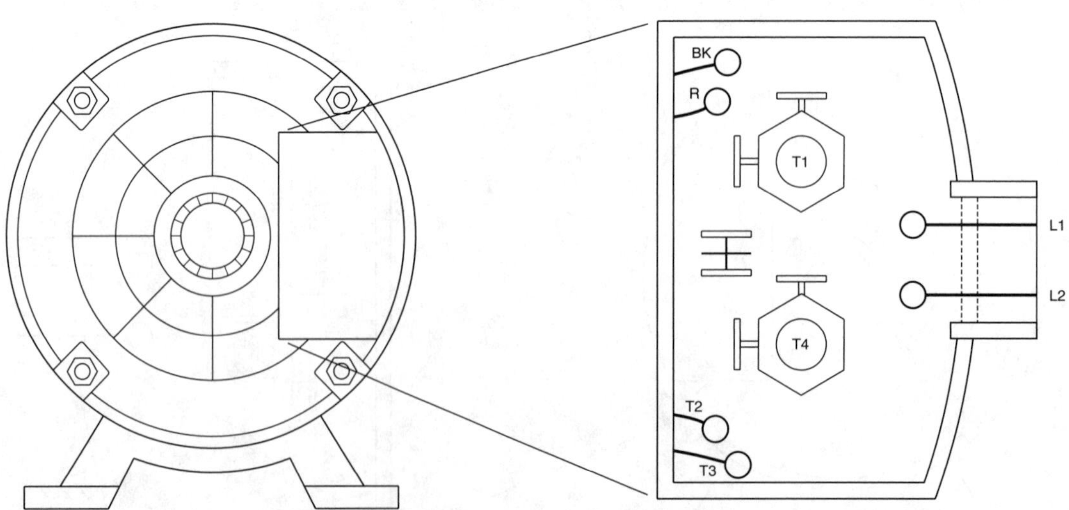

◯ Activity 1-13. Wiring Multispeed, Single-Phase Motors

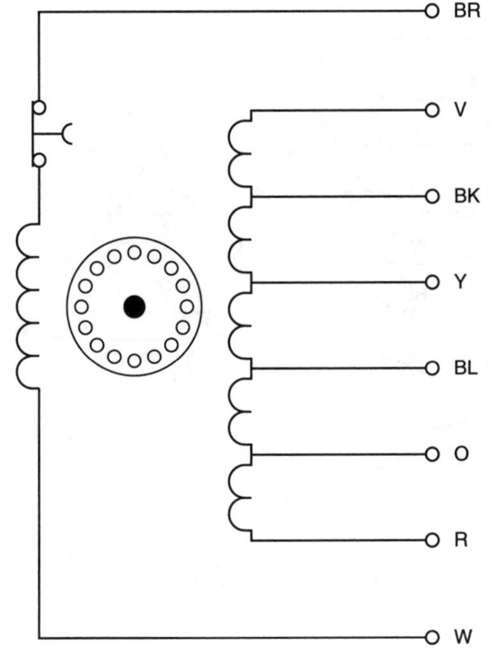

SPEED	L1	L2	INSULATE SEPARATELY
HIGH	BR-V	BK-W	Y, BL, O, R
MED-HIGH	BR-V	Y-W	BK, BL, O, R
MED	BR-V	BL-W	BK, Y, O, R
MED-LOW	BR-V	O-W	BK, Y, BL, R
LOW	BR-V	R-W	BK, Y, BL, O

FOR CLOCKWISE ROTATION
INTERCHANGE BROWN AND WHITE

1. Connect the motor and power leads inside the terminal box for low-speed counterclockwise rotation.

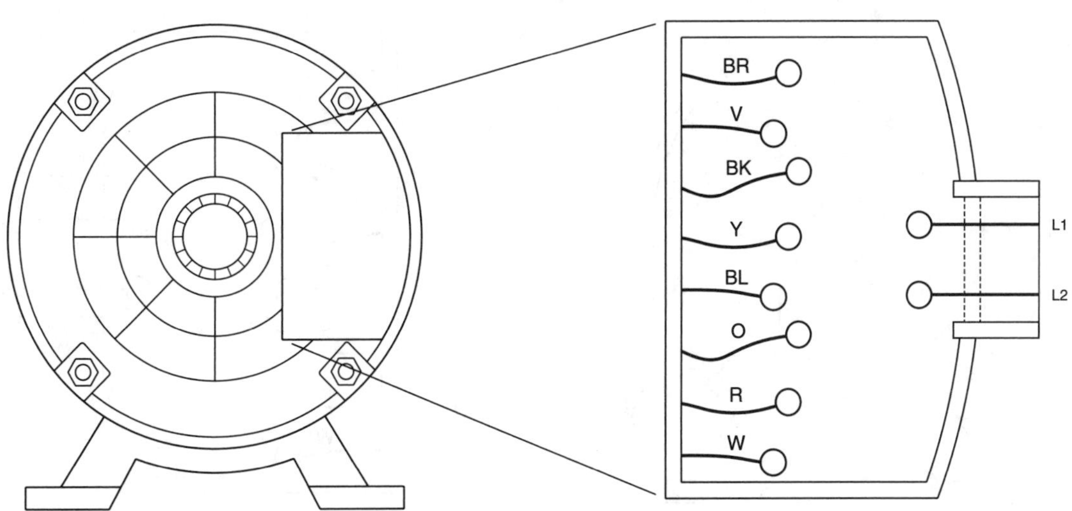

2. Connect the motor and power leads inside the terminal box for medium-speed counterclockwise rotation.

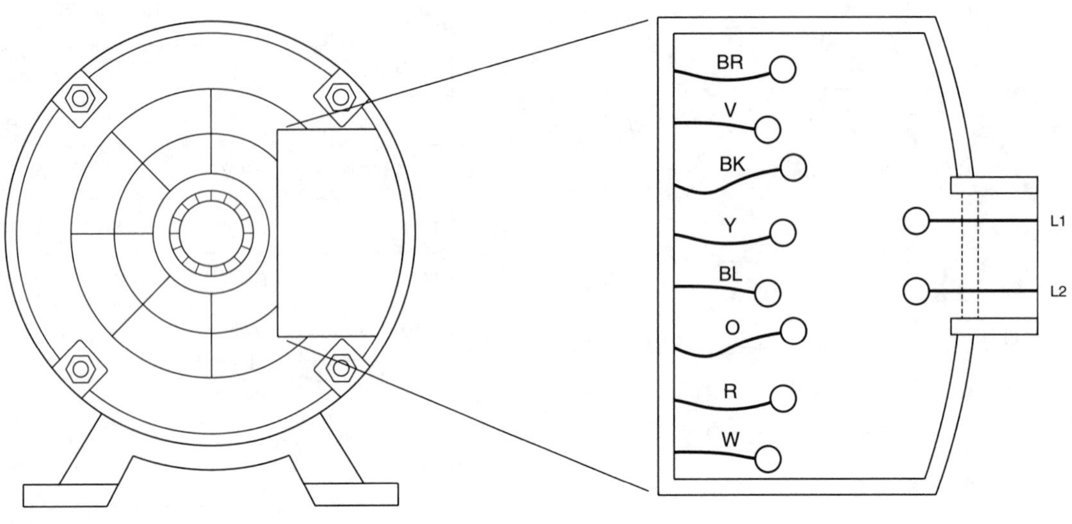

3. Connect the motor and power leads inside the terminal box for high-speed clockwise rotation.

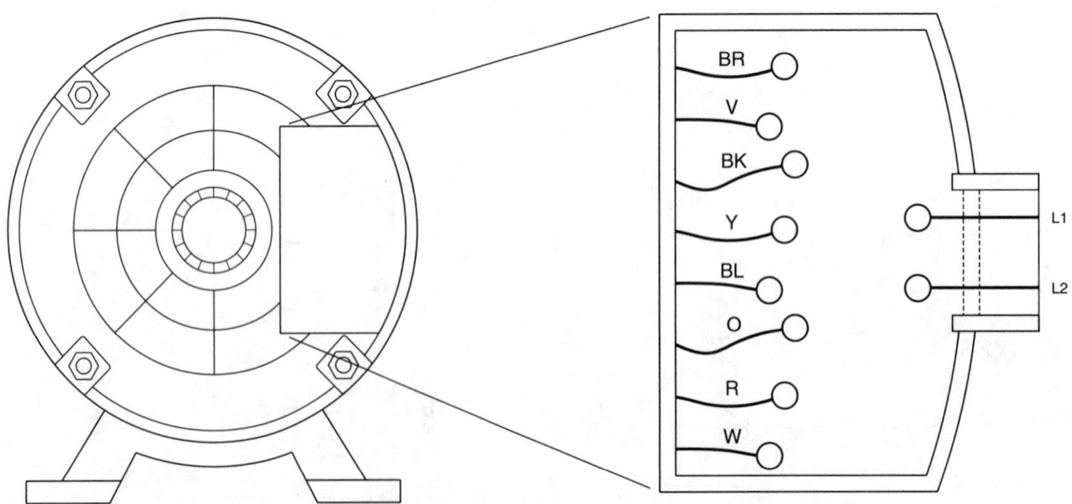

Name ______________________________ Date ______________

chapter 1

TRADE TEST

SINGLE-PHASE MOTORS

Completion

__________ 1. ________ current reverses its direction of flow twice per cycle.

__________ 2. The ________ is the rotating part of a motor.

__________ 3. Slip is the difference between ________ speed and the actual speed of a motor.

__________ 4. Line frequency is the number of ________ of supplied voltage per second.

__________ 5. ________ is the force that produces rotation in a motor.

__________ 6. ________ force moves rotating bodies away from the center of rotation.

__________ 7. Split-phase motors are generally available in sizes ranging from $\frac{1}{30}$ HP to ________ HP.

__________ 8. A(n) ________ connection provides only one path for current flow.

__________ 9. The dual-voltage rating of 1ϕ motors is usually ________ V.

__________ 10. A(n) ________ is a device that stores an electric charge.

__________ 11. ________ is the number of complete electric cycles per second.

__________ 12. The capacitor start-and-run motor uses ________ capacitors.

__________ 13. ________ torque is the torque a motor produces when the rotor is stationary and full power is applied to the motor.

__________ 14. Many small businesses and almost all dwellings operate on ________-phase power.

__________ 15. A(n) ________ is the stationary part of a motor to which the power is directly connected.

__________ 16. The simplest method used to start a 1ϕ motor is by ________ the stator poles.

__________ 17. A(n) ________ switch operates its contacts when a preset temperature is reached.

__________ 18. ________ is the positive or negative state of an object.

__________ 19. In normal operation, a thermal switch is in the ________ position.

__________ 20. ________ is the amount of current for which a conductor or device is rated.

True-False

T F 1. A split-phase motor can run on one or more phases.

T F 2. Alternating current is usually generated and distributed as 3ϕ power.

T F 3. The magnetic field of a 1ϕ motor produces poles on the rotor, which are the same polarity as the stator poles.

T F 4. A starting method is required to start a 1ϕ motor.

T F 5. Inductive reactance is the flow of alternating current in a circuit caused by inductance.

T F 6. The capacitor-run motor leaves the starting winding and capacitor in the circuit at all times.

T F 7. Many 1ϕ motors can be connected for either of two voltages.

T F 8. Ambient temperature is the temperature of the air around a piece of equipment.

T F 9. A dual-voltage motor develops the same amount of power for either voltage.

T F 10. A two-speed, split-phase motor is commonly wound to run on either two or four poles.

Multiple Choice

__________ 1. The starting torque of a split-phase motor is ________% of the full-load torque.

A. 50–100
B. 75–200
C. 250–350
D. 350–450

__________ 2. In a split-phase motor, the main winding current lags the applied voltage by about ________%.

A. 20
B. 30
C. 40
D. 50

__________ 3. A 1725 rpm motor (1800 rpm synchronous speed) has a slip of approximately ________%.

A. 2
B. 4
C. 8
D. 24

__________ 4. Shaded-pole motors are commonly ________.

A. ¼ HP or less
B. used as cooling fans in small appliances
C. both A and B
D. neither A nor B

__________ 5. When a split-phase motor is first connected to power, the ________.

A. inductive reactance of the starting winding is lower
B. resistance is lower than the running winding
C. running winding is in phase with the starting winding
D. neither A, B, nor C

__________ 6. The centrifugal switch of a split-phase motor is ________.

A. often located outside the enclosure for easier repair
B. connected in series with the starting winding
C. used to automatically de-energize the starting winding at a set speed
D. A, B, and C

__________ 7. A 1ϕ, dual-voltage, split-phase motor typically is set for ________ V.

A. 110/220
B. 115/230
C. 120/240
D. neither A, B, nor C

__________ 8. A(n) ________° phase difference is required to produce maximum starting torque in a split-phase motor.

A. 20
B. 60
C. 90
D. 180

__________ 9. The industrial standard for reversing the direction of rotation of a 1ϕ motor is ________.

A. reversing the starting winding
B. reversing the running winding
C. both A and B
D. neither A nor B

__________ 10. A ½ HP capacitor motor requires a capacitor with a value of ________ μF.

A. 90–110
B. 110–150
C. 150–190
D. 190–260

Problems

1. Determine the total voltage and total capacitance.

A. _______ V

B. _______ μF

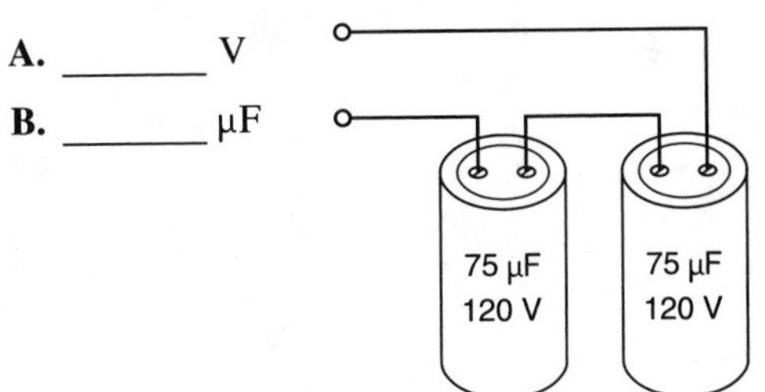

C. _______ V

D. _______ μF

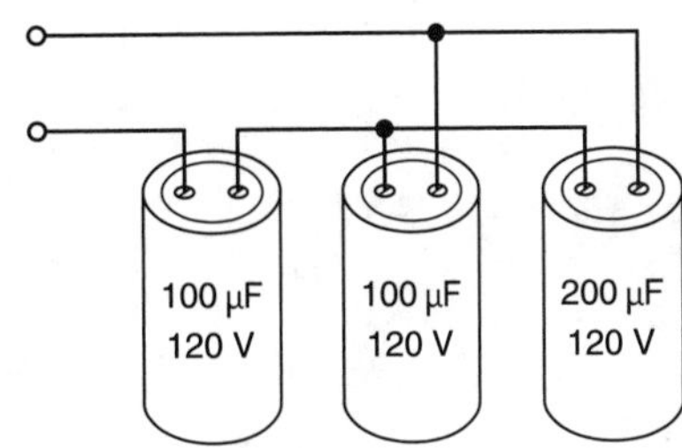

E. _______ V

F. _______ μF

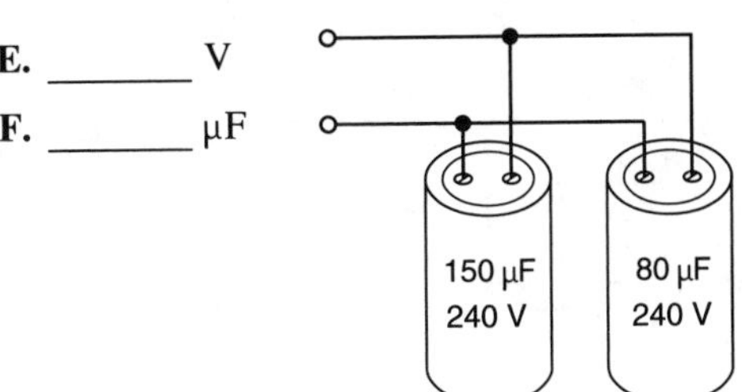

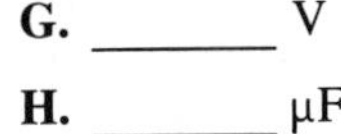

G. _______ V

H. _______ μF

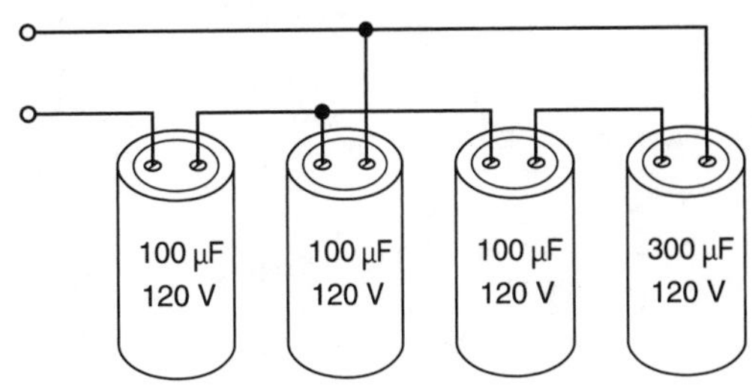

2. Determine the actual speed of each motor.

ACTUAL SPEED	POLES	SYNCHRONOUS SPEED	% SLIP
A. __________ rpm	2	3600 RPM	4.2
B. __________ rpm	4	1800 RPM	4.5
C. __________ rpm	6	1200 RPM	5.0
D. __________ rpm	8	900 RPM	5.1

3. State the value and tolerance of each resistor. See Resistor Color Codes.

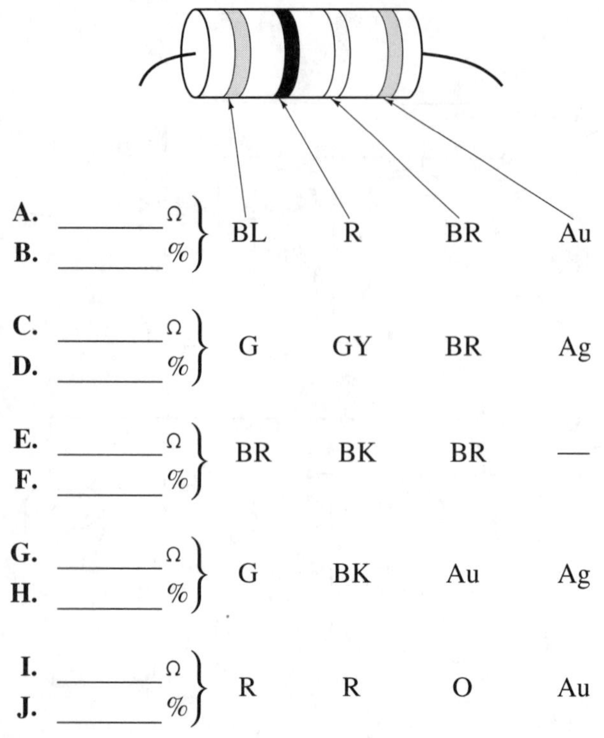

RESISTOR COLOR CODES				
Color	Number		Multiplier	Tolerance (%)
	1st	2nd		
Black (BK)	0	0	1	0
Brown (BR)	1	1	10	—
Red (R)	2	2	100	—
Orange (O)	3	3	1000	—
Yellow (Y)	4	4	10,000	—
Green (G)	5	5	100,000	—
Blue (BL)	6	6	1,000,000	—
Violet (V)	7	7	10,000,000	—
Gray (GY)	8	8	100,000,000	—
White (W)	9	9	1,000,000,000	—
Gold (Au)	—	—	0.1	5
Silver (Ag)	—	—	0.01	10
None	—	—	0	20

4. Based on the meter readings, is the thermal switch good or defective?

A. The thermal switch is ______________.

B. The thermal switch is ______________.

C. The thermal switch is ______________.

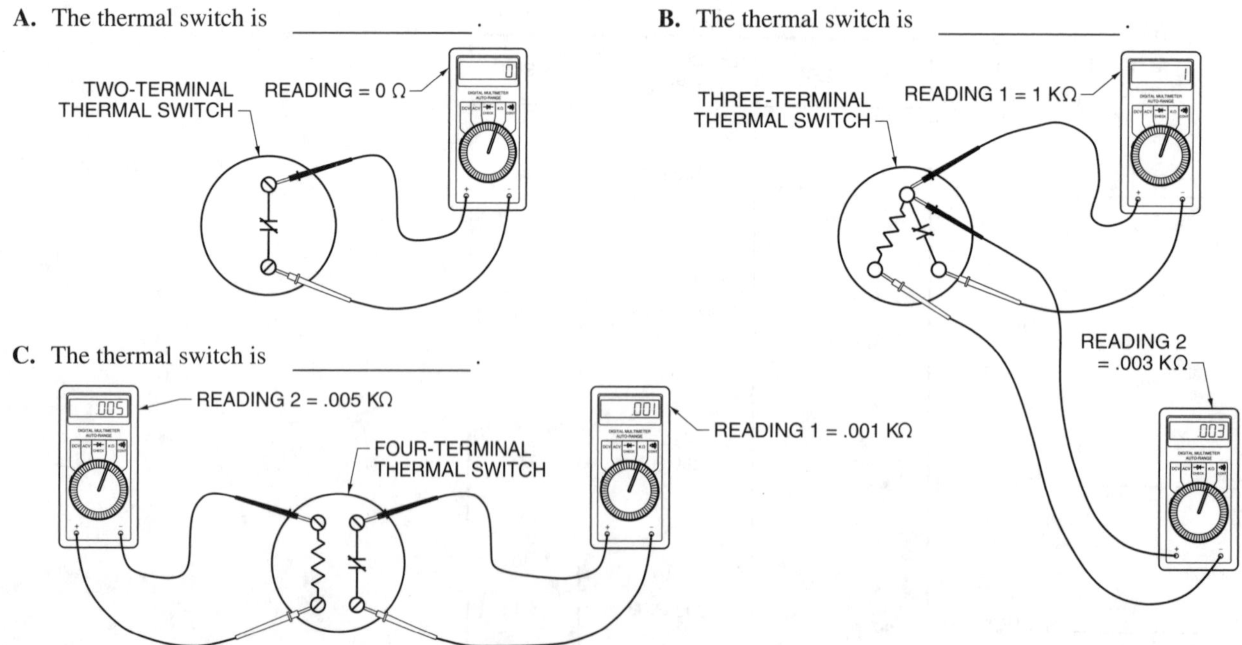

5. A split-phase, dual-voltage motor has eight terminals. The motor manufacturer has brought out each motor winding and the centrifugal switch to a terminal lug. There are no internal motor connections, and the centrifugal switch is not connected to the motor windings. See Ohmmeter Readings.

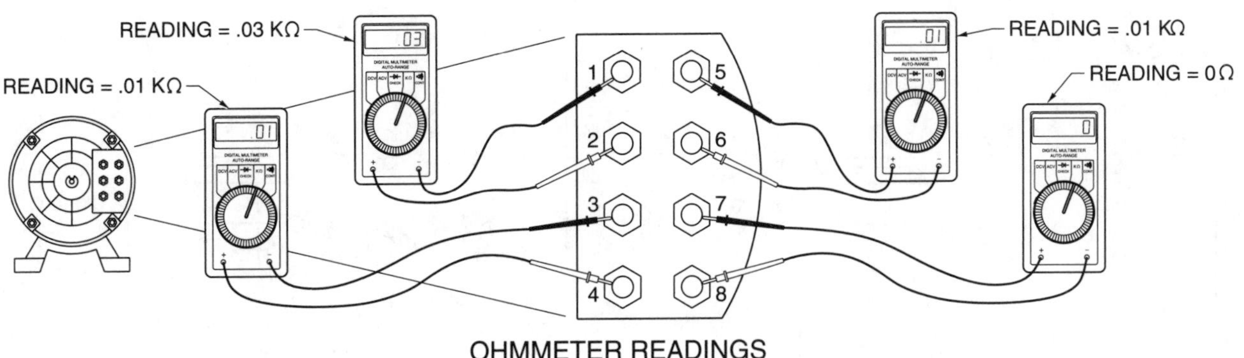

OHMMETER READINGS

Using Ohmmeter Readings, mark the following:

__________ **A.** Lower-numbered terminals for one section of the running winding

__________ **B.** Higher-numbered terminals for one section of the running winding

__________ **C.** Terminals for centrifugal switch

__________ **D.** Terminals for starting winding

Using the answers from **A–D**, mark terminal post numbers on Motor Diagram.

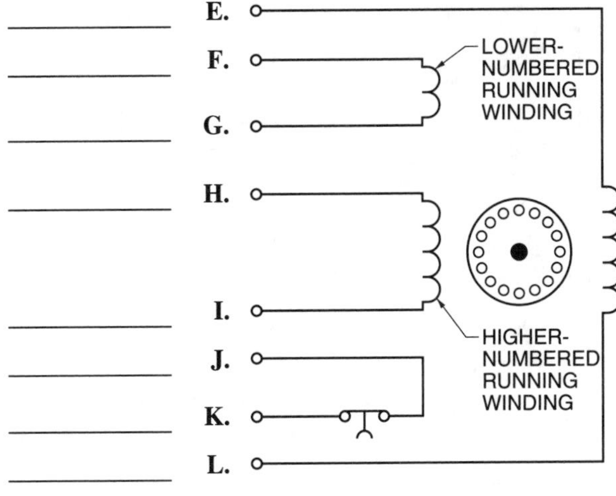

MOTOR DIAGRAM

M. Using Motor Diagram, wire Low-Voltage Connection.

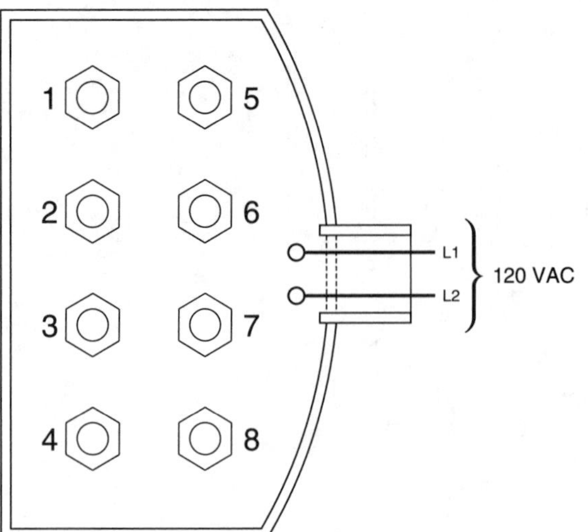

LOW-VOLTAGE CONNECTION

N. Using Motor Diagram, wire Low-Voltage Connection (Changing Direction of Rotation).

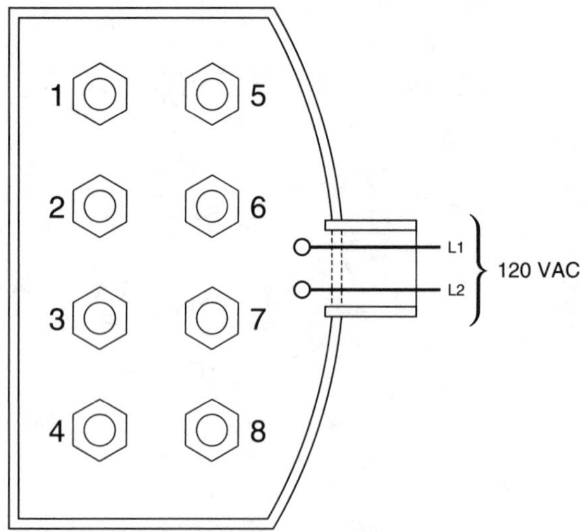

LOW-VOLTAGE CONNECTION
(CHANGING DIRECTION OF ROTATION)

O. Using Motor Diagram, wire High-Voltage Connection.

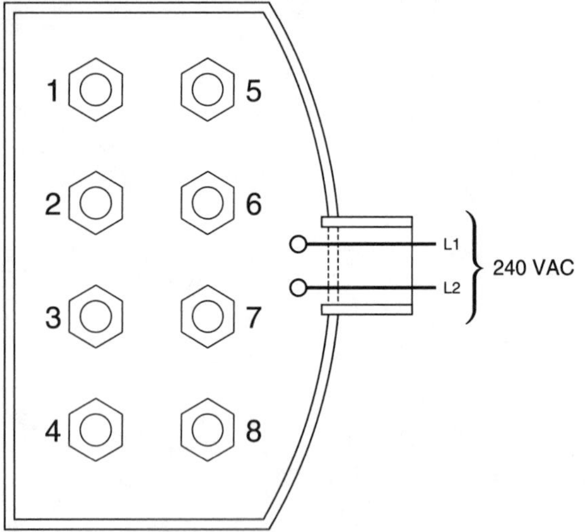

HIGH-VOLTAGE CONNECTION

P. Using Motor Diagram, wire High-Voltage Connection (Changing Direction of Rotation).

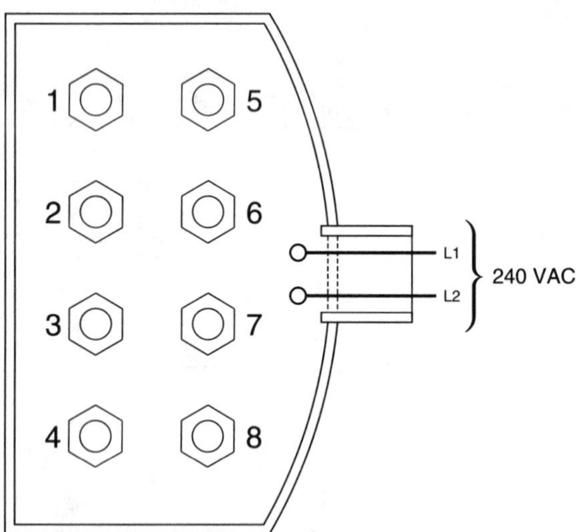

HIGH-VOLTAGE CONNECTION
(CHANGING DIRECTION OF ROTATION)

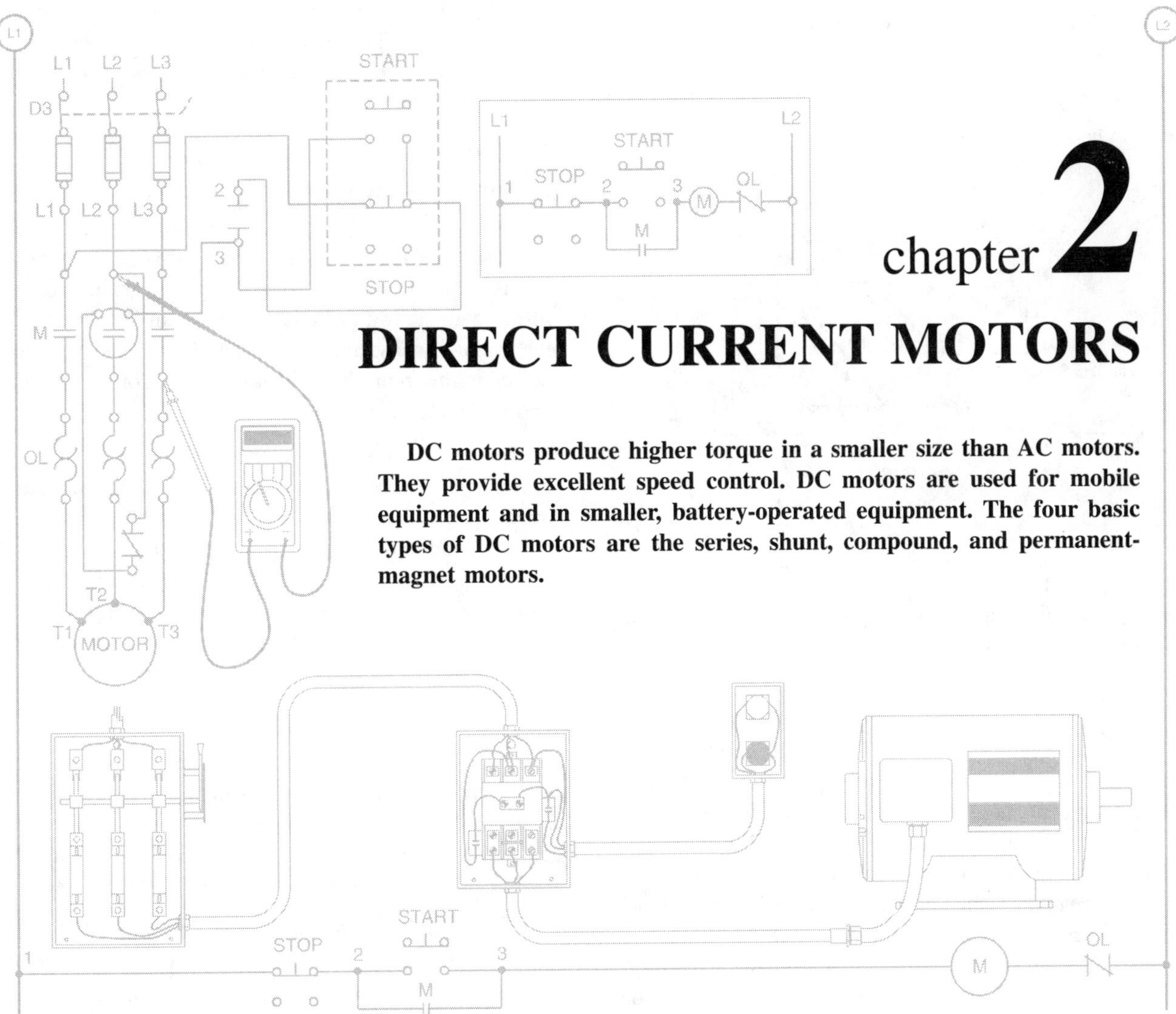

chapter 2
DIRECT CURRENT MOTORS

DC motors produce higher torque in a smaller size than AC motors. They provide excellent speed control. DC motors are used for mobile equipment and in smaller, battery-operated equipment. The four basic types of DC motors are the series, shunt, compound, and permanent-magnet motors.

DIRECT CURRENT MOTORS

A *DC (direct current) motor* is a motor that uses direct current connected to the field and armature to produce rotation. *Direct current* is current that flows in one direction only. By connecting voltage directly to the field and armature, the DC motor produces higher torque in a smaller size than AC motors.

The selection of any type of motor is based on the requirements of the load that the motor is to drive. DC motors are more expensive to purchase and maintain than AC motors of the same size. Therefore, AC motors are usually the first choice for most applications.

DC motors provide excellent speed control for acceleration and deceleration with effective and simple torque control. DC motors perform better than AC motors in most traction equipment. DC motors are used for mobile equipment, such as golf carts, quarry and mining equipment, and locomotives. DC motors are also used in smaller, battery-operated equipment.

The four basic types of DC motors are:

DC series motor

DC shunt motor

DC compound motor

Permanent-magnet motor

These motors have the same external appearance, but differ in their internal construction and output performance. The selection of the type of DC motor to use is based on the mechanical requirements of the applied load.

The field windings of a DC motor are used to develop a magnetic field. See Figure 2-1. When current is passed through a conductor in the magnetic field, a mechanical force is exerted on the conductor. This conductor is connected to the shaft of the motor. The amount of force exerted on the conductor (motor shaft) is dependent upon the following factors:

- Intensity (strength) of the magnetic field
- Current passing through the conductor inside the magnetic field
- Length (or number) of the conductor inside the magnetic field

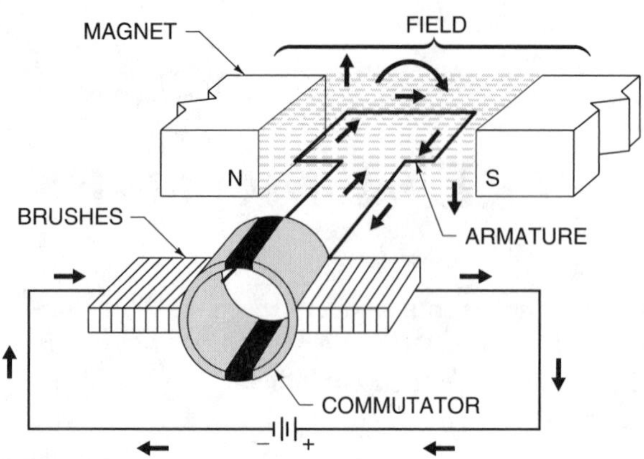

Figure 2-1. The field windings of a DC motor are used to develop a magnetic field.

By increasing any of these factors, the force on the motor shaft can be increased. Generally, the intensity of the field and the current are changed to increase force. The length of the conductors inside the magnetic field is not commonly changed in the field. The conductor length is fixed when the motor is manufactured.

An *armature* is the rotating part of a DC motor, which is mounted on the motor shaft. A *commutator* is the part of an armature that connects each armature winding to insulated copper bars on which the brushes ride. As the armature rotates, brushes make contact with successive copper bars.

Brushes are the sliding contacts that make the connection between the rotating armature and the stationary part of the DC motor. Brushes are made of carbon or graphite.

The armature windings, commutator, and brushes are arranged so that the flow of current is in one direction in the windings on one side of the armature. The flow of current is in the opposite direction in the windings on the opposite side of the armature. DC power is delivered into the armature through the brushes, which ride on the commutator sections. The commutator is mounted on the same shaft as the armature and rotates with it.

To increase the torque of the motor, the armature has a large number of coils connected to a large number of commutator sections. The field coils may be electromagnets or permanent magnets.

In DC motors, the rotating part of the motor is the armature. In AC motors, the rotating part of the motor is the rotor. In DC motors, the stationary part of the motor is the field. In AC motors, the stationary part of the motor is the stator.

Motor Construction

The frame of a DC motor is made of steel or cast iron and is constructed so that the field poles can be mounted inside with screws or bolts or can be an integral part of the frame on very small motors. Two end plates are connected to the frame. They bear the weight of the armature and commutator assembly.

The end plates contain the bearings in which the motor shaft rotates. The brushes are located in brush holders, which are mounted to a brush assembly commonly mounted on the front end plate. The brush assembly is constructed so that the brush position can be changed if required. The main parts of a DC motor are the field, interpoles, armature, commutator, and brushes.

Field. A *field* is the stationary windings, or magnets, of a DC motor. Depending upon the type of DC motor, field windings are connected in series or in parallel with the armature windings. The field provides a magnetic field around the armature.

The field structure includes a yoke that holds the pole bodies. The field provides a magnetic field by permanent magnets or by electromagnets. The electromagnets are supplied with power by an external DC power supply. In some motors, interpoles are added between the main poles.

Interpoles. *Interpoles* are auxiliary poles placed between the main field poles of the motor. See Figure 2-2. The interpoles are made with larger size wire than the main field poles, in order to carry armature current. They are smaller in overall size than the main field poles because they require less windings. The interpoles are connected in series with the armature windings. Interpoles are also known as commutating field poles.

Interpoles are used to reduce sparking at the brushes of larger DC motors. They are used with shunt and compound DC motors of .5 HP or more. The interpoles reduce sparking at the brushes by helping to overcome the effect of armature reaction.

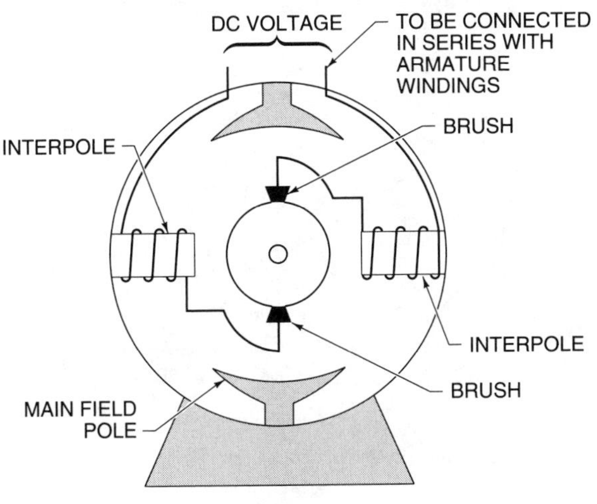

Figure 2-2. Interpoles are auxiliary poles placed between the main field poles of the motor.

Armature. The armature is the rotating part of a DC motor. See Figure 2-3. It consists of laminated steel slots connected to the shaft. The armature core is made of notched laminations, which form slots when stacked. The armature conductors are pressed into the slots. These conductors are then connected to the commutator.

Commutator. The commutator consists of a series of copper segments connected to the armature winding. The commutator and the brushes supply the coil windings with current and reverse the current flow as needed. The commutators function is to act as a rotating rectifier. A *rectifier* is a component that converts AC to DC by allowing the current to move in only one direction.

A typical commutator is constructed of copper commutator bars, which are insulated from one another. The armature coils are connected to each of the copper commutator bars.

Brushes. The brushes provide contact between the external power source and the commutator. See Figure 2-4. The current is supplied to the commutator by the brushes, which ride on the commutator, and make contact as it is turned. The brushes are usually made from various grades of carbon and are held in a stationary position by brush holders. A pigtail connects the brushes to the external circuit. A *pigtail* is an extended, flexible connection. The pigtail for the brushes is a braided copper conductor.

Each brush is free to move up and down on the brush holder. This freedom allows the brush to follow irregularities in the surface of the commutator. A spring placed behind each brush forces the brush to make contact on the commutator. The spring pressure is usually adjustable, as is the entire brush-holder assembly, allowing shifting of the position of the brushes on the commutator.

DC Series Motor

A *DC series motor* is a motor with the field connected in series with the armature. The field must carry the load current passing through the armature. It has comparatively few turns of heavy-gauge wire.

The DC series motor is used as a traction motor because it produces the highest torque of all DC motors. The DC series motor can develop 500% of its full-load torque upon starting. Typical applications include traction bridges, hoists, gates, and starting motors in automobiles.

The speed regulation of a DC series motor is poor. As the mechanical load on the motor is reduced, a simultaneous reduction of current occurs in the field and the armature. If the mechanical load is entirely removed, the speed of the motor increases without limit and may destroy the motor. For this reason, series motors are always permanently connected to the load they control.

The wires extending from the series coil are marked S1 and S2. The wires extending from the armature are marked A1 and A2. See Figure 2-5.

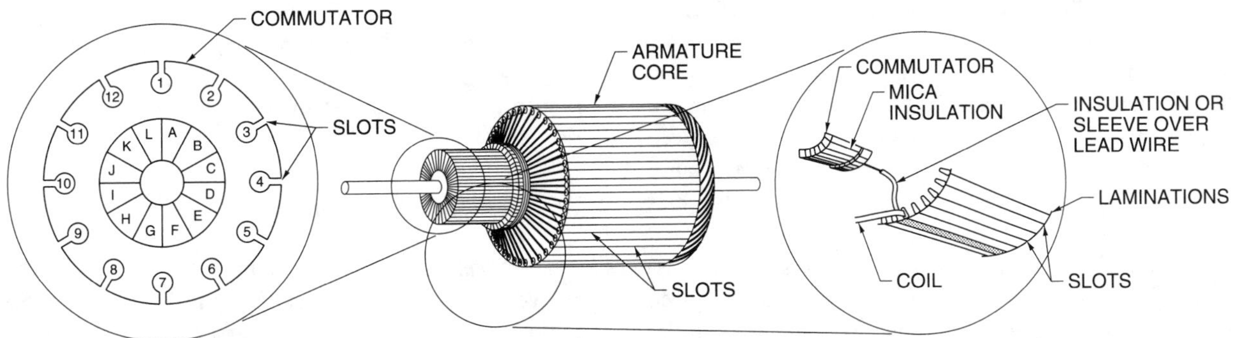

Figure 2-3. The armature is the rotating part of a DC motor.

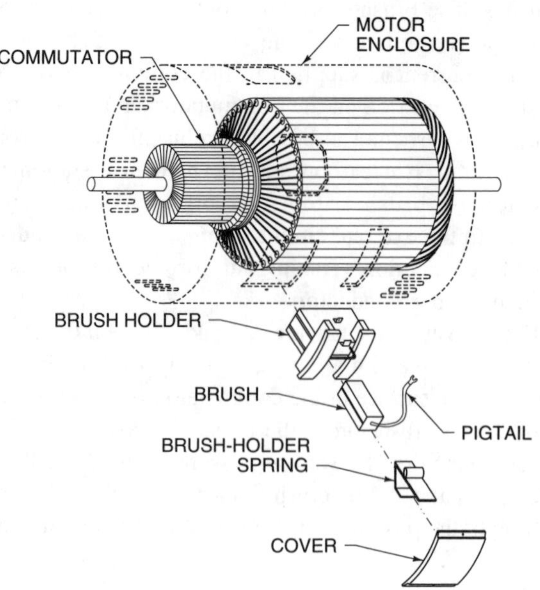

Figure 2-4. Brushes provide contact between the external power source and the commutator.

DC Shunt Motor

A *DC shunt motor* is a motor with the field connected in shunt (parallel) with the armature. See Figure 2-6. The field has numerous turns of wire, and the current in the field is independent of the armature, providing the DC shunt motor with excellent speed control.

The DC shunt motor is used where constant or adjustable speed is required and starting conditions are moderate. Typical applications include fans, blowers, centrifugal pumps, conveyors, elevators, woodworking machinery, and metalworking machinery.

The field windings extending from the shunt field of a DC shunt motor are marked F1 and F2. The armature windings are marked A1 and A2.

The shunt field may be connected to the same power supply as the armature or may be connected to another power supply. A *self-excited shunt field* is a shunt field connected to the same power supply as the armature. A *separately excited shunt field* is a shunt field connected to a different power supply than the armature.

The speed of a separately excited, DC shunt motor can be controlled by varying the field current. Field speed control is accomplished by inserting external resistance in series with the shunt field circuit. As resistance is increased in the field circuit, field current reduces, and the speed of the motor increases. Conversely, as resistance is decreased, field current increases, and the speed of the motor decreases. Selection of the proper controller assures a specific speed-control range.

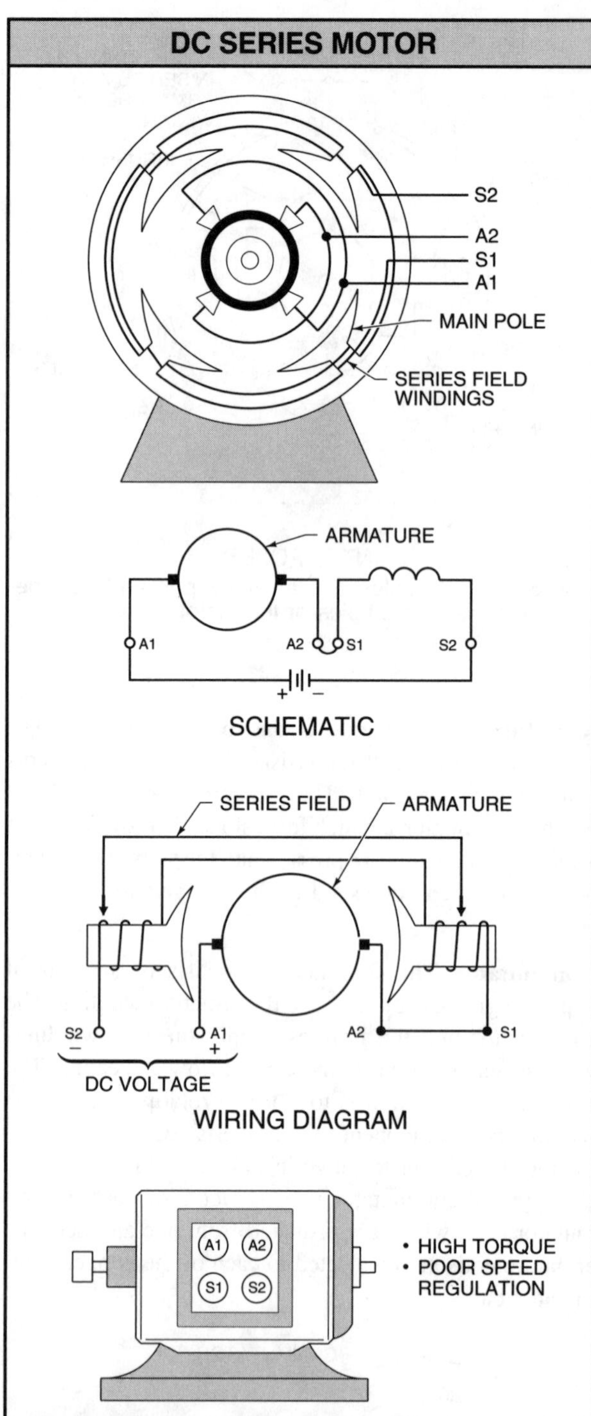

Figure 2-5. A DC series motor is a motor with the field connected in series with the armature.

DC Compound Motor

A *DC compound motor* is a motor with a field connected in both series and shunt with the armature. See Figure 2-7. In a DC compound motor, the field coil is a combination of the series field (S1 and S2) and

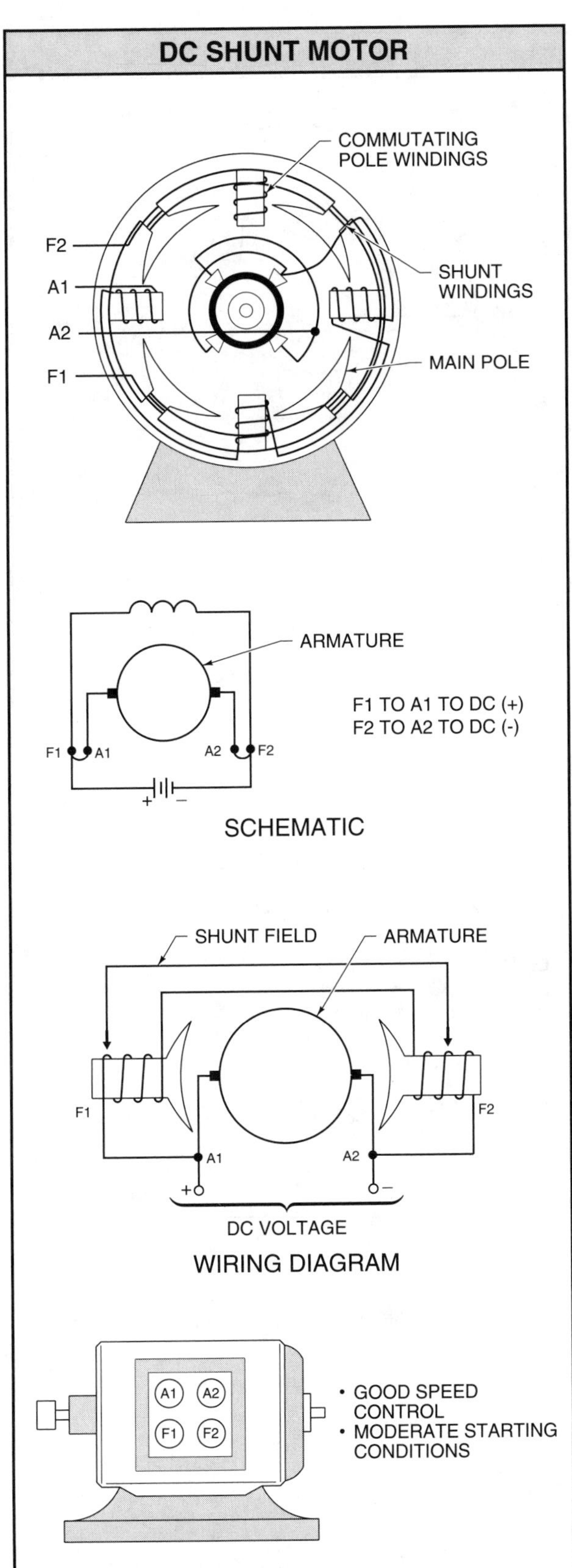

Figure 2-6. A DC shunt motor is a motor with the field connected in shunt (parallel) with the armature.

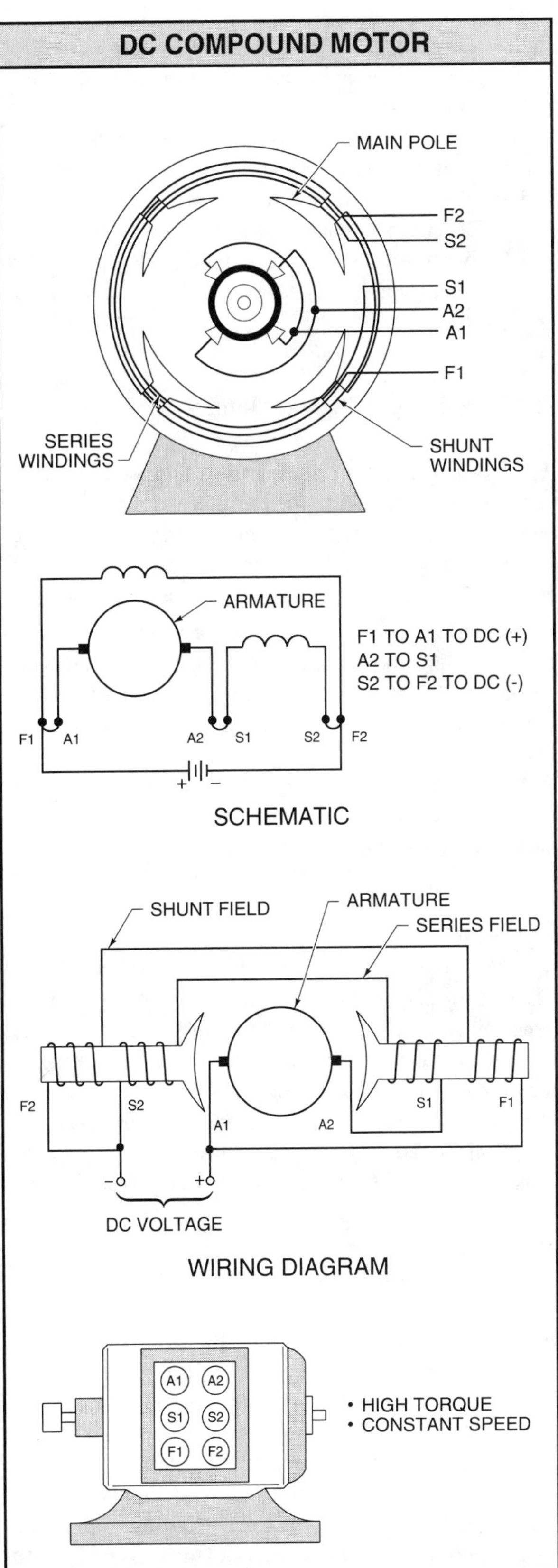

Figure 2-7. A DC compound motor is a motor with a field connected in both series and shunt with the armature.

shunt field (F1 and F2). The series field is connected in series with the armature. The shunt field is connected in parallel with the series field and armature. This arrangement gives the motor some of the advantages of both the DC series motor (high torque) and the DC shunt motor (constant speed).

The DC compound motor is used when starting torque and fairly constant speed are required. Typical applications include punch presses, shears, bending machines, and hoists.

DC Permanent-Magnet Motor

A *DC permanent-magnet motor* is a motor that uses magnets, not a coil of wire, for the field winding. The DC permanent-magnet motor has molded magnets mounted into a steel shell. The permanent magnets are the field coils. DC power is supplied only to the armature.

The DC permanent-magnet motor is used in automobiles to control power seats, power windows, and windshield wipers. It produces relatively high torque at low speeds and provides some self-braking when removed from power.

DC permanent-magnet motors are not designed to run continuously because they overheat rapidly. Overheating destroys the permanent magnets.

Reversing

The direction of rotation of the shaft of all DC motors depends on the direction of the current in the field circuit and the armature circuit. To reverse the direction of rotation, the current direction in either the field or the armature is reversed. Reversing the power leads does not reverse the direction of armature rotation because this situation causes both the field and armature currents to be reversed.

UNIVERSAL MOTOR

A *universal motor* is a motor that can be operated on either DC or 1ϕ, AC. The motor characteristics are approximately the same on AC as on DC, provided the AC voltage does not exceed 60 cycles. The universal motor is electrically the same as the DC series motor. Current flows from the supply, through the field, through the armature windings, and back to the supply. The main parts of a universal motor are the field coils, which are stationary, and the armature, which rotates. See Figure 2-8.

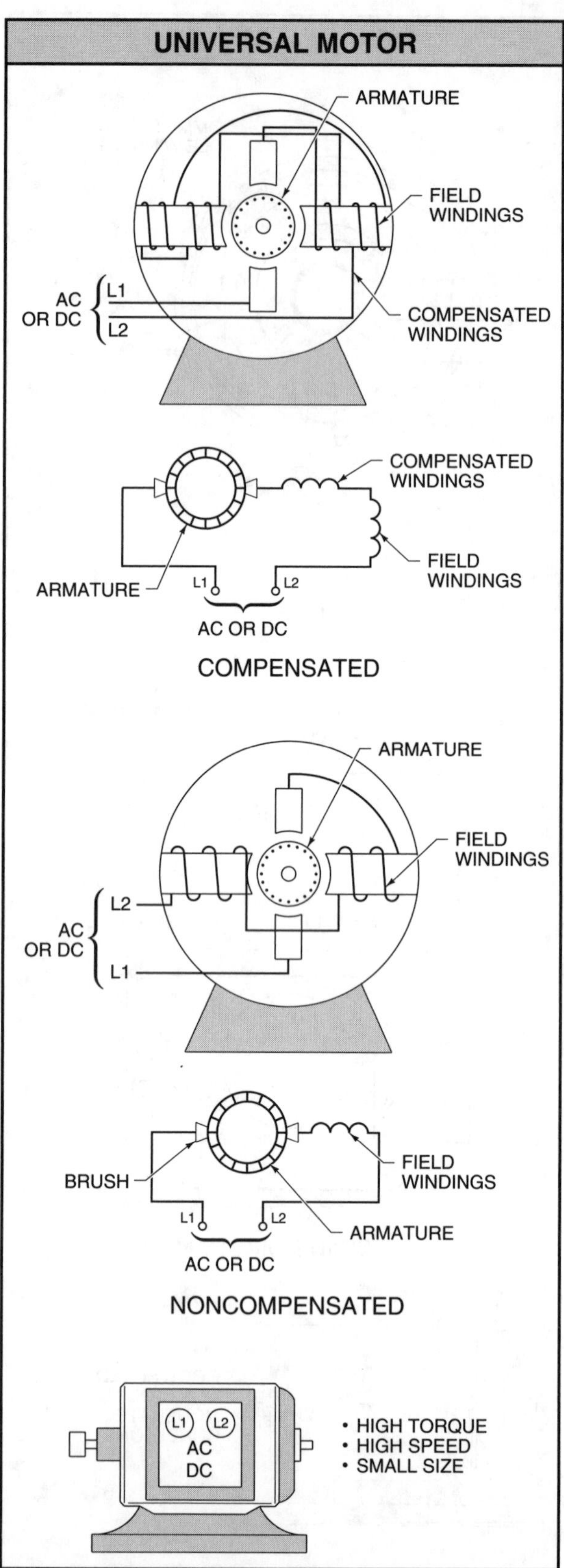

Figure 2-8. A universal motor is a motor that can be operated on either DC or 1ϕ, AC.

The universal motor is the most common motor found in dwellings. The main advantages of the universal motor are its high torque, high speed, and smaller size when compared to other AC motors. It provides high torque in a minimum of space. Universal motors are commonly used in such applications as:

- Kitchen appliances (garbage disposals, mixers, blenders, food processors, and can openers)
- Sewing machines
- Vacuum cleaners
- Portable hand tools (saws, drills, routers, grinders, etc.)
- Electric razors
- Cameras
- Calculators with printouts

The principle of operation of the universal motor is basically the same as the DC series motor. The ends of the armature coils are connected to segments of a split-ring commutator. The segments of the commutator are usually made of copper or brass and are fastened to the armature shaft. Mica, or a hard fiber, is used to electrically insulate the commutator segments from one another. The soft carbon brushes are mounted in fixed, insulated holders that allow them to slide across the commutator segments as the armature rotates.

When the universal motor is connected to an AC voltage supply, the current flows through the armature and the field windings. The field produces an AC flux that reacts with the current flowing through the armature to produce torque. Because the armature current and the flux reverse simultaneously as the AC current changes direction, the torque always acts in the same direction. Unlike an AC motor, no revolving field is produced in the universal motor.

Compensated Universal Motor

A *compensated universal motor* is a universal motor with extra windings added to the field poles. These extra windings are connected in series with the armature windings. Compensated universal motors are usually ¼ HP and larger and are the most common type of universal motor.

Noncompensated Universal Motor

A *noncompensated universal motor* is a universal motor without extra windings added to the field poles. Noncompensated universal motors are more simple in construction and are less expensive than compensated universal motors. They are commonly used for lower-power output and higher-speed applications.

Operating a noncompensated universal motor on AC poses some problems, such as inefficiency due to hysteresis and eddy-current losses. *Hysteresis* is power loss due to molecular friction because of the inability of individual molecules to instantly change their direction when the current changes direction. This condition occurs when the universal motor is connected to AC.

Eddy current is unwanted current induced in the metal field structure of the motor, due to the rate of change in the induced magnetic flux. Eddy current produces unwanted heat and a loss of power resulting in motor inefficiency. To help reduce inefficiency, the field structures of universal motors are laminated.

Reversing

Universal motors may be nonreversible or reversible. See Figure 2-9. A nonreversible universal motor has two power leads and a ground wire coming out of the motor. The ground wire is used for grounding the frame of the motor. Grounding is required on portable tools, due to the danger of electrocution. The standard direction of rotation for a nonreversible motor is counterclockwise facing the end opposite the shaft extension.

A reversible motor also has two power leads and a ground wire coming out of the motor. Additionally, it has three or more leads available at the reversing switch. When reversing a universal motor, the armature connections must be on electric neutral in order to obtain satisfactory operation in both directions of rotation.

The load neutral is the best position for running a universal motor. However, when reversing a universal motor, the load neutral is not the same for each direction. For one direction, the load neutral is to one side of the neutral plane, and for the other, it is to the other side. Consequently, the motor operates well in one direction, but not in the other direction.

A reversible universal motor may be reversed by using one coil for the forward direction and the other for the reverse direction. A reversible universal motor may also be reversed by reversing the direction of current in the field with a double-pole, double-throw (DPDT) switch. The same field is used for both directions.

Speed Control

Because universal motors are series wound, their no-load speed is very high. Under a no-load condition, a universal motor tends to run away, like the DC series motor. However, this high speed is usually not high enough to damage the universal motor, as it does with larger, DC series

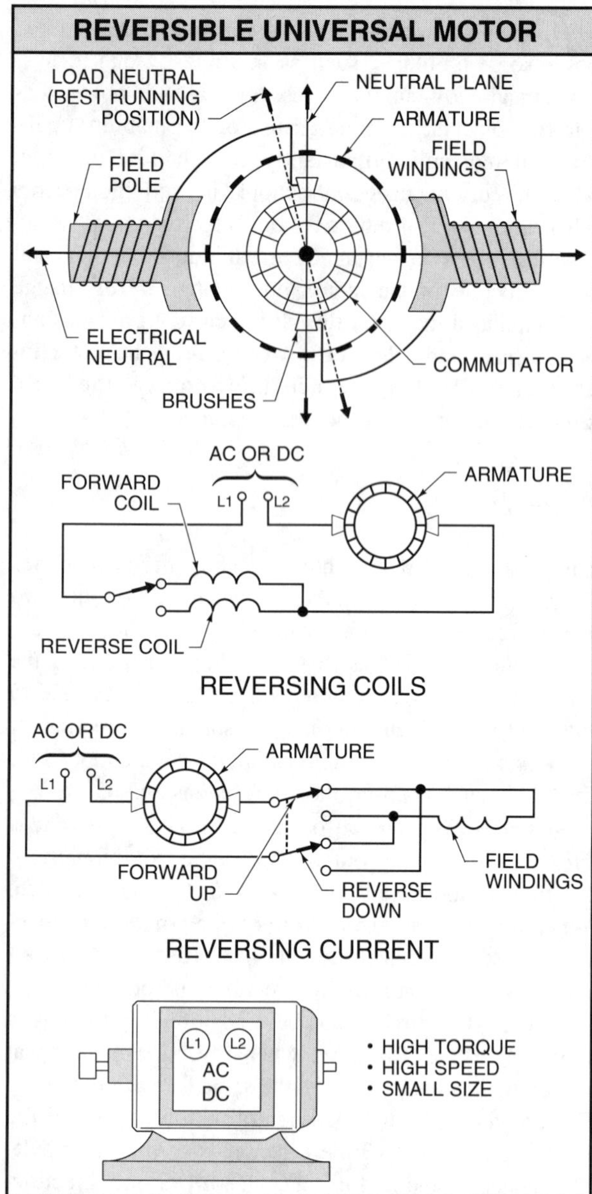

Figure 2-9. Universal motors may be nonreversible or reversible.

motors. The universal motor usually has adequate resistance, due to internal friction. Larger universal motors are often connected directly to the load in order to limit the motor speed.

When a load is placed on a universal motor, the motor speed decreases. As the load is increased, the motor speed continues to decrease. Thus, as small appliances using universal motors are loaded, the speed of the appliance decreases. For example, an electric drywall screwdriver with a universal motor decreases in speed as the drywall screw is turned into the stud. The speed of a universal motor may be controlled by an external resistor, a tapped field, brushes, or solid-state devices. See Figure 2-10.

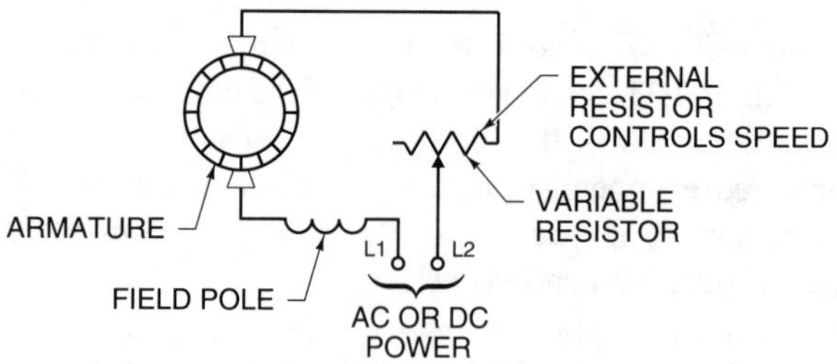

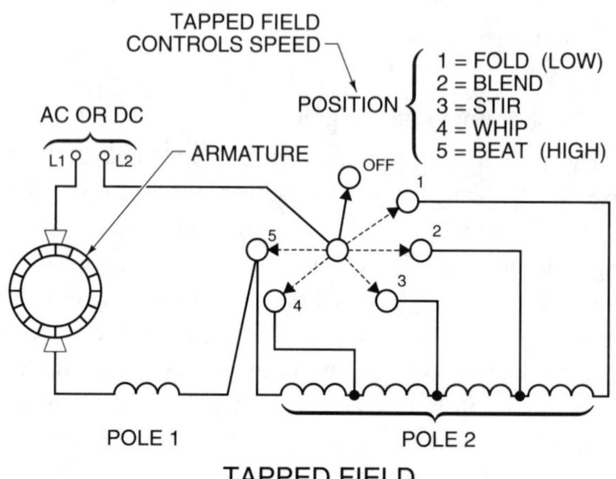

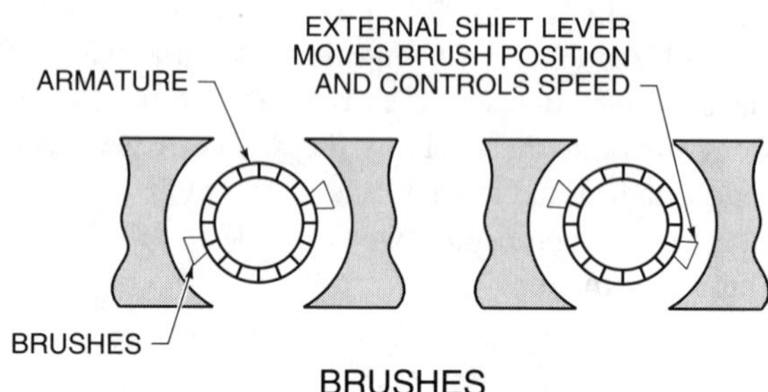

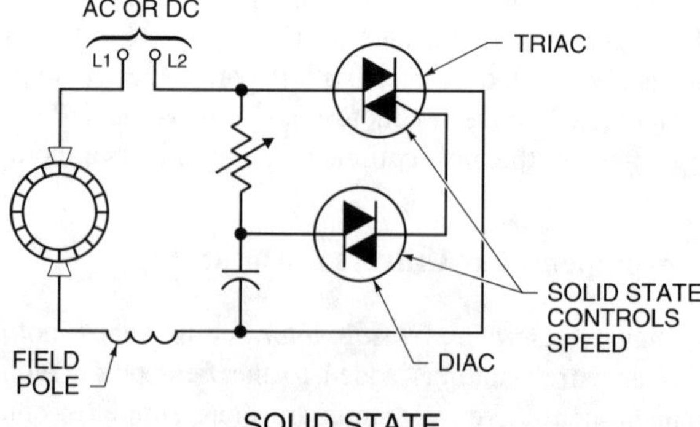

Figure 2-10. The speed of a universal motor may be controlled by either an external resistor, a tapped field, brushes, or solid-state devices.

External Resistor. An external resistor can be connected to control the speed of a universal motor. A fixed resistor has a fixed value for one set speed. A variable resistor has variable values for multiple speeds. The greater the resistor value (in ohms), the slower the motor runs. The lower the resistor value, the faster the motor runs.

Variable speed is required in applications, such as a sewing machine or variable-speed reversible (VSR) drill. In addition to the speed control provided by an external resistor, the external resistor also reduces the torque of the motor. The added resistance of the external resistor reduces applied current and voltage at the armature.

Tapped Field. A tapped field may be used to vary the speed of a universal motor. In these circuits, the speed of the motor is controlled by tapping one field pole at various points. This varies the field strength of the field poles, and thus the speed.

The more field poles connected into the circuit, the slower the motor runs. As field poles are removed from the circuit, the motor speed increases. A selector switch with multiple positions is used to change the number of field poles.

Universal motors with tapped fields are used in food mixers because they develop high torque and have adjustable speeds. The different speed ranges are usually divided into a set number of speeds, such as three speed or five speed.

Brushes. The strength of the field poles of a universal motor may also be changed by moving the brushes on the commutator. The brush position is moved by means of an externally located brush shift lever. Moving the brushes changes the brushes away from the position in which the motor develops maximum torque (load neutral) and speed.

Changing the speed of a universal motor by changing the position of the brushes is not recommended for motors that are used to drive larger loads. The larger the load, the greater the current flow through the brushes. Since changing brush position increases arcing at the brushes, current should be kept to a minimum to prevent brush wear.

Solid-State Devices. Electronic controllers that use thyristors to vary voltage are also used to control universal motors. A *thyristor* is a solid-state switching device that switches current ON by a quick pulse of control current. Once the current is switched ON, the thyristor does not require control current to remain ON. Two types of thyristors used to control motors are the triac and the silicon controlled rectifier (SCR).

A *triac* is a three-terminal thyristor that is triggered into conduction in either direction by a small current to its gate. Since it can be triggered into conduction in either direction, the triac is used to control AC loads, such as lamps, heating elements, AC motors, and universal motors. See Figure 2-11.

The three terminals of a triac are the main terminal 1 (MT_1), main terminal 2 (MT_2), and the gate (G). When control current is applied to G, current flows between MT_1 and MT_2. The triac is triggered for each half wave. The point at which the control circuit triggers the triac determines the point on the wave at which current begins to flow. This point also determines the amount of output voltage applied to the load.

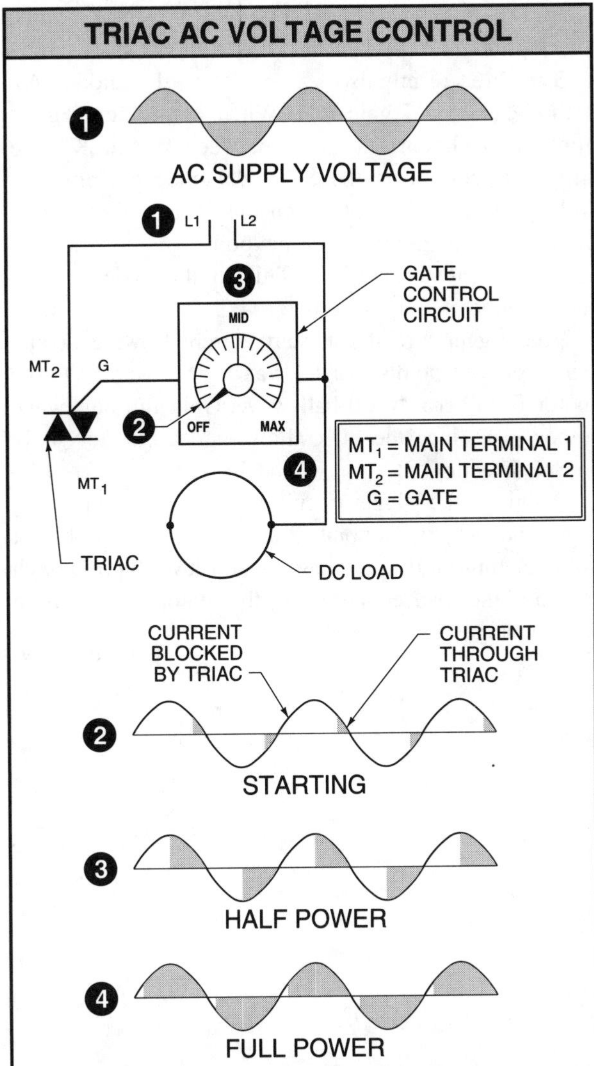

Figure 2-11. A triac is used to control output voltage of an AC load.

The trigger circuit can start current flowing at any point between points 2 and 4, varying the voltage to the motor from zero to full wave. When triggered at the beginning of each half wave (point 4), there is full voltage out and the motor runs at full speed. When triggered in the middle of each half wave (point 3), there is half voltage out and the motor runs at half speed.

Although the trigger circuit can start current flowing at any point between points 2 and 4, the motor does not start rotating until the voltage is at a level high enough to move the load connected to the motor. This turn-on point changes for different loads.

An *SCR* is a three-terminal semiconductor thyristor that is normally an open circuit until a signal applied to the gate switches it to the conducting state in one direction. Since it can be triggered into conduction in only one direction, it is used to control DC loads, such as lamps, spark plugs, DC motors, and universal motors. See Figure 2-12.

The three terminals of an SCR are the anode (A), cathode (K), and gate (G). When control current is applied to G, current flows between A and K. The trigger circuit turns the SCR ON once during each full cycle. The point at which the control circuit triggers the SCR determines the point on the wave at which current starts to flow. This point also determines the amount of output voltage.

The trigger circuit can start current flowing at any point between points 2 and 4, varying the voltage to the motor from zero to full half wave. Only full half wave is possible, since the SCR allows current to flow only in one direction.

Although the trigger circuit can start current flowing at any point between points 2 and 4, the motor does not start rotating until the voltage is at a level high enough to move the load connected to the motor. This turn-on point changes for different loads.

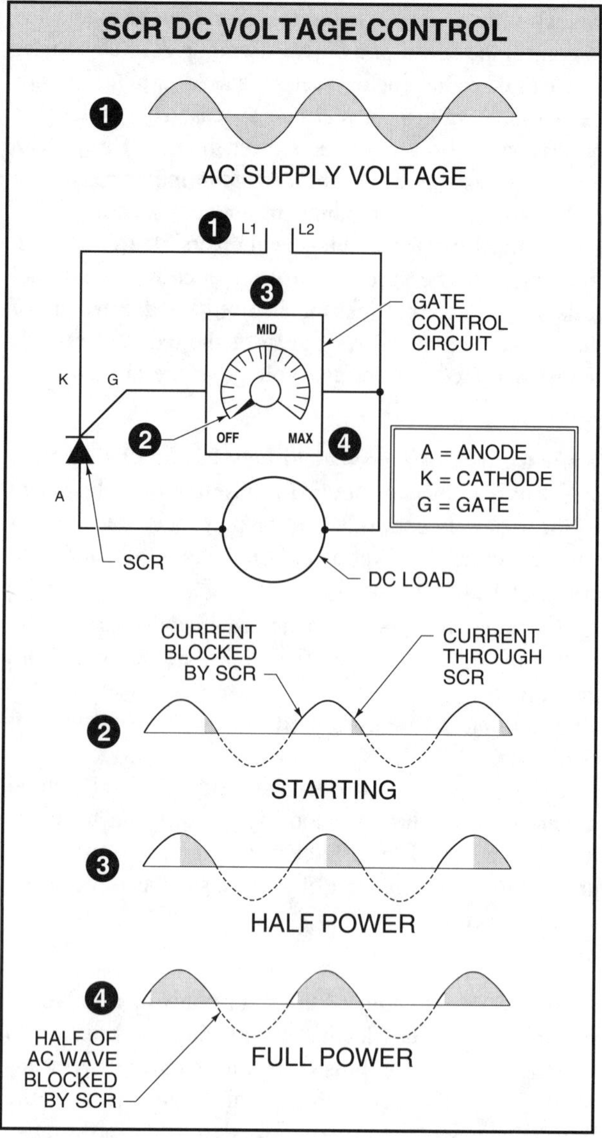

Figure 2-12. An SCR is used to control output voltage of a DC load.

chapter 2

DIRECT CURRENT MOTORS

APPLICATIONS

Application — DC Motor Speed Control

Speed control of a DC series motor is accomplished by inserting an external resistance (rheostat) in series with the field and armature. This resistance reduces the starting voltage. The reduced starting voltage reduces the starting current. See DC Series Motor.

Speed control of DC shunt and DC compound motors is accomplished by inserting a rheostat in series with the shunt field. The moveable arm of the speed-control rheostat is connected directly to the positive side of the power supply to control the speed. As resistance increases in the field, the speed of the motor increases. See DC Shunt and DC Compound Motors.

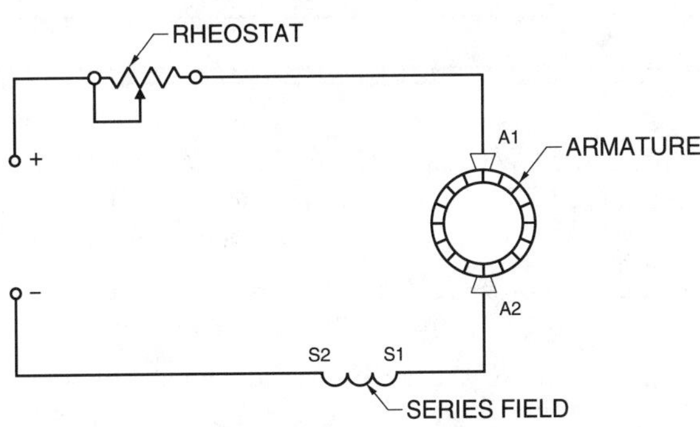

DC SERIES MOTOR

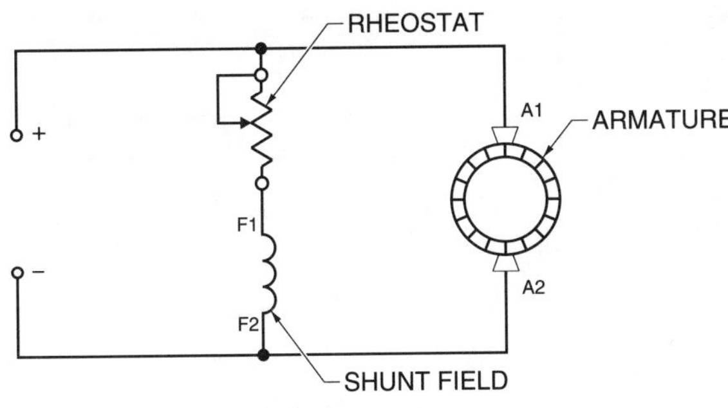

DC SHUNT MOTOR

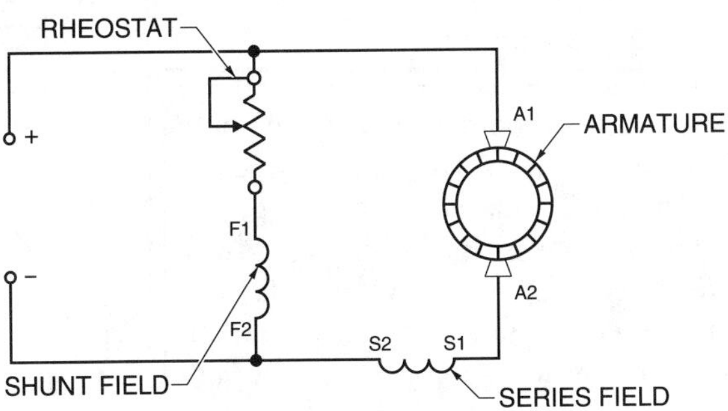

DC COMPOUND MOTOR

Application — DC Motor Reduced-Voltage Starting

DC motors smaller than one-half horsepower draw low current and are started by placing full-line voltage across the motor terminals. DC motors larger than one-half horsepower typically require reduced-voltage starting. To start large DC motors, a resistance unit is placed in series with the motor during starting. The moveable arm of the starting rheostat is connected directly to the positive side of the power supply and the motor is connected to the fixed side of the rheostat. The starter decreases the resistance as the motor accelerates. See Standard Wiring Procedures on page 50.

STANDARD WIRING PROCEDURES			
	Series Motor	**Shunt Motor**	**Compound Motor**
Power supply	+ to A1 – to S2	+ to A1 + to F1 – to A2 – to F2	+ to A1 + to F1 – to F2 – to S2
Starting rheostat	Connect between positive side of power supply and motor with control arm on positive side of power supply	Connect between positive side of power supply and motor with control arm on positive side of power supply	Connect between positive side of power supply and motor with control arm on positive side of power supply
Speed-control rheostat	Connect between power supply and motor with control arm on positive side of power supply	Connect in series with field circuit with control arm on positive side of power supply	Connect in series with field circuit with control arm on positive side of power supply

The starting resistance unit is not needed when the motor is running because the motor generates a counterelectromotive force (counter EMF). *Counter EMF* is a voltage that is opposite to the supply voltage. The amount of counter EMF depends on the speed of the motor. The faster the motor runs, the greater the counter EMF. For example, a DC motor that has a resistance of 4 Ω at standstill draws 57.5 A when connected to 230 V (230 V ÷ 4 Ω = 57.5 A).

When the motor accelerates to a speed that generates a counter EMF of 100 V, the total voltage in the motor is 130 V (230 V – 100 V = 130 V), and the current drawn is 32.5 A (130 V ÷ 4 Ω = 32.5 A).

When the motor accelerates to full speed and generates a counter EMF of 200 V, the total voltage in the motor is 30 V (230 V – 200 V = 30 V), and the current drawn is 7.5 A (30 V ÷ 4 Ω = 7.5 A).

Application — DC Voltage Variations

DC motors should be operated on pure DC power. *Pure DC power* is power obtained from a battery or DC generator. DC power is also obtained from rectified AC power. Most industrial DC motors obtain power from a rectified AC power supply. DC power obtained from a rectified AC power supply varies from almost-pure DC power to half-wave DC power. Half-wave rectified power is obtained by placing a diode in one of the AC power lines. Full-wave rectifed power is obtained by placing a bridge rectifier (four diodes) in the AC power line. Rectified DC power is filtered by connecting a capacitor in parallel with the output of the rectifier circuit. See DC Power Types.

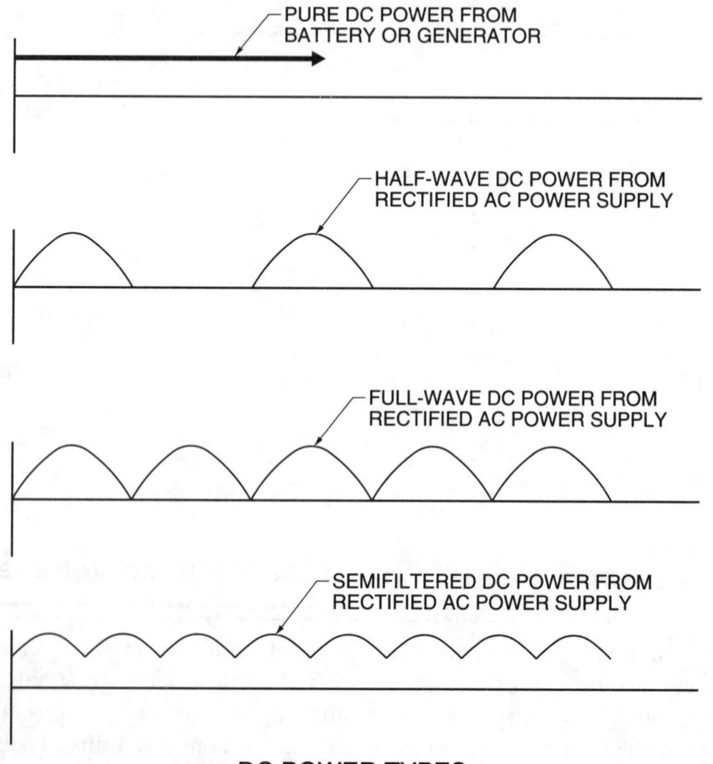

DC POWER TYPES

DC motor operation is affected by a change in voltage. The change may be intentional, as in a speed-control application, or the change may be caused by variations in the power supply.

Typically, the power supply voltage should not vary by more than 10 % of the motor's rated voltage. Motor speed, current, torque, and temperature are affected if the DC voltage varies from the motor rating. See DC Motor Performance Characteristics.

DC MOTOR PERFORMANCE CHARACTERISTICS

Performance Characteristics	Voltage 10% below Rated Voltage		Voltage 10% above Rated Voltage	
	Shunt	Compound	Shunt	Compound
Starting torque	↓ 15%	↓ 15%	↑ 15%	↑ 15%
Speed	↓ 5%	↓ 6%	↑ 5%	↑ 6%
Current	↑ 12%	↑ 12%	↓ 8%	↓ 8%
Field temperature	↑	↓	↑	↑
Armature temperature	↑	↑	↓	↓
Commutator temperature	↑	↑	↓	↓

Application — Reversing DC Motors

The current direction in the field or armature is changed to reverse the direction of DC motors. To determine the conductor connections of a DC motor for forward and reverse directions, apply the procedure:

1. Determine the number of power lines that must be switched. In a DC motor, the positive power line is switched and the negative power line is connected directly to the motor.
2. Use the information provided on the motor wiring diagram to record the connections that must be made to operate the motor in the forward and reverse directions. Record the conductors that must be interchanged in the forward direction. Interchange their position in the reverse direction. For DC motors, the armature or field windings are interchanged.
   - **A.** Show the motor terminals that are connected to the conductors that are interchanged. For DC motors, the positive power line is interchanged.

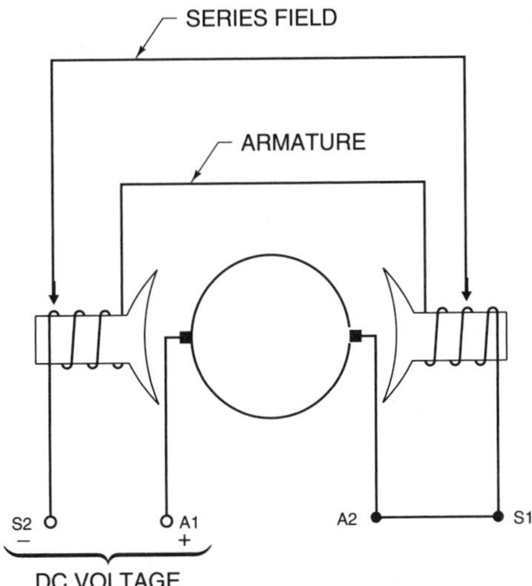

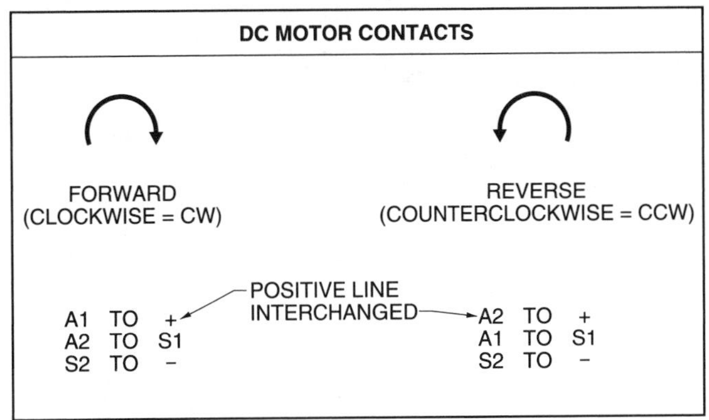

Note: No common connections.

DC MOTOR CONNECTIONS

B. Remove any common conductor connections that are not power lines and remain connected in the forward and reverse directions. Connect the common conductors at the motor and select the name of the lowest number for the common name. For DC motors, there may not be any common connections in a series or a shunt motor unless the motor has interpoles or a split-field winding. See DC Motor Connections.

3. Connect the power line that is not switched. If a power line is not a hot power line, connect it directly to the motor. In DC motors, the negative power line is typically connected directly to the motor.
4. Determine the number of contacts required and their connections. A set of electric contacts is required for each place the word "to" appears in the connections.
5. Draw the wiring diagram. Connect all lines that are the same. List the name of the common line only on the forward contacts. See Motor Control Wiring Diagram.

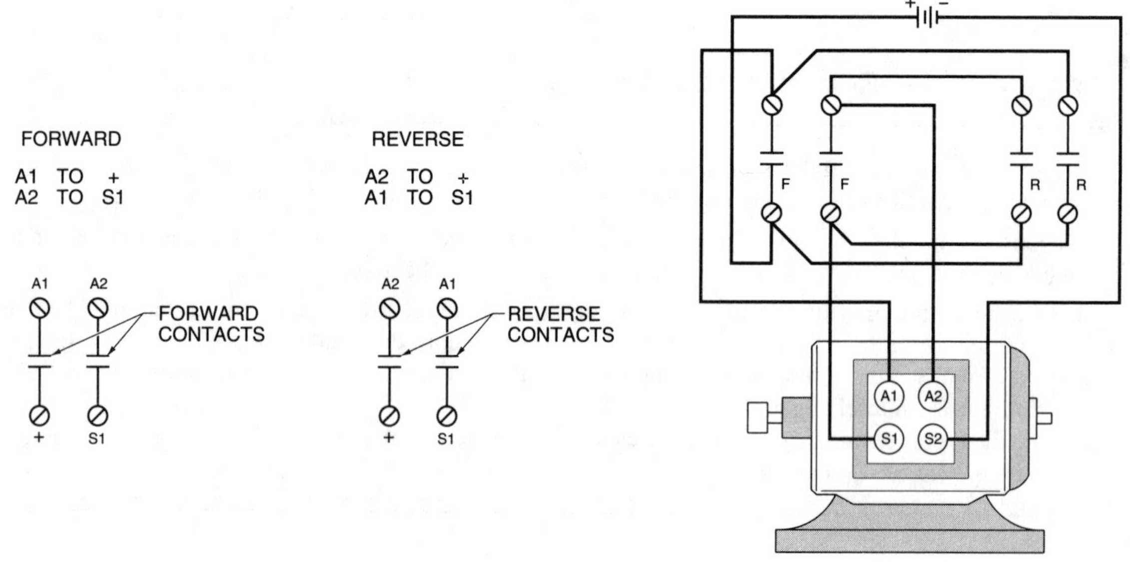

MOTOR CONTROL WIRING DIAGRAM

Name ______________________ Date ____________

DIRECT CURRENT MOTORS

chapter 2 ACTIVITIES

Activity 2-1. DC Motor Speed Control

Connect the motors so that the starting rheostat is used for reduced-voltage starting and the speed-control rheostat controls the motor running speed. Use Standard Wiring Procedures on page 50.

1.

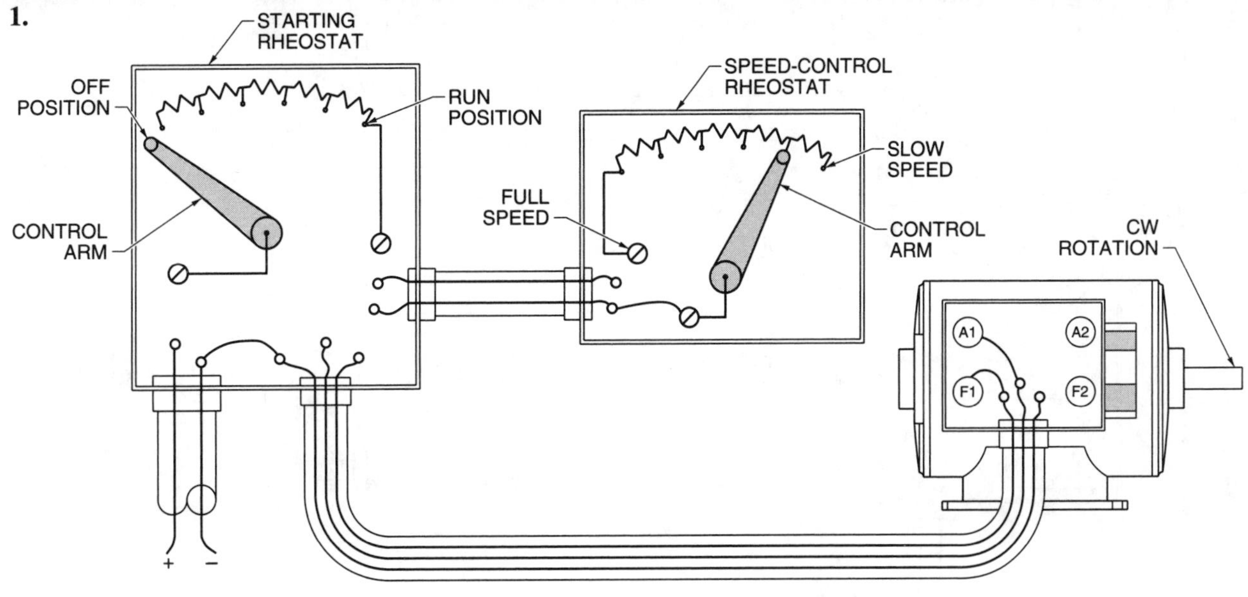

2.

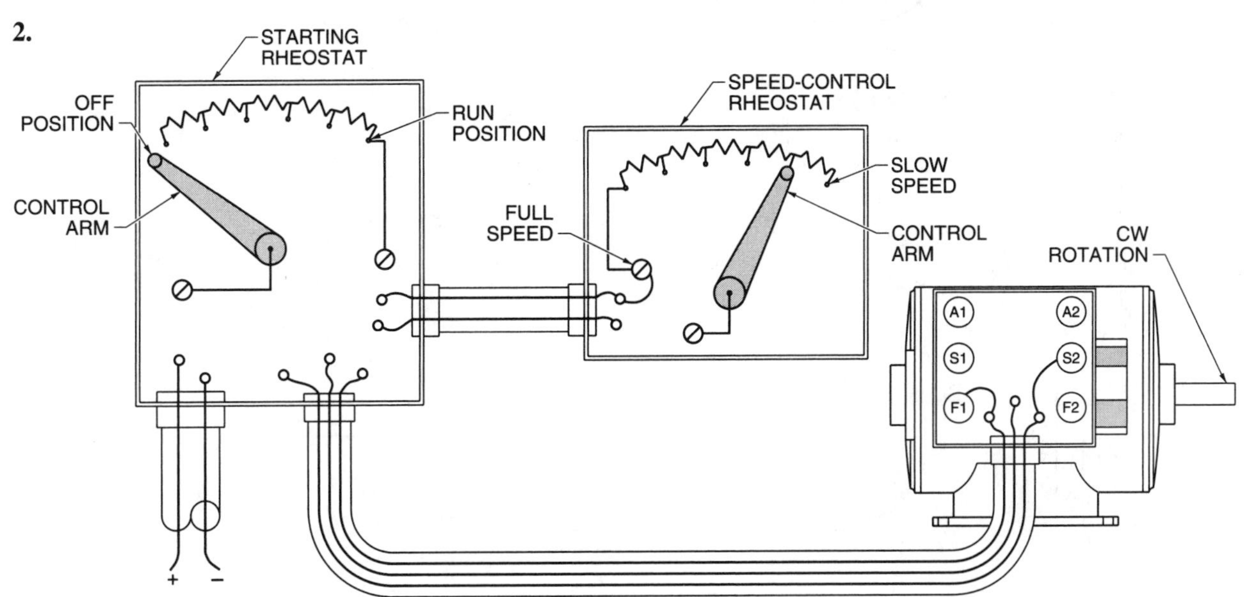

◯ Activity 2-2. DC Motor Reduced-Voltage Starting

Connect the motors through the starting rheostats so that the motors start at reduced voltage. Use Standard Wiring Procedures on page 50.

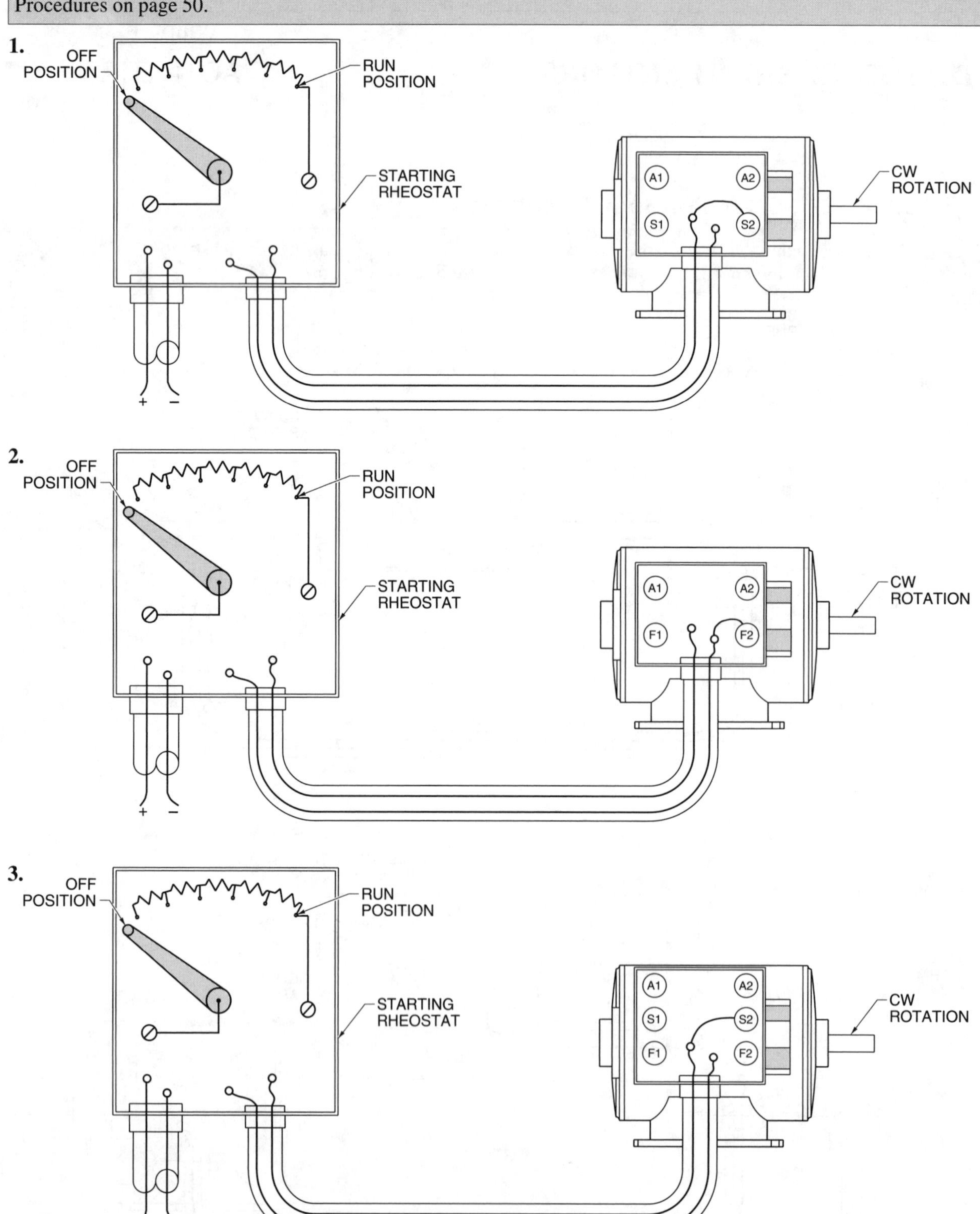

Activity 2-3. DC Voltage Variations

Calculate the adjusted ratings based on the variation in the power supply.

1. The motor is connected to a 108 VDC power supply.

_____ **A.** The adjusted motor starting torque is _____ lb-ft.

_____ **B.** The adjusted motor speed is _____ rpm.

_____ **C.** The adjusted motor current rating is _____ A.

QXP600 INDUSTRIAL MOTOR			
CATALOG #	600112	DUTY	CONT
FRAME	56	HP	1
VOLTS	120	AMPS	9.5
RPM	1750	AMBIENT TEMPERATURE	40°C
WOUND	COM	SF	1.00
CLASS	F	STARTING TORQUE (LB-FT)	11.55

2. The motor is connected to a 122 VDC power supply.

_____ **A.** The adjusted motor starting torque is _____ lb-ft.

_____ **B.** The adjusted motor speed is _____ rpm.

_____ **C.** The adjusted motor current rating is _____ A.

QXP600 INDUSTRIAL MOTOR			
CATALOG #	600112	DUTY	CONT
FRAME	56	HP	1
VOLTS	120	AMPS	9.5
RPM	1750	AMBIENT TEMPERATURE	40°C
WOUND	COM	SF	1.00
CLASS	F	STARTING TORQUE (LB-FT)	11.55

3. The motor is connected to a 264 VDC power supply.

_____ **A.** The adjusted motor starting torque is _____ lb-ft.

_____ **B.** The adjusted motor speed is _____ rpm.

_____ **C.** The adjusted motor current rating is _____ A.

QXP1800 INDUSTRIAL MOTOR			
CATALOG #	18001125	DUTY	CONT
FRAME	365T	HP	20
VOLTS	240	AMPS	72
RPM	850	AMBIENT TEMPERATURE	40°C
WOUND	COM	SF	1.20
CLASS	F	STARTING TORQUE (LB-FT)	208

4. The motor is connected to a 216 VDC power supply.

_______ **A.** The adjusted motor starting torque is _______ lb-ft.

_______ **B.** The adjusted motor speed is _______ rpm.

_______ **C.** The adjusted motor current rating is _______ A.

QXP1700 INDUSTRIAL MOTOR			
CATALOG #	1700112X	DUTY	CONT
FRAME	365T	HP	20
VOLTS	240	AMPS	25
RPM	1150	AMBIENT TEMPERATURE	40° C
WOUND	SHUNT	SF	1.00
CLASS	F	STARTING TORQUE (LB-FT)	170

5. The motor is connected to a 450 VDC power supply.

_______ **A.** The adjusted motor starting torque is _______ lb-ft.

_______ **B.** The adjusted motor speed is _______ rpm.

_______ **C.** The adjusted motor current rating is _______ A.

QXP1000 INDUSTRIAL MOTOR			
CATALOG #	1000112B	DUTY	CONT
FRAME	256T	HP	10
VOLTS	500	AMPS	18
RPM	650	AMBIENT TEMPERATURE	40° C
WOUND	SHUNT	SF	1.00
CLASS	F	STARTING TORQUE (LB-FT)	105

6. The motor is connected to an 10.8 VDC power supply.

_______ **A.** The adjusted motor starting torque is _______ lb-ft.

_______ **B.** The adjusted motor speed is _______ rpm.

_______ **C.** The adjusted motor current rating is _______ A.

QXP10 INDUSTRIAL MOTOR			
CATALOG #	10001122	DUTY	CONT
FRAME	48	HP	$\frac{1}{4}$
VOLTS	12	AMPS	5.1
RPM	650	AMBIENT TEMPERATURE	40° C
WOUND	SHUNT	SF	1.00
CLASS	F	STARTING TORQUE (LB-FT)	3

Activity 2-4. Reversing DC Motors

Connect the motor for forward and reverse directions.

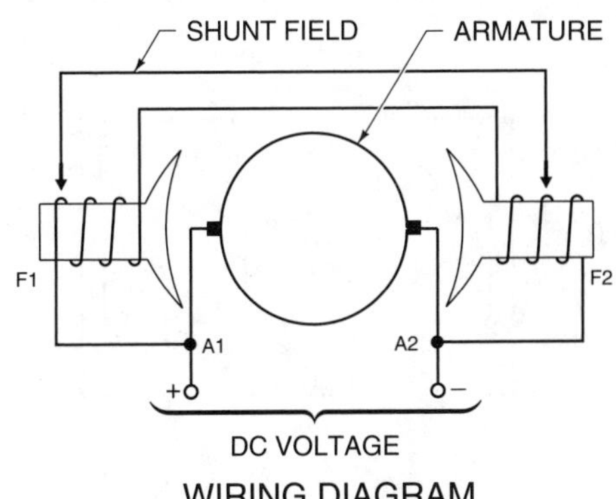

WIRING DIAGRAM

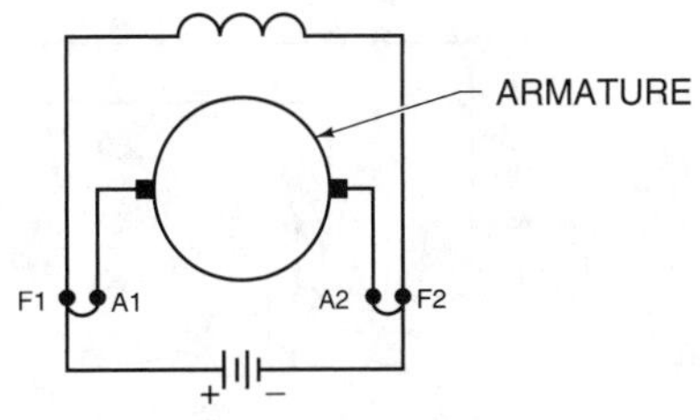

SCHEMATIC

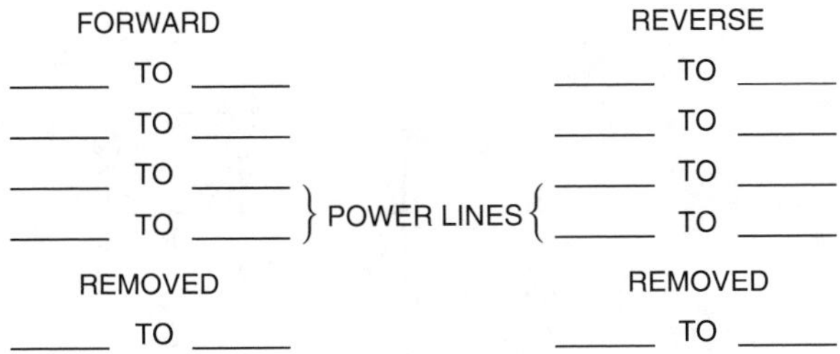

FORWARD

______ TO ______
______ TO ______
______ TO ______
______ TO ______ } POWER LINES

REMOVED

______ TO ______

REVERSE

______ TO ______
______ TO ______
______ TO ______
POWER LINES { ______ TO ______

REMOVED

______ TO ______

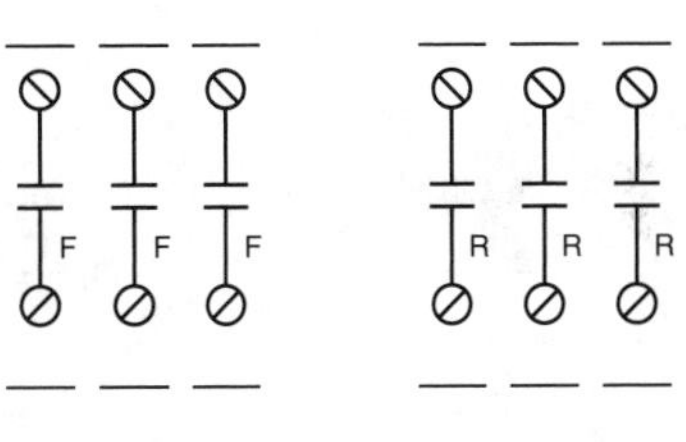

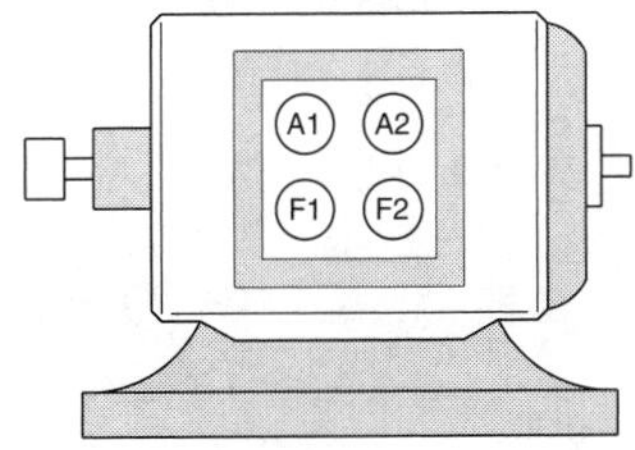

◯ Activity 2-5. Reversing DC Compound Motors

Connect the motor for forward and reverse directions.

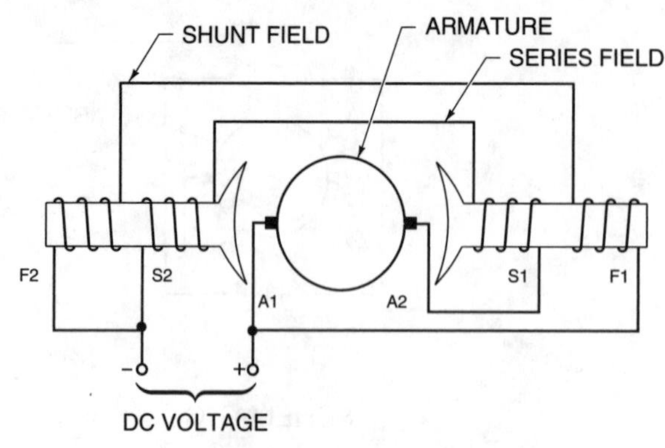

WIRING DIAGRAM

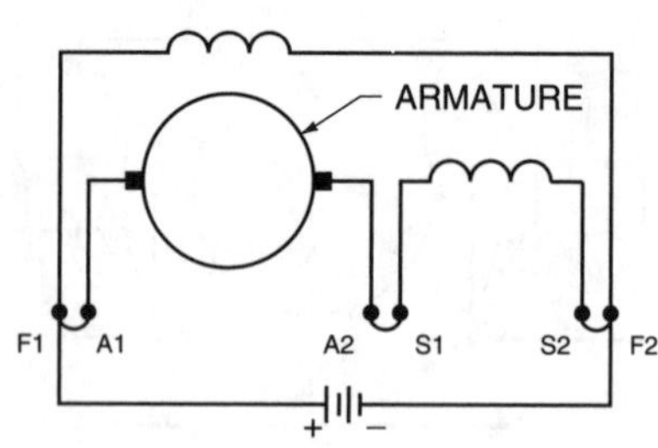

SCHEMATIC

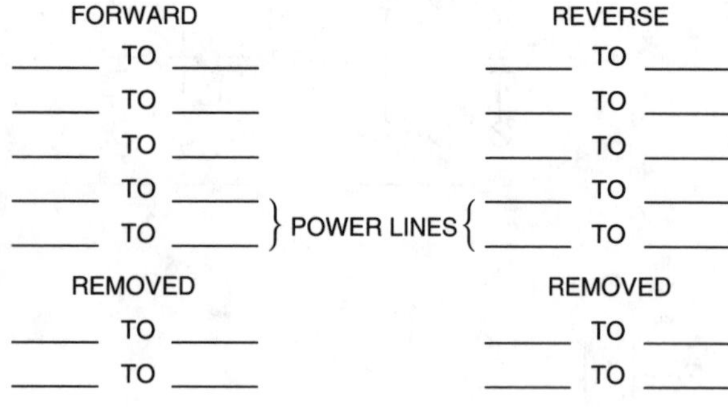

FORWARD			REVERSE		
______	TO	______	______	TO	______
______	TO	______	______	TO	______
______	TO	______	______	TO	______
______	TO	______	______	TO	______
______	TO	______ } POWER LINES {	______	TO	______
REMOVED			REMOVED		
______	TO	______	______	TO	______
______	TO	______	______	TO	______

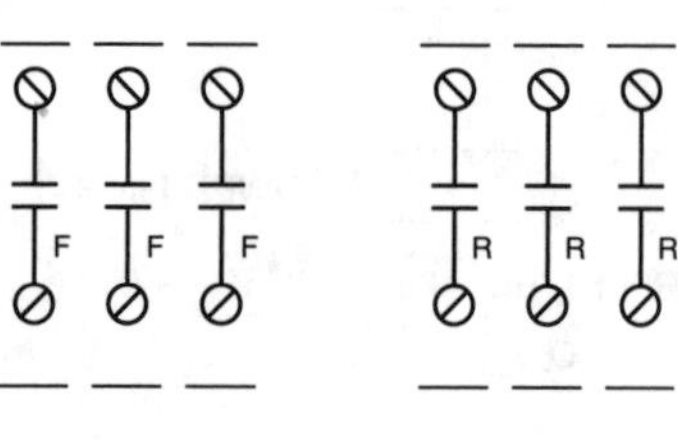

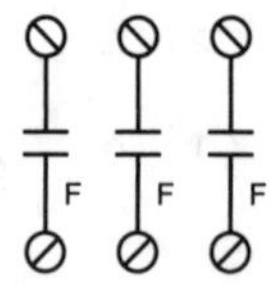

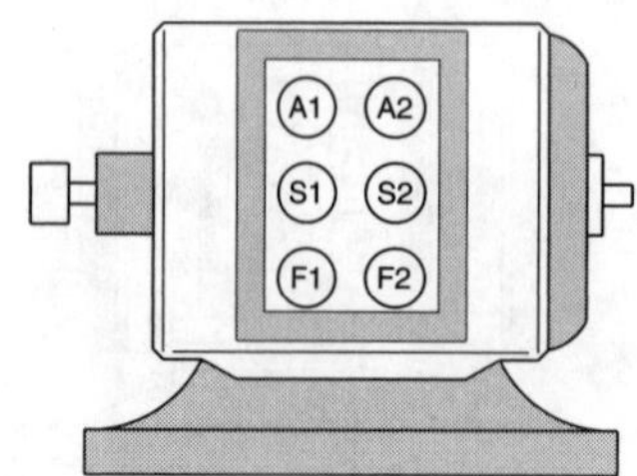

Name ______________________________ Date ______________

chapter 2

DIRECT CURRENT MOTORS

TRADE TEST

STOP START 2 3 M OL 1

Completion

______ **1.** The DC current of a motor is connected to the field and _________ to produce rotation.

______ **2.** _________ are auxiliary poles placed between the main field poles of the motor.

______ **3.** A(n) _________ is a device that converts AC to DC by allowing the current to move in only one direction.

______ **4.** A(n) _________ is an extended, flexible connection.

______ **5.** The DC permanent-magnet motor produces relatively _________ torque at low speeds.

______ **6.** A(n) _________ universal motor is a universal motor with extra windings added to the field poles.

______ **7.** _________ current is unwanted current induced in the metal field structure of a motor, due to the rate of change in the induced magnetic flux.

______ **8.** A(n) _________ is a solid-state switching device that switches current ON by a quick pulse of control current.

______ **9.** A(n) _________ is the rotating part of a DC motor.

______ **10.** A(n) _________ is the rotating part of an AC motor.

______ **11.** A(n) _________ is the stationary part of a DC motor.

______ **12.** A(n) _________ is the stationary part of an AC motor.

______ **13.** _________ is the power loss that occurs when a universal motor is connected to AC.

______ **14.** The _________ windings of a DC motor are used to develop a magnetic field.

______ **15.** A(n) _________ field may be used to vary the speed of a universal motor.

______ **16.** Brushes are made of carbon or _________.

______ **17.** The DC permanent-magnet motor uses magnets for the _________.

______ **18.** Compensated universal motors are usually _________ HP and larger.

______ **19.** An SCR can be triggered into _________ in only one direction.

______ **20.** The armature core is made up of notched _________, which form slots when stacked.

True-False

T F **1.** A universal motor can be operated on either DC or 1ϕ, AC.

T F **2.** Universal motors may be nonreversible or reversible.

T F **3.** A revolving field is produced in a universal motor.

T F **4.** The no-load speed of a universal motor is very low.

T F **5.** A fixed resistor has a fixed value for one set speed.

T F **6.** A triac is triggered by a large current to its gate.

T F **7.** The load neutral is the best position for running a universal motor.

T F **8.** The field pole strength of a universal motor may be changed by moving the brushes.

T F **9.** AC motors perform better than DC motors in most traction equipment.

T F **10.** DC power is delivered into the armature through the brushes.

Multiple Choice

_________ **1.** The field of a DC shunt motor is connected in ________ with the armature.

A. shunt
B. parallel
C. both A and B
D. neither A nor B

_________ **2.** When a load is placed on a universal motor, the motor speed ________ .

A. increases
B. decreases
C. remains the same
D. fluctuates rapidly

_________ **3.** The amount of force exerted on the shaft of a DC motor is based on the ________ .

A. current passing through the conductor inside the magnetic field
B. intensity of the magnetic field
C. length (or number) of the conductor inside the magnetic field
D. A, B, and C

_________ **4.** Interpoles are used ________.

A. to increase sparking at the brushes
B. with shunt and compound motors less than ½ HP
C. both A and B
D. neither A nor B

_________ **5.** The DC series motor ________.

A. has the field connected in parallel with the armature
B. has good speed regulation
C. produces the highest torque of all DC motors
D. neither A, B, nor C

_________ **6.** The DC compound motor has ________.

A. a series field
B. a shunt field
C. high torque
D. A, B, and C

_________ **7.** A compensated universal motor ________.

A. has extra windings added to the field poles
B. is usually smaller than ¼ HP
C. both A and B
D. neither A nor B

_________ **8.** The three terminals of an SCR are the ________.

A. thyristor, anode, and gate
B. anode, gate, and cathode
C. cathode, thyristor, and anode
D. neither A, B, nor C

_________ **9.** A reversible universal motor may be reversed by ________.

A. using one coil for the forward direction and the other for the reverse direction
B. reversing the direction of current in the field
C. both A and B
D. neither A nor B

_________ **10.** The armature is the ________ part of a DC motor.

A. rotating
B. reciprocating
C. oscillating
D. stationary

Problems

1. Connect the motor through the control switch to the power supply.

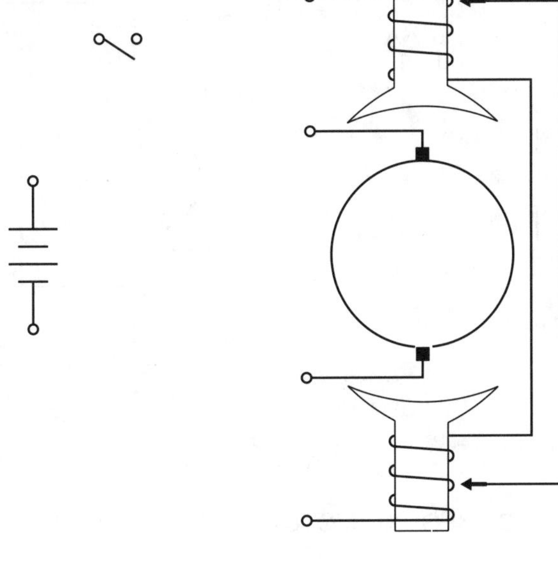

SERIES MOTOR

2. Connect the motor through the control switch to the power supply.

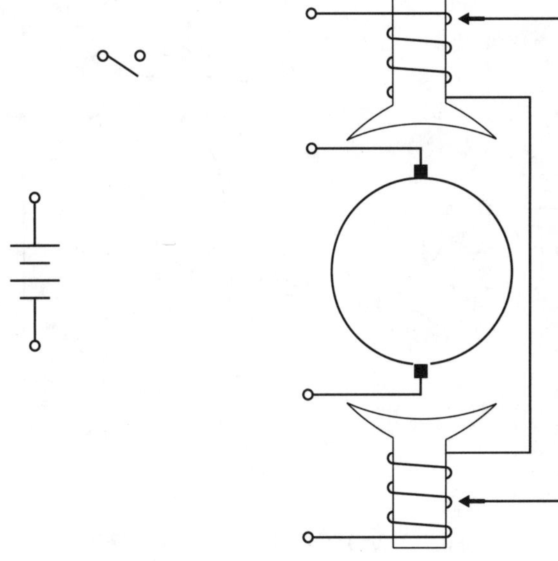

SHUNT MOTOR

3. Connect the motor through the control switch to the power supply.

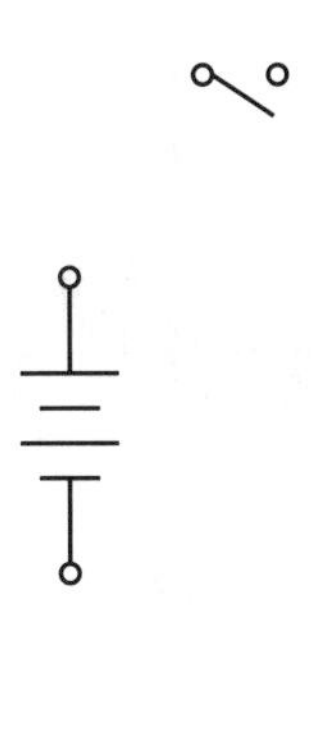

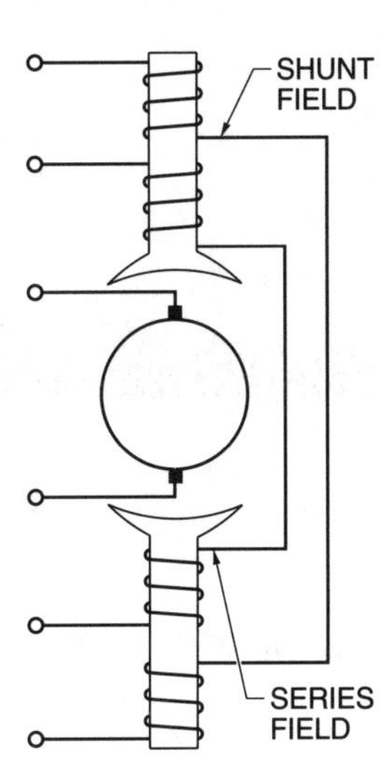

COMPOUND MOTOR

4. Connect the motor to start at reduced voltage.

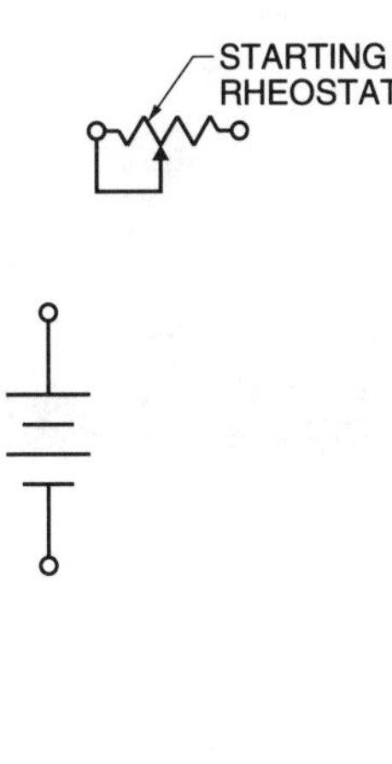

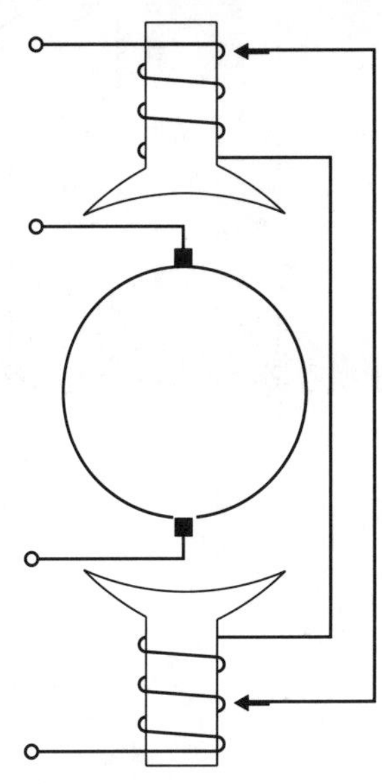

SERIES MOTOR, REDUCED-VOLTAGE STARTING

5. Connect the motor to start at reduced voltage with speed control.

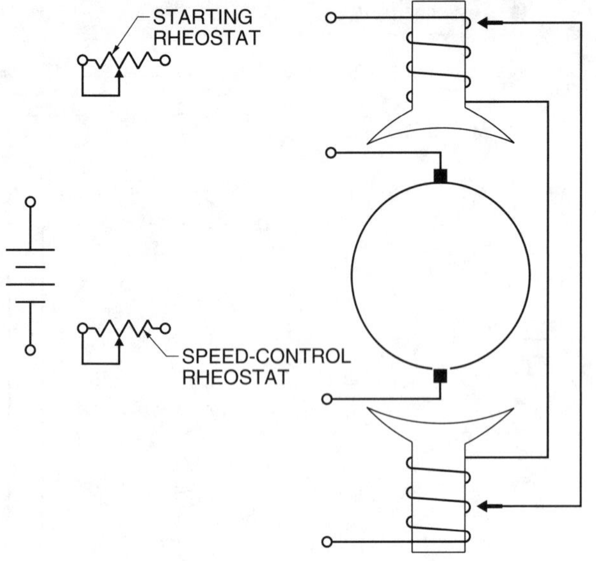

SHUNT-MOTOR SPEED CONTROL

6. Connect the motor to start at reduced voltage with speed control.

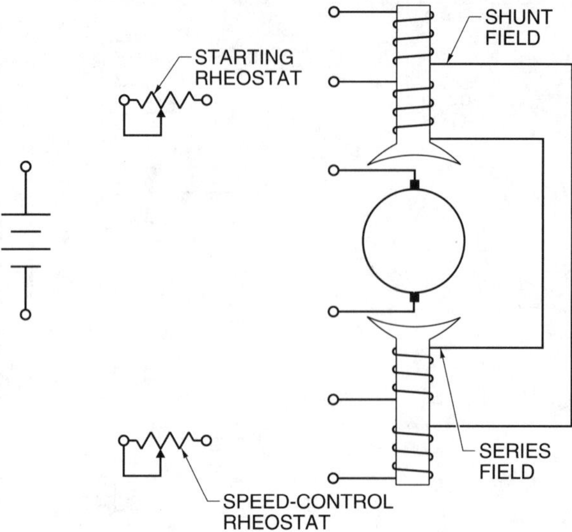

COMPOUND-MOTOR SPEED CONTROL

7. Connect the motor for speed control using two power supplies.

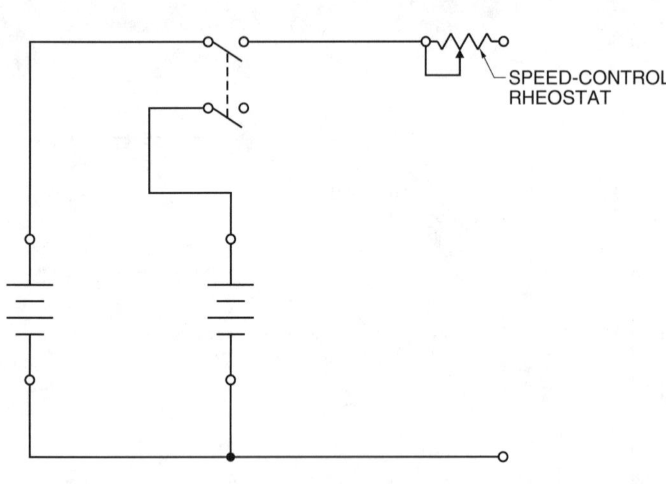

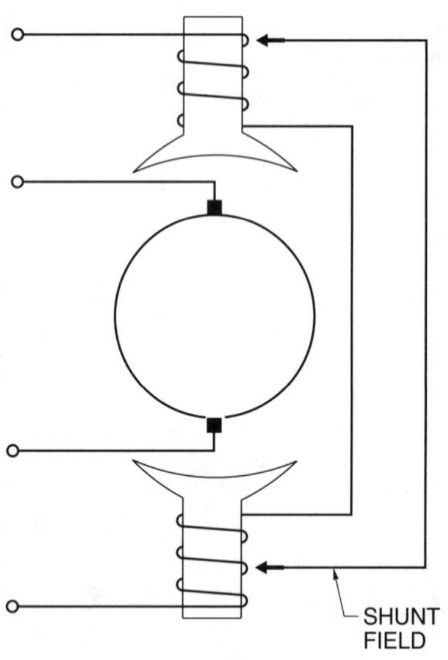

SEPARATELY EXCITED SHUNT MOTOR SPEED CONTROL

chapter 3

THREE-PHASE MOTORS

Three-phase motors are the standard motor type used in industry. These motors vary in size, from fractional horsepower to thousands of horsepower. Three-phase motors operate at a fairly constant speed and are manufactured in designs with a variety of torque characteristics. The primary advantages of three-phase motors are low maintenance requirements and economy of operation.

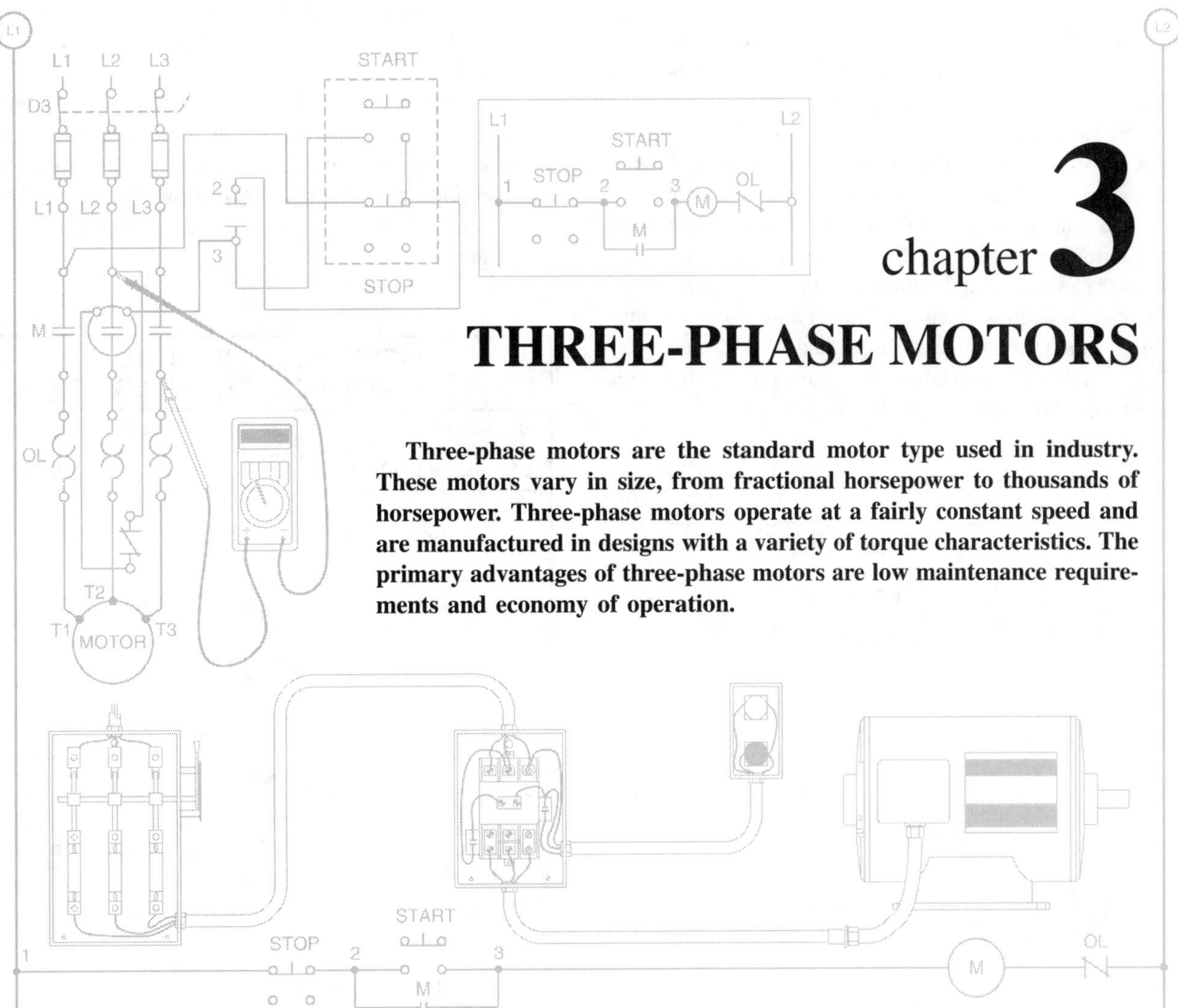

THREE-PHASE MOTORS

The most common 3ϕ motor used in industry is the induction motor. An *induction motor* is a motor that has no physical electrical connection to the rotor. Induction motors have no brushes. Current in the rotor is induced by the magnetic field of the stator.

Approximately 5% of the 3ϕ motors used in industry are repulsion motors. A *repulsion motor* is a motor with the rotor connected to the power supply through brushes that ride on a commutator. Repulsion motors can develop more torque than induction motors.

The extensive use of 3ϕ induction motors for almost all industrial applications is due to the following:

- Three-phase power is the standard power supplied by electrical power companies to almost all commercial and industrial locations. The 3ϕ motor can be connected to the supplied power with very little modification or control required.
- Three-phase motors are simple in construction, rugged, and require very little maintenance. It is not uncommon to find 3ϕ motors that have run in an application for ten or more years without a failure.
- Three-phase motors are less expensive than other motor types of the same horsepower rating. They are also available in a larger selection of sizes, speeds, and frames than other motors.
- Three-phase motors cost less to operate per horsepower than 1ϕ motors or DC motors.
- Three-phase motors have a fairly constant speed characteristic and are available in a wide variety of torque characteristics.
- Three-phase motors are self-starting. No starting method is required.

Motor Construction

The *stator* is the stationary part of an AC motor. The *rotor* is the rotating part of an AC motor. Like the 1ϕ motor, the 3ϕ motor requires a rotating magnetic field. However, unlike the 1ϕ motor, the 3ϕ motor does not require any additional components to produce this rotating magnetic field.

The rotating magnetic field is set up automatically in the stator when the motor is connected to the 3ϕ power lines. The coils in the stator are connected to form three separate windings (phases). Each phase contains one-third of the total number of individual coils in the motor. These composite windings, or phases, are the A phase, B phase, and C phase. See Figure 3-1.

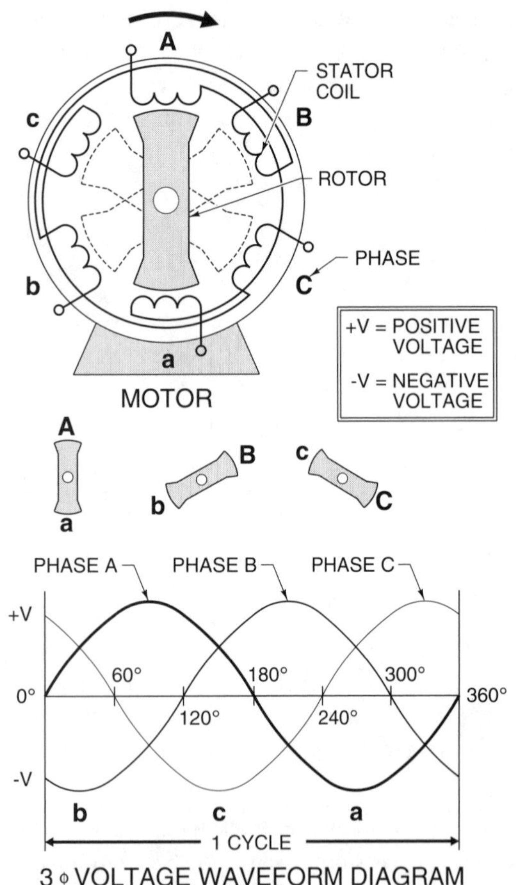

Figure 3-1. The coils in the stator are connected to form three separate windings (phases).

Each phase is placed in the motor so that it is 120° from the other phases. Since each phase reaches its peak value 120° apart from the other phases, a rotating magnetic field is produced in the stator.

Electrical degrees and mechanical degrees differ. In electric motors and generators, the distance traveled past one pole represents 180 electrical degrees. There are 360° (mechanical) in one revolution.

For example, a rotor, during one revolution in a 4-pole motor, passes from one north pole, through a south pole, through a north pole, through a south pole, and back to the original north pole, completing 720 electrical degrees (4 poles × 180 electrical degrees = 720 electrical degrees). See Figure 3-2.

MECHANICAL VERSUS ELECTRICAL DEGREES

MECHANICAL DEGREES IN ONE REVOLUTION	MOTOR POLES x 180 =	ELECTRICAL DEGREES IN ONE REVOLUTION
360		2 x 180 = 360
360		4 x 180 = 720
360		6 x 180 = 1080
360		8 x 180 = 1440

Figure 3-2. There are 360 mechanical degrees in one revolution. There are 180 electrical degrees from one pole to the next.

Single-Voltage Motors

To develop a rotating magnetic field in the motor, the windings must be connected to the proper voltage. This voltage level is determined by the manufacturer and stamped on the motor nameplate.

A *single-voltage motor* is a motor that operates at only one voltage level. Single-voltage, 3ϕ motors are less expensive to manufacture than dual-voltage, 3ϕ motors, but are limited to locations having the same voltage as the motor. Typical single-voltage, 3ϕ motor ratings are 230 V, 460 V, and 575 V. Other single-voltage, 3ϕ motor ratings are 200 V, 208 V, 220 V, and 280 V.

Wye-Connected Motor. In a wye-connected, 3ϕ motor, one end of each of the three phases is internally connected to the other phases. The remaining end of each phase is then brought out externally and connected to the incoming power source. See Figure 3-3.

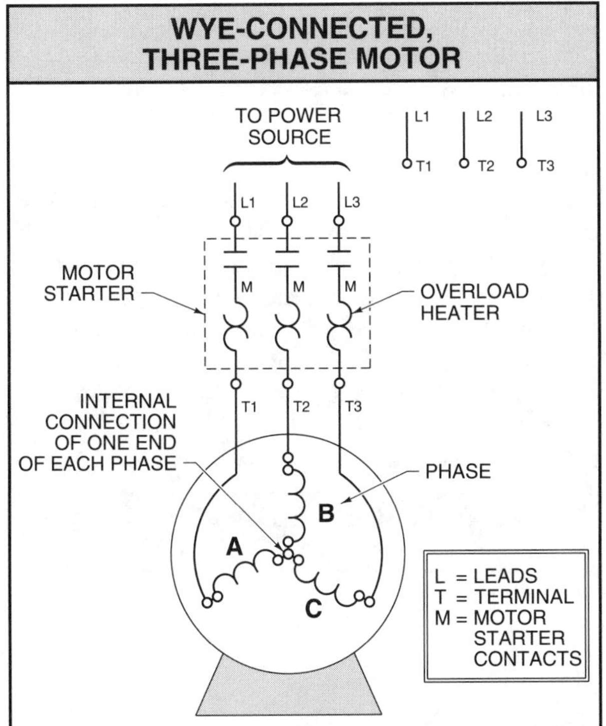

Figure 3-3. In a wye-connected, 3ϕ motor, one end of each of the three phases is internally connected to the other phases.

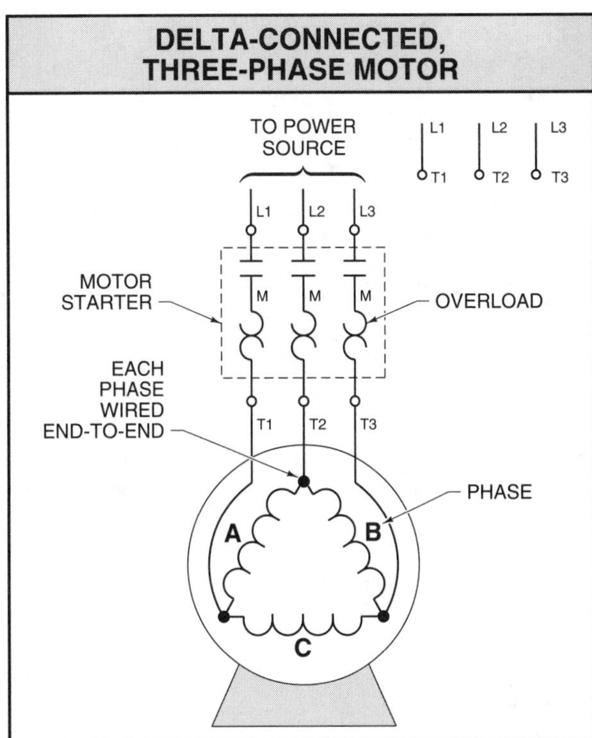

Figure 3-4. In a delta-connected, 3ϕ motor, each phase is wired end-to-end to form a completely closed loop.

The leads, which are brought out externally, are labeled terminals one, two, and three (T1, T2, and T3). When connecting a wye-connected, 3ϕ motor to the 3ϕ power lines, the power lines and motor terminals are connected L1 to T1, L2 to T2, and L3 to T3.

Delta-Connected Motor. In a delta-connected, 3ϕ motor, each phase is wired end-to-end to form a completely closed loop circuit. At each point where the phases are connected, leads are brought out externally to form T1, T2, and T3. See Figure 3-4.

T1, T2, and T3, like the terminals of a wye-connected motor, are connected to the three power lines. L1 is connected to T1, L2 to T2, and L3 to T3. The 3ϕ line supplying power to the motor must have the same voltage and frequency rating as the motor.

Dual-Voltage Motors

A *dual-voltage motor* is a motor that operates at more than one voltage level. Most 3ϕ motors are manufactured so that they can be connected for either of two voltages. The purpose in making motors for two voltages is to enable the same motor to be used with two different power line voltages.

A typical dual-voltage, 3ϕ motor rating is 230/460 V. Other common dual-voltage, 3ϕ motor ratings are 240/480 V and 208–230/460 V. The dual-voltage rating of the motor is listed on the nameplate of the motor. If both voltages are available, the higher voltage is usually preferred because the motor uses the same amount of power, given the same horsepower output, for either high or low voltage. As the voltage is doubled (e.g., 230 V to 460 V), the current drawn on the power lines is cut in half. With the reduced current, the wire size is reduced, and the material cost is decreased.

Dual-Voltage, Wye-Connected Motor. In a dual-voltage, wye-connected, 3ϕ motor, each phase coil (A, B, and C) is divided into two equal parts. By dividing the phase coils in two, nine terminal leads are available. These motor leads are marked terminals one through nine (T1–T9). The nine terminal leads can be connected for high or low voltage. See Figure 3-5.

To connect a dual-voltage, wye-connected, 3ϕ motor for high voltage, connect L1 to T1, L2 to T2, and L3 to T3 at the motor starter. Using wire nuts, tie T4 to T7, T5 to T8, and T6 to T9. By making these connections, the individual coils in each phase are connected in series. Since the coils are connected in series, the applied voltage divides equally among the coils.

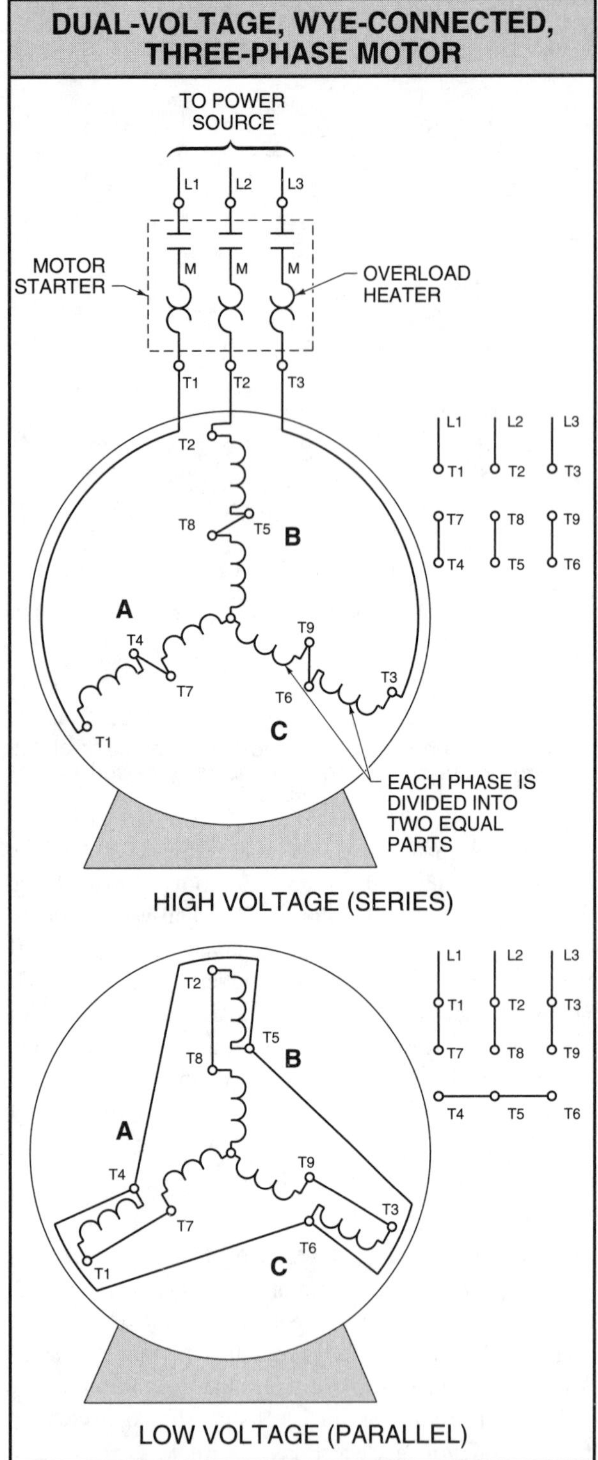

Figure 3-5. In a dual-voltage, wye-connected, 3ϕ motor, each phase coil is divided into two equal parts.

To connect a dual-voltage, wye-connected, 3ϕ motor for low voltage, connect L1 to T1 and T7, L2 to T2 and T8, and L3 to T3 and T9 at the motor starter. Using a wire nut, tie T4, T5, and T6 together. By making these connections, the individual coils in each phase are connected in parallel. Since the coils are connected in parallel, the applied voltage is present across each set of coils.

Dual-Voltage, Delta-Connected Motor. In a dual-voltage, delta-connected, 3ϕ motor, each phase coil (A, B, and C) is divided into two equal parts. By dividing the phase coils in two, nine terminal leads are available. These motor leads are marked terminals one through nine (T1–T9). The nine terminal leads can be connected for high or low voltage. See Figure 3-6.

To connect a dual-voltage, delta-connected, 3ϕ motor for high voltage, connect L1 to T1, L2 to T2, and L3 to T3 at the motor starter. Using wire nuts, tie T4 to T7,

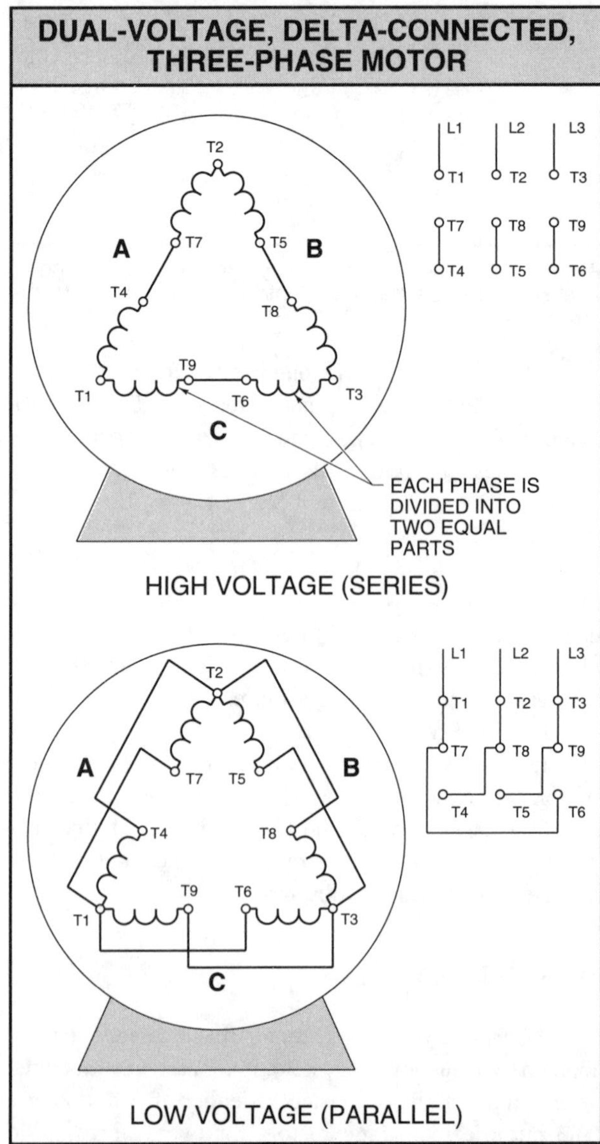

Figure 3-6. In a dual-voltage, delta-connected, 3ϕ motor, each phase coil is divided into two equal parts.

T5 to T8, and T6 to T9. By making these connections, the individual coils in each phase are connected in series. Since the coils are connected in series, the applied voltage divides equally among the coils.

To connect a dual-voltage, delta-connected, 3ϕ motor for low voltage, connect L1 to T1, L2 to T2, and L3 to T3 at the starter motor. Using wire nuts, tie T1 to T7 and T6, T2 to T8 and T4, and T3 to T9 and T5. By making these connections, the individual coils in each phase are connected in parallel. Since the coils are connected in parallel, the applied voltage is present across each set of coils.

Reversing

The direction of rotation of 3ϕ motors can be reversed by interchanging any two of the 3ϕ power lines to the motor. Although any two lines can be interchanged, the industrial standard is to interchange T1 and T3. This standard holds true for all 3ϕ motors. For example, to reverse the direction of rotation of a delta-connected, 3ϕ motor, interchange T1 and T3.

Interchanging T1 and T3 is a standard for safety reasons. When first connecting a motor, the direction of rotation is not usually known until the motor is started. It is common practice to temporarily connect the motor to determine the direction of rotation before making permanent connections. Motor leads of temporary connections are not taped. By always interchanging T1 and T3, T2 can be permanently connected to L2, creating an insulated barrier between T1 and T3. See Figure 3-7.

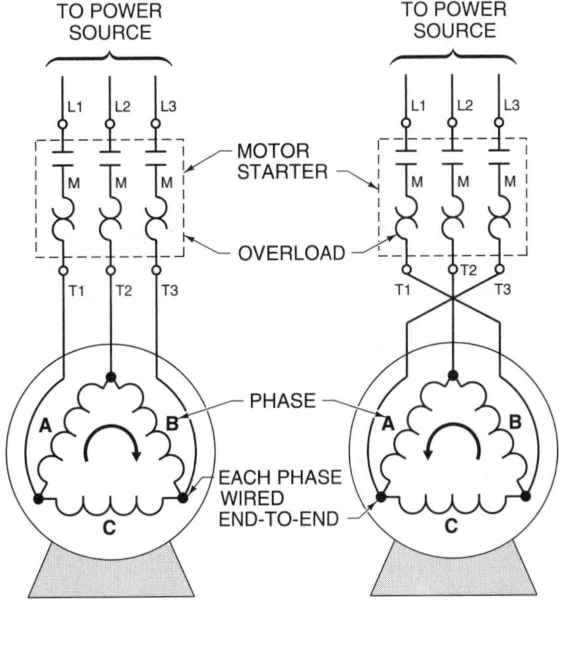

Figure 3-7. A 3ϕ motor can be reversed by interchanging any two of the 3ϕ power lines to the motor. The industrial standard is to interchange T1 and T3.

Multiple-Speed Motors

Multiple-speed, 3ϕ motors are designed to operate at two, three, or four speeds. The motor's operating speed is dependent upon the number of poles used. The speed of the motor varies inversely with the number of poles.

When the speed of a motor changes, the horsepower and torque required at the new speed may be higher, lower, or the same. The type of load and application determines if a change in horsepower or torque is required. To meet these requirements, multiple-speed, 3ϕ motors are designed with different operating characteristics.

The three motor types available are constant horsepower, constant torque, and variable torque motors. Constant horsepower motors are designed to give the same maximum horsepower at all speeds. Constant torque motors are designed to give the same maximum torque at all speeds. Variable torque motors are designed to produce an increase in torque with an increase in speed.

Constant Horsepower. In a constant horsepower motor, torque decreases in the same ratio as the speed increases, maintaining a constant horsepower. More current flows at the lower speed, increasing the torque. Less current flows at the higher speed, decreasing the torque.

Constant horsepower motors are used to drive loads that require the same horsepower output at different speeds. Typical applications include most machine-tool machines, such as boring machines, drilling machines, wheel-driven grinders, lathes, and milling machines. The number of poles in a constant horsepower motor is effectively changed by changing the direction of current through the motor windings. See Figure 3-8.

Constant Torque. In a constant torque motor, horsepower changes proportionally to the speed. A *proportional change* is a change in which factors increase or decrease at the same rate. The horsepower and the line

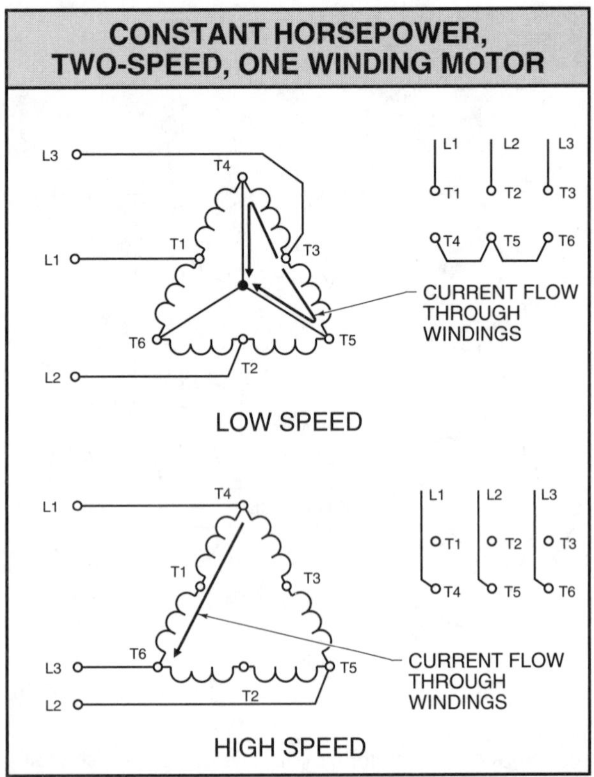

Figure 3-8. Constant horsepower motors are designed to give the same maximum horsepower at both speeds.

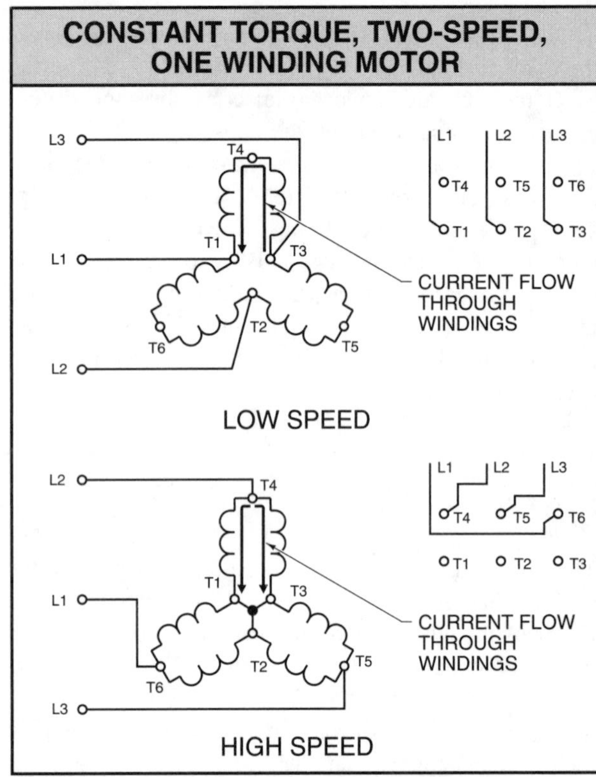

Figure 3-9. Constant torque motors are designed to give the same maximum torque at both speeds.

current increase in the same ratio as the motor speed to provide constant torque. Constant torque motors are used to drive loads that require a constant torque output at different speeds.

Typical applications include rotary and reciprocating compressors, conveyors, displacement fans, and printing presses. The number of poles in the motor is effectively changed by changing the direction of current through the motor windings. See Figure 3-9.

Variable Torque. In a variable torque motor, torque varies inversely with the speed. An *inverse change* is a change in which one factor increases at the same rate the other factor decreases. The horsepower varies with the square of the speed change. Torque and horsepower increase at higher speed and decrease at lower speed. The variable torque, multiple-speed motor is used to drive fans, pumps, and blowers that require an increase in both torque and horsepower when speed is increased. The number of poles in the motor is effectively changed by changing the direction of current through the motor windings. See Figure 3-10.

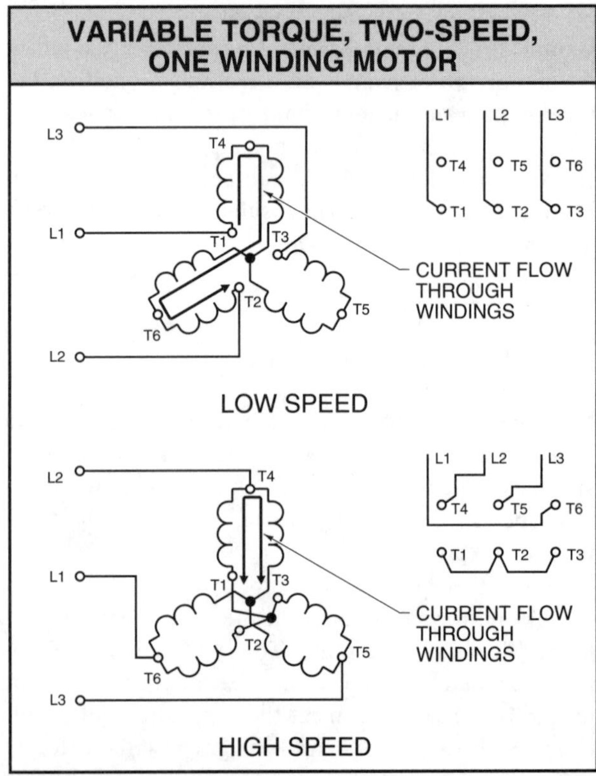

Figure 3-10. Variable torque motors are designed to produce an increase in torque with an increase in speed.

THREE-PHASE MOTORS

chapter 3

APPLICATIONS

Application — Gear Reducer Selection

Gear reducers transmit power from a motor to the driven machine. They efficiently change torque, speed, direction, and position.

Gear reducers amplify torque for most motor applications. The torque is increased proportionally to the reducer ratio. See Gear Reducer.

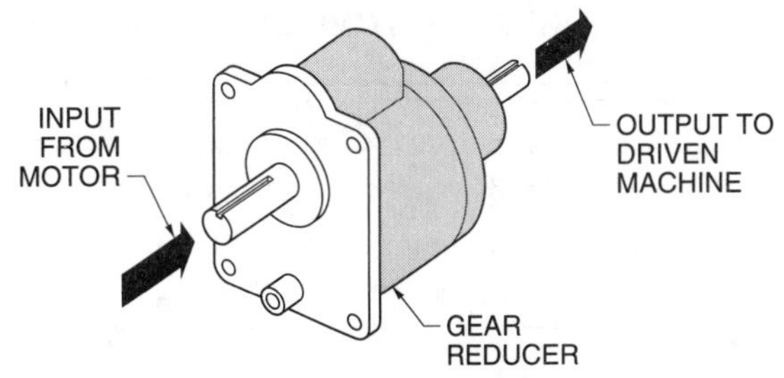

GEAR REDUCER

To find the output torque of a gear reducer, apply the formula:

$$O_T = I_T \times R_R \times R_E$$

where

O_T = output torque (in lb-ft)

I_T = input torque (in lb-ft)

R_R = gear reducer ratio

R_E = reducer efficiency (percentage)

Example: Finding Output Torque

A motor has 6 lb-ft of torque. A gear reducer has a ratio of 30:1 and an efficiency of 85%. Find the output torque of the gear reducer.

$$O_T = I_T \times R_R \times R_E$$

$$O_T = 6 \times 30 \times .85$$

$$O_T = \mathbf{153\ lb\text{-}ft}$$

To find the output speed of a gear reducer, apply the formula:

$$O_S = \frac{I_S}{R_R} \times R_E$$

where

O_S = output speed (in rpm)

I_S = input speed (in rpm)

R_R = gear reducer ratio

R_E = reducer efficiency (percentage)

Example: Finding Output Speed

A motor turns at 1750 rpm. A gear reducer has a ratio of 30:1 and an efficiency of 85%. Find the output speed of the gear reducer.

$$O_S = \frac{I_S}{R_R} \times R_E$$

$$O_S = \frac{1750}{30} \times .85$$

$$O_S = 58.33 \times .85$$

$$O_S = \mathbf{49.58\ rpm}$$

To find the output horsepower of a gear reducer, apply the formula:

$O_{HP} = I_{HP} \times R_E$

where

O_{HP} = output horsepower

I_{HP} = input horsepower

R_E = reducer efficiency (percentage)

Example: Finding Output Horsepower

A 2 HP motor turns a gear reducer that has an efficiency of 85%. Find the output horsepower of the gear reducer.

$O_{HP} = I_{HP} \times R_E$

$O_{HP} = 2 \times .85$

$O_{HP} = \mathbf{1.7\ HP}$

Note: The same formulas are used when chains or belts are used as reducers.

Application — Reversing Three-Phase Motors

A 3ϕ motor is reversed by interchanging power lines one and three (L1 and L3). To determine the wire arrangement of a 3ϕ motor for forward and reverse directions, apply the procedure:

1. Determine the number of power lines that must be switched. Every hot power line must be switched. All lines are hot in a 3ϕ power system. See Three-Phase Motors.

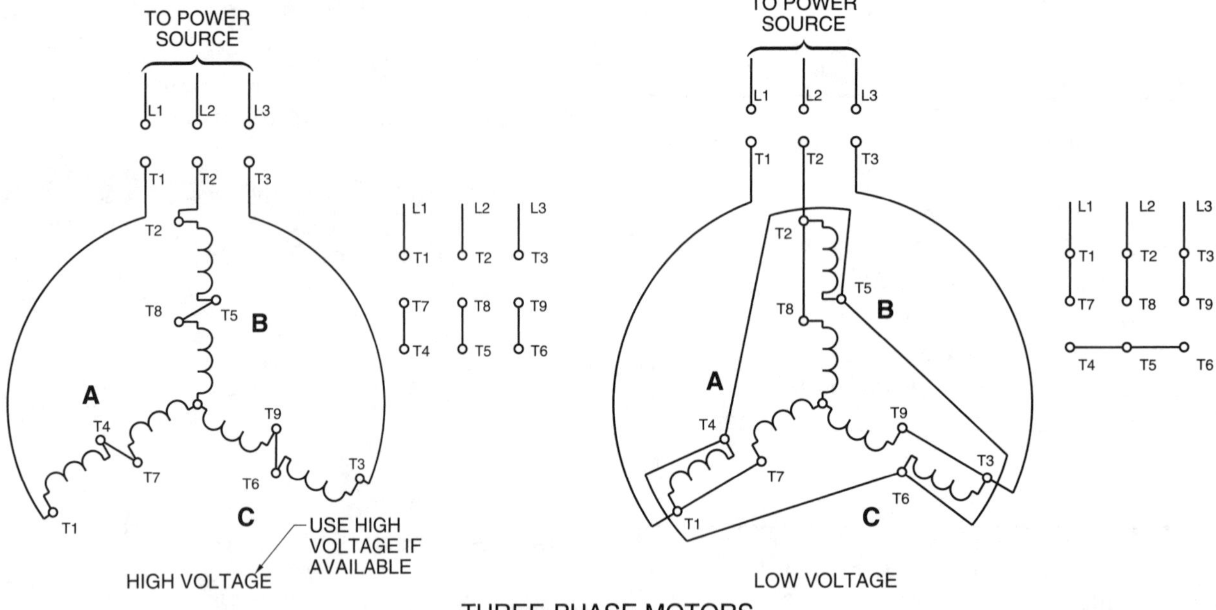

THREE-PHASE MOTORS

2. Determine the required voltage. If a motor is a dual-voltage motor, select the higher available voltage.

3. Use the information provided on the motor wiring diagram to record the connections that must be made to operate the motor in the forward and reverse directions. Record the conductors that must be interchanged in the forward direction. Interchange their position in the reverse direction. For 3ϕ motors, L1 and L3 are interchanged.

A. Show the motor terminals that are connected to the conductors that are interchanged. Do not include any power lines.

B. Add the power lines. Do not show them connected to the lines that are interchanged. See Motor Connections.

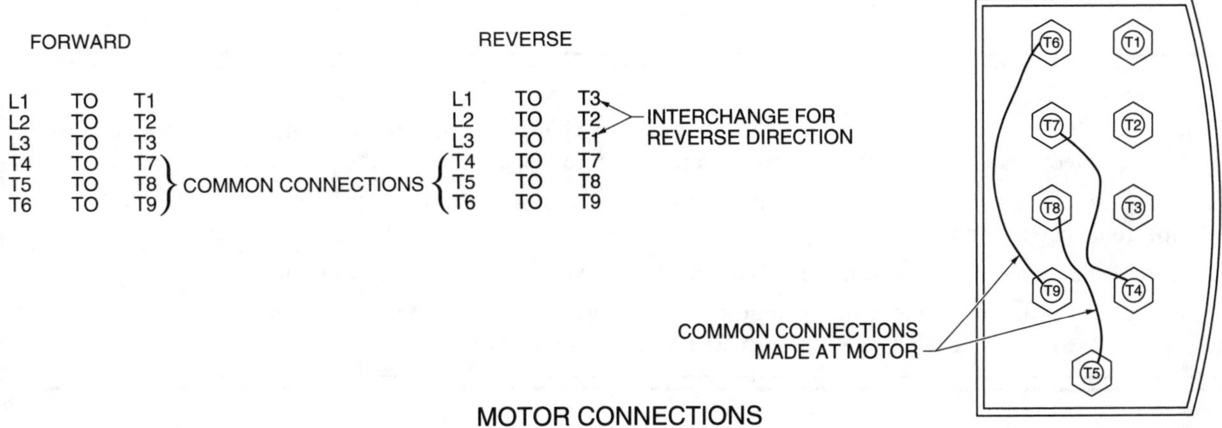

MOTOR CONNECTIONS

4. Remove any common connections that are not power lines and remain connected in the forward and reverse directions. Connect the common conductors at the motor and select the name of the lowest number for the common name.
5. Determine the contacts. A set of electric contacts is required for each place the word "to" appears in the connections.
6. Draw the wiring diagram. Connect all lines that are the same. List the name of the common line only on the forward contacts. See Motor Control Wiring Diagram.

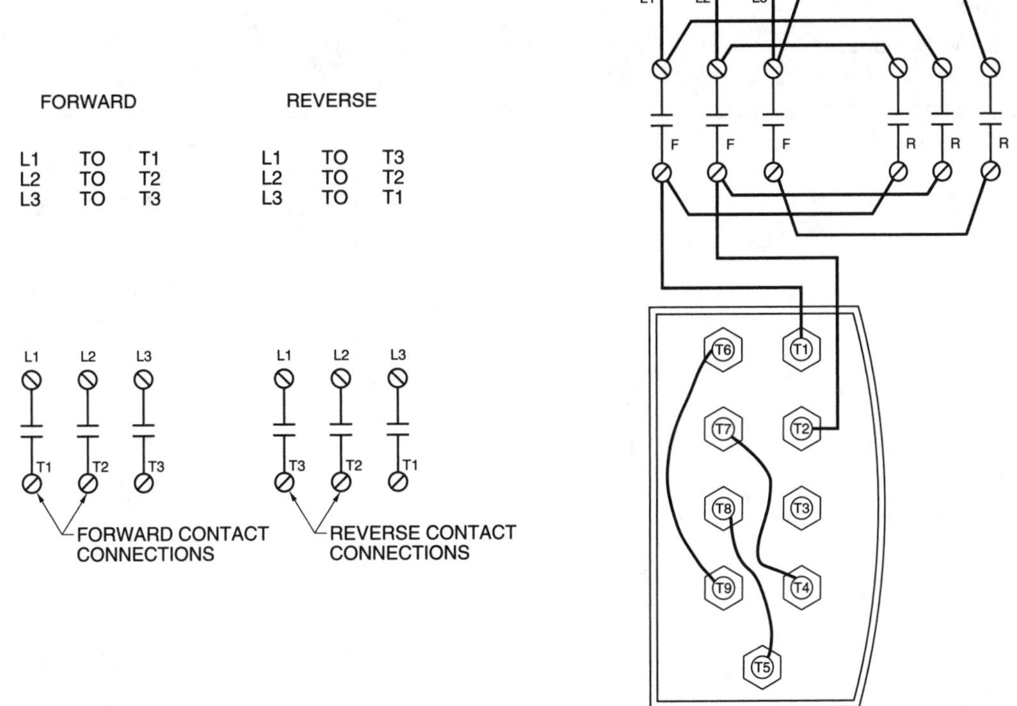

MOTOR CONTROL WIRING DIAGRAM

Application — Connecting Multispeed, Three-Phase Motors

Three-phase motors are available in two, three, and four speeds. One or all speeds may be used in an application. The speed is changed as the current drawn is changed. Each speed should have overload protection. To connect a multispeed, 3ϕ motor to operate at different speeds, apply the procedure:

1. Determine the number of power lines that must be switched. Each hot power line must be switched for the different speeds of a motor.
2. Determine required speeds. A motor nameplate lists the different speeds of a motor.
3. Use the information provided on the motor wiring diagram to record the connections that must be made to operate the motor in each speed required. See Motor Connections.

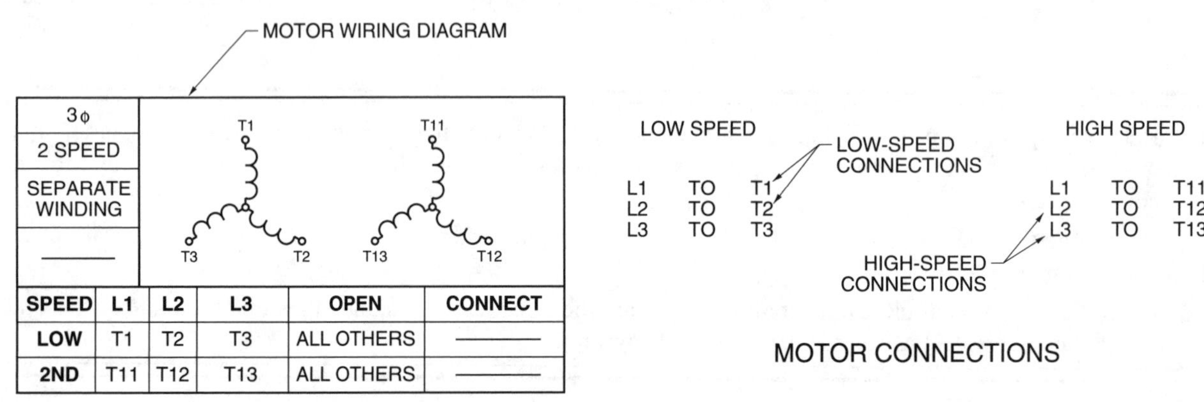

MOTOR CONNECTIONS

4. Determine the contacts. A set of electric contacts is required for each place the word "to" appears in the connections.
5. Draw the wiring diagram. Connect all lines that are the same. List the name of the common line only on the forward contacts. See Motor Control Wiring Diagram.

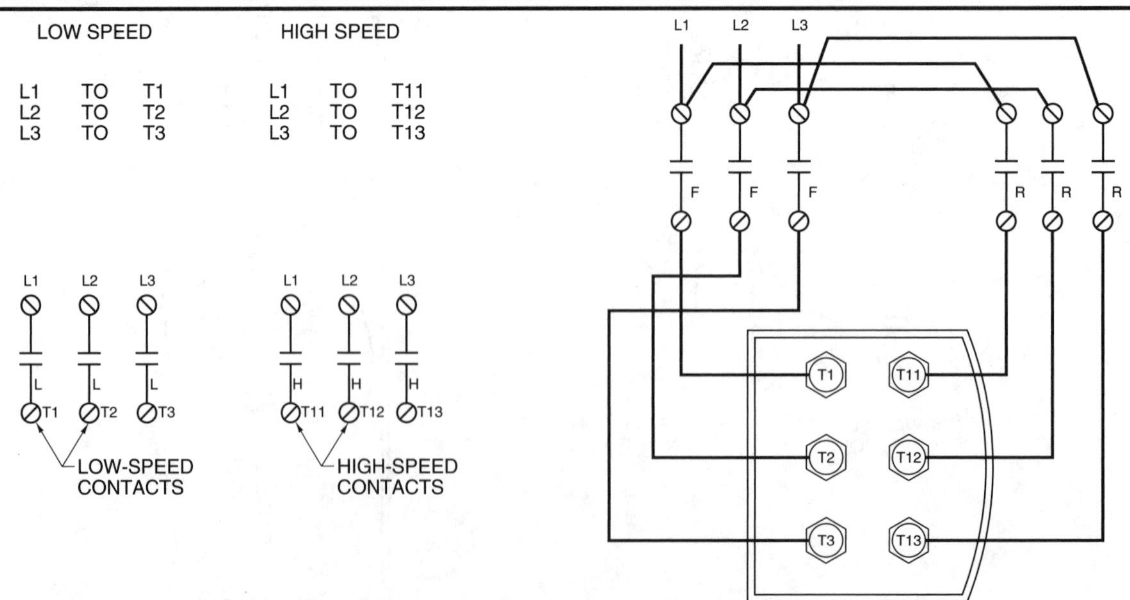

MOTOR CONTROL WIRING DIAGRAM

Application — Motor Line and Motor Wiring Diagrams

The two types of diagrams used with motor circuits are line diagrams and wiring diagrams. A line diagram shows only the control circuit. A wiring diagram shows the control circuit and the power circuit. See Motor Control and Power Circuits.

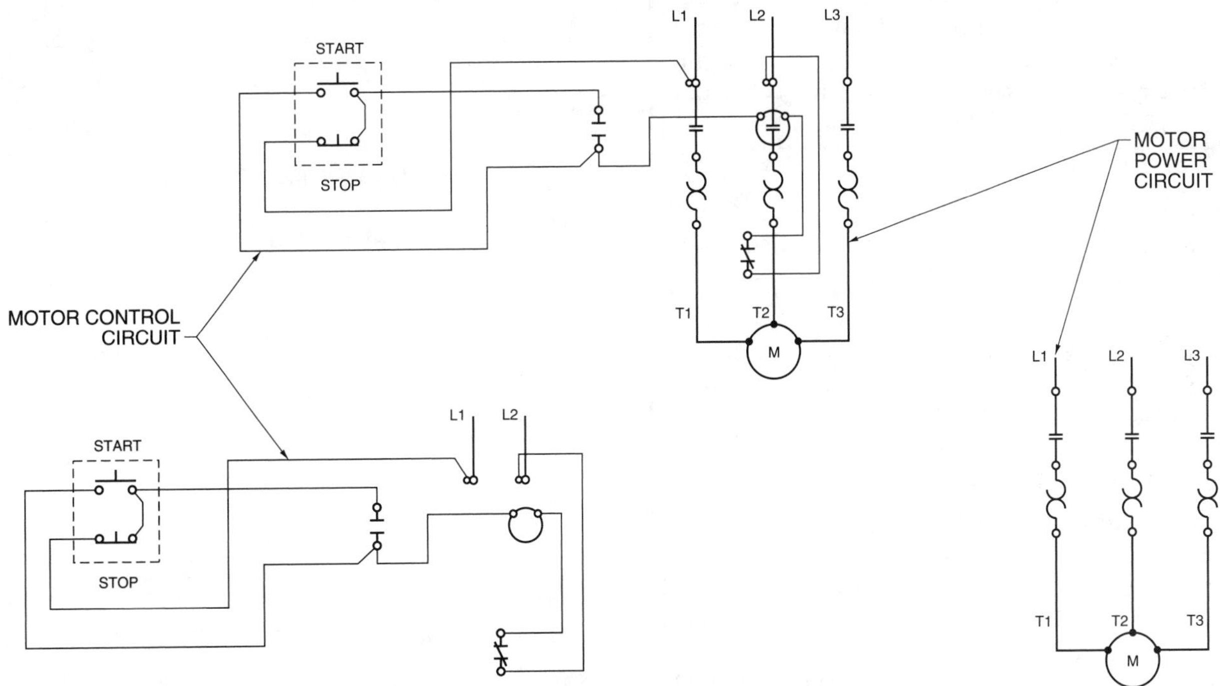

MOTOR CONTROL AND POWER CIRCUITS

Line Diagrams

Line diagrams show the operational logic of the motor circuit. The line diagram shows the electric connections between the components in the control circuit, and it shows how the components control the power circuit. For example, the diagram shows that the start and stop pushbuttons are connected by a conductor. When the start pushbutton is pressed, the circuit is completed through the motor starter. The starter's contacts are connected in parallel with the start pushbutton. The motor starter remains energized until the stop pushbutton is pressed, or until the overload contacts open. The line diagram does not show the location of the components in the circuit. See Motor Line Diagram.

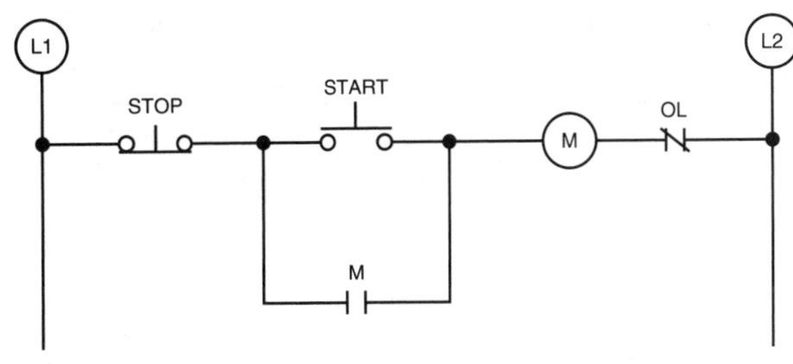

MOTOR LINE DIAGRAM

Wiring Diagrams

A wiring diagram shows the actual location of each component used in the control circuit and power circuit. For example, the diagram shows that the start and stop pushbuttons are located in the same pushbutton station and the start pushbutton is located on top. See Motor Wiring Diagram.

Wiring diagrams are useful in troubleshooting because they show the layout and connections of the components. However, wiring diagrams can hinder circuit understanding because the conductor connections are often hard to follow.

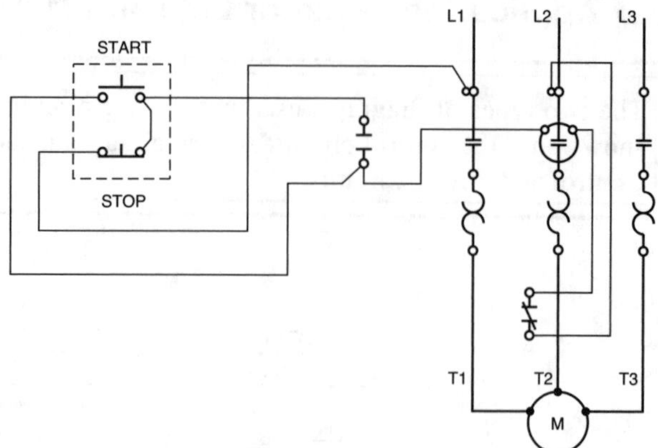

MOTOR WIRING DIAGRAM

Application — Dual-Voltage Control Transformer Installation

In most industrial applications, the motor power circuit is at a high voltage that produces the required power at the motor. The control circuit is at a low voltage for safety reasons. A control transformer reduces the high voltage of the power circuit to a low voltage for the control circuit.

Most control transformers have a dual-voltage primary. A dual-voltage primary allows the transformer to be connected to a 240 V or 480 V power circuit. See Dual-Voltage Transformer Connections. The primary coils of the transformer are connected in series for high voltage and in parallel for low voltage. The secondary side of the transformer delivers a low output (normally 120 V) for the control circuit. See Transformer Wiring Diagram.

The secondary side of the transformer is shown in the line diagram. A fuse is added to protect the control circuit. The fuse is connected between the start of the control circuit and the X1 terminal of the transformer. The fuse is typically located on the transformer in a holder provided by the transformer manufacturer. See Transformer Line Diagram.

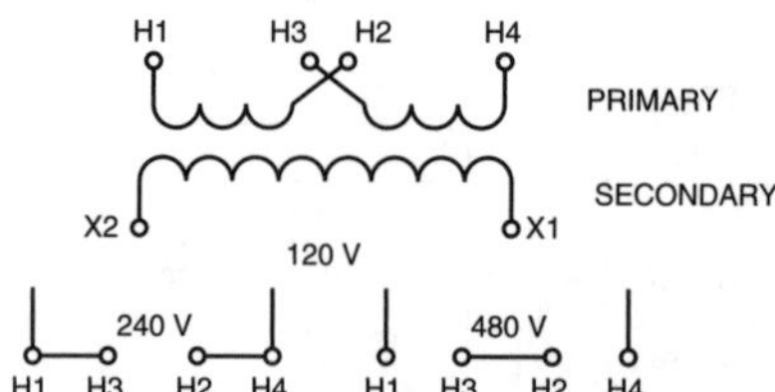

DUAL-VOLTAGE TRANSFORMER CONNECTIONS

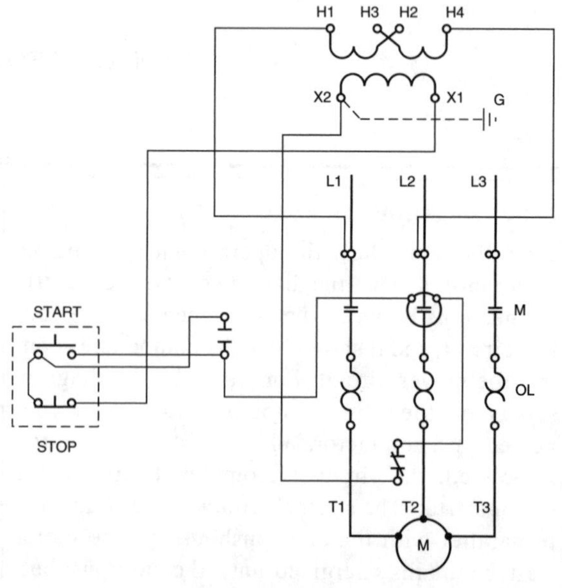

TRANSFORMER WIRING DIAGRAM

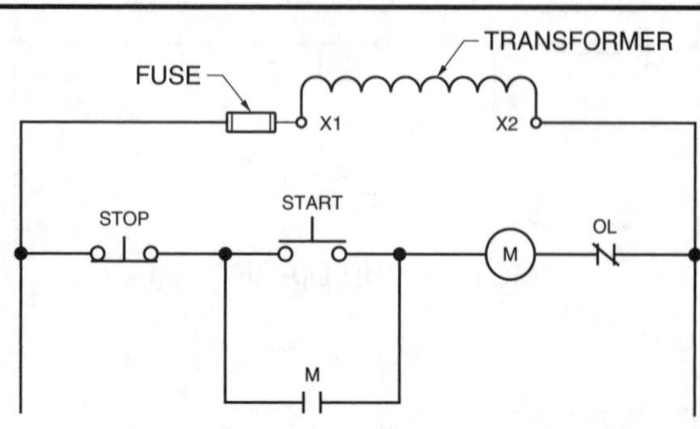

TRANSFORMER LINE DIAGRAM

Name ______________________________ Date ______________

THREE-PHASE MOTORS

chapter 3 ACTIVITIES

Activity 3-1. Gear Reducer Selection

Calculate the output torque, speed, and horsepower.

1. A 1 HP motor is connected to a gear reducer with a ratio of 15:1 and an efficiency rating of 93%. The motor turns at 1200 rpm and has an input torque of 4.5 lb-ft.

__________ **A.** The output torque is ________ lb-ft.

__________ **B.** The output speed is ________ rpm.

__________ **C.** The output horsepower is ________.

2. A 1.5 HP motor is connected to a gear reducer with a ratio of 50:1 and an efficiency rating of 85%. The motor turns at 3600 rpm and has an input torque of 2.2 lb-ft.

__________ **A.** The output torque is ________ lb-ft.

__________ **B.** The output speed is ________ rpm.

__________ **C.** The output horsepower is ________.

3. A 2 HP motor is connected to a gear reducer with a ratio of 25:1 and an efficiency rating of 79%. The motor turns at 1200 rpm and has an input torque of 8.9 lb-ft.

__________ **A.** The output torque is ________ lb-ft.

__________ **B.** The output speed is ________ rpm.

__________ **C.** The output horsepower is ________.

4. A 3 HP motor is connected to a gear reducer with a ratio of 7:1 and an efficiency rating of 96%. The motor turns at 1800 rpm and has an input torque of 9 lb-ft.

__________ **A.** The output torque is ________ lb-ft.

__________ **B.** The output speed is ________ rpm.

__________ **C.** The output horsepower is ________.

5. A 5 HP motor is connected to a gear reducer with a ratio of 3:1 and an efficiency rating of 80%. The motor turns at 1200 rpm and has an input torque of 22.5 lb-ft.

__________ **A.** The output torque is ________ lb-ft.

__________ **B.** The output speed is ________ rpm.

__________ **C.** The output horsepower is ________.

6. A 7.5 HP motor is connected to a gear reducer with a ratio of 42:1 and an efficiency rating of 84%. The motor turns at 1800 rpm and has an input torque of 21.4 lb-ft.

__________ **A.** The output torque is ________ lb-ft.

__________ **B.** The output speed is ________ rpm.

__________ **C.** The output horsepower is ________.

7. A 10 HP motor is connected to a gear reducer with a ratio of 12:1 and an efficiency rating of 90%. The motor turns at 1200 rpm and has an input torque of 44.8 lb-ft.

_________ **A.** The output torque is _________ lb-ft.

_________ **B.** The output speed is _________ rpm.

_________ **C.** The output horsepower is _________.

8. A 15 HP motor is connected to a gear reducer with a ratio of 32:1 and an efficiency rating of 95%. The motor turns at 1200 rpm and has an input torque of 66.7 lb-ft.

_________ **A.** The output torque is _________ lb-ft.

_________ **B.** The output speed is _________ rpm.

_________ **C.** The output horsepower is _________.

9. The motor is connected to a gear reducer with a ratio of 18:1 and an efficiency rating of 80%.

TYPE	AC	PHASE	3
HP	20	RPM	1800
VOLTS	460	AMPS	34
CYCLE	60	DUTY	CONT
TORQUE (lb-ft)	59.3	TEMP RISE	40° C

_________ **A.** The output torque is _________ lb-ft.

_________ **B.** The output speed is _________ rpm.

_________ **C.** The output horsepower is _________.

10. The motor is connected to a gear reducer with a ratio of 30:1 and an efficiency rating of 85%.

TYPE	AC	PHASE	3
HP	25	RPM	1800
VOLTS	460	AMPS	40
CYCLE	60	DUTY	CONT
TORQUE (lb-ft)	74	TEMP RISE	40° C

_________ **A.** The output torque is _________ lb-ft.

_________ **B.** The output speed is _________ rpm.

_________ **C.** The output horsepower is _________.

❍ Activity 3-2. Reversing Three-Phase Motors

Connect the motor for forward and reverse directions using low voltage.

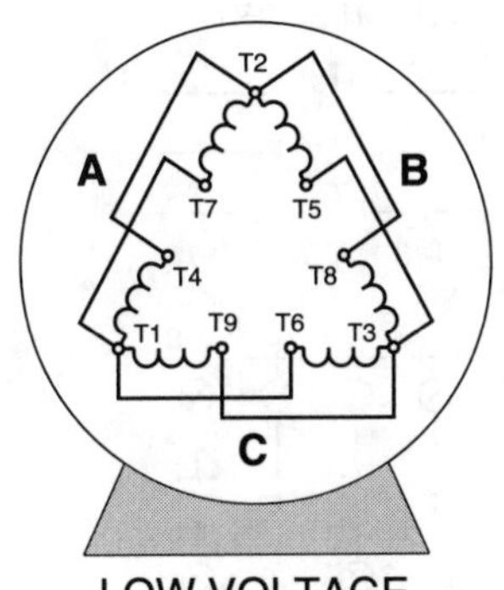

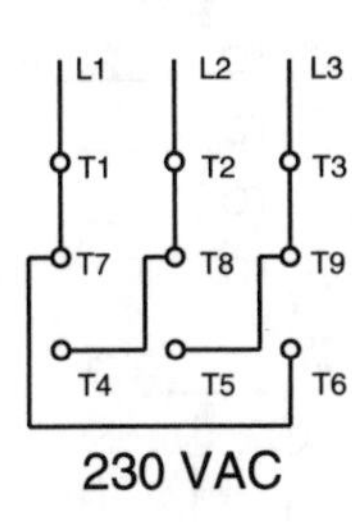

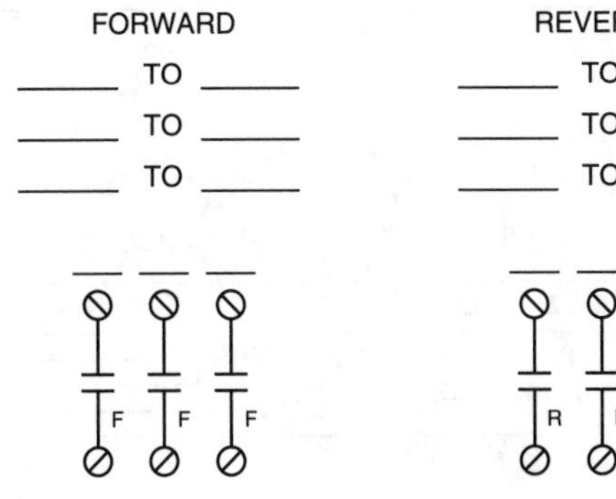

L1 L2 L3

F F F

R R R

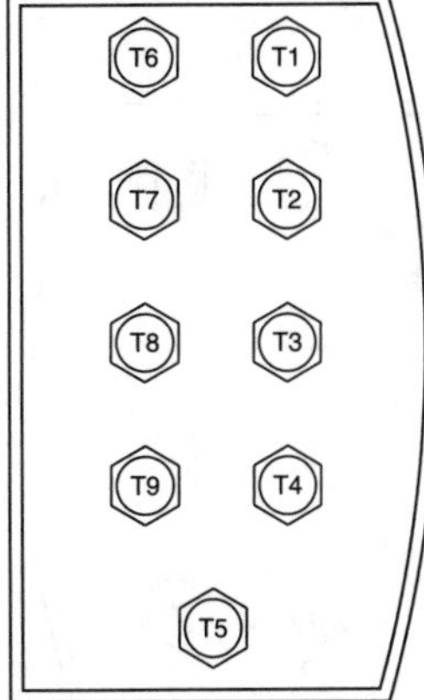

Activity 3-3. Connecting Multispeed, Three-Phase Motors

1. Connect the motor for low and high speeds.

3 φ	
2 SPEED	
SEPARATE WINDING	
______	

SPEED	L1	L2	L3	OPEN	CONNECT
LOW	T1	T2	T3, T7	ALL OTHERS	______
HIGH	T11	T12	T13, T17	ALL OTHERS	______

LOW SPEED

______ TO ______
______ TO ______
______ TO ______
T3 TO T7

HIGH SPEED

______ TO ______
______ TO ______
______ TO ______
T13 TO T17

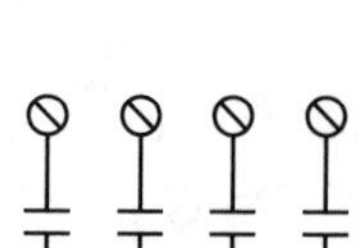

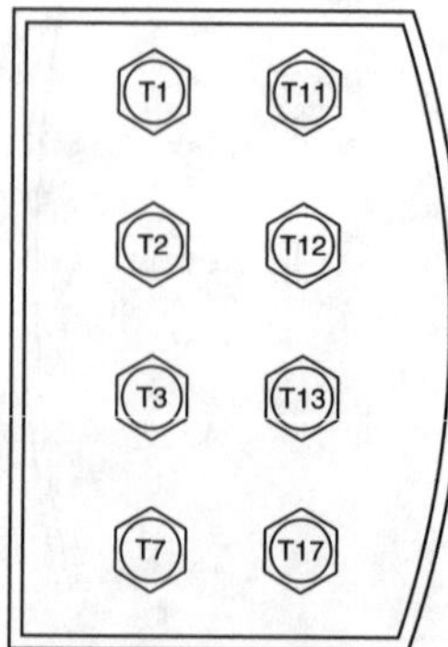

2. Connect the motor for low, second (medium), and high speeds.

3 φ	
2 SPEED	
SEPARATE WINDING	
VARIABLE TORQUE	

SPEED	L1	L2	L3	OPEN	CONNECT
LOW	T1	T2	T3	ALL OTHERS	———
2ND	T6	T4	T5	ALL OTHERS	T1, T2, T3
HIGH	T11	T12	T13	ALL OTHERS	———

LOW SPEED			SECOND SPEED (MEDIUM)			HIGH SPEED		
______	TO	T1	______	TO	T6	______	TO	T11
______	TO	T2	______	TO	T4	______	TO	T12
______	TO	T3	______	TO	T5	______	TO	T13
			T1	TO	T2			
			T3	TO	T2			

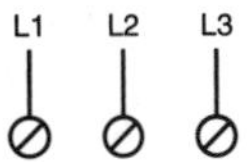

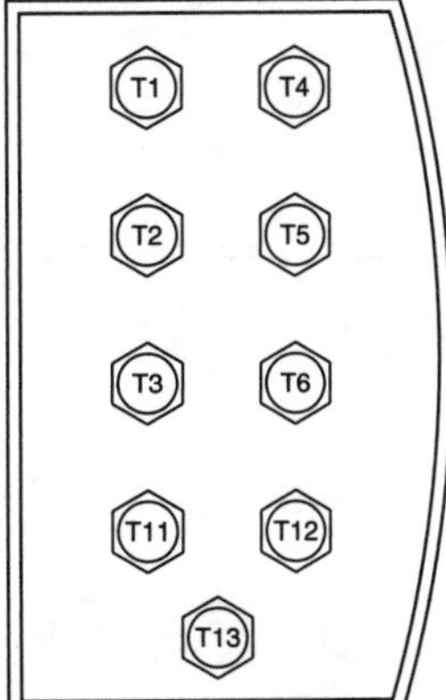

3. Connect the motor for low, second, third, and high speeds.

3 φ
4 SPEED
2 WINDING
CONSTANT HP

SPEED	L1	L2	L3	OPEN	CONNECT
LOW	T1	T2	T3	ALL OTHERS	T4, T5, T6, T7
2ND	T6	T4	T5, T7	ALL OTHERS	———
3RD	T11	T12	T13	ALL OTHERS	T14, T15, T16, T17
HIGH	T16	T14	T15, T17	ALL OTHERS	———

LOW SPEED	SECOND SPEED	THIRD SPEED	HIGH SPEED
____ TO ____	____ TO ____	____ TO ____	____ TO ____
____ TO ____	____ TO ____	____ TO ____	____ TO ____
____ TO ____	____ TO ____	____ TO ____	____ TO ____
T4 TO T5	T5 TO T7	T14 TO T15	T15 TO T17
T5 TO T6		T15 TO T16	
T6 TO T7		T16 TO T17	

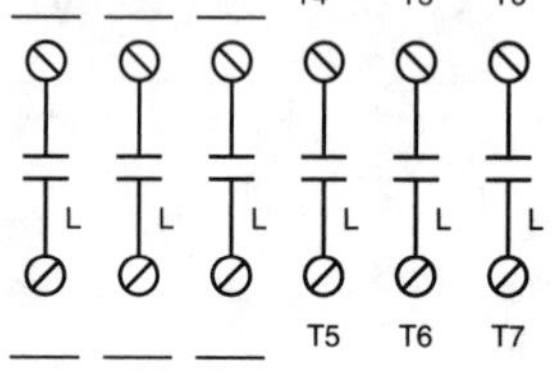

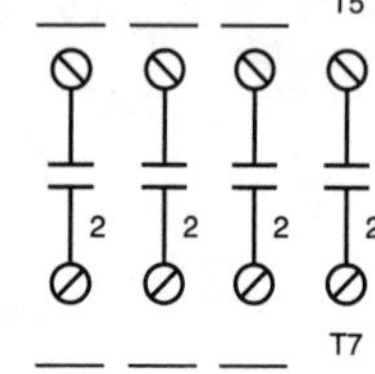

L1 L2 L3

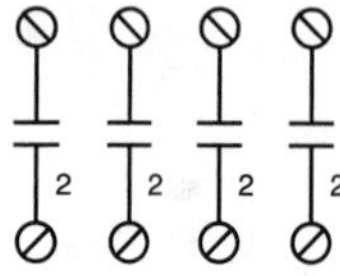

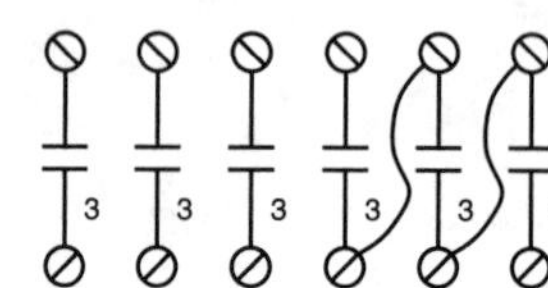

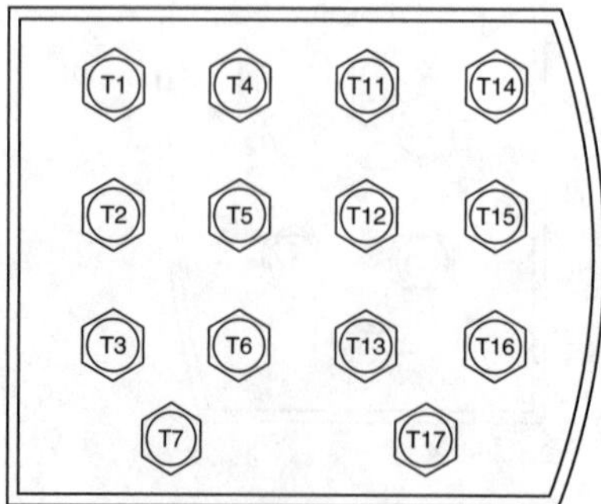

Activity 3-4. Motor Line and Motor Wiring Diagrams

1. Draw the line diagram from the wiring diagram.

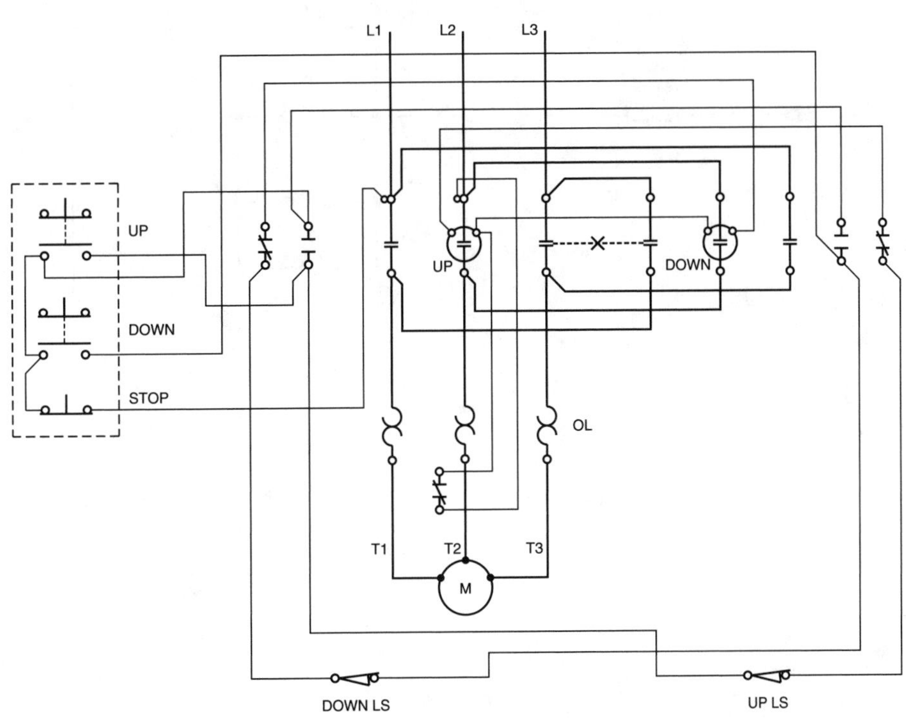

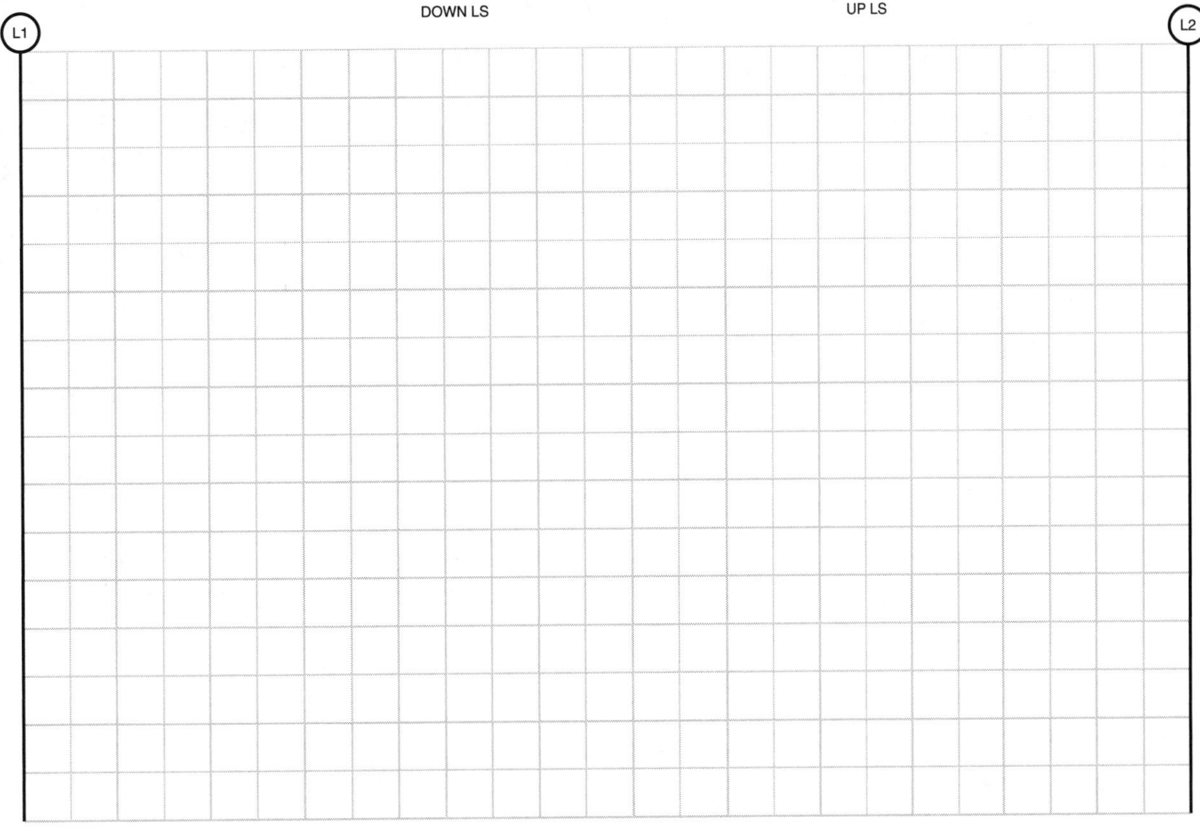

2. Draw the wiring diagram from the line diagram.

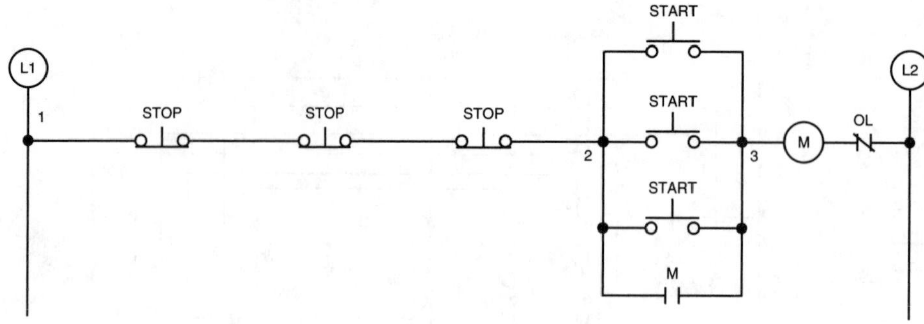

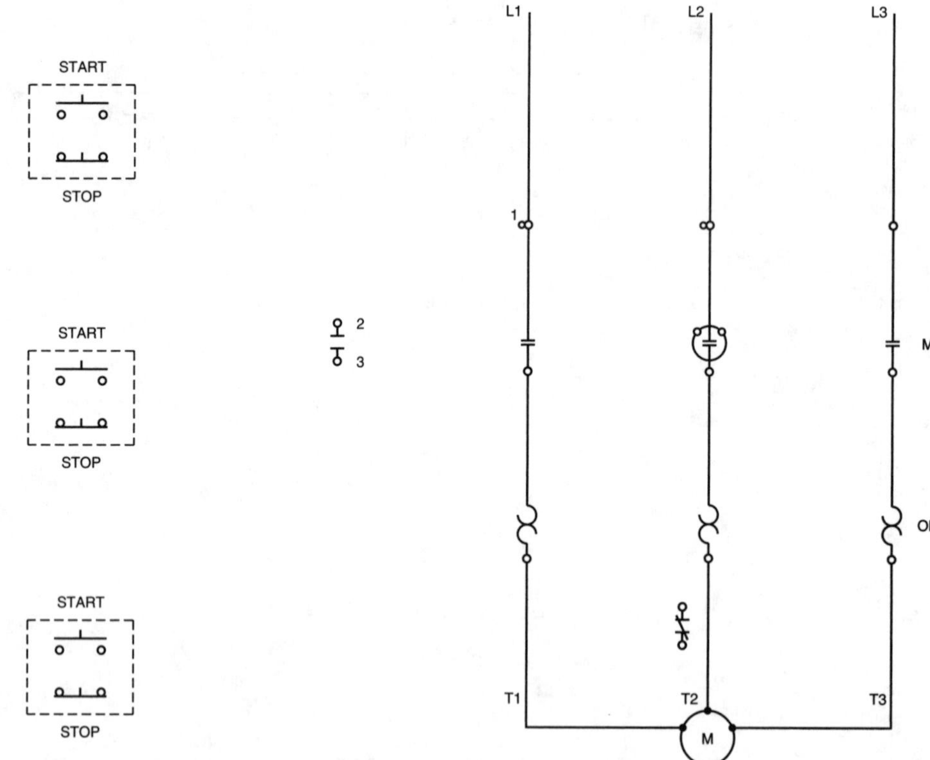

○ Activity 3-5. Dual-Voltage Control Transformer Installation

1. Draw the line diagram from the wiring diagram.

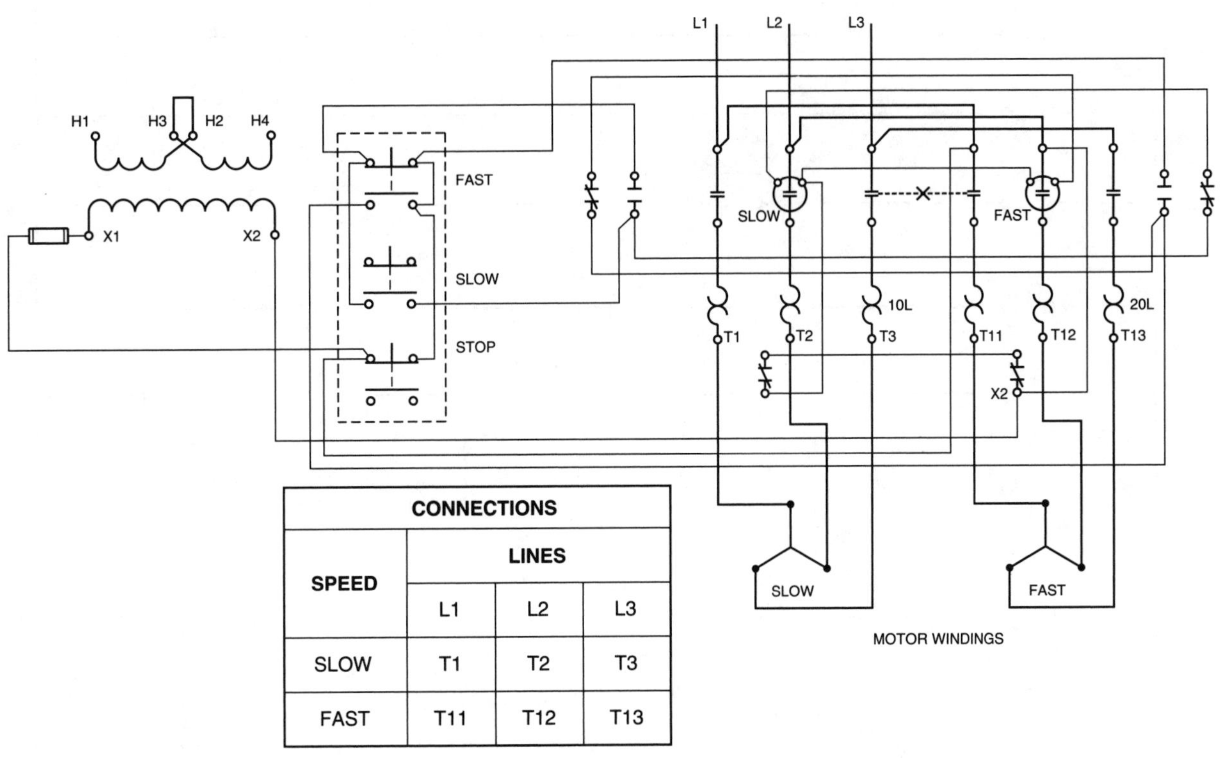

CONNECTIONS			
SPEED	LINES		
	L1	L2	L3
SLOW	T1	T2	T3
FAST	T11	T12	T13

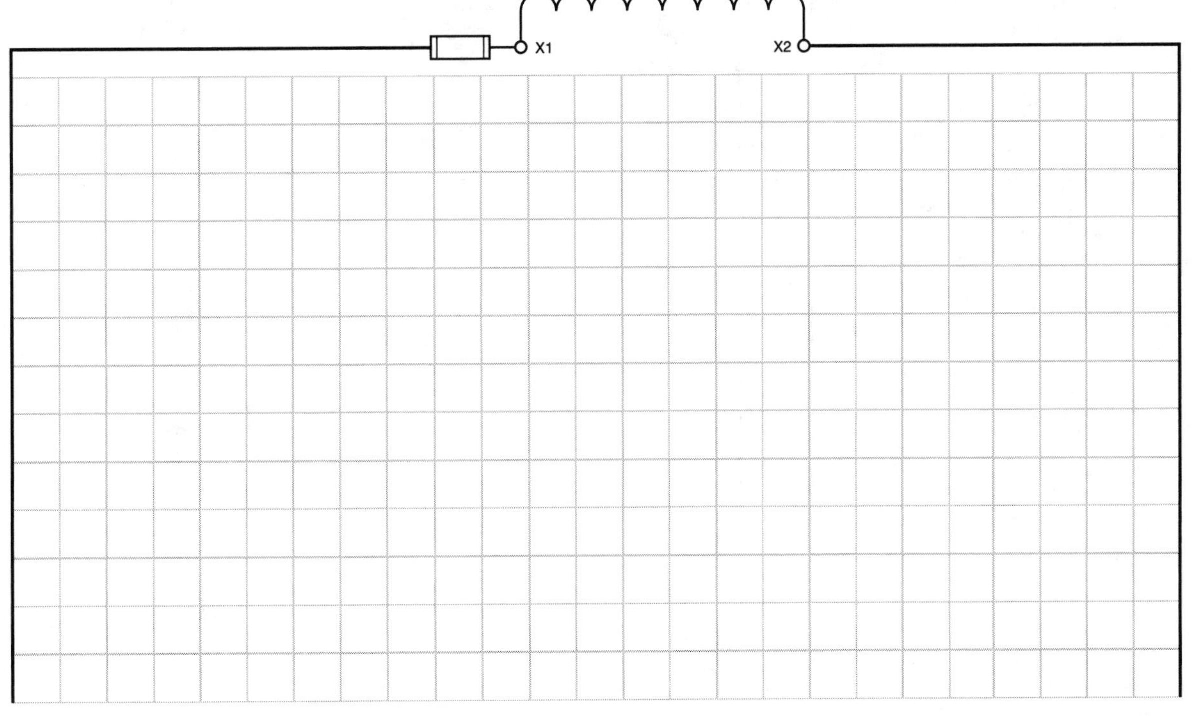

2. Draw the wiring diagram from the line diagram. Include the required connections at the transformer.

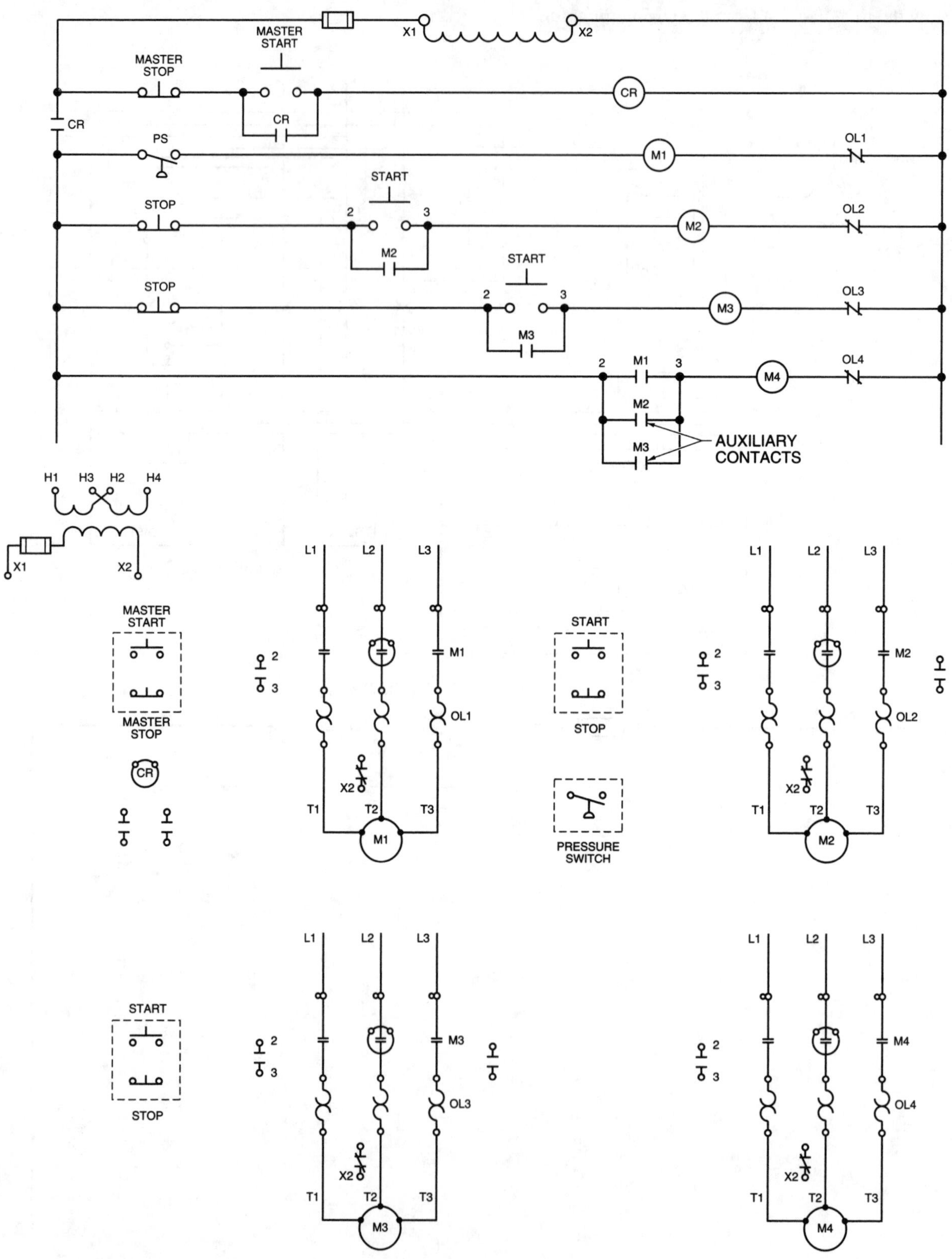

Name ______________________ Date ______________

chapter **3**

THREE-PHASE MOTORS

TRADE TEST

STOP START 2 3 M OL M

Completion

______ **1.** A(n) ______ motor has no physical, electrical connection to the rotor.

______ **2.** ______ power is the standard power supplied to almost all commercial and industrial locations.

______ **3.** The ______ is the stationary part of a 3ϕ motor.

______ **4.** The ______ is the rotating part of a 3ϕ motor.

______ **5.** There are ______ mechanical degrees in one revolution.

______ **6.** There are ______ electrical degrees from one pole to the next.

______ **7.** A(n) ______ motor has the rotor connected to the power supply through brushes.

______ **8.** If both voltages of a dual-voltage motor are available, the ______ voltage is usually preferred.

______ **9.** The coils of a dual-voltage, wye-connected, 3ϕ motor are connected in ______ for high voltage.

______ **10.** The coils of a dual-voltage, delta-connected, 3ϕ motor are connected in ______ for low voltage.

______ **11.** Three-phase motors cost ______ to operate per horsepower than 1ϕ motors.

______ **12.** Each phase of a 3ϕ motor contains ______ of the total number of individual coils.

______ **13.** The voltage level of a motor is stamped on the motor ______.

______ **14.** The ______ of a motor determines if a change of horsepower or torque is required.

______ **15.** ______ torque motors produce an increase in torque with an increase in speed.

______ **16.** The most common 3ϕ motor used in industry is the ______ motor.

______ **17.** As the voltage of a dual-voltage motor is doubled, ______ is cut in half.

______ **18.** The industrial standard for reversing a 3ϕ motor is to interchange ______ and T3.

______ **19.** ______ horsepower motors give the same maximum horsepower at all speeds.

______ **20.** In a variable torque motor, torque varies ______ with the speed.

True-False

T F **1.** Three-phase motors have fairly constant speed.

T F **2.** Three-phase motors require extensive maintenance.

T F **3.** The three windings of a 3ϕ motor are known as phases 1, 2, and 3.

T F **4.** Each of the phases of a wye-connected, 3ϕ motor is internally connected to the other phases.

T F **5.** A typical single-voltage motor operates at 230/460 V.

T F **6.** Most 3ϕ motors can operate at either of two voltages.

T F 7. A 3ϕ motor's operating speed depends upon its number of poles.

T F 8. A dual-voltage motor can operate at more than one voltage level.

T F 9. If the coils of a motor are connected in parallel, the voltage divides equally.

T F 10. The number of poles in a constant horsepower motor is effectively changed by changing the direction of current through the motor windings.

Multiple Choice

__________ 1. Three-phase motors are _________.

A. self-starting
B. less expensive than other motor types of the same HP rating
C. simple in construction
D. A, B, and C

__________ 2. During one revolution, a rotor completes _________ electrical degrees in a 6-pole motor.

A. 180
B. 360
C. 1080
D. 2160

__________ 3. In a single-voltage, delta-connected, 3ϕ motor, each phase is _________.

A. divided with two equal parts
B. wired end-to-end to form a closed circuit
C. neither A nor B
D. both A and B

__________ 4. In a dual-voltage, wye-connected, 3ϕ motor, _________ terminal loads are available.

A. 3
B. 4
C. 6
D. 9

__________ 5. To reverse the direction of rotation of a delta-connected, 3ϕ motor, _________.

A. interchange T1 and T2
B. interchange T1 and T3
C. tie T1 to T2
D. tie T1 to T3

__________ 6. Multiple-speed, 3ϕ motors are assigned to operate at _________ speeds.

A. two
B. three
C. four
D. A, B, and C

__________ 7. In a constant horsepower motor, torque _________ as speed increases.

A. decreases
B. increases
C. neither A nor B
D. both A and B

__________ 8. In a constant torque motor, horsepower changes _________ to the speed.

A. proportionally
B. inversely
C. either A or B
D. horsepower does not change

__________ 9. In a variable torque motor, torque and horsepower _________ at higher speed and _________ at lower speed.

A. decrease; increase
B. increase; decrease
C. decrease; remain the same
D. increase; remain the same

__________ 10. To connect a dual-voltage, wye-connected, 3ϕ motor, connect L1, L2, and L3 to T1, T2, and T3 and use wire nuts to connect _________.

A. T4 to T5, T6 to T7, and T8 to T9
B. T4 to T6, T5 to T7, and T6 to T9
C. T4 to T7, T5 to T8, and T6 to T9
D. neither A, B, nor C

Problems

Identify the wiring as a high-speed connection or a low-speed connection.

1. ________speed

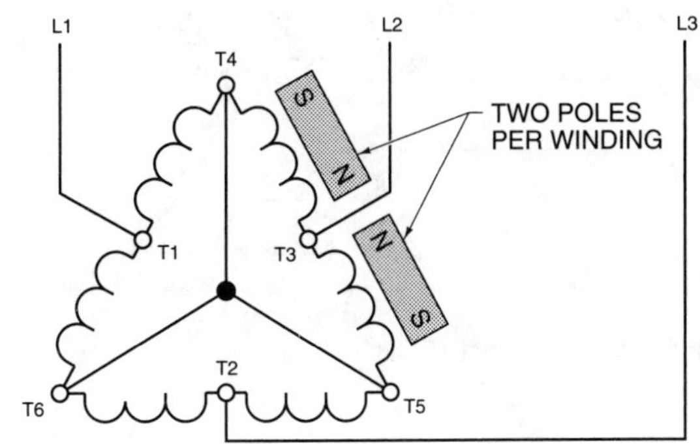

2. ________speed

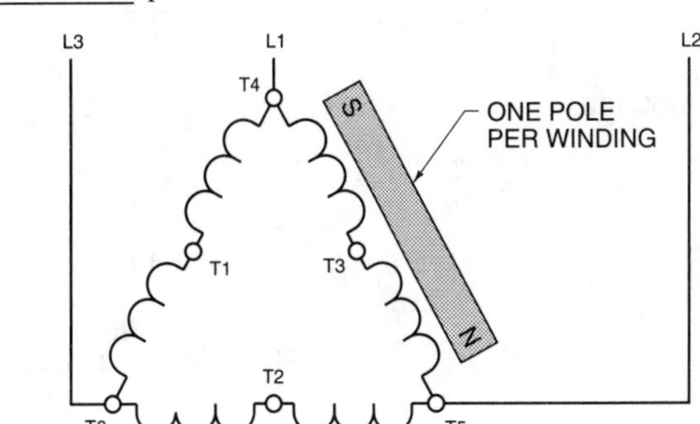

3. ________speed

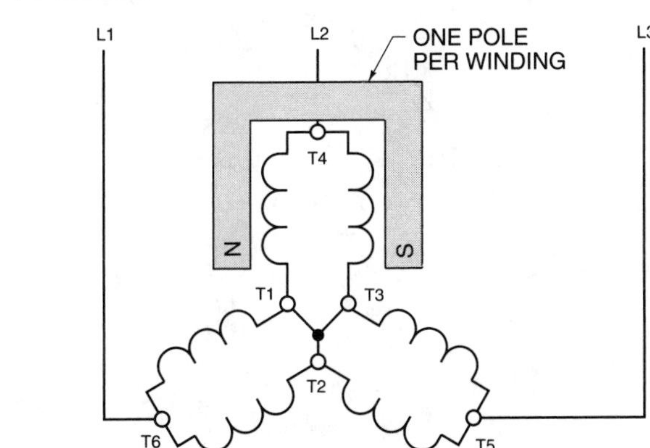

4. ________speed

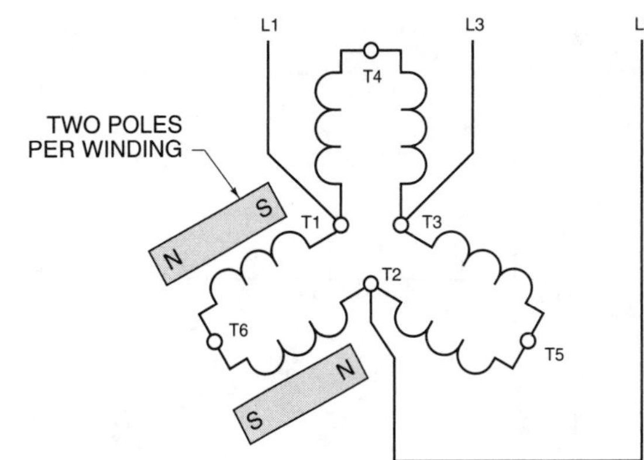

5. ________speed

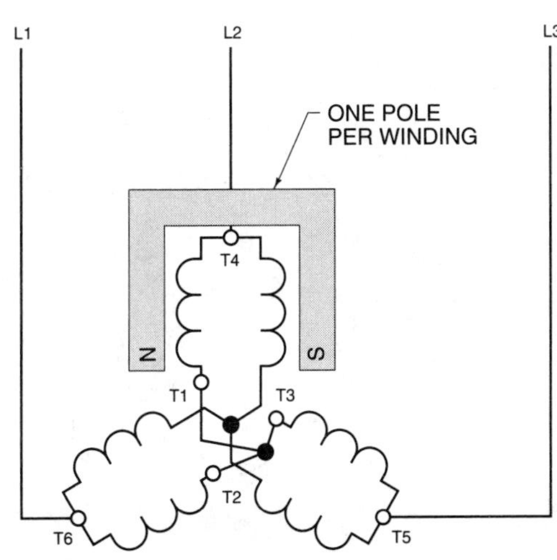

6. ________speed

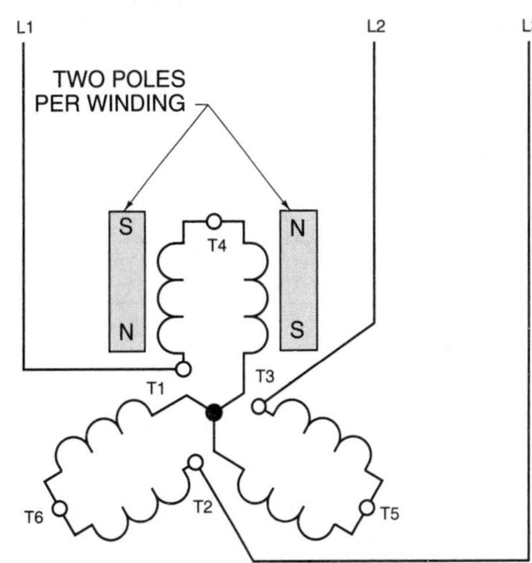

7. Connect the motor to run in forward or reverse directions. Use industrial standards.

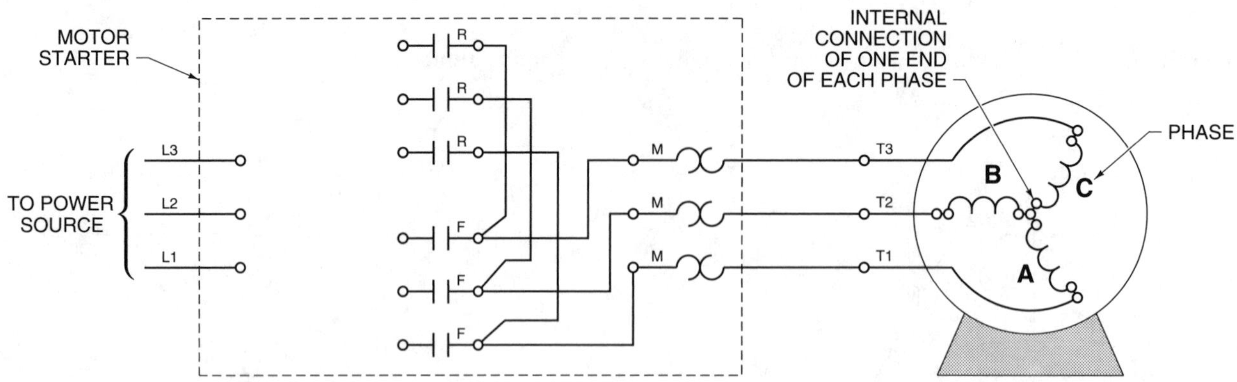

SINGLE-VOLTAGE, WYE-CONNECTED, 3ϕ MOTOR

8. Connect the motor to the 460 V power supply.

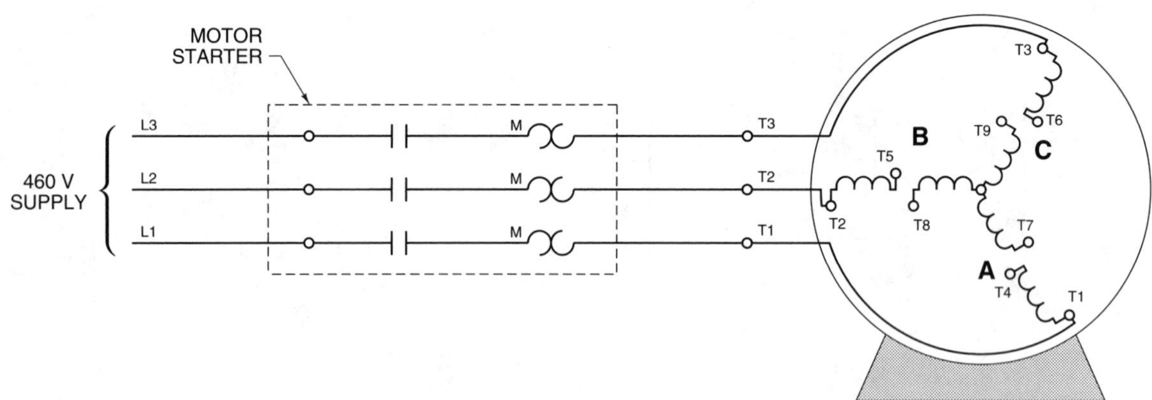

DUAL-VOLTAGE, WYE-CONNECTED, 3ϕ MOTOR

9. Connect the motor to the 230 V power supply.

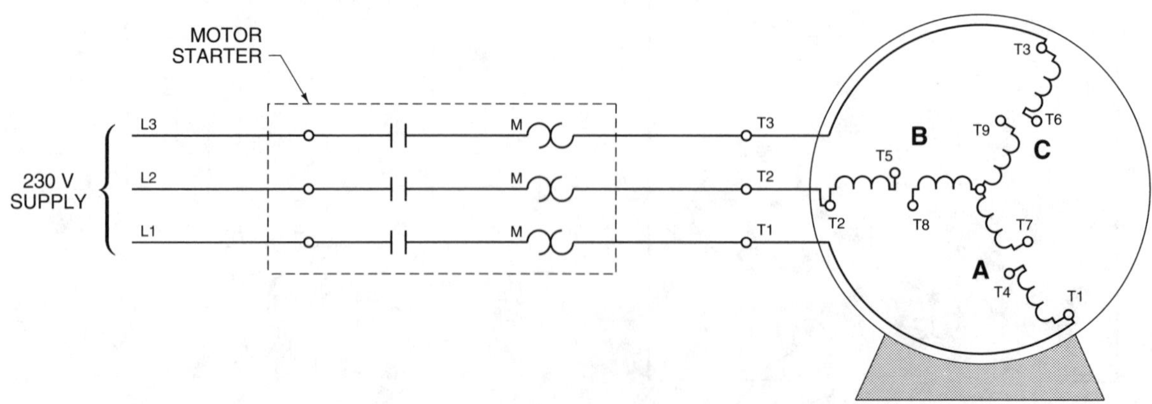

DUAL-VOLTAGE, WYE-CONNECTED, 3ϕ MOTOR

10. Connect the motor to the 460 V power supply.

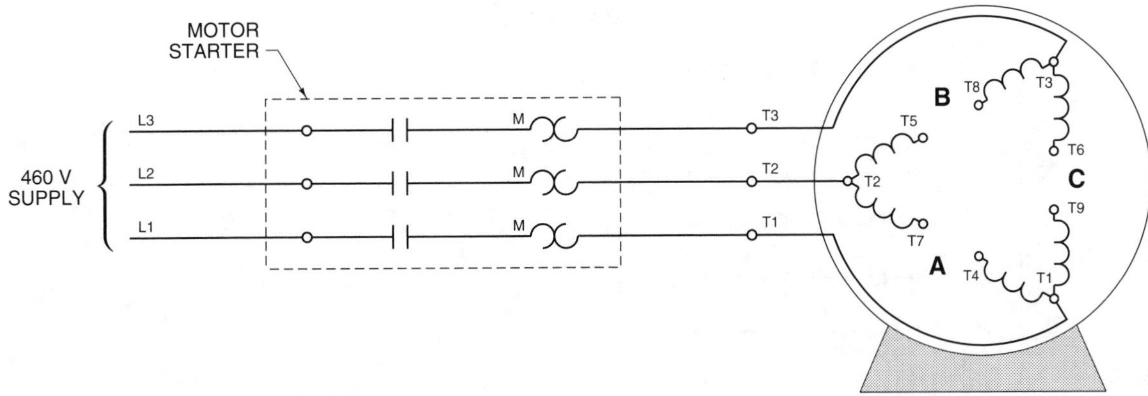

DUAL-VOLTAGE, DELTA-CONNECTED, 3ϕ MOTOR

11. Connect the motor to the 230 V power supply.

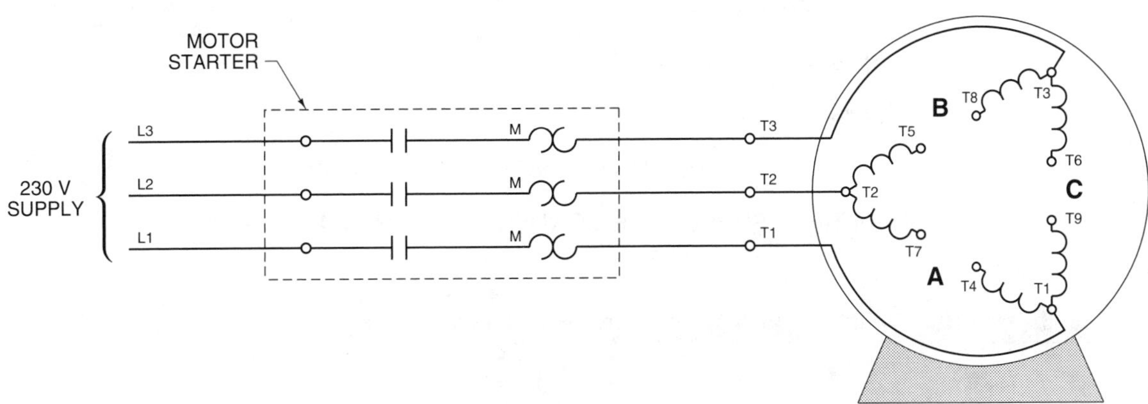

DUAL-VOLTAGE, DELTA-CONNECTED, 3ϕ MOTOR

12. Connect the motor to operate at low or high speed.

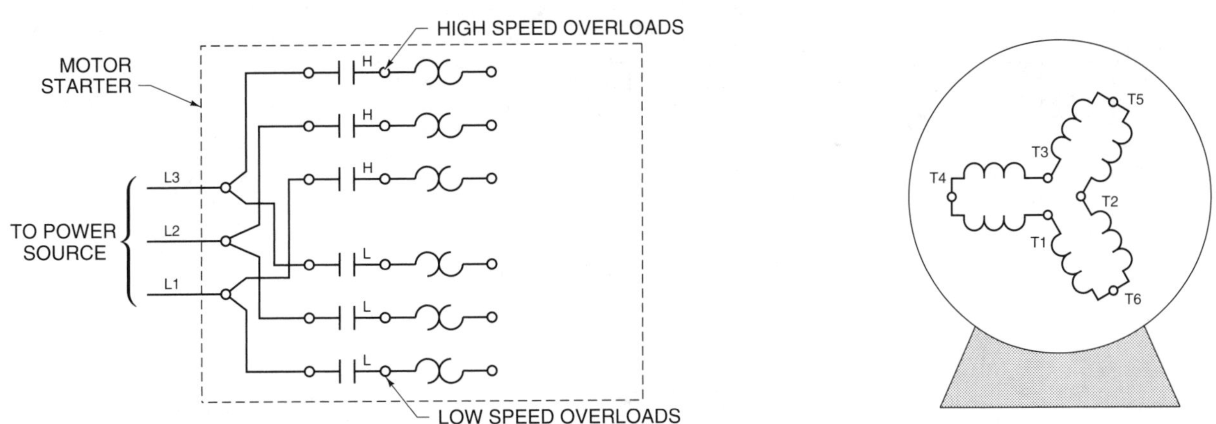

CONSTANT TORQUE, TWO-SPEED, ONE WINDING MOTOR

13. Connect the motor to operate at low or high speed.

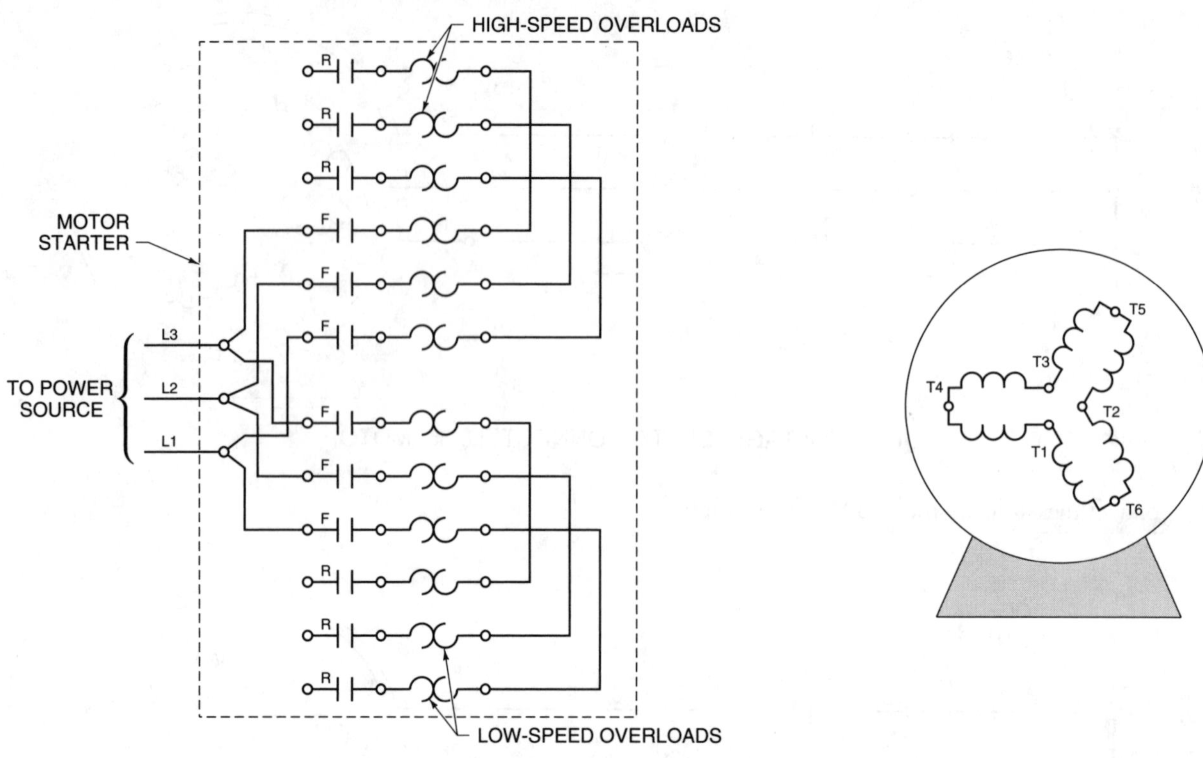

MULTIPLE-SPEED, WYE-CONNECTED, 3ϕ MOTOR

14. Connect the motor to run in forward or reverse directions in high speed.

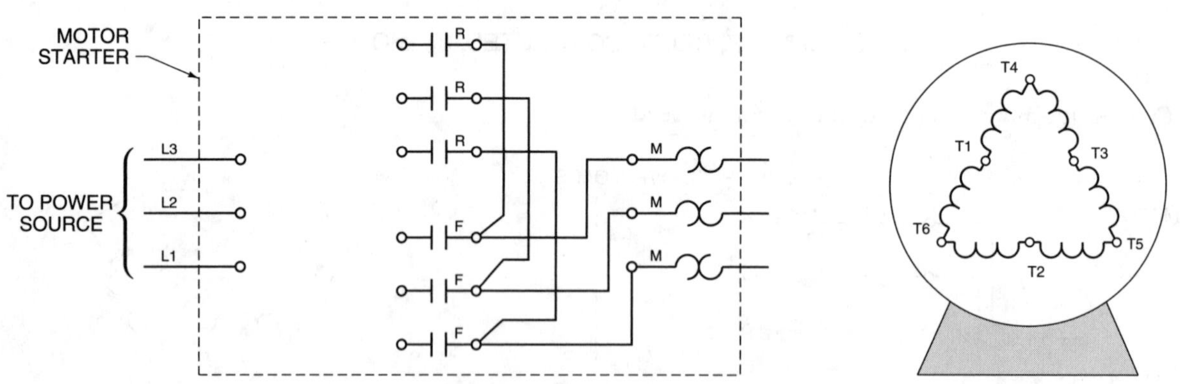

HIGH-SPEED, DELTA-CONNECTED, 3ϕ MOTOR

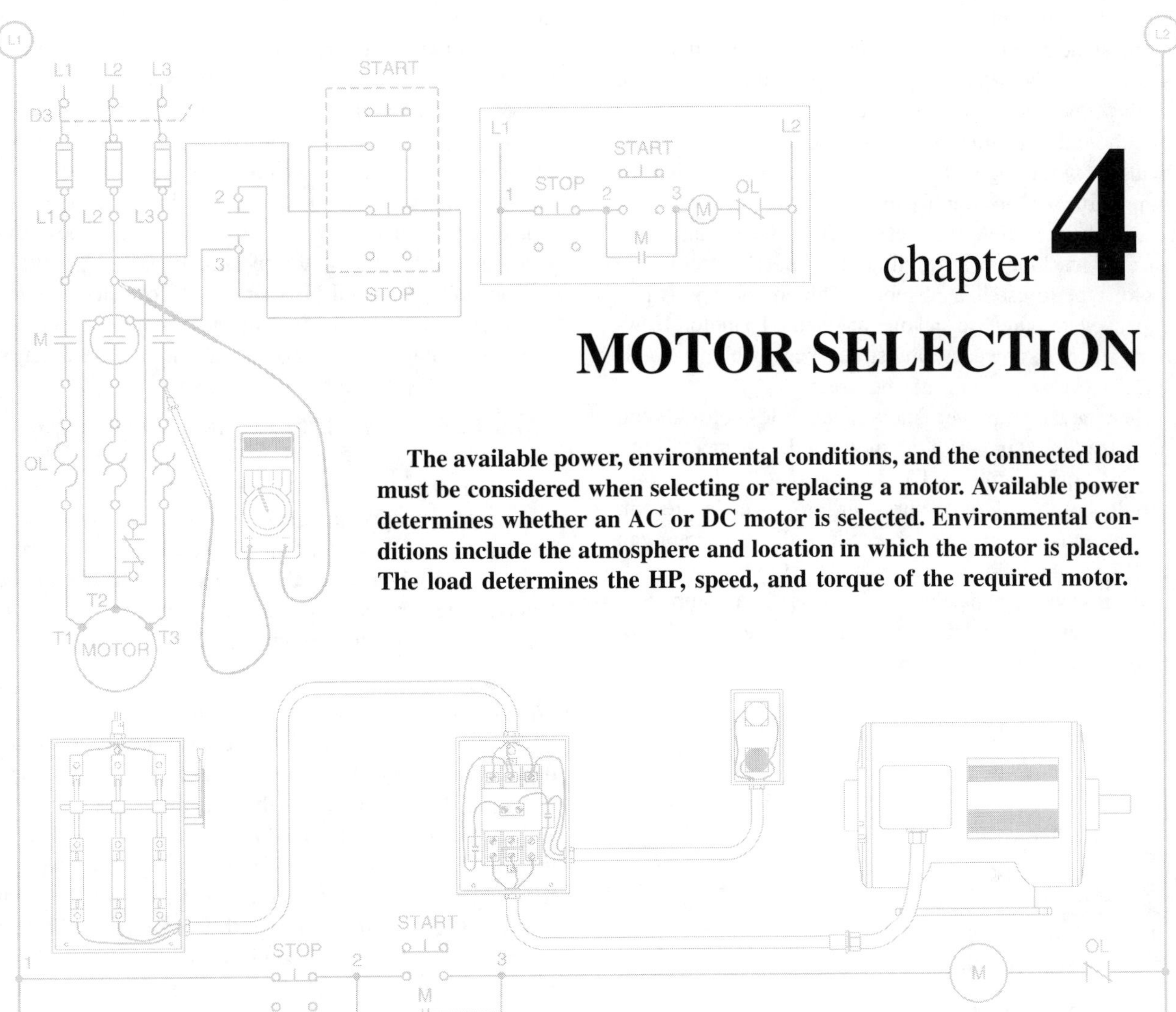

chapter 4 MOTOR SELECTION

The available power, environmental conditions, and the connected load must be considered when selecting or replacing a motor. Available power determines whether an AC or DC motor is selected. Environmental conditions include the atmosphere and location in which the motor is placed. The load determines the HP, speed, and torque of the required motor.

MOTOR SELECTION

The electric motor performs more work in residential, commercial, and industrial applications than any other type of machine. Motors are used to operate pumps, fans, air conditioners, tools, appliances, conveyors, and many other types of machines.

All electric motors are machines used to change electrical energy into mechanical energy. Thus, all motors are used to perform some type of work. The type of work that motors do today is almost unlimited. However, as diversified as the use of motors is, there is usually a motor type that will solve almost any problem or application satisfactorily.

Determining the correct motor for an application involves a wide range of considerations. The choice of a motor is obvious in some applications. In other applications, the choice of a motor is more involved. To make the best choice, several things must be collectively and simultaneously taken into account. It is highly unlikely that simply running down a checklist will determine the correct motor for a given application.

The application in which the motor is to be used must be considered, and then a logical motor type and size can be tried. Even after the most logical motor is selected, field testing and the performance of the motor may require a change to a different type or size. Items to consider when selecting a motor type include the available power, load to be driven, and environmental conditions. See Figure 4-1.

Available Power

In selecting a motor type for any application, the available electrical power source must be considered. All electric motors require either direct current (DC), single-phase, alternating current (1ϕ, AC), or three-phase, alternating current (3ϕ, AC).

In some applications, any of these electrical power sources may be selected. In other applications, only one of these electrical power sources is practical. For example, the only electrical power source available for practical use with a golf cart is DC. It is not practical or safe to run AC to a golf cart.

Another example requires a motor to drive an appliance or machine in a dwelling. The most cost-effective motor type to use is a 3ϕ motor. This motor type is less expensive to purchase and operate than a 1ϕ motor. However, since 3ϕ power is almost never available in dwellings, a 3ϕ motor could not be used.

Whenever 3ϕ power is available, a 3ϕ motor should be considered first. If a 3ϕ motor will not meet application requirements, a 1ϕ, AC motor or a DC motor should be considered. Wherever 3ϕ power is present, 1ϕ power is usually available. Since direct current can easily be obtained from a rectifier, DC motors can almost always be considered. A *rectifier* is a component that converts AC to DC by allowing the current to move in only one direction.

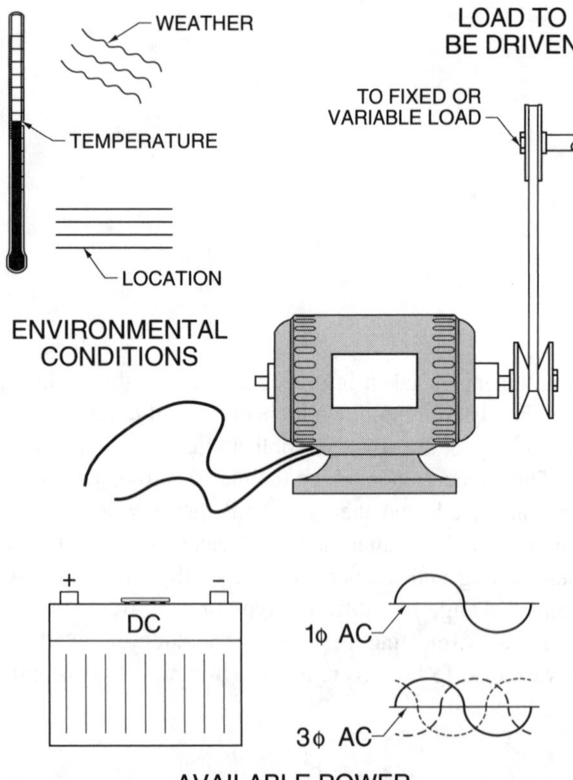

Figure 4-1. Available power, load to be driven, and environmental conditions should be considered when selecting a motor type.

Variations from Motor Specifications. For any motor to operate properly, the power delivered to the motor must be very close to the motor specifications. It is almost impossible to meet exact specifications when delivering power to a motor. The performance characteristics of a motor are affected by any variation from specifications. Motor efficiency is usually poorer when a motor is operated at the far ends of the permissible range. Motors will operate properly when the voltage, frequency, and speed are within the motor specifications.

The voltage should be + or – 10% of rated voltage at the rated frequency. AC voltages usually vary more than DC voltages. This variation should not be a major problem, unless it becomes excessive.

The frequency should be + or – 5% of rated frequency at the rated voltage. Variation in frequency is almost never a problem. The frequency problem that is most common is connecting a 50 cycle motor to a 60 cycle line or connecting a 60 cycle motor to a 50 cycle line. This usually only occurs when 60 cycle motors are sent out of the United States or when foreign 50 cycle motors (usually as part of a machine) are brought into the United States.

When a motor is operated below its rated speed, the driven load should be reduced in order to avoid overheating the motor. Overheating usually results from reduced ventilation. As a motor runs more slowly, there is less air flow around and through the motor.

When a motor is operated above its rated speed, centrifugal forces must be considered. Not only can the motor or part of the motor come apart, but the bearing lubrication can be forced out of the motor. An AC motor can be operated above its rated speed by using a variable frequency drive. Some frequency drives operate a motor at four times, or more, of the motor's rated nameplate speed. The manufacturer's recommendations should be followed to determine the maximum speed of a motor. Typical speeds for motors vary, depending upon the type. Motor speeds are measured in revolutions per minute (rpm). See Figure 4-2.

Driven Load

Since the function of the motor is to do work, the motor must be able to operate the load to which it is connected. To do this correctly, the motor must be matched to the load that it will drive. When the motor and load are properly matched, the motor should successfully drive the load under all given conditions for a reasonable period of time, using the most economical means.

TYPICAL MOTOR SPEEDS*		
	Synchronous Speed	**Rated Speed (Nameplate)**
1φ, AC and 3φ, AC	900	825
	1200	1140
	1800	1725
	3600	3450
Permanent Magnet DC	None	1725
DC	**Base Speed**	**Rated Top Speed**
	1150	1380
	1750	2050
	2500	2750

* Speeds in rpm.

Figure 4-2. Manufacturer's recommendations should be followed to determine the maximum speed of a motor.

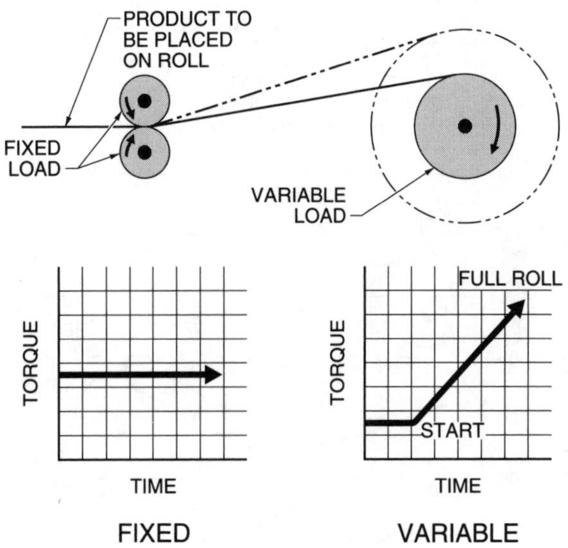

Figure 4-3. Loads may be fixed or variable.

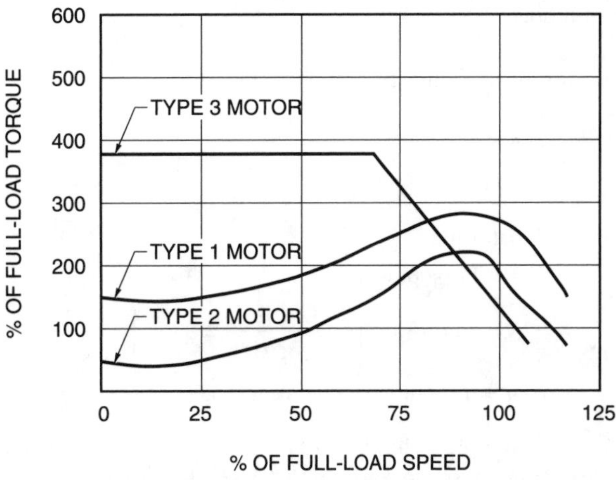

Figure 4-4. A speed-torque graph is used to determine motor characteristics.

Undersized and oversized motors will also drive most loads within a given range. However, if a motor is undersized, it may drive the load for a shorter period of time than is desirable. This is a typical problem with motors that require frequent replacement. To simply oversize a motor is not always the solution. An oversized motor costs more to purchase and operate than a properly sized motor. Additionally, oversized motors require more space. If the proper size motor is not available, it is usually better to oversize than to undersize.

To drive a load at a set speed, the motor must produce a certain amount of torque. If the motor's output torque is large enough, the load will be driven. If the motor's output torque is too small, the load will not be driven, or will be driven at a reduced speed.

The torque-speed characteristic of a motor must match the load the motor is to drive. A load may have a definite torque-speed characteristic, such as a pump or fan that has a fixed load. Or the load may be a variable one, such as a hoist or conveyor belt used to move loads of varying weights. See Figure 4-3.

The motor manufacturer provides technical data on each motor type manufactured. A speed-torque graph is used to determine motor characteristics. See Figure 4-4.

Motor Torque. The torque required to operate a load from initial startup to final shutdown is considered when determining the type and size of motor required for a given application. *Torque* is the force that produces rotation in a motor. It is measured in pound-feet (lb-ft). The four types of torque related to motors are locked rotor torque, full-load torque, pull-up torque, and breakdown torque. See Figure 4-5.

Locked rotor torque is the torque a motor produces when the rotor is stationary and full power is applied to the motor. This is the minimum torque that a motor at rest develops for all angular positions of the shaft with rated voltage applied at rated frequency. Locked rotor torque is also referred to as breakaway or starting torque. *Starting torque* is the torque required to start a motor. Starting torque is usually expressed as a percentage of full-load torque. *Full-load torque* is the torque required to produce the rated power at full speed of the motor.

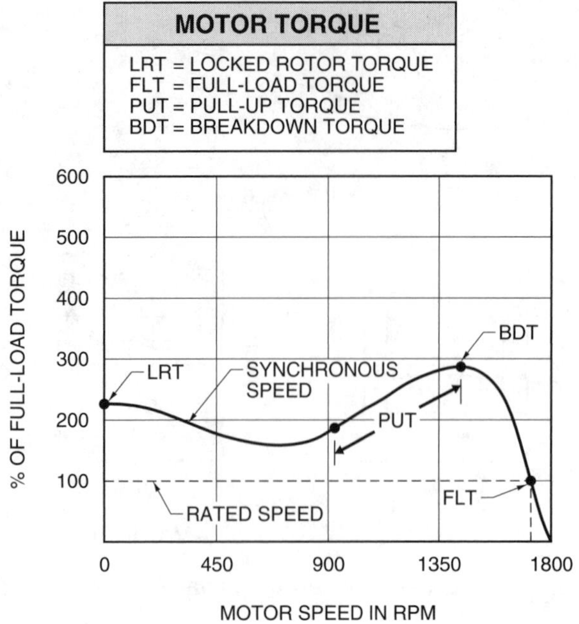

Figure 4-5. Torque is the force which produces shaft rotation.

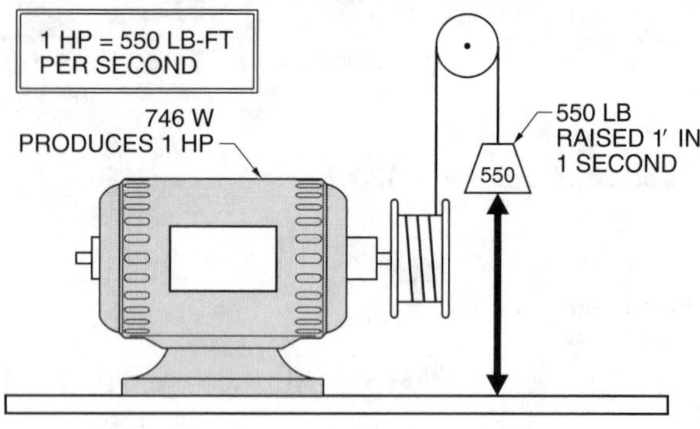

MECHANICAL ENERGY	ELECTRICAL ENERGY
$\frac{1}{2}$ HP	373 W
1 HP	746 W
2 HP	1492 W
5 HP	3730 W
100 HP	74,600 W

Figure 4-6. Motor power is rated in horsepower or watts.

Torque is found by applying the formula:

$$T = \frac{HP \times 5252}{rpm}$$

where

T = torque

HP = horsepower

5252 = constant $\left(\frac{33.000\text{ lb-ft}}{\pi \times 2} = 5252\right)$

rpm = revolutions per minute

For example, what is the full-load torque of a 60 HP, 240 V, 3ϕ motor, turning at 1725 rpm?

$$T = \frac{HP \times 5252}{rpm}$$

$$T = \frac{60 \times 5252}{1725}$$

$$T = \frac{315{,}120}{1725}$$

T = **182.7 lb-ft**

Motor power is rated in horsepower or watts. See Figure 4-6. A *horsepower* (HP) is a unit of power equal to 746 watts or 33,000 pound-feet per minute (550 pound-feet per second). A watt (W) is the base unit of electrical power. Larger motors are rated in kilowatts (kW). For example, the output of a 5 HP motor is 3.73 kW.

$$\left(\frac{5\text{ HP} \times 746\text{ W}}{1000} = 3.73\text{ kW}\right)$$

Horsepower is used to measure the energy produced by a motor while doing work. The horsepower of a motor, when the current and voltage are known, is found by applying the formula:

$$HP = \frac{E \times I \times E_{ff}}{746}$$

where

HP = horsepower

E = voltage (volts)

I = current (amps)

E_{ff} = efficiency

For example, what is the horsepower of a 240 V motor pulling 15 A and having 85% efficiency?

$$HP = \frac{E \times I \times E_{ff}}{746}$$

$$HP = \frac{240 \times 15 \times .85}{746}$$

$$HP = \frac{3060}{746}$$

HP = **4.1 HP**

The horsepower of a motor determines how fast a load will turn. The horsepower of a motor, when the speed and torque are known, is found by applying the formula:

$$HP = \frac{rpm \times T}{5252}$$

where

HP = horsepower

rpm = revolutions per minute

T = torque (lb-ft)

$$5252 = \text{constant} \left(\frac{33.000 \text{ lb-ft}}{\pi \times 2} = 5252 \right)$$

For example, what is the horsepower of a 1725 rpm motor with a full-load torque of 15.2 lb-ft?

$$HP = \frac{rpm \times T}{5252}$$

$$HP = \frac{1725 \times 15.2}{5252}$$

$$HP = \frac{26,220}{5252}$$

HP = **5 HP**

The horsepower or torque of a motor may also be found with a conversion table when the rpm is known. For example, to find the horsepower, place a straightedge along the rpm and torque of the motor. To find the torque, place a straightedge along the rpm and HP. See Appendix.

Pull-up torque (accelerating torque) is the torque required to bring a load up to the correct speed. If a motor is properly sized to the load, pull-up torque is brief. If a motor does not have sufficient pull-up torque, the locked rotor torque may start the load turning, but the pull-up torque will not bring it up to rated speed. Once a motor is up to rated speed, full-load torque keeps the load turning.

Breakdown torque is the maximum torque a motor can provide without an abrupt reduction in motor speed. As the load on a motor shaft increases, the motor produces more torque. As the load continues to increase, the point at which the motor stalls is reached. This point is the breakdown torque.

Motors are designed for high efficiency, high starting torque, or high power factor, but they are not designed to have all three. The National Electrical Manufacturers Association (NEMA) has established minimum starting torque for motors. The starting torque of all motors is in a range. For example, the starting torque range of a capacitor-start motor is from 200% to 350% of the motor's full-load torque. See Figure 4-7.

STARTING TORQUE	
Motor Type	**Starting Torque***
DC Motors	
Series	400–450%
Shunt	125–250%
Compound	300–400%
1ϕ Motors	
Shaded-pole	50–100%
Split-phase	75–200%
Capcitor-start	200–350%
Capacitor-run	50–100%
Capacitor start-and-run	350–450%
3ϕ Motors	
Induction	100–275%
Wound rotor	200–300%
Synchronous	40–160%
Universal Motors	
Noncompensated	300–350%
Compensated	300–400%

*Percent of full-load torque

Figure 4-7. The starting torque of all motors is in a range.

Torque Classification. Motors are classified by NEMA according to their electrical characteristics. The starting torque of a motor varies with the classification of the motor. Motors are classified as Classes A through F. Each class of motor has a different value of starting torque. Classes B, C, and D are most common, but most manufacturer's catalogs also list Class A. See Figure 4-8.

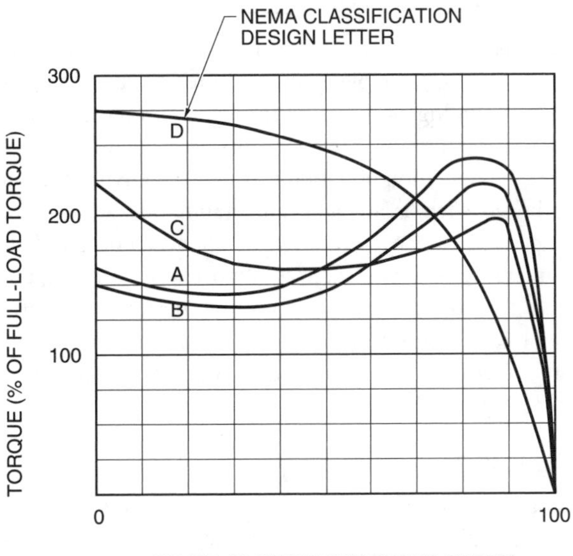

Figure 4-8. The starting torque varies with the classification of the motor.

Class B motors are the most widely used motors in the electrical industry. A Class B motor increases the starting torque of the motor by 150%. A Class C motor increases the starting torque of the motor by 225%. A Class D motor increases the starting torque of the motor by 275%. Subtract 25% from each of these values to avoid overloading the starting torque of the motor. For example, to find the starting torque of a motor, use the formula:

$$T = \frac{HP \times 5252}{rpm} \times \%$$

where

HP = horsepower

$$5252 = \text{constant}\left(\frac{33{,}000\,\text{lb-ft}}{\pi \times 2} = 5252\right)$$

rpm = revolutions per minute

% = motor class percentage

For example, what is the starting torque of a 60 HP, 240 V, 3ϕ, Class B motor turning at 1725 rpm?

$$T = \frac{HP \times 5252}{rpm} \times \%$$

$$T = \frac{60 \times 5252}{1725} \times 125\%$$

$$T = \frac{315{,}120}{1725} \times 125\%$$

T = **228.35 lb-ft**

Environmental Conditions

Environmental conditions are those conditions that surround a motor. Ambient temperature, altitude, atmosphere, mounting surface, and mechanical forces, such as shock and vibration, are environmental conditions that affect the operation of a motor. Abnormal environmental conditions such as ambient temperature and altitude are compensated for by derating the motor. Abnormal environmental conditions such as atmosphere are compensated for by selecting the correct motor enclosure. Abnormal environmental conditions such as the mounting surface and mechanical conditions are compensated for during installation and maintenance.

Usual Service Conditions. Satisfying a motor's electrical requirements can assure that the motor runs. Satisfying a motor's mechanical and environmental requirements determine how long the motor will run. Standard motors are designed to operate under usual service conditions. See Figure 4-9. Usual service conditions include:

- An ambient temperature of not more than 40°C
- Exposure to an altitude of not more than 3300′
- Installation on a rigid mounting surface
- Installation in areas that will not seriously interfere with the ventilation of the motor

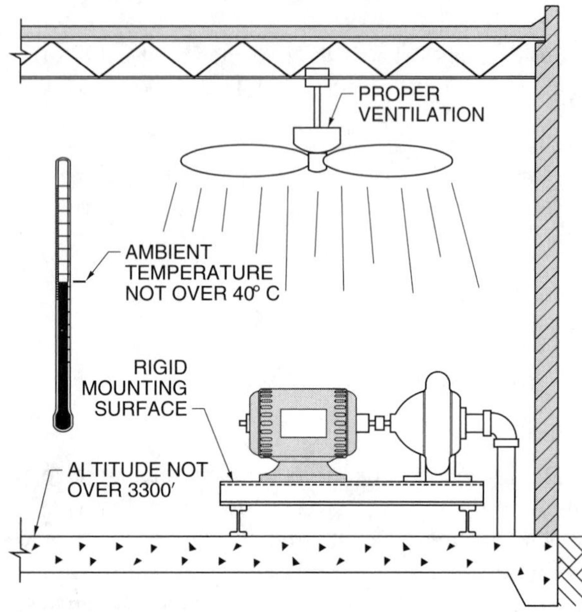

Figure 4-9. Standard motors are designed to operate under usual service conditions.

Unusual Service Conditions. Unusual service conditions can affect the operation of a motor. If a motor is required to operate in an unusual service condition, a special purpose motor should be used. See Figure 4-10. Unusual service conditions include:

- Areas with combustible or explosive gases or dust
- Lint or very dirty operating conditions. The accumulation of dirt reduces the normal cooling of the motor and increases the motor's temperature.
- Chemical fumes, steam, salt, or farm animals
- Nuclear radiation
- Very damp or very dry locations
- Above normal vibration or shock conditions
- Operation above or below rated speed. Operation above rated speed is possible with some variable speed drives. For example, some motors may be operated two, three, or even four times higher than the rated speed with some variable speed drives. Operation below rated speed is possible

if a large load is driven or a variable speed drive is used to control the speed.

- Shaft overloading, misalignment, incorrect sizing of couplings, belts, or chains

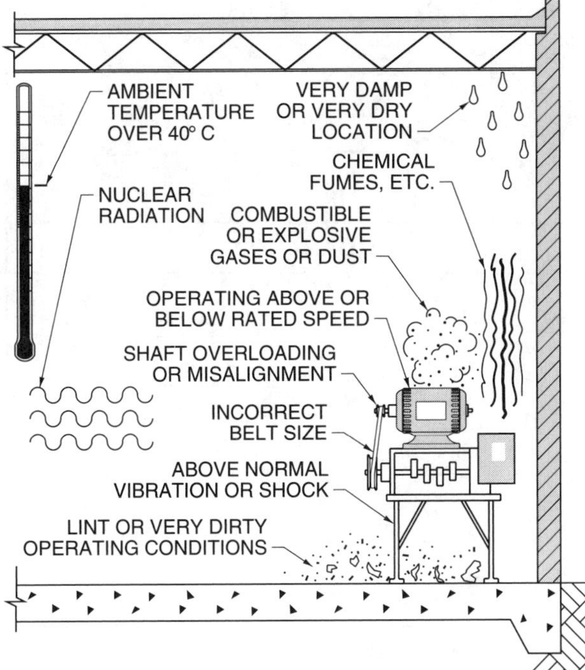

Figure 4-10. Special purpose motors should be used for unusual service conditions.

Motor Frames. Motors must be mounted properly before operation. All motors with frames provide some means of mounting. Motor frames are classified by NEMA. A standard number is used to indicate the motor's mounting dimensions. Motors with the same frame number can be interchanged. For example, a motor with a number 48 frame from one manufacturer will fit a number 48 frame of another manufacturer. See Figure 4-11.

Motor manufacturers assign motor frame numbers (FR), which designate standards that follow NEMA specifications. The frame number is listed on the motor's nameplate. A motor frame number is assigned by multiplying the base-to-shaft center distance by 16 for #48 and #56 frames. See Motor Frame Dimensions in Appendix.

For motors with frames larger than #48 or #56, a three (or four) digit frame number is assigned. The first two digits of the frame number are assigned by multiplying the base-to-shaft center distance by four. When the calculated number is not a whole number, round to the next higher whole number. The third digit of the frame number is assigned by doubling Dimension F and applying the 3rd-4th Digit Frame Number Table. For example, a motor with a base-to-shaft center dimension of 12½″ and an F dimension of 9″ requires a #505 frame. See Appendix. The letter immediately following the frame number indicates variations.

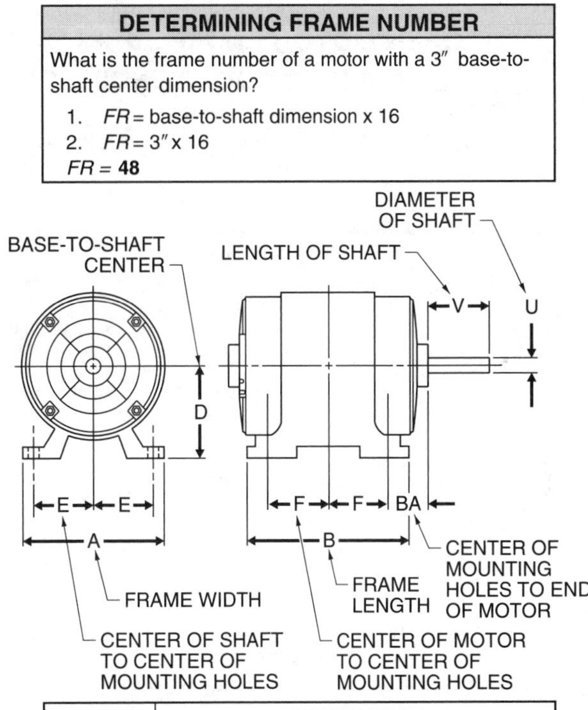

LETTER	DESIGNATION
G	Gasoline pump motor
K	Sump pump motor
M and N	Oil burner motor
S	Standard short shaft for direct connection
T	Standard dimensions established
U	Previously used as frame designation for which standard dimensions are established
Y	Special mounting dimensions required from manufacturer
Z	Standard mounting dimensions except shaft extension

Figure 4-11. Motor frames are classified by NEMA.

Motor Enclosures. The motor enclosure protects the motor against environmental conditions, reduces maintenance, and increases safety. A wide variety of motor enclosures are commercially available. The type of motor enclosure affects the cost of the motor.

The two general classifications for motor enclosures are open motor enclosures and totally enclosed motor enclosures. An *open motor enclosure* is a motor enclosure with openings to allow passage of air to cool the windings. See Figure 4-12. A *totally enclosed motor enclosure* is a motor enclosure that prevents air from entering the enclosure. See Figure 4-13.

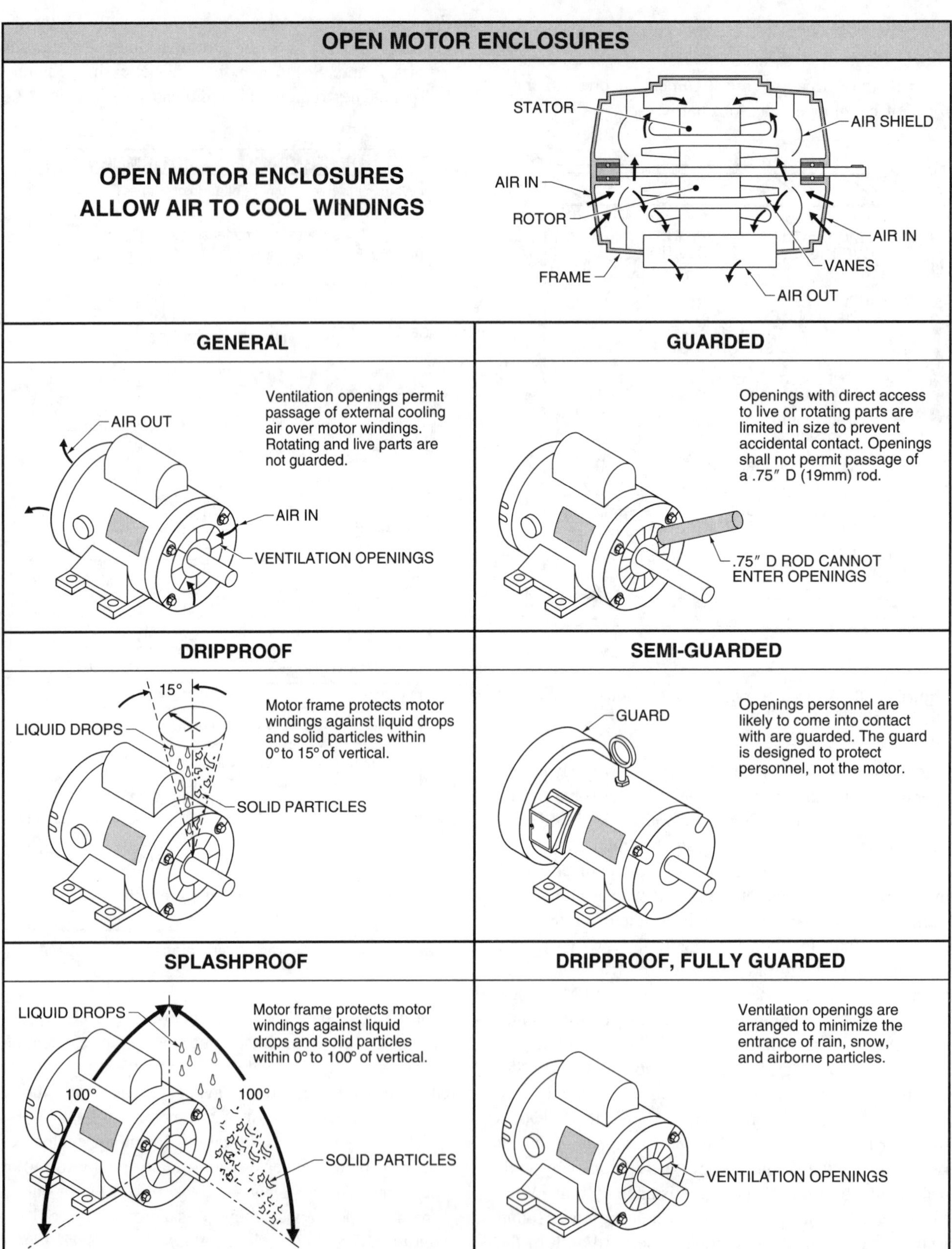

Figure 4-12. An open motor enclosure allows air to cool the windings.

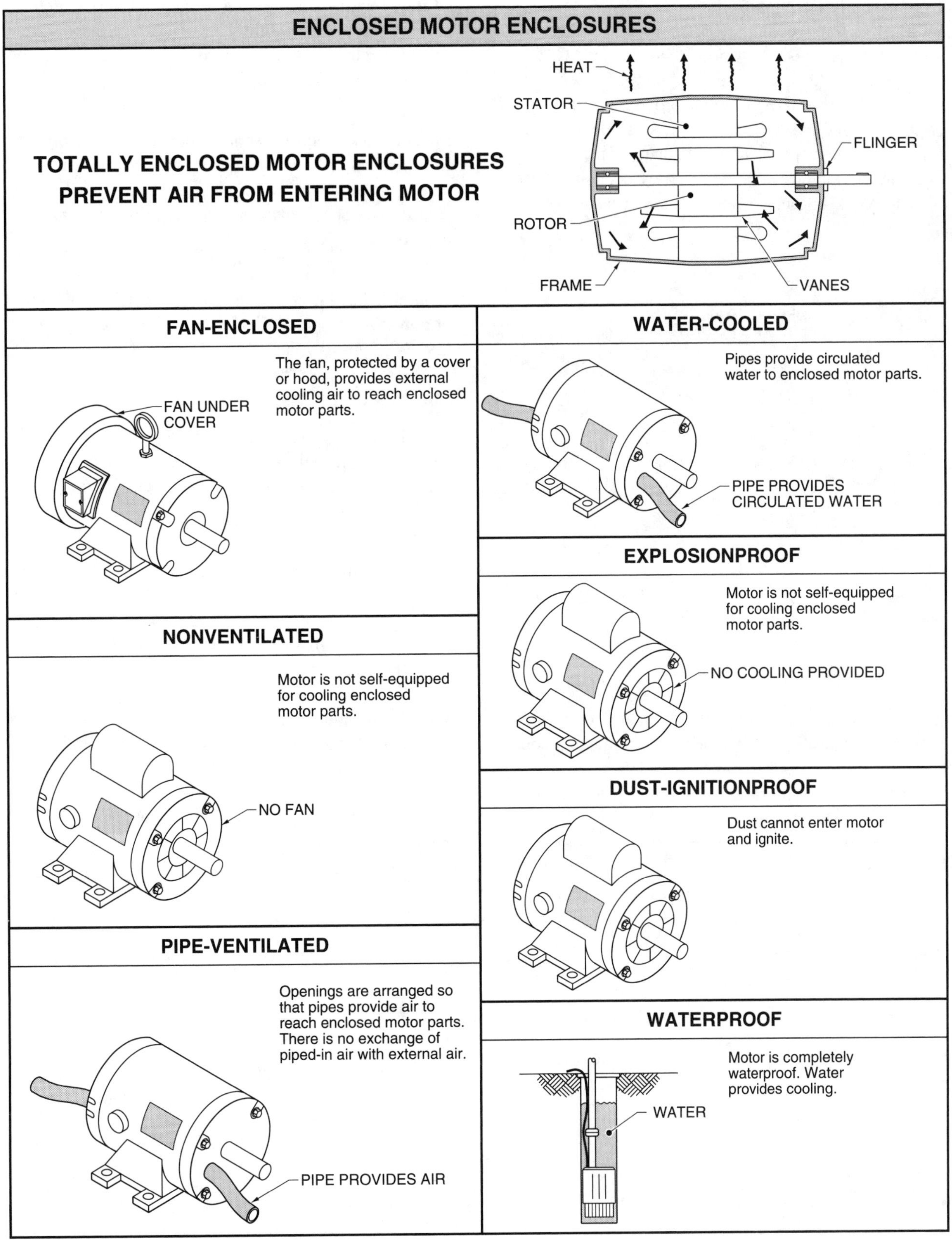

ENCLOSED MOTOR ENCLOSURES

TOTALLY ENCLOSED MOTOR ENCLOSURES PREVENT AIR FROM ENTERING MOTOR

HEAT
STATOR
FLINGER
ROTOR
FRAME
VANES

FAN-ENCLOSED

The fan, protected by a cover or hood, provides external cooling air to reach enclosed motor parts.

FAN UNDER COVER

WATER-COOLED

Pipes provide circulated water to enclosed motor parts.

PIPE PROVIDES CIRCULATED WATER

NONVENTILATED

Motor is not self-equipped for cooling enclosed motor parts.

NO FAN

EXPLOSIONPROOF

Motor is not self-equipped for cooling enclosed motor parts.

NO COOLING PROVIDED

PIPE-VENTILATED

Openings are arranged so that pipes provide air to reach enclosed motor parts. There is no exchange of piped-in air with external air.

PIPE PROVIDES AIR

DUST-IGNITIONPROOF

Dust cannot enter motor and ignite.

WATERPROOF

Motor is completely waterproof. Water provides cooling.

WATER

Figure 4-13. A totally enclosed motor enclosure prevents air from entering the enclosure.

DC MOTOR CHARACTERISTICS

The DC motor is commonly used where an AC motor will not do a satisfactory job, there is no AC power available, or physical space is a problem. See Figure 4-14. DC motors provide high torque and good speed control in smaller sizes than AC motors. However, they usually require more maintenance than a typical AC motor. The DC motor can be reversed by reversing current flow through the field or through the armature.

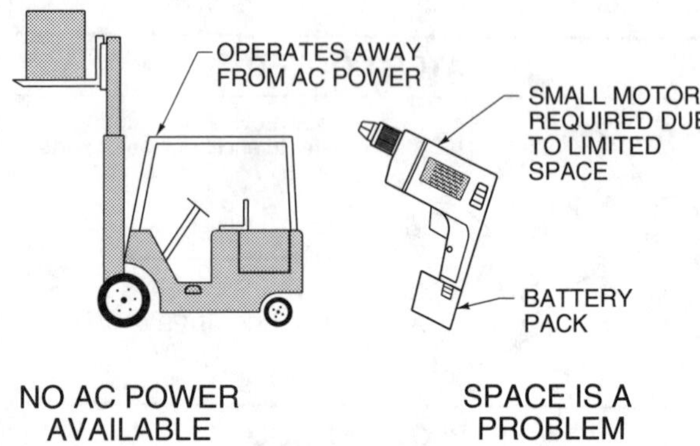

Figure 4-14. DC motors are used where AC power is not available or space is a problem.

Series Motor

The series motor is used where a high starting torque is required, such as with hoists, bridges, and traction equipment. Since there is the danger of high speeds at low loads, the series motor should not be used with belt drives or low torque loads. See Figure 4-15.

Motor Torque. The starting torque of a series motor is 400% to 450% of its full-load torque, which is very high for an electric motor. The torque varies approximately as the square of the armature current.

Speed. The speed of a series motor can vary from zero to full speed, depending on load and control. The speed varies greatly with a change in load. As the load decreases, the speed increases. Variable resistor units are used for speed control.

Available Power. The series motor must have a DC source of power, such as a battery or a rectifier that changes AC into DC. Typical voltage levels are 12, 90, 120, or 180 V.

Shunt Motor

The shunt motor is used where a constant or variable speed is required, such as with wood- and metal-working machines, elevators, and centrifugal pumps. See Figure 4-16.

Motor Torque. The starting torque of a shunt motor is good, but not as good as the series motor. The starting torque of a shunt motor is about 125% to 250% of its full-load torque and increases directly with the load.

Speed. The shunt motor runs at almost the same speed at any load within its rating. Solid-state circuitry can be used to control the motor speed over a wide range. The shunt motor has much better speed control than the series motor.

SERIES MOTORS

POWER	DC
VOLTS	12, 90, 120, 180 V
HP	Fractional to 100 HP
PHASE	Rectified 1ϕ or 3ϕ

TERMINALS	
A1 A2	Armature
S1 S2	Series field

ROTOR	SPEED(S)	BUILT-IN AUTO STARTING	APPROX. COST*
Drum-wound commutator	Variable from 0 to full speed	None	175%-225%

TORQUE	CHARACTERISTICS	USES	ENVIRONMENTAL CONDITIONS
• High starting torque • Starting torque is 400% to 450% of full-load torque	• High torque • Variable speed	• Hoists, bridges, traction equipment • Do not use with belt drives or low torque loads	• Do not use in hazardous locations due to sparking of brushes

* Based on standard 3ϕ induction motor

Figure 4-15. The series motor has high starting torque.

SHUNT MOTORS			
POWER	DC	TERMINALS	
VOLTS	12, 90, 120, 180 V	A1 A2	Armature
HP	Fractional to 100 HP	F1 F2	Shunt field
PHASE	Rectified 1ϕ or 3ϕ		

ROTOR	SPEED(S)	BUILT-IN AUTO STARTING	APPROX. COST*
Drum-wound commutator	Constant or adjustable	None	175%-225%

TORQUE	CHARACTERISTICS	USES	ENVIRONMENTAL CONDITIONS
• Good starting torque • Starting torque is 125% to 250% of full-load torque	• Used where constant or variable speed is required • Has better speed control than DC series motor	• Woodworking machines, metalworking machines, elevators, centrifugal pump	• Do not use in hazardous locations due to sparking of brushes

* Based on standard 3ϕ induction motor

Figure 4-16. The shunt motor has a constant or variable speed.

Available Power. The shunt motor must have a DC source of power, such as a battery or a rectifier that changes AC into DC. Typical voltage levels are 12, 90, 120, or 180 V.

Compound Motor

The compound motor is used where a high starting torque and a relatively constant speed is required, such as with elevators, hoists, conveyors, printing presses, and pumps. See Figure 4-17.

Motor Torque. The starting torque of a compound motor is usually higher than a shunt motor, but less than a series motor. The starting torque of a compound motor is about 300% to 400% of its full-load torque.

Speed. The speed of a compound motor changes with a load change. It does not change as much as the speed of a series motor, but changes more than the speed of a shunt motor.

Available Power. The compound motor must have a DC source of power, such as a battery or a rectifier that changes AC into DC. Typical voltage levels are 12, 90, 120, or 180 V.

SINGLE-PHASE MOTOR CHARACTERISTICS

The 1ϕ, AC motor is generally used where only 1ϕ power is available, such as in dwellings and small commercial buildings. For example, smaller fans, pumps,

COMPOUND MOTORS			
POWER	DC	TERMINALS	
VOLTS	12, 90, 120, 180 V	A1 A2	Armature
HP	Fractional to 100 HP	S1 S2	Series field
PHASE	Rectified 1ϕ or 3ϕ	F1 F2	Shunt field

ROTOR	SPEED(S)	BUILT-IN AUTO STARTING	APPROX. COST*
Drum-wound commutator	Varies with load change	None	175%-225%

TORQUE	CHARACTERISTICS	USES	ENVIRONMENTAL CONDITIONS
• High starting torque • Starting torque is 300% to 400% of full-load torque	• Has advantages of series (high torque) and shunt (good speed control) motor	• Elevators, hoists, conveyors, printing presses	• Do not use in hazardous locations due to sparking of brushes

* Based on standard 3ϕ induction motor

Figure 4-17. The compound motor has high starting torque and relatively constant speed.

saws, and portable tools of less than 1 HP contain 1ϕ, AC motors. Some industrial applications use fractional horsepower motors. See Figure 4-18.

All 1ϕ motors require a starting method, since they are not self-starting. The name of the motor is determined by the starting method. The direction of 1ϕ motors is reversed by reversing the current flow in the starting windings. The end opposite the shaft is the front of the motor. When viewed from the front, forward rotation is clockwise and reverse rotation is counterclockwise.

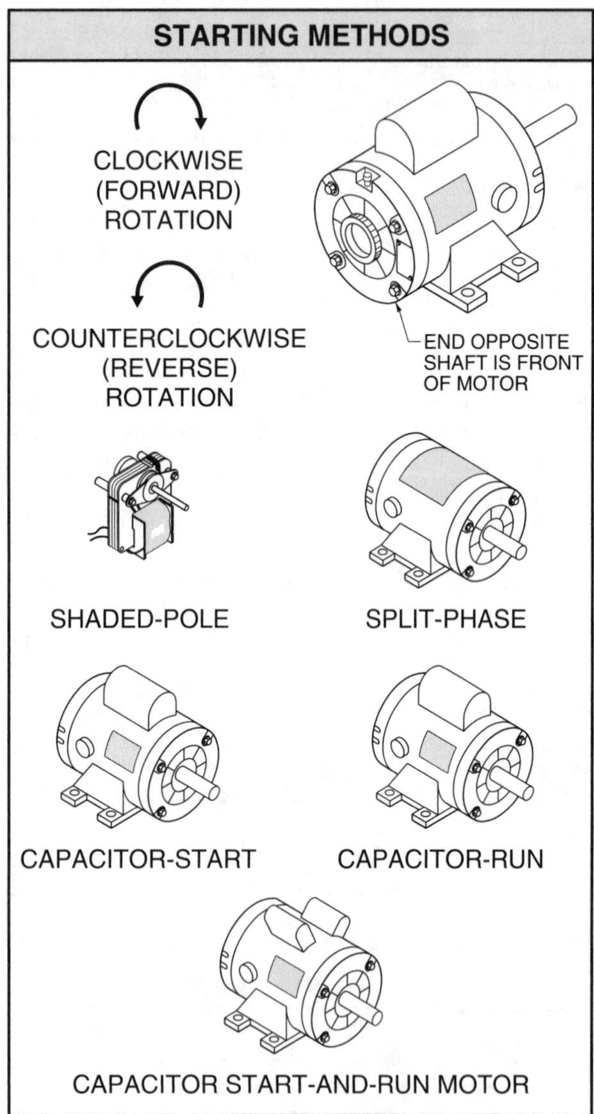

Figure 4-18. All 1ϕ, AC motors require a starting method.

Shaded-Pole Motor

The shaded-pole motor is the most simple and least expensive 1ϕ, AC motor. It is commonly used to drive very low torque loads, such as small fans. The motor is used in most small machines that require a cooling fan, such the central processing units (CPU's) of computers. See Figure 4-19.

Motor Torque. The shaded-pole motor develops the lowest starting and running torque of all motor types. Starting torque is 50% to 100% of full-load torque.

Speed. The shaded-pole motor is a constant (fixed) speed motor that is not designed to have a varying speed. The standard rated speed is commonly 3600 or 1800 rpm.

Available Power. The shaded-pole motor requires 1ϕ, AC power at the same voltage level and frequency as the motor. The typical voltage level is 115/230 V, 60 cycle.

Split-Phase Motor

The split-phase motor is used where a constant speed is required and high starting torque is not required. It is used widely for pumps, blowers, fans, machine tools, and other easily started loads. See Figure 4-20.

Motor Torque. The low starting torque of a split-phase motor is about 75% to 200% of its full-load torque. The starting current is four to eight times the full-load running current. Because of their high starting current, split-phase motors are usually limited to ⅓ HP or less in applications that require frequent starts.

Speed. The split-phase motor is usually a fixed-speed motor. The speed of the motor drops about 10% from no load to full load. Some split-phase motors have two, three, or four fixed speeds.

Available Power. The split-phase motor must have a source of 1ϕ power at the same voltage and frequency as the motor. Typical voltage levels are 115/230 V, 60 cycle.

Capacitor-Start Motor

The capacitor in a capacitor-start motor improves the starting torque of the motor, but has no effect on the motor when running. The centrifugal switch removes the capacitor after the motor reaches speed. The capacitor-start motor uses the capacitor for starting only. The capacitor increases the starting torque of the motor.

	SHADED-POLE MOTOR			
	POWER	AC	TERMINALS	
	VOLTS	115/230 V	L1 L2 AC Power line	
	HP	Fractional		
	PHASE	1ϕ		
	ROTOR	SPEED(S)	BUILT-IN AUTO STARTING	APPROX. COST*
	Squirrel-cage	Constant	None	75%-85%

TORQUE	CHARACTERISTICS	USES	ENVIRONMENTAL CONDITIONS
• Lowest starting torque of all motor types • Starting torque is 50% to 100% of full-load torque	• Usually has no frame • Motor is part of machine in which it is placed	• Fan motor for small machines, dryers, recorders	• Dirt must be cleaned from motor at least once per year

* Based on standard 3ϕ induction motor

Figure 4-19. The shaded-pole motor is used to drive very low torque loads.

	SPLIT-PHASE MOTORS			
	POWER	AC	TERMINALS	
	VOLTS	115/230 V	T1 T2 Starting winding	
	HP	$\frac{1}{3}$ or less	T3 T4 Running winding	
	PHASE	1ϕ		
	ROTOR	SPEED(S)	BUILT-IN AUTO STARTING	APPROX. COST*
	Squirrel-cage	Fixed-1120, 1780, 1960, 2400, constant speed	Centrifugal switch	85%-95%

TORQUE	CHARACTERISTICS	USES	ENVIRONMENTAL CONDITIONS
• Low starting torque • Starting torque is 75% to 200% of full-load torque	• Constant speed • Low starting torque	• Pumps, blowers, fans, machine tools	• Enclosure must match application • Must be cleaned as needed • Must be used as designed

* Based on standard 3ϕ induction motor

Figure 4-20. The split-phase motor has a constant speed and low starting torque.

The capacitor-start motor is used where a constant speed is required even under changing conditions and where higher starting torque is required. This is the most common 1ϕ motor. It is used in higher starting applications, such as with refrigerator compressors, air compressors, and power tools. See Figure 4-21.

Motor Torque. The capacitor-start motor has a higher starting torque than the split-phase motor. The starting torque is 200% to 350% of its full-load torque.

Speed. The capacitor-start motor is usually a fixed-speed motor. The speed drops about 10% from no load to full load. Some capacitor-start motors have two or three fixed speeds.

Available Power. The capacitor-start motor must have a source of 1ϕ power at the same voltage and frequency as the motor. Typical voltage levels are 115/230 V, 60 cycle.

Capacitor-Run Motor

In the capacitor-run (permanent) motor, the capacitor remains in the circuit for both starting and running. The capacitor improves both starting and running

CAPACITOR-START MOTORS				
POWER	AC	TERMINALS		
VOLTS	115/230 V	Single voltage	J1 J2	Capacitor
HP	Fractional to 3 HP		T1 T2	Starting winding
PHASE	1ϕ		T3 T4	Running winding

ROTOR	SPEED(S)	BUILT-IN AUTO STARTING	APPROX. COST*
Squirrel-cage	Fixed speeds	Centrifugal switch	90%-110%

TORQUE	CHARACTERISTICS	USES	ENVIRONMENTAL CONDITIONS
• Higher starting torque than split-phase motors • Starting torque is 200% to 350% of full-load torque	• Constant speed	• Refrigerator compressors, air compressors, power tools	• Enclosure must match application • Must be cleaned as needed • Must be used as designed

* Based on standard 3ϕ induction motor

Figure 4-21. The capacitor-start motor has a constant speed and higher starting torque.

torque. To do this, a large capacitor rated for continuous duty is required. Capacitor-run motors are used for pumps, blowers, coolers, compressors, conveyors, etc. See Figure 4-22.

Motor Torque. The capacitor-run motor has a lower starting torque than the capacitor-start motor because the capacitor must be rated to compromise between a good starting and a good running value. The starting torque is 50% to 100% of the full-load torque.

Speed. The capacitor-run motor is usually a fixed-speed motor. The speed of the motor drops about 10% from no load to full load. Some capacitor-run motors have two, three, or four fixed speeds.

Available Power. The capacitor-run motor must have a source of 1ϕ power at the same voltage and frequency as the motor. Typical voltage levels are 115/230 V, 60 cycle.

Capacitor Start-and-Run Motor

The capacitor start-and-run motor uses two capacitors to provide an advantage in both starting and running. One capacitor starts the motor and a second capacitor runs the motor. Capacitor start-and-run motors are often used to drive the compressors of small air conditioning units. See Figure 4-23.

CAPACITOR-RUN MOTORS				
POWER	AC	TERMINALS		
VOLTS	115/230 V	Single voltage	J1 J2	Capacitor
HP	Fractional to 5 HP		T1 T2	Starting winding
PHASE	1ϕ		T3 T4	Running winding

ROTOR	SPEED(S)	BUILT-IN AUTO STARTING	APPROX. COST*
Squirrel-cage	Fixed speeds	Centrifugal switch	90%-110%

TORQUE	CHARACTERISTICS	USES	ENVIRONMENTAL CONDITIONS
• Low starting torque • Starting torque is 50% to 100% of full-load torque	• Improved starting and running	• Pumps, blowers, coolers, compressors, conveyors	• Enclosure must match application • Must be cleaned as needed • Must be used as designed

* Based on standard 3ϕ induction motor

Figure 4-22. The capacitor-run motor usually has a fixed speed and lower starting torque.

CAPACITOR START-AND-RUN MOTORS

POWER	AC	TERMINALS	
VOLTS	115/230 V	J1 J2	Capacitor
HP	Fractional to 10 HP	Single voltage T1 T2	Starting winding
PHASE	1ϕ	T3 T4	Running winding

ROTOR	SPEED(S)	BUILT-IN AUTO STARTING	APPROX. COST*
Squirrel-cage	Fixed speeds	Centrifugal switch	100%-115%

TORQUE	CHARACTERISTICS	USES	ENVIRONMENTAL CONDITIONS
• Good starting torque and running torque • Starting torque is 350% to 450% of full-load torque	• Good starting and running	• AC compressors, conveyors, grinders, pumps	• Enclosure must match application • Must be cleaned as needed • Must be used as designed

* Based on standard 3ϕ induction motor

Figure 4-23. The capacitor start-and-run motor has good starting and running torque.

Motor Torque. The capacitor start-and-run motor has good starting and running torque. The starting torque is 350% to 450% of the full-load torque.

Speed. The capacitor start-and-run motor is usually a fixed-speed motor. The speed drops about 10% from no load to full load. Some motors have two, three, or four fixed speeds.

Available Power. The capacitor start-and-run motor must have a source of 1ϕ power at the same voltage and frequency as the motor. Typical voltage levels are 115/230 V, 60 cycle.

THREE-PHASE MOTOR CHARACTERISTICS

Three-phase motors are simple in design. They are the most rugged of all electric motors and are the most common motor used in industry. See Figure 4-24. Three-phase motors are used for most machine tool and general applications.

Induction Motor

The induction motor is used where a constant speed is required and starting torque is not excessively high. Induction motors are the most common motor used for industrial applications. They are used

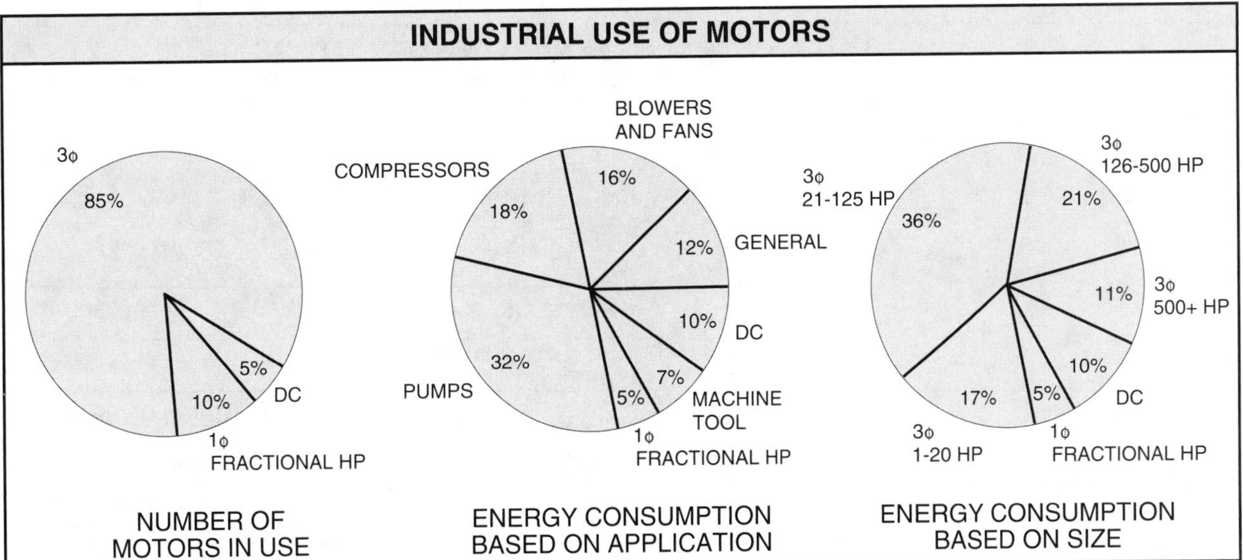

Figure 4-24. Three-phase motors are the most common motors used in industry.

with conveyors, blowers, fans, and feeders, etc. See Figure 4-25.

Motor Torque. The induction motor has moderate starting torque. The starting torque of an induction motor is 100% to 275% of the full-load torque.

Speed. The induction motor has good speed regulation. It is considered a constant-speed motor even though it does not run at exact synchronous speed. The induction motor runs from within 1% to 4% of synchronous speed. It is commercially available with one fixed speed or two speeds.

Available Power. The induction motor must have a source of 3ϕ power at the same voltage and frequency as the motor. Typical voltage levels are 230/460 V, 60 cycle.

Wound-Rotor Motor

The wound-rotor motor has a rotor that is brought out through slip rings and connected to an external circuit. By inserting a high external resistance in the rotor circuit at starting, a high starting torque with a low starting current is developed. It is used where very high starting torque is required, such as on cranes, hoists, and elevators. See Figure 4-26.

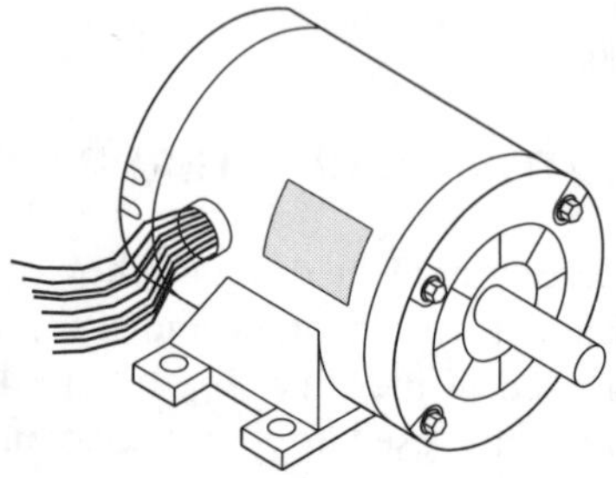

INDUCTION MOTORS

POWER	AC	TERMINALS
VOLTS	230/460 V	T1 T2 T3
HP	Fractional to over 500 HP	T4 T5 T6 Dual voltage
PHASE	3ϕ	T7 T8 T9

ROTOR	SPEED(S)	BUILT-IN AUTO STARTING	APPROX. COST*
Squirrel-cage	Constant speeds	None	100%

TORQUE	CHARACTERISTICS	USES	ENVIRONMENTAL CONDITIONS
• Starting torque is 100% to 275% of full-load torque	• Good speed control	• Commonly used in industry • Conveyors, blowers, fans, feeders, machine tools, mixers, pumps	• Enclosure must match application • Must be cleaned as needed • Must be used as designed

* Based on standard 3ϕ induction motor

Figure 4-25. The induction motor has good speed control.

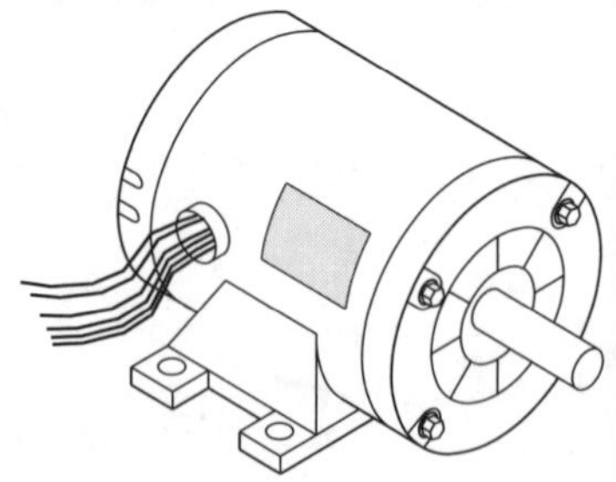

WOUND-ROTOR MOTORS

POWER	AC	TERMINALS
VOLTS	230/460 V	T1 T2 T3 Stator winding
HP	$\frac{1}{2}$ to 200 HP	
PHASE	3ϕ	M1 M2 M3 Rotor winding

ROTOR	SPEED(S)	BUILT-IN AUTO STARTING	APPROX. COST*
Wound rotor with slip rings	Depends on resistance in rotor circuit	None	250% to 350%

TORQUE	CHARACTERISTICS	USES	ENVIRONMENTAL CONDITIONS
• High starting torque • Starting torque is 200% to 300% of full-load torque	• Smooth acceleration	• Cranes, hoists, elevators, pumps, air compressors	• Enclosure must match application • Must be cleaned as needed • Must be used as designed

* Based on standard 3ϕ induction motor

Figure 4-26. The wound-rotor motor has very high starting torque.

Motor Torque. The wound-rotor motor has good starting torque. The starting and breakdown torque is 200% to 300% of the full-load torque, depending upon the external setting of the resistor.

Speed. The speed control of a wound-rotor motor is obtained by using resistors in the rotor circuit. The operating speed depends on the amount of resistance in the rotor circuit. The wound-rotor motor has smooth acceleration, making it good for large pumps, air compressors, and hoist applications, such as cranes, and trolley drives.

Available Power. The wound-rotor motor must have a source of 3ϕ power at the same voltage and frequency as the motor. Typical voltage levels are 230/460 V, 60 cycle.

Synchronous Motor

The synchronous motor is used where a very constant speed is required, power factor correction is required, or for slow-speed machines. The motor revolves at the same speed as the rotating magnetic field of the stator. It is used to correct a very low power factor. See Figure 4-27.

Motor Torque. The synchronous motor has generally poor starting torque. The starting torque is 40% to 160% of the full-load torque.

Speed. The speed of a synchronous motor is determined by the frequency of the power supply and the number of poles in the motor. Direct current is delivered directly to the rotor through brushes and slip rings to make the motor run at exact synchronous speed.

Available Power. The synchronous motor must have a source of 3ϕ power at the same voltage and frequency as the motor. Typical voltage levels are 230/460 V, 60 cycle. A DC power source is also required for the rotor winding.

UNIVERSAL MOTOR CHARACTERISTICS

The universal motor can operate on AC or DC. It is usually used in appliances and tools requiring good torque and speed control.

Universal Motor

The universal motor is a series motor usually only available in small sizes of less than 1 HP. It is used frequently in portable tools, such as drills and routers, and small household appliances such as vacuum cleaners, fans, food mixers, blenders, etc. See Figure 4-28.

Starting Torque. The universal motor has high starting torque. The starting torque is 300% to 400% of the full-load torque.

Speed. The speed of a universal motor can be adjusted by adding resistance in series. The speed changes with a change in the load.

Available Power. The universal motor can operate on AC or DC voltage. Voltage must be the same as listed on the nameplate. Typical voltage levels are 115/230 VAC, 50 and 60 cycle, and 12, 24, 36, or 120 VDC.

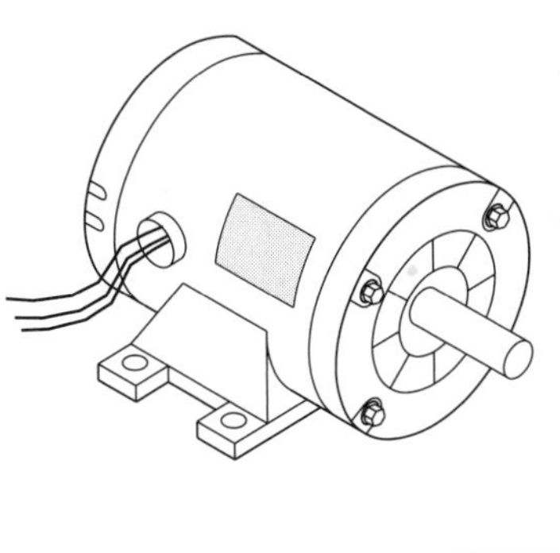

SYNCHRONOUS MOTORS

POWER	VOLTS	HP	PHASE
AC (stator) DC (rotor)	230/460 V	Fractional to 250 HP	3ϕ

TERMINALS	
T1 T2 T3	Stator winding
+ −	Rotor winding

ROTOR	SPEED(S)	BUILT-IN AUTO STARTING	APPROX. COST*
Consists of a series of DC-excited poles	Exact constant speeds	None	200% to 250%

TORQUE	CHARACTERISTICS	USES	ENVIRONMENTAL CONDITIONS
• Poor starting torque • Starting torque is 40% to 100% of full-load torque	• Constant speed	• Used where power factor correction and efficiency is needed • Slow-speed motors	• Enclosure must match application • Must be cleaned as needed • Must be used as designed

* Based on standard 3ϕ induction motor

Figure 4-27. The synchronous motor has very constant speed.

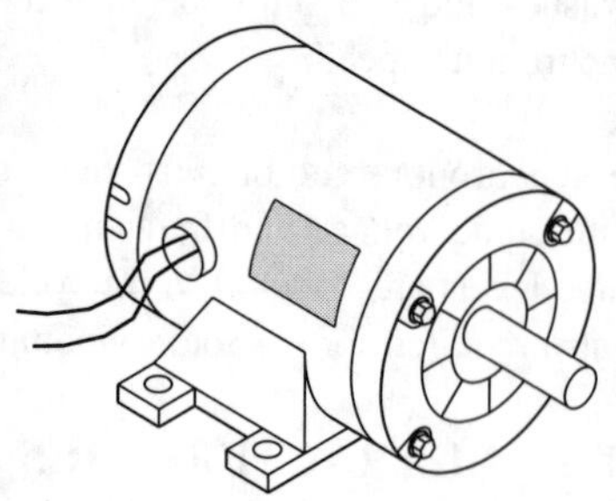

UNIVERSAL MOTORS			
POWER	AC/DC	TERMINALS	
VOLTS	115/230 VAC 12, 24, 36, 120 VDC	T1 T2 T3	Stator winding
HP	Less than 1HP	+ −	Rotor winding
PHASE	1ϕ or rectified 3ϕ		

ROTOR	SPEED(S)	BUILT-IN AUTO STARTING	APPROX. COST*
Drum-wound commutator	Variable	None	175% to 225%

TORQUE	CHARACTERISTICS	USES	ENVIRONMENTAL CONDITIONS
• High starting torque • Starting torque is 300% to 400% of full-load torque	• Can operate on AC or DC • Good torque and speed control	• Drills, routers, vacuum cleaners, fans, food mixers, blenders	• Enclosure must match application • Must be cleaned as needed • Must be used as designed

* Based on standard 3ϕ induction motor

Figure 4-28. The universal motor can operate on AC or DC.

MOTOR SELECTION

Application — Motor Ambient Temperature Correction

Motor installations with ambient temperatures above or below the rated ambient temperature of a motor require a temperature correction factor. A correction factor derates motor specifications to prevent damage caused by environmental conditions other than those stated by the manufacturer on the motor nameplate.

An ambient temperature correction chart provides temperature correction factors to derate motor characteristics for ambient temperatures above or below the rated ambient temperature of the motor. The ambient temperature of the motor installation is located on the horizontal axis of the chart. A vertical line is drawn from the ambient temperature of the motor installation until it intersects the temperature correction factor line. A horizontal line is drawn from the intersection of the vertical line and the temperature correction factor line to the vertical axis. The intersection of the horizontal line and the vertical axis is the temperature correction factor for the ambient temperature of the motor application. The temperature correction factor is multiplied by the motor's rated horsepower to obtain the motor's horsepower for the application's ambient temperature. See Ambient Temperature Correction Chart.

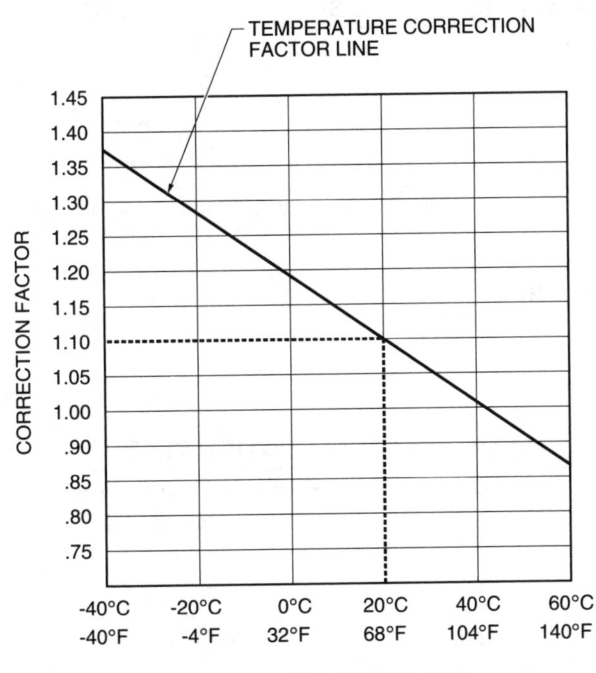

AMBIENT TEMPERATURE CORRECTION CHART

Example: Finding Temperature Correction Factor

A 104°F rated motor is installed in a 68°F ambient temperature location. Find the temperature correction factor.

A vertical line is drawn from 68°F on the horizontal axis to the temperature correction factor line. A horizontal line is drawn from the intersection of the vertical line and the temperature correction factor line to the vertical axis. The correction factor is 1.1 (from Ambient Temperature Correction Chart).

Note: For ambient temperatures above and below 40°C, round the temperature correction factor to the next lowest number. For example, a temperature correction factor of .87 is rounded to .85.

The starting, pull-up, and breakdown torque remain the same when a motor is derated. The bearings, capacitors, fuses, overloads, and motor controllers are sized for the corrected ambient temperature rating.

Application — Voltage and Frequency Variations

Voltage Variations

Motors are rated for operation at specific voltages. Motor performance is affected when the supply voltage varies from a motor's rated voltage. A motor operates satisfactorily with a voltage variation of +10% to −10% from the voltage rating listed on the motor nameplate. See Voltage Variation Characteristics.

VOLTAGE VARIATION CHARACTERISTICS

Performance Characteristics	10% above Rated Voltage	10% below Rated Voltage
Starting current	+10% to 12%	−10% to 12%
Full-load current	−7%	+11%
Motor torque	+20% to 25%	−20% to 25%
Motor efficiency	Little change	Little change
Speed	+1%	−1.5%
Temperature rise	−3°C to 4°C	+6°C to 7°C

Frequency Variations

Motors are rated for operation at specific frequencies. Motor performance is affected when the frequency varies from a motor's rated frequency. A motor operates satisfactorily with a frequency variation of +5% to −5% from the frequency rating listed on the motor nameplate. See Frequency Variation Characteristics.

FREQUENCY VARIATION CHARACTERISTICS

Performance Characteristics	5% above Rated Frequency	5% below Rated Frequency
Starting current	−5% to 6%	+5% to 6%
Full-load current	−1%	+1%
Motor torque	−10%	+11%
Motor efficiency	Slight increase	Slight decrease
Speed	+5%	−5%
Temperature rise	Slight decrease	Slight increase

Application — Altitude Correction

The temperature rise of motors is based on motor operation at altitudes of 3300 feet or less. A motor is derated when the motor operates at altitudes above 3300 feet. See Motor Altitude Deratings.

MOTOR ALTITUDE DERATINGS

Altitude Range (in ft)	1.0 SF	1.15 SF
3300–9000	93%	100%
9000–9900	91%	98%
9900–13,200	86%	92%
13,200–16,500	79%	85%
Over 16,500	Consult manufacturer	Consult manufacturer

Application — Allowable Motor Starting Time

A motor must accelerate to its rated speed within a limited time period. The longer a motor takes to accelerate, the higher the temperature rise in the motor. The larger the load, the longer the acceleration time. The maximum recommended acceleration time depends on the motor frame size. Large motor frames dissipate heat faster than small motor frames. See Maximum Acceleration Time.

MAXIMUM ACCELERATION TIME

Frame Number	Maximum Acceleration Time (in seconds)
48 and 56	8
143–286	10
324–326	12
364–505	15

Application — Motor Coupling Selection

Motor Couplings

A *motor coupling* is a device that connects the motor shaft to the equipment the motor is driving. A motor coupling allows the motor to operate the driven equipment, allows for a slight misalignment between the motor and the driven equipment, and allows for horizontal and axial movement of the shafts.

Misalignment

When connecting equipment, angular misalignment and parallel misalignment occur. *Angular misalignment* is misalignment when two shafts are not parallel. *Parallel misalignment* is misalignment when two shafts are parallel but not on the same line. See Motor Couplings.

Motor Coupling Rating

Motor couplings are rated according to the amount of torque they can handle. Couplings are rated in pound-inches (lb-in) or pound-feet (lb-ft). The coupling torque rating must be correct for the application to prevent the coupling from bending or breaking. A bent coupling causes misalignment and vibration. A broken coupling prevents the motor from doing work.

Selecting Motor Couplings

The correct coupling for an application is selected by determining the nominal torque rating of the power source, determining the application service factor, calculating the coupling torque rating, selecting a coupling with an equal or greater torque rating, and ensuring that the coupling has the correct shaft size to fit the drive unit.

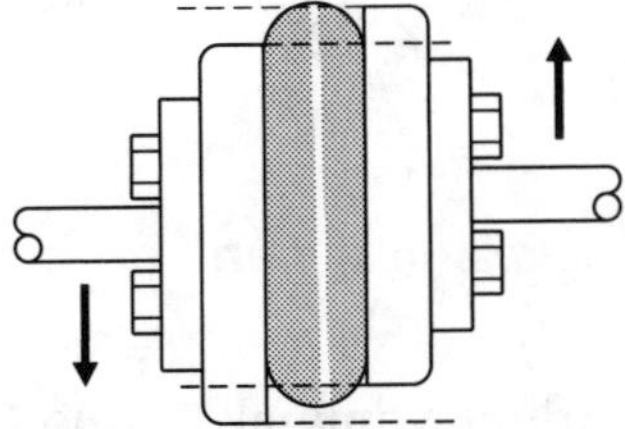

PARALLEL MISALIGNMENT

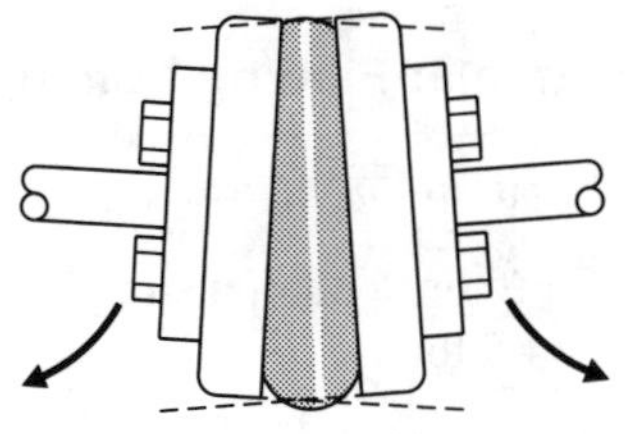

ANGULAR MISALIGNMENT

To select the correct coupling for an application, apply the procedure:

Step 1. Determine the nominal torque rating of the power source (electric motor or other power source). The nominal torque rating is calculated or found on a conversion table.

Finding Nominal Torque Rating — Calculation

To calculate the nominal torque rating of a motor in lb-in, apply the formula:

$$T = \frac{HP \times 63{,}000}{rpm}$$

where

T = nominal torque rating (in lb-in)

HP = horsepower

63,000 = constant

rpm = speed (in revolutions per minute)

To calculate the nominal torque rating of a motor in lb-ft, apply the formula:

$$T = \frac{HP \times 5252}{rpm}$$

where

T = nominal torque rating (in lb-ft)

HP = horsepower

5252 = constant

rpm = speed (in revolutions per minute)

Example: Finding Nominal Torque Rating — Calculation

A 10 HP motor operates at 1725 rpm. Find the nominal torque rating of the motor in lb-ft.

$$T = \frac{HP \times 5252}{rpm}$$

$$T = \frac{10 \times 5252}{1725}$$

$$T = \frac{52{,}520}{1725}$$

$T =$ **30.45 lb-ft**

Note: 30.45 lb-ft = 365.4 lb-in (30.45 × 12)

CONVERSION FACTOR		
Multiply	**By**	**To obtain**
lb-ft	12	lb-in
Divide	**By**	**To obtain**
lb-in	12	lb-ft

Finding Nominal Torque Rating — Conversion Table

To find the nominal torque rating of a motor using a conversion table, place one end of a straightedge on the rpm and the other end on the horsepower. The point where the straightedge crosses the torque scale is the torque rating. See Horsepower To Torque Conversion in Appendix.

Example: Finding Nominal Torque Rating — Conversion Table

A 1 HP motor operates at 1140 rpm. Find the nominal torque rating in lb-ft.

Place one end of a straightedge on 1140 rpm and the other end at 1 HP. The straightedge crosses the torque scale at 4.5 lb-ft.

Step 2. Determine application service factor. An *application service factor* is a multiplier that corrects for the operating conditions of the coupling. The greater the stress placed on the coupling, the larger the multiplier. By applying a multiplier, the size of the coupling is increased to adjust for severity of the load placed on the motor. See Common Service Factors in Appendix.

Step 3. Calculate the coupling torque rating by multiplying the nominal torque rating of the power source by the service factor of the application. Coupling torque rating is found by applying the formula:

$$C_{TR} = N_{TR} \times SF$$

where

C_{TR} = coupling torque rating (in lb-in or lb-ft)

N_{TR} = nominal torque rating (in lb-in or lb-ft)

SF = service factor

Example: Finding Coupling Torque Rating

The nominal torque rating of a motor is 4 lb-ft. The motor/coupling application is a heavy-duty conveyor. Find the coupling torque rating.

$C_{TR} = N_{TR} \times SF$

$C_{TR} = 4 \times 2$ (from Common Service Factors in Appendix)

C_{TR} = **8 lb-ft**

Note: 8 lb-ft = 96 lb-in

Step 4. Select a coupling with an equal or greater torque rating. See Coupling Selections in Appendix.

Step 5. Ensure coupling has the correct shaft size to fit the drive unit. The exact size of a motor shaft can be determined by the motor frame number. Typical shaft sizes for motors from ¼ HP to 200 HP are ½″, ⅝″, ⅞″, 1⅛″, 1⅜″, 1⅝″, 1⅞″, 2⅛″, 2⅜″, 2 ⅞″, and 3⅜″.

Example: Motor Coupling Selection

A 2 HP motor operating at 1725 rpm is used in a uniformly loaded conveyor. Select the coupling for the application.

Step 1. Determine nominal torque rating.

$$T = \frac{HP \times 63{,}000}{rpm}$$

$$T = \frac{2 \times 63{,}000}{1725}$$

$$T = \frac{126{,}000}{1725}$$

$T =$ **73.04 lb-in**

Note: 73.04 lb-in = 6.09 lb-ft (73.04 ÷ 12)

Step 2. Determine application service factor.

From Common Service Factors in Appendix, the service factor for a uniformly loaded conveyor is 1.50.

Step 3. Calculate the coupling torque rating.

$C_{TR} = N_{TR} \times SF$

$C_{TR} = 73.04 \times 1.50$

$C_{TR} =$ **109.56 lb-in**

Step 4. Select a coupling with an equal or greater torque rating.

From Coupling Selections in Appendix, the coupling with a torque rating equal to or greater than 109.56 lb-in is a 10-104-A.

Step 5. Ensure coupling has the correct shaft size to fit the drive unit.

A 2 HP motor normally has a 145T frame. The shaft size of a 145T frame motor is ⅞″. The coupling must have a bore size that would accept the ⅞″ motor shaft.

Application — Determining Motor Horsepower

The horsepower of a motor is found by using a conversion table when the required speed and torque rating of a motor application is known. To find the required horsepower, place one end of a straightedge on the rpm and the other end on the torque rating. The point where the straightedge crosses the horsepower scale is the required horsepower rating. See Horsepower to Torque Conversion in Appendix.

Example: Finding Motor Horsepower — Conversion Table

A motor with a torque rating of 3 lb-ft turns at 1800 rpm. Find the motor's horsepower.

Place one end of a straightedge on 1800 rpm and the other end on 3 lb-ft. The straightedge crosses the horsepower scale at 1HP.

Once the horsepower for an application is determined, select the next largest standard motor size. See Standard Motor Sizes.

STANDARD MOTOR SIZES	
Classification	**Size (HP)**
Milli	1, 1.5, 2, 3, 5, 7.5, 10, 15, 25, 35
Fractional	1⁄20, 1⁄12, 1⁄8, 1⁄6, 1⁄4, 1⁄3, 1⁄2, 3⁄4
Full	1, 1½, 2, 3, 5, 7½, 10, 15, 20, 25, 30, 40, 50, 60, 75, 100, 125, 150, 200, 250, 300
Full—Special Order	350, 400, 450, 500, 600, 700, 800, 900, 1000, 1250, 1500, 1750, 2000, 2250, 2500, 3000, 3500, 4000, 4500, 5000, 5500, 6000, 7000, 8000, 9000, 10,000, 11,000, 12,000, 13,000, 14,000, 15,000, 16,000, 17,000, 18,000, 19,000, 20,000, 22,500, 30,000, 32,500, 35,000, 37,500, 40,000, 45,000, 50,000

❒ Application — Determining Motor Speed

The speed of a motor is found by using a conversion table when the required horsepower and torque rating of a motor application is known. To find the required speed, place one end of a straightedge on the horsepower and the other end on the torque rating. The point where the straightedge crosses the speed scale is the required rpm rating. See Horsepower to Torque Conversion and Appendix.

Example: Finding Motor Speed — Conversion Table

A 7 HP, 3ϕ induction motor has a torque rating of 70 lb-ft. Find the motor's speed.

Place one end of a straightedge on 7 HP and the other end on 70 lb-ft. The straightedge crosses the rpm scale at 600 rpm.

Once the required speed for an application is determined, select the next slowest standard speed. See Standard Motor Speeds.

A 3ϕ induction motor with a standard speed of 514 rpm is selected (from Standard Motor Speeds).

STANDARD MOTOR SPEEDS	
Motor Type	**Speed (rpm)**
1ϕ	3600, 1800, 1200, 900
3ϕ Induction	3600, 1800, 1200, 900, 720, 600, 514, 450
Synchronous	3600, 1800, 1200, 900, 720, 600, 514, 450, 400, 360, 327, 300, 277, 257, 240, 225, 200, 180, 164, 150, 138, 129, 120

HORSEPOWER TO TORQUE CONVERSION

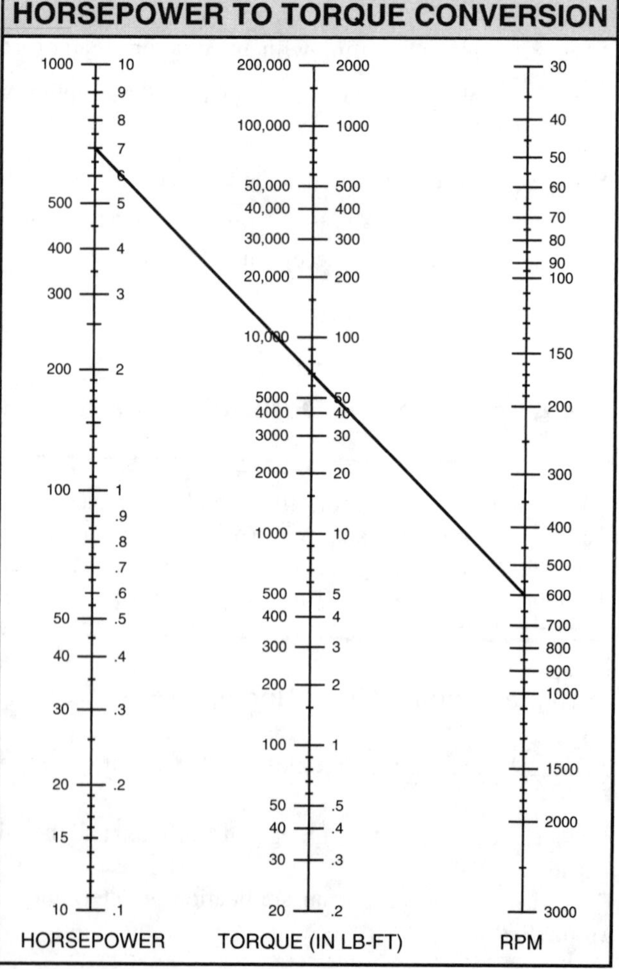

Control Circuit Selection

All motors require a control circuit for proper operation. The control circuit determines when and how the motor operates. A control circuit is shown as a wiring diagram and/or line diagram.

Wiring Diagrams

A wiring diagram shows the placement and connection of all components in the control circuit and power circuit. It is difficult to see the operation of a circuit because a wiring diagram usually contains many wires. A line diagram is used for better understanding of the circuit operation. See Wiring Diagram and Line Diagram.

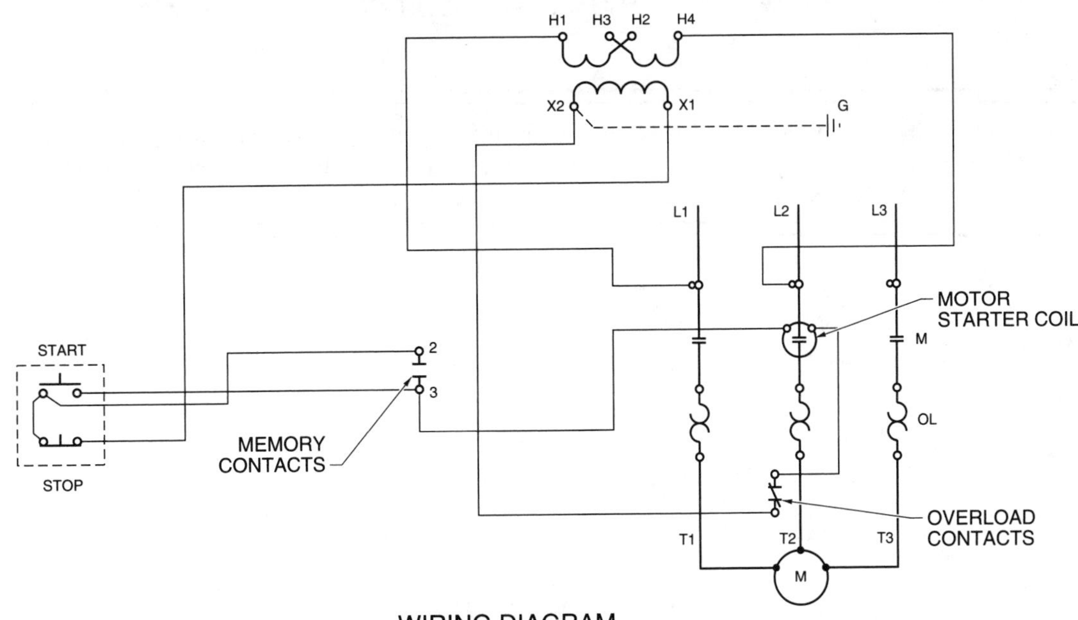

WIRING DIAGRAM

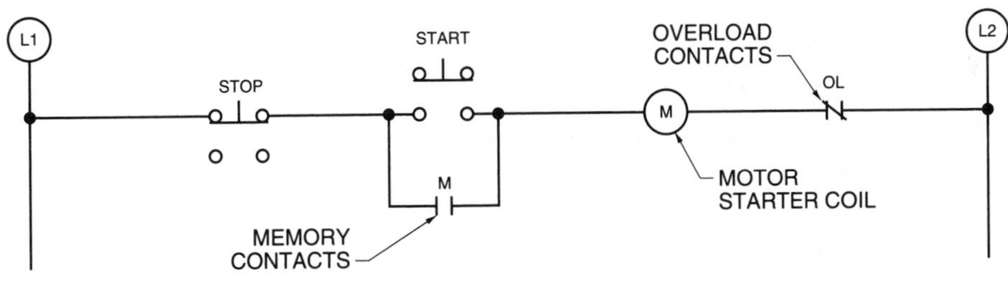

LINE DIAGRAM

Line Diagram

A line diagram shows the logic of a control circuit in simple form. A line diagram does not show the location of each component in relation to the other components in the circuit, but is used when designing, modifying, or explaining a circuit.

Manual, mechanical, and automatic inputs are used to control a motor. Manual inputs are activated by a person. Foot switches and pushbuttons are typical manual inputs. Manual inputs include normally open (NO) or normally closed (NC) switches. A normally open switch is added in parallel when an additional start function is required. A normally closed switch is added in series when an additional stop function is required. See Manual Input Addition.

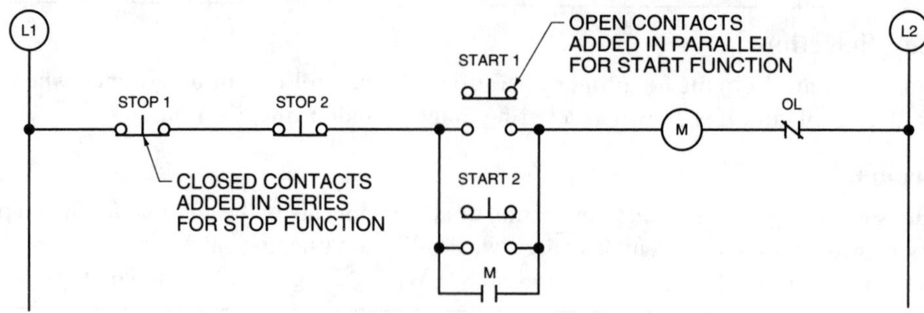

MANUAL INPUT ADDITION

Mechanical inputs are activated by a moving part. Limit switches are mechanical inputs. Automatic inputs respond to a change in the system. Flow switches, temperature switches, and pressure switches are typical automatic inputs. See Mechanical and Automatic Input Addition.

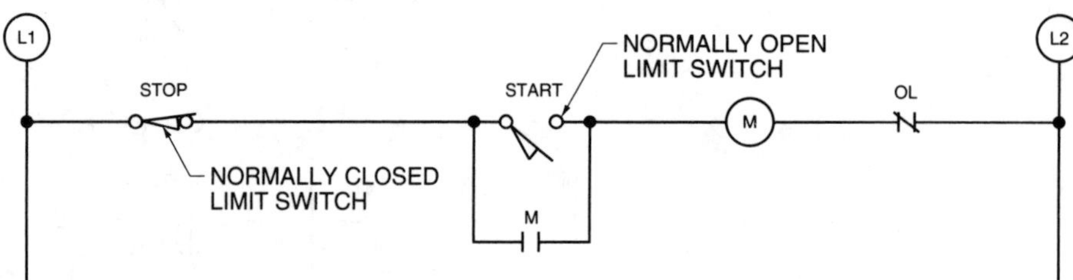

MECHANICAL INPUT ADDITION

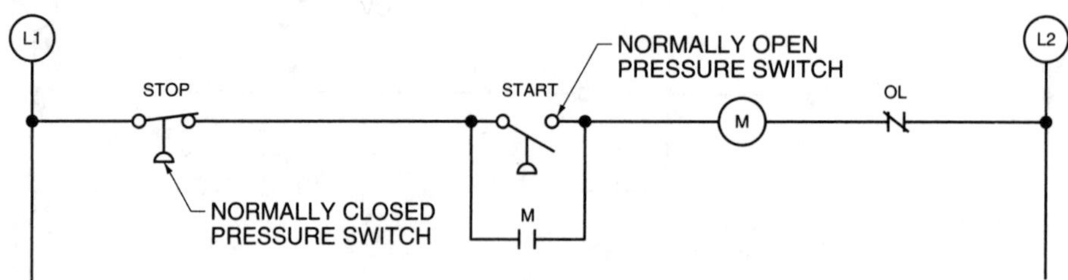

AUTOMATIC INPUT ADDITION

Control Circuit Modification

A control circuit often requires modification to improve its operation or to reinforce its safety. Modification includes adding start, stop, or protection functions, which may be manual, mechanical, or automatic. Protection functions include controls, such as temperature, pressure, and flow switches, that shut down a system if a problem occurs.

Name ______________________ Date ______________

chapter **4**

MOTOR SELECTION

ACTIVITIES

Activity 4-1. Motor Ambient Temperature Correction

Calculate the horsepower ratings for the motor installations.

______ **1.** A ½ HP motor is used as an attic fan. The attic temperature reaches 60°C during the summer. The motor rating adjusted for ambient temperature is ______ HP.

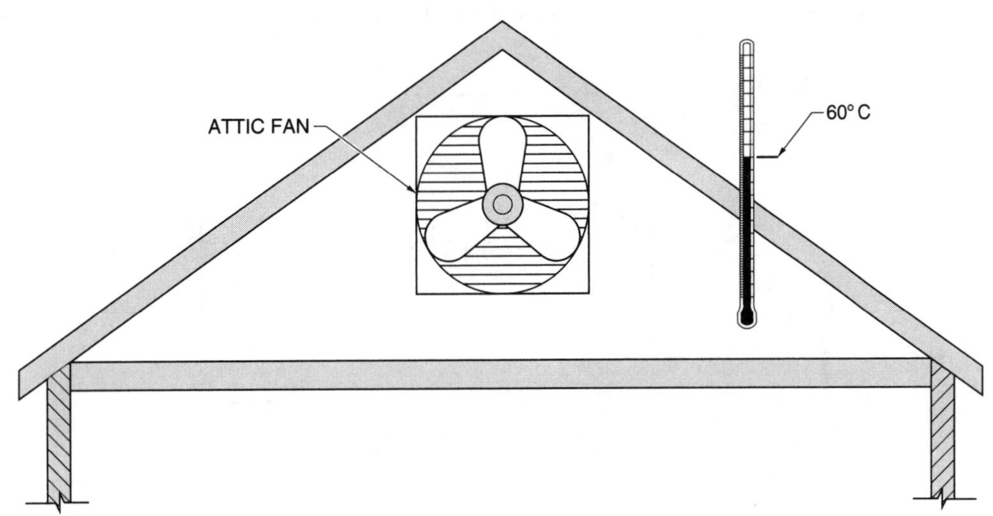

______ **2.** A 7½ HP motor is used in a well pump. The water temperature in the well is a constant 55°F. The motor rating adjusted for ambient temperature is ______ HP.

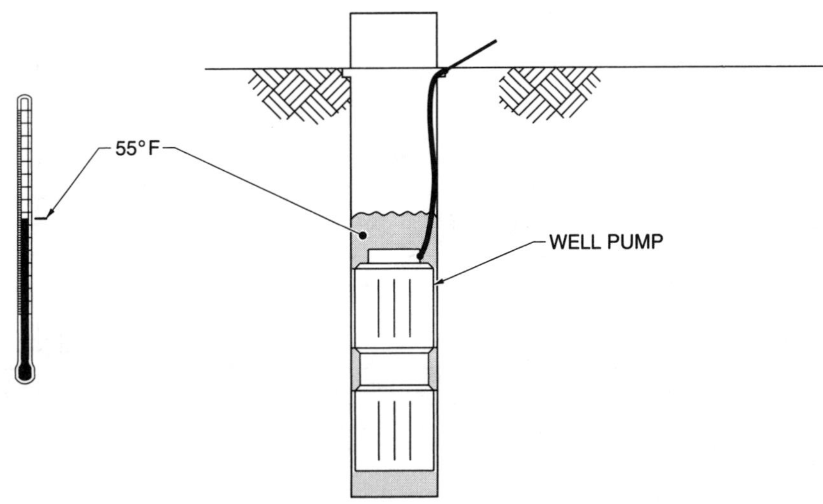

_______ **3.** A 5 HP motor is used in a compressor application in which the ambient temperature varies from 60°F to 120°F. The motor rating adjusted for ambient temperature is _______ HP.

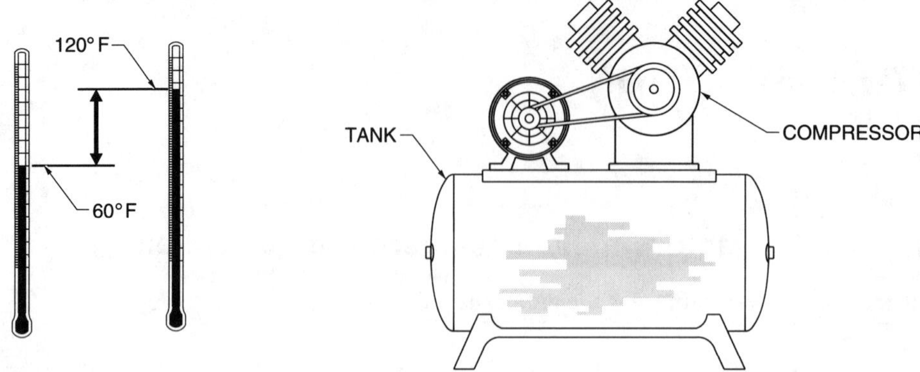

_______ **4.** A ¾ HP motor is located indoors near an annealing furnace. The temperature around the motor reaches 140°F. The motor rating adjusted for ambient temperature is _______ HP.

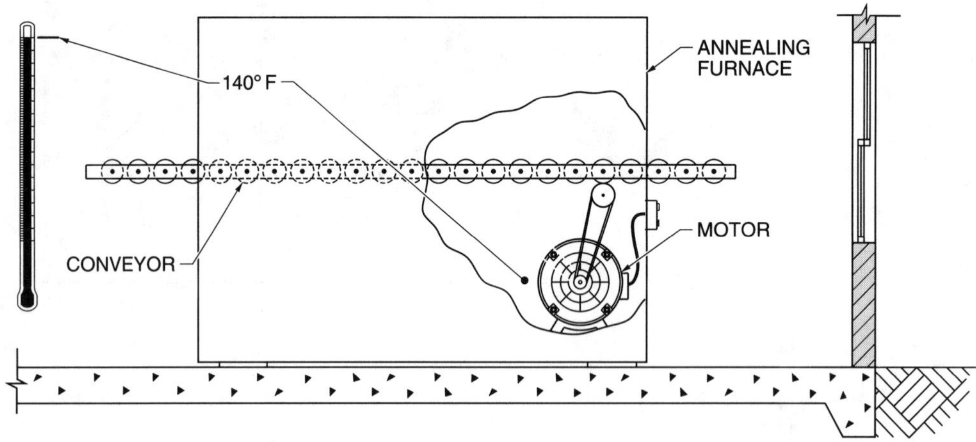

_______ **5.** A 2 HP motor is used in a refrigerated warehouse that has a maintained temperature of –5°C to –8°C. The motor rating adjusted for ambient temperature is _______ HP.

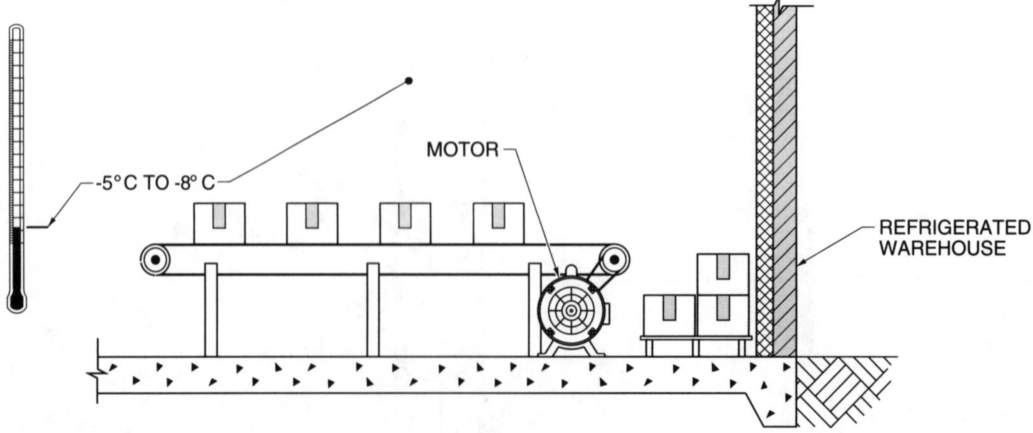

Activity 4-2. Voltage and Frequency Variations

Use the motor's starting current to select the size of the fuse.

1. A motor has a rated running current of 8.5 A and a starting current six times the rated running current.

_________ **A.** The rated current at the rated voltage is _________ A.

_________ **B.** The rated current at 10% above rated voltage is _________ A.

_________ **C.** The rated current at 10% below rated voltage is _________ A.

_________ **D.** The starting current at rated voltage is _________ A.

_________ **E.** The starting current at 10% above rated voltage is _________ A.

_________ **F.** The starting current at 10% below rated voltage is _________ A.

Determine the motor's torque rating for the given voltages.

2. A 10 HP, 3ϕ motor turns at 1800 rpm, and has a 30 lb-ft full-load torque rating and a 165 lb-ft locked rotor torque rating at full voltage.

_________ **A.** The rated full-load torque at the rated voltage is _________ lb-ft.

_________ **B.** The rated full-load torque at 10% above the rated voltage is _________ lb-ft.

_________ **C.** The rated full-load torque at 10% below the rated voltage is _________ lb-ft.

_________ **D.** The rated locked rotor torque at the rated voltage is _________ lb-ft.

_________ **E.** The rated locked rotor torque at 10% above the rated voltage is _________ lb-ft.

_________ **F.** The rated locked rotor torque at 10% below the rated voltage is _________ lb-ft.

Using the following information, state whether the motor's performance increases or decreases. *Note:* The standard AC line frequency in the U.S. is 60 cycles per second (cps). The standard AC line frequency in some foreign countries is 50 cps.

_________ **3.** The starting current of a motor with a rated frequency of 60 cps _________ when operated at 50 cps.

_________ **4.** The starting current of a motor with a rated frequency of 50 cps _________ when operated at 60 cps.

_________ **5.** The full-load current of a motor with a rated frequency of 60 cps _________ when operated at 50 cps.

_________ **6.** The full-load current of a motor with a rated frequency of 50 cps _________ when operated at 60 cps.

_________ **7.** The torque of a motor with a rated frequency of 60 cps _________ when operated at 50 cps.

_________ **8.** The torque of a motor with a rated frequency of 50 cps _________ when operated at 60 cps.

_________ **9.** The efficiency of a motor with a rated frequency of 60 cps _________ when operated at 50 cps.

_________ **10.** The efficiency of a motor with a rated frequency of 50 cps _________ when operated at 60 cps.

__________ **11.** The speed of a motor with a rated frequency of 60 cps ________ when operated at 50 cps.

__________ **12.** The speed of a motor with a rated frequency of 50 cps ________ when operated at 60 cps.

__________ **13.** The temperature rise of a motor with a rated frequency of 60 cps ________ when operated at 50 cps.

__________ **14.** The temperature rise of a motor with a rated frequency of 50 cps ________ when operated at 60 cps.

Activity 4-3. Altitude Correction

Calculate the horsepower rating for the motor installations.

__________ **1.** A ¾ HP motor with a 1.15 SF installed at an altitude of 2500′ has a(n) ________ HP altitude-adjusted rating.

__________ **2.** A 20 HP motor with a 1.15 SF installed at an altitude of 5000′ has a(n) ________ HP altitude-adjusted rating.

__________ **3.** A 7.5 HP motor with a 1.0 SF installed at an altitude of 13,000′ has a(n) ________ HP altitude-adjusted rating.

__________ **4.** A ⅓ HP motor with a 1.0 SF installed at an altitude of 14,500′ has a(n) ________ HP altitude-adjusted rating.

__________ **5.** A ¾ HP motor with a 1.15 SF installed at an altitude of 9500′ has a(n) ________ HP altitude-adjusted rating.

Activity 4-4. Allowable Motor Starting Time

State whether the motor's acceleration time is within the permissible limit.

__________ **1.**

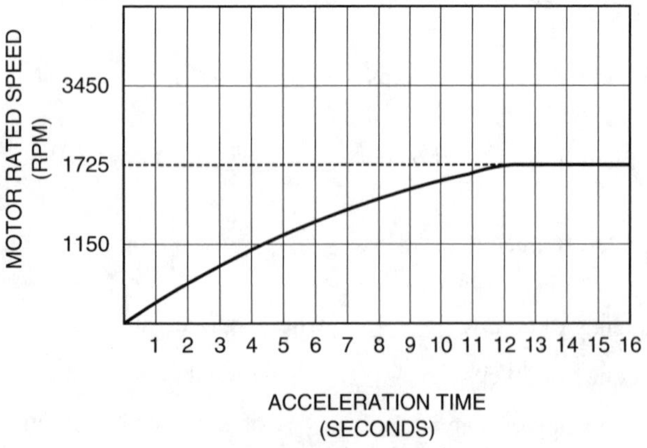

MOTOR RATED SPEED (RPM)
3450
1725
1150
1 2 3 4 5 6 7 8 9 10 11 12 13 14 15 16
ACCELERATION TIME (SECONDS)

NO. 48 FRAME

__________ **2.**

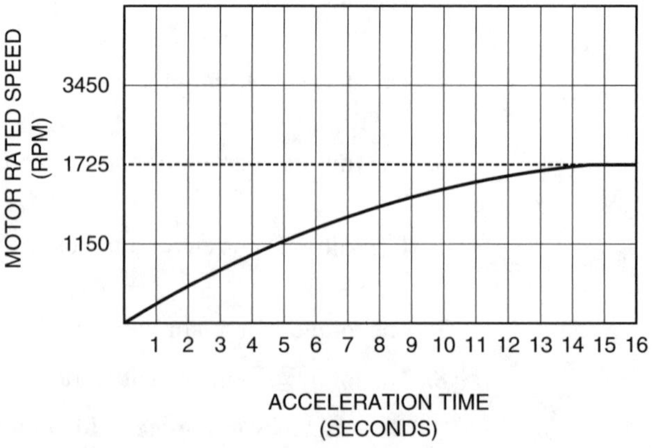

MOTOR RATED SPEED (RPM)
3450
1725
1150
1 2 3 4 5 6 7 8 9 10 11 12 13 14 15 16
ACCELERATION TIME (SECONDS)

NO. 213 FRAME

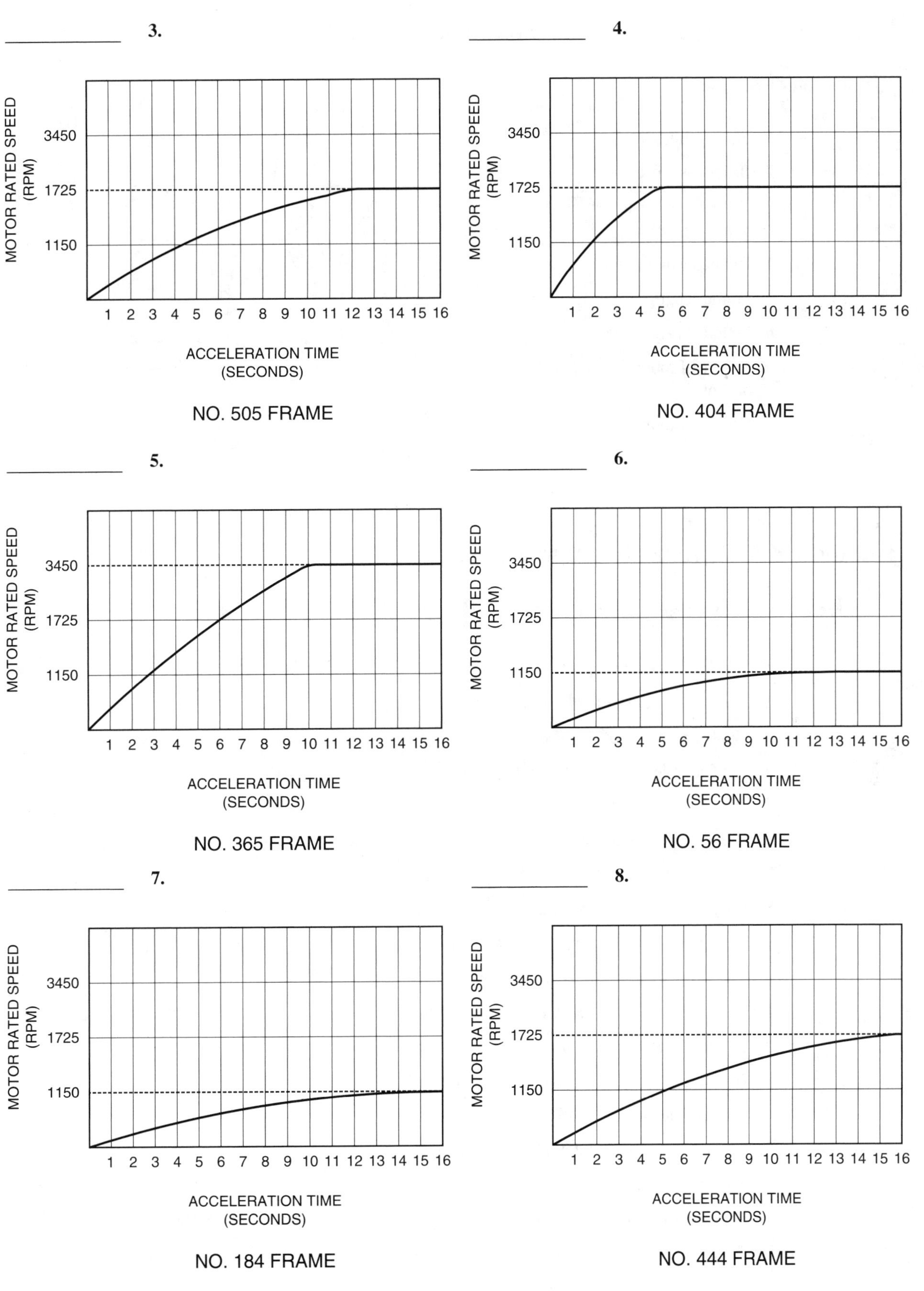

______ 3.
MOTOR RATED SPEED (RPM)
3450
1725
1150
1 2 3 4 5 6 7 8 9 10 11 12 13 14 15 16
ACCELERATION TIME (SECONDS)
NO. 505 FRAME
______ 4.
MOTOR RATED SPEED (RPM)
3450
1725
1150
1 2 3 4 5 6 7 8 9 10 11 12 13 14 15 16
ACCELERATION TIME (SECONDS)
NO. 404 FRAME
______ 5.
MOTOR RATED SPEED (RPM)
3450
1725
1150
1 2 3 4 5 6 7 8 9 10 11 12 13 14 15 16
ACCELERATION TIME (SECONDS)
NO. 365 FRAME
______ 6.
MOTOR RATED SPEED (RPM)
3450
1725
1150
1 2 3 4 5 6 7 8 9 10 11 12 13 14 15 16
ACCELERATION TIME (SECONDS)
NO. 56 FRAME
______ 7.
MOTOR RATED SPEED (RPM)
3450
1725
1150
1 2 3 4 5 6 7 8 9 10 11 12 13 14 15 16
ACCELERATION TIME (SECONDS)
NO. 184 FRAME
______ 8.
MOTOR RATED SPEED (RPM)
3450
1725
1150
1 2 3 4 5 6 7 8 9 10 11 12 13 14 15 16
ACCELERATION TIME (SECONDS)
NO. 444 FRAME

Activity 4-5. Motor Frame Dimension Identification

Identify the motor frame dimensions.

_________ **1.** Frame width

_________ **2.** Base-to-shaft center

_________ **3.** Center of shaft to center of mounting holes

_________ **4.** Diameter of shaft

_________ **5.** Frame length

_________ **6.** Length of shaft

_________ **7.** Center of mounting holes to end of motor

_________ **8.** Center of motor to center of mounting holes

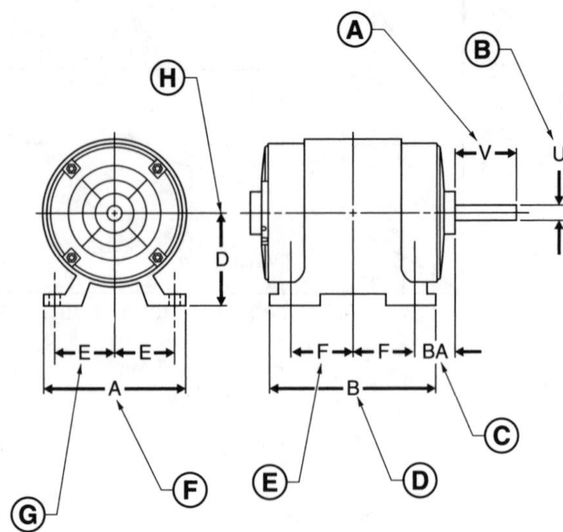

Activity 4-6. Motor Frame Dimensions

Complete the following using Motor Frame Dimensions in Appendix.

_________ **1.** The shaft diameter of a #48 motor frame is _________″.

_________ **2.** The shaft length of a #48 motor frame is _________″.

_________ **3.** The frame width of a #48 motor frame is _________″.

_________ **4.** The frame length of a #48 motor frame is _________″.

_________ **5.** The center-to-center length between the mounting holes of a #48 motor frame is _________″.

_________ **6.** The center-to-center width between the mounting holes of a #48 motor frame is _________″.

_________ **7.** The shaft diameter of a #182T motor frame is _________″.

_________ **8.** The shaft length of a #182T motor frame is _________″.

_________ **9.** The frame width of a #182T motor frame is _________″.

_________ **10.** The frame length of a #182T motor frame is _________″.

_________ **11.** The center-to-center length between the mounting holes of a #182T motor frame is _________″.

_________ **12.** The center-to-center width between the mounting holes of a #182T motor frame is _________″.

_________ **13.** The shaft diameter of a #404T motor frame is _________″.

_________ **14.** The shaft length of a #404T motor frame is _________″.

_________ **15.** The frame width of a #404T motor frame is _________″.

_________ **16.** The frame length of a #404T motor frame is _________″.

_________ **17.** The center-to-center length between the mounting holes of a #404T motor frame is _________″.

_________ **18.** The center-to-center width between the mounting holes of a #404T motor frame is _________″.

◯ Activity 4-7. Motor Coupling Selection

State the required torque rating and select a coupling of each application using Common Service Factors and Coupling Selections in Appendix.

1. The centrifugal compressor motor turns at 1800 rpm.

__________ **A.** The coupling torque rating is __________ lb-in.

__________ **B.** A #__________ coupling is used for the application.

10 HP, 460 V, 3ϕ CENTRIFUGAL COMPRESSOR

2. The sewage pump motor turns at 1200 rpm.

__________ **A.** The coupling torque rating is __________ lb-in.

__________ **B.** A #__________ coupling is used for the application.

7 HP, 230 V, 3ϕ MOTOR

SEWAGE PUMP

3. The conveyor motor turns at 900 rpm.

__________ **A.** The coupling torque rating is __________ lb-in.

__________ **B.** A #__________ coupling is used for the application.

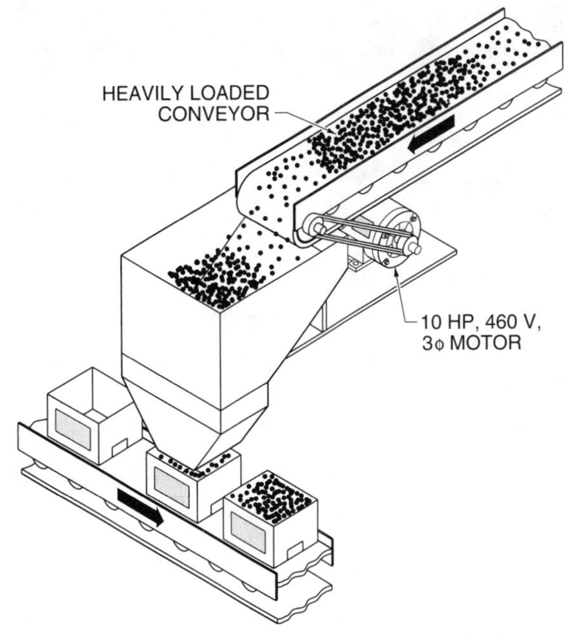

❍ Activity 4-8. Determining Motor Horsepower

Determine the required horsepower for each application using Horsepower to Torque Conversion in Appendix. Round answers to next largest size. Select a standard motor size for the application.

1. A motor application requires a speed of 1200 rpm and torque rating of 9 lb-ft.

__________ **A.** A(n) ________ HP motor is required.

__________ **B.** A(n) ________ HP standard size motor is used.

2. A motor application requires a speed of 1800 rpm and torque rating of 1000 lb-ft.

__________ **A.** A(n) ________ HP motor is required.

__________ **B.** A(n) ________ HP standard size motor is used.

3. A motor application requires a speed of 900 rpm and torque rating of 90 lb-ft.

__________ **A.** A(n) ________ HP motor is required.

__________ **B.** A(n) ________ HP standard size motor is used.

4. A motor application requires a speed of 1200 rpm and torque rating 1600 lb-ft.

__________ **A.** A(n) ________ HP motor is required.

__________ **B.** A(n) ________ HP standard size motor is used.

❍ Activity 4-9. Determining Motor Speed

Determine the required speed for each application using Horsepower to Torque Conversion in Appendix. Round answers to next smallest size. Select a standard motor speed for the application.

1. A 5 HP, 1ϕ motor is used in an application that requires 20 lb-ft of torque.

__________ **A.** The motor turns at ________ rpm.

__________ **B.** A motor with a standard speed of ________ rpm is used.

2. A 50 HP, 3ϕ motor is used in an application that requires 100 lb-ft of torque.

__________ **A.** The motor turns at ________ rpm.

__________ **B.** A motor with a standard speed of ________ rpm is used.

3. A 125 HP, 3ϕ motor is used in an application that requires 700 lb-ft of torque.

__________ **A.** The motor turns at ________ rpm.

__________ **B.** A motor with a standard speed of ________ rpm is used.

4. A ¾ HP, 1ϕ motor is used in an application that requires 3 lb-ft of torque.

__________ **A.** The motor turns at ________ rpm.

__________ **B.** A motor with a standard speed of ________ rpm is used.

◯ Activity 4-10. Control Circuit Modification

1. Redraw the line diagram so that the pump motor cannot start unless the level of oil in the tank is at a specified height. Add a pressure switch so that the pump turns OFF if excessive pressure occurs in the system. Include a bell that sounds if there is no flow in the system after the pump is started. Include a start/stop pushbutton and switches that regulate level, pressure, and flow.

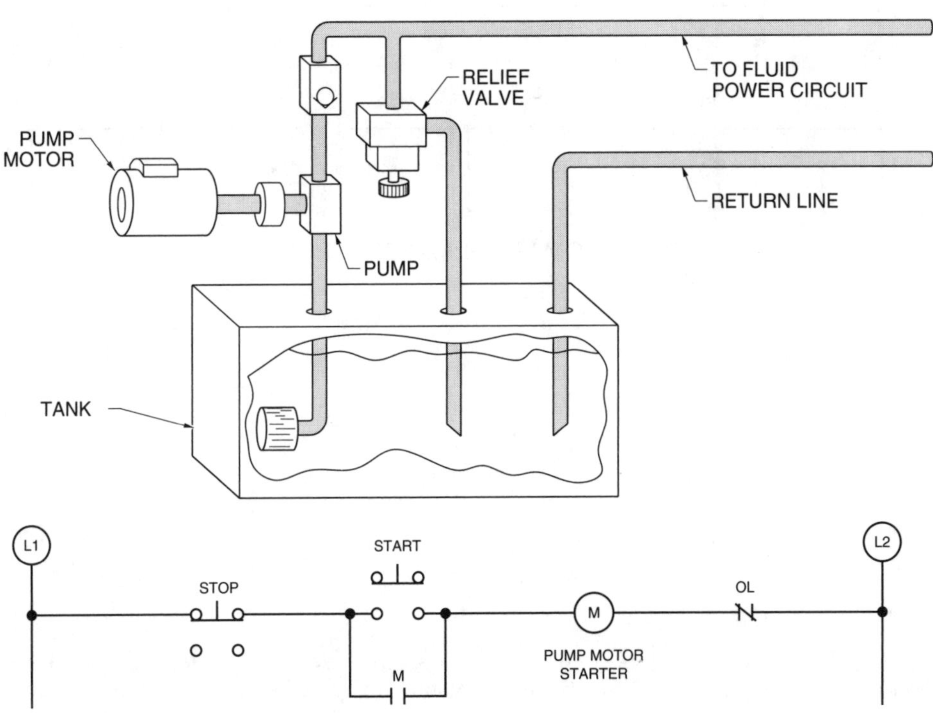

FLUID POWER PUMP PROTECTION

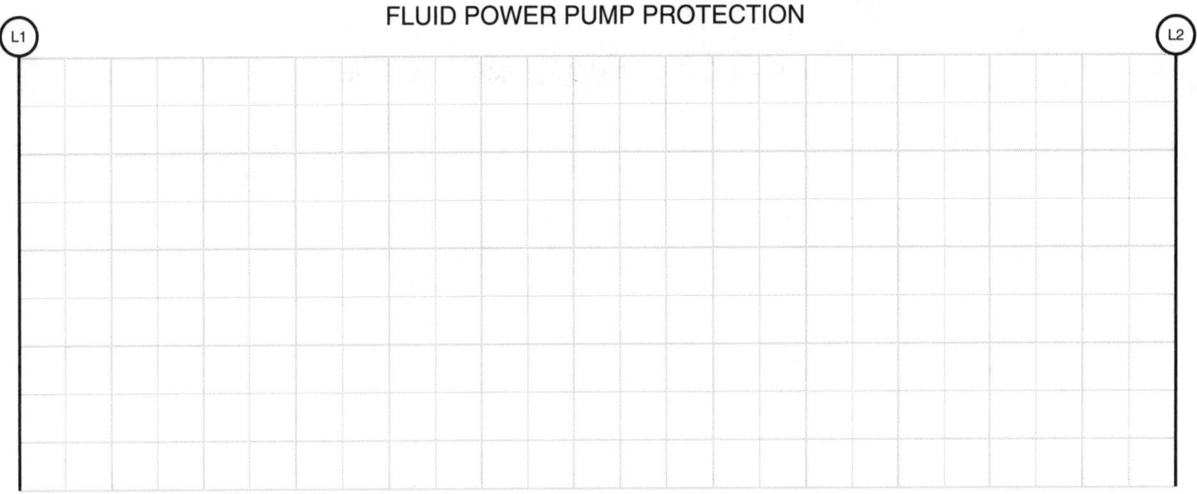

2. Redraw the line diagram so that the pump motor is automatically controlled by a level switch.

PUMP MOTOR
PUMP

L1
START
STOP
M
PUMP MOTOR STARTER
OL
L2

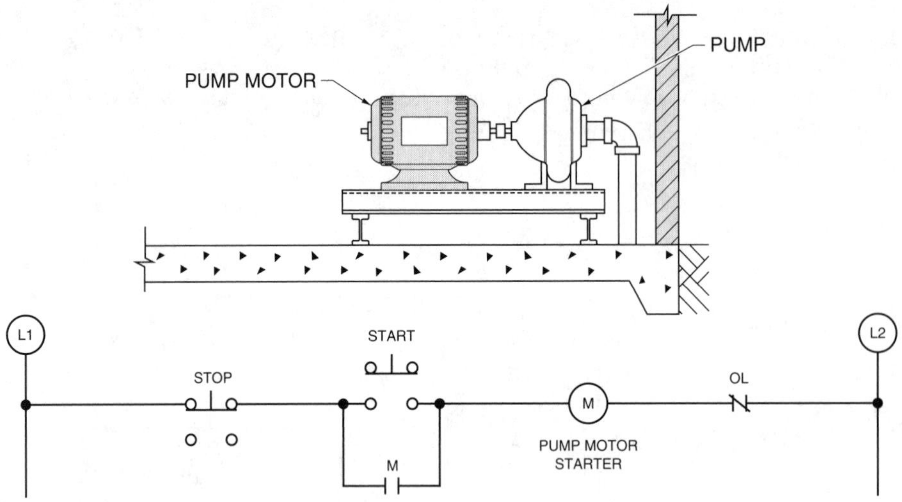

AUTOMATIC PUMP CONTROL

L1
L2

3. Redraw the line diagram to include a two-position selector switch that sets the circuit in manual or automatic mode. In the manual mode, the pump motor is controlled by a start/stop pushbutton station. In the automatic mode, the pump is controlled by a level switch.

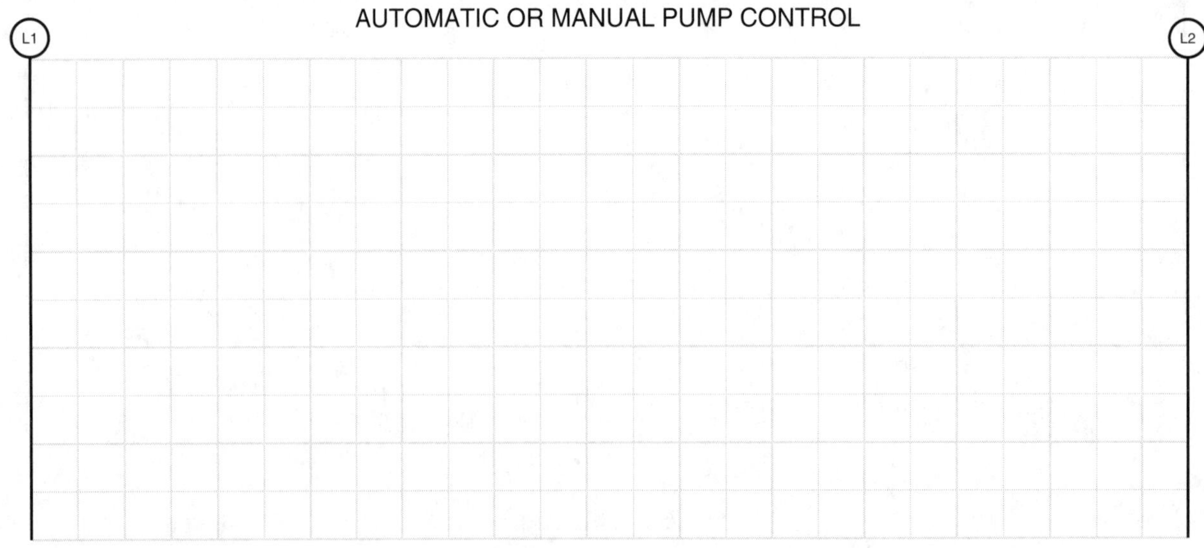

Name ______________________ Date ____________

chapter 4

MOTOR SELECTION

TRADE TEST

Completion

______ **1.** ______ is the force that produces rotation in a motor.

______ **2.** Usual service conditions for a motor include exposure to an altitude of not more than ______′.

______ **3.** Motor frames are classified by ______.

______ **4.** To find a large motor frame number, multiply the base-to-shaft center distance by ______.

______ **5.** The openings of a guarded, open motor enclosure does not permit passage of a(n) ______″ D rod.

______ **6.** DC motors provide high ______ in smaller sizes than AC motors.

______ **7.** The DC ______ motor is used where a constant or variable speed is required.

______ **8.** The direction of rotation for 1ϕ motors is reversed by reversing the current flow in the ______.

______ **9.** The capacitor start-and-run motor uses ______ capacitors.

______ **10.** ______-phase motors are the most common motors used in industry.

______ **11.** An induction motor runs from within 1% to ______% of synchronous speed.

______ **12.** The universal motor is usually available in sizes of less than ______ HP.

______ **13.** The voltage of a motor should be ±______% of rated voltage.

______ **14.** ______ torque is the maximum torque a motor can provide without an abrupt reduction in motor speed.

______ **15.** A splashproof, open motor enclosure provides protection against liquid drops and solid particles within 0° to ______° of vertical.

True-False

T F **1.** AC voltages usually vary more than DC voltages.

T F **2.** Open motor enclosures allow air to cool the motor windings.

T F **3.** The synchronous motor has generally good starting torque.

T F **4.** The universal motor can operate on AC or DC.

T F **5.** Electric motors change electrical energy into mechanical energy.

T F **6.** Full-load torque is the torque required to bring a load up to the correct speed.

T F **7.** The horsepower of a motor determines how fast a load turns.

T F **8.** An explosionproof, enclosed motor enclosure is not self-equipped for cooling enclosed parts.

T F **9.** A series motor is used when high starting torque is required.

T F **10.** A shunt motor runs at almost the same speed at any load within its rating.

T F **11.** The most cost-efficient motor type is a 3ϕ motor.

T F **12.** Very damp or very dry locations are classified as unusual service conditions.

T F **13.** The starting torque of a shunt motor is about 250% to 350% of its full-load torque.

T F **14,** Motor frequency should be within ±5% of rated frequency at the rated voltage.

T F **15.** A permanent-magnet motor has a synchronous speed.

Multiple Choice

________ **1.** A rectifier is a component that converts AC to DC by allowing the current to be ________.

A. increased C. removed
B. decreased D. moved in one direction

________ **2.** A horsepower is a unit of power equal to ________.

A. 550 lb-ft/second C. 33,000 lb-ft/minute
B. 746 W D. A, B, and C

________ **3.** ________ torque is the torque a motor produces when the rotor is stationary and full power is applied.

A. Locked rotor C. Breakdown
B. Pull-up D. Full-load

________ **4.** A Class B motor increases the starting torque of the motor by ________%.

A. 150 C. 275
B. 225 D. neither A, B, nor C

________ **5.** Usual service conditions to satisfy a motor's environmental requirements include an ambient temperature of not more than ________°C.

A. 20 C. 40
B. 30 D. neither A, B, nor C

________ **6.** A motor frame with the letter(s) ________ can be used with a gasoline pump motor.

A. G C. M and N
B. K D. S

________ **7.** A dripproof, open motor enclosure protects motor windings against liquid drops and solid particles within ________ of vertical.

A. 0° to 15° C. 0° to 100°
B. 0° to 30° D. neither A, B, nor C

________ **8.** The starting torque of a DC series motor is ________ its full-load torque.

A. 125% to 250% C. 300% to 400%
B. 150% to 300% D. 400% to 500%

________ **9.** The ________ motor is the most simple and least expensive 1ϕ, AC motor.

A. split-phase C. capacitor-start
B. shaded-pole D. capacitor-run

________ **10.** When a motor is viewed from the front, ________.

A. forward rotation is clockwise C. both A and B
B. reverse rotation is counterclockwise D. neither A nor B

Problems

For problems 1–4,

A. Identify the load the motor must drive as fixed or variable.
B. Identify the motor type best suited for the application.
C. Identify the service conditions as usual or unusual.
D. Identify the motor enclosure type best suited for the application.

1. 30 HP, AC MOTOR

__________ **A.** The load is ________.

__________ **B.** The motor type is ________.

A. 3ϕ induction
B. series
C. split phase
D. capacitor start-and-run

__________ **C.** The service condition is ________.

__________ **D.** The motor enclosure type is ________.

A. general
B. dripproof
C. guarded
D. explosionproof

AMBIENT TEMPERATURE	= 30° C
ALTITUDE	= 1000′
ATMOSPHERE	= OIL REFINERY
SERVICE FACTOR	= 1.25

12° C TO 30° C CRUDE OIL
OIL PUMP

2. ¾ HP, AC MOTOR

__________ **A.** The load is ________.

__________ **B.** The motor type is ________.

A. series
B. synchronous
C. capacitor-start
D. shaded-pole

__________ **C.** The service condition is ________.

__________ **D.** The motor enclosure type is ________.

A. water-cooled
B. nonventilated
C. waterproof
D. splashproof

AMBIENT TEMPERATURE	= 25° C
ALTITUDE	= 500′
ATMOSPHERE	= INDOOR WOODWORKING SHOP
SERVICE FACTOR	= 1.15

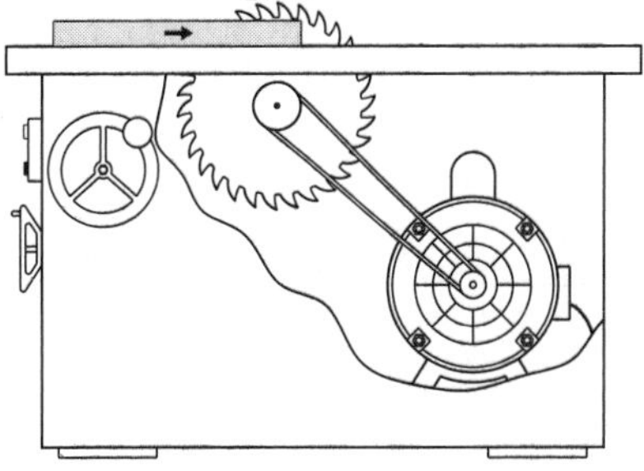

3. ¼ HP, DC MOTOR

_______ **A.** The load is _______.

_______ **B.** The motor type is _______.

A. shaded-pole
B. universal
C. wound-rotor
D. capacitor-start

_______ **C.** The service condition is _______.

_______ **D.** The motor enclosure type is _______.

A. waterproof
B. explosionproof
C. pipe-ventilated
D. dripproof, fully guarded

AMBIENT TEMPERATURE	= 0° C TO 30° C
ALTITUDE	= 1500′
ATMOSPHERE	= OUTDOOR CONSTRUCTION SITE
SERVICE FACTOR	= 1.25

BATTERY PACK

4. 5 HP, AC MOTOR

_______ **A.** The load is _______.

_______ **B.** The motor type is _______.

A. series
B. synchronous
C. shaded-pole
D. capacitor start-and-run

_______ **C.** The service condition is _______.

_______ **D.** The motor enclosure type is _______.

A. waterproof
B. explosionproof
C. water-cooled
D. dripproof

AMBIENT TEMPERATURE	= 10° C
ALTITUDE	= -50′
ATMOSPHERE	= SALT WATER
SERVICE FACTOR	= 1.15

DEEP WELL PUMP

5. What is the full-load torque of a 50 HP, 240 V, 3ϕ motor turning at 1725 rpm?

6. What is the horsepower of a 230 V motor pulling 20 A and having 88% efficiency?

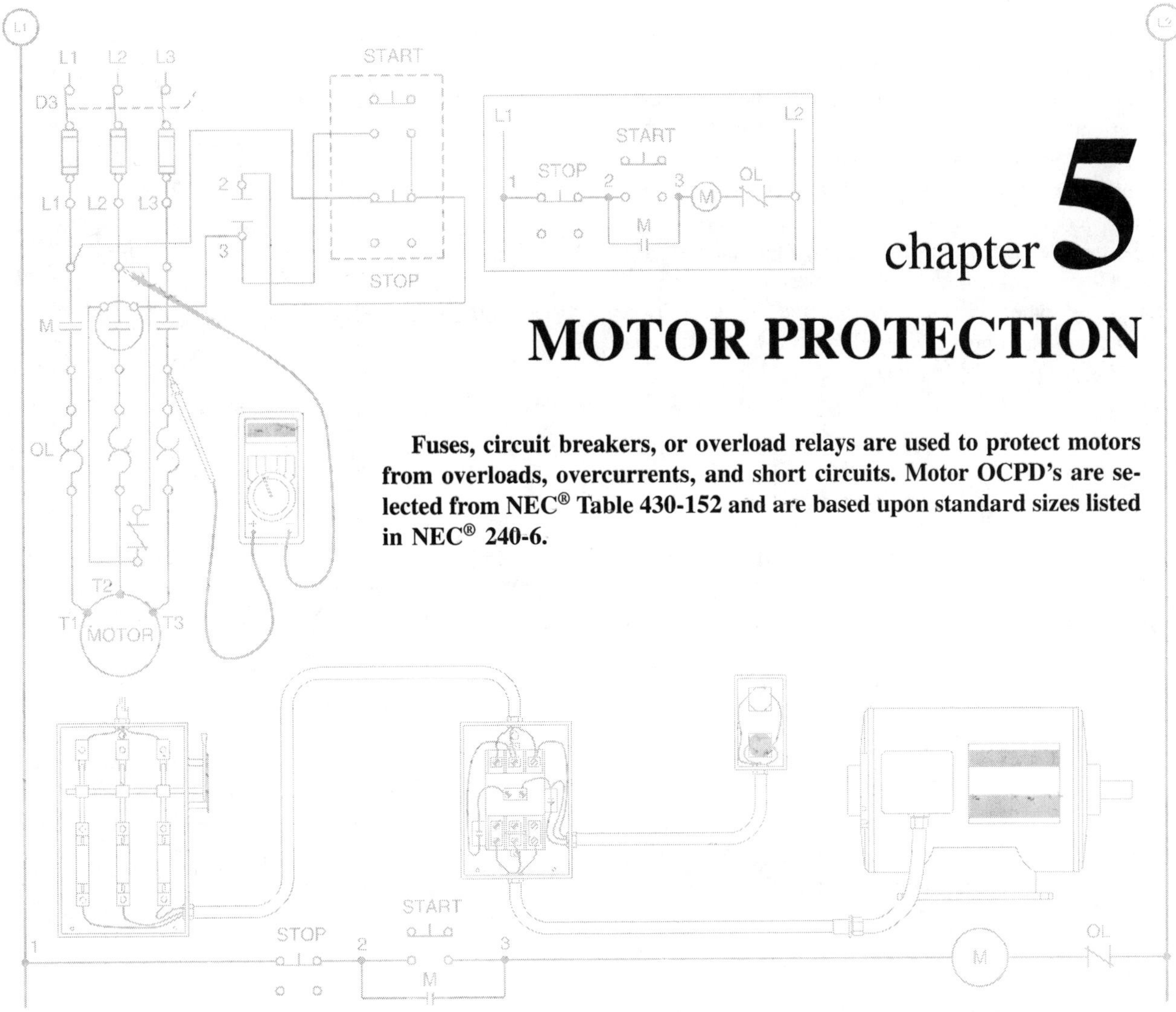

chapter 5

MOTOR PROTECTION

Fuses, circuit breakers, or overload relays are used to protect motors from overloads, overcurrents, and short circuits. Motor OCPD's are selected from NEC® Table 430-152 and are based upon standard sizes listed in NEC® 240-6.

MOTOR PROTECTION

Motors must be properly protected from overloads, overcurrents, and short circuits. Fuses, circuit breakers (CB's), or overload relays are typically used to protect the motor. Fuses and CB's are used for overcurrent and short-circuit protection. Overload relays are used for overload protection. See Figure 5-1. When properly selected, these devices provide a safety link in the motor circuit. They disconnect the circuit when there is a problem and are the first place to start when troubleshooting a motor or motor circuit.

The motor will not run when the fuses have blown, the CB has tripped, or the overload relay contacts have opened. Changing the fuses, resetting the CB, or resetting the overload relay contacts often allow the motor to restart. However, the reason the protection devices malfunctioned may remain.

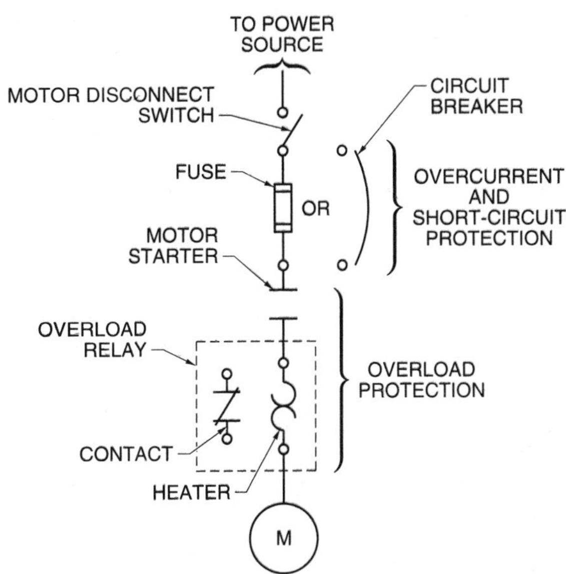

Figure 5-1. Fuses, CB's, or overload relays protect the motor.

Overcurrent

Current flows through and is confined to the conductive paths provided by conductors and other components when a load is turned ON. Every load draws a normal amount of current. This normal amount of current is the current level for which the load is designed. An *overcurrent* is any current over the normal current level. An overcurrent may be an overload current or a short-circuit current.

Some overcurrents are to be expected and are normal. Others are very dangerous. One normal overcurrent occurs whenever a motor is started. A motor draws many times its running (normal) current when starting. See Figure 5-2.

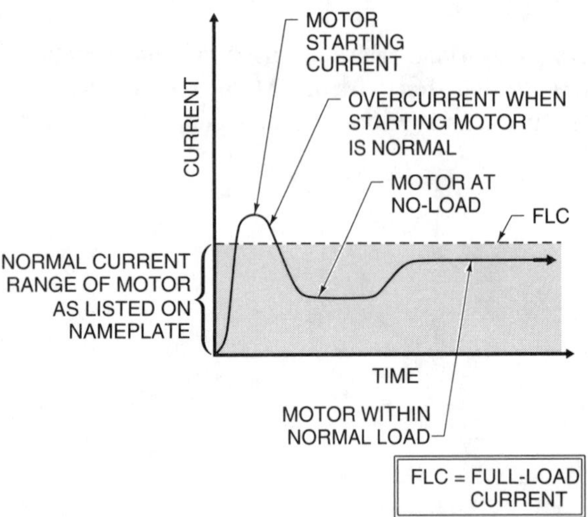

Figure 5-2. An overcurrent is any current over the normal current level.

Overcurrent Protection. Overcurrent protection devices (OCPD's) protect the motor branch-circuit conductors, control equipment, and motor from short circuits or grounds. The OCPD's commonly used to sense and clear overcurrents are fuses and circuit breakers. The NEC® requires overload protection of motor installations.

Short Circuit. A *short circuit* is current that leaves the normal current-carrying path by going around the load and back to the power source or ground. Overloads occur in most circuits at modest levels. However, a short circuit causes the current to rise hundreds of times higher than normal at a very fast rate.

A short circuit occurs when the current in the circuit does not follow its designed path. A typical short circuit occurs when the insulation between two wires is broken. The current bypasses the load and returns to the source through the bare wire and not through the load. See Figure 5-3.

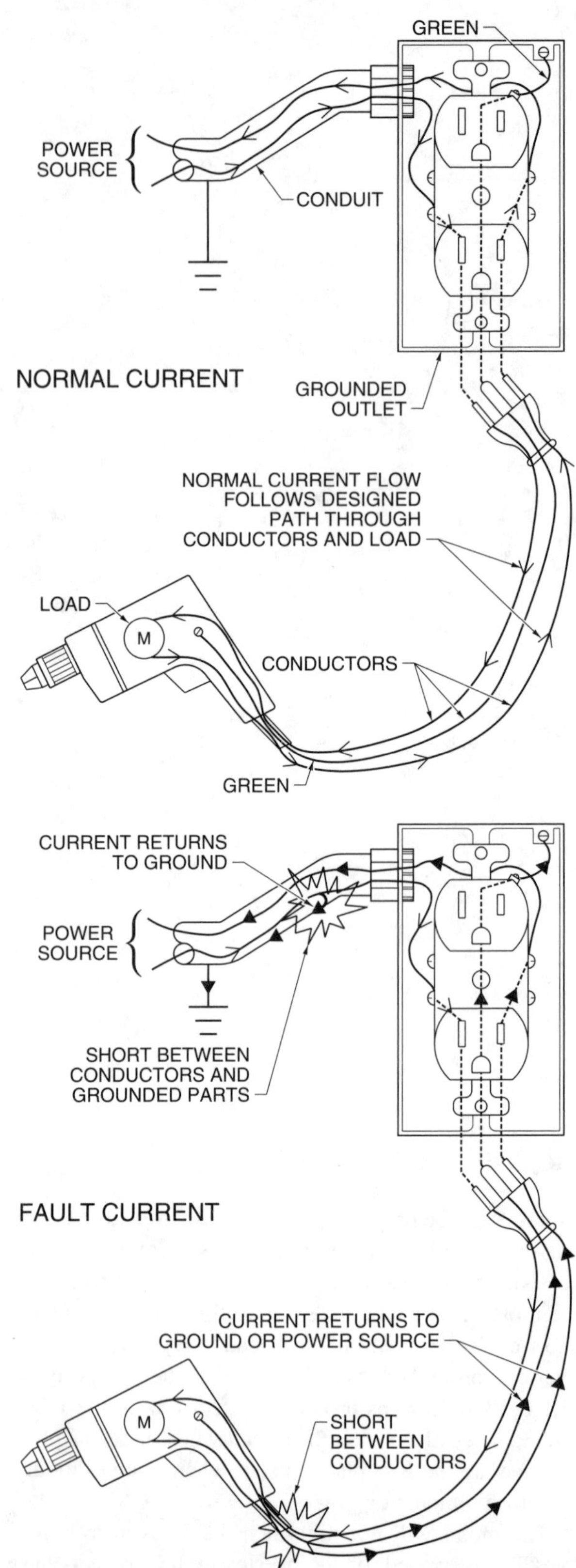

Figure 5-3. A short occurs when current takes a short cut around the load and returns to the power source or the ground.

Overload

An *overload* is the condition that occurs when the load connected to the motor exceeds the full-load torque rating of the motor. An overload occurs whenever the current in a circuit rises above the normal current level for which the circuit has been designed to operate. When overloaded, the motor still attempts to drive the load. To produce the higher torque, the motor draws a higher current. Overloads produce higher-than-normal current levels than the circuit was designed to operate. Overloads are usually between one and six times the normal current level of the circuit.

An overload is usually caused by the temporary surge current that occurs whenever motors are started. This temporary overload is brief and harmless to the circuit. An overload can also occur if a motor is overloaded while running. See Figure 5-4.

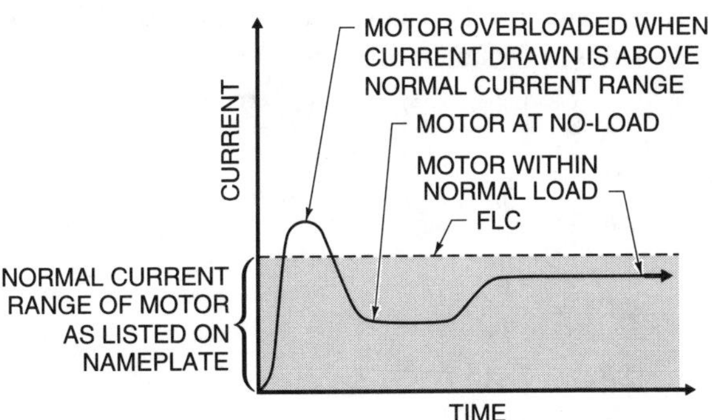

Figure 5-4. An overload occurs when the load connected to the motor is above the normal current level of the motor.

Overload Protection. All overloads shorten motor life by deteriorating motor insulation. Small overloads of short duration cause little damage. However, a sustained overload, even though small, will damage the motor.

An overload protection device is designed to carry harmless overloads, but quickly remove the motor from the supply voltage when an overload has remained too long. Overload protection devices commonly used to sense and clear overloads are dual-element fuses, time-delay fuses, and thermal or magnetic overload relays. See Figure 5-5. The NEC® requires overload protection of motor installations.

Current

Current is the amount of electron flow in a circuit. Current equals voltage divided by resistance ($I = E/R$). It is denoted as a capital I in electrical formulas. Current is measured in amperes (A). The types of current include line current, inrush current, locked rotor current, and full-load current.

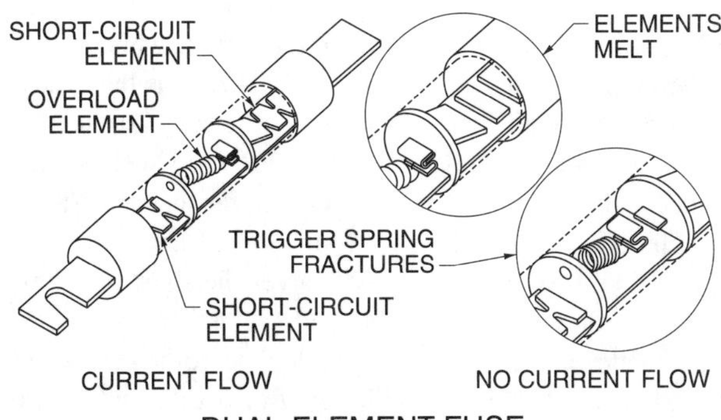

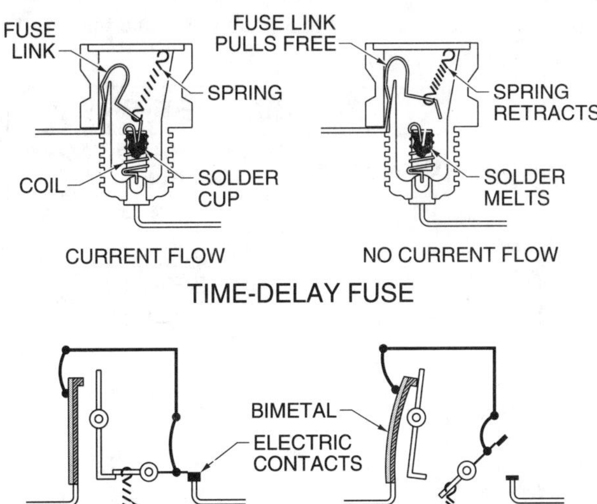

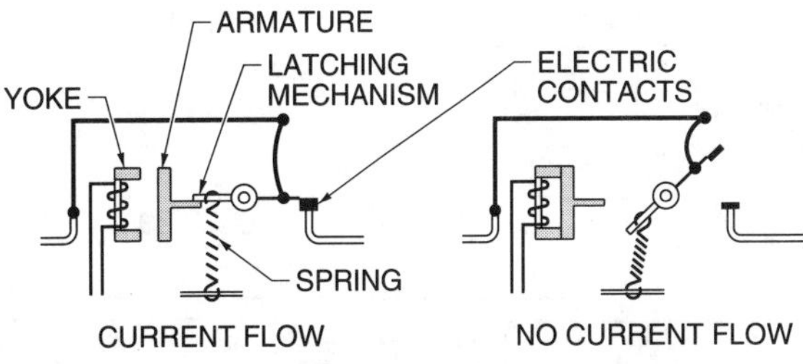

Figure 5-5. Overload protection devices are used to sense and clear overloads.

Locked Rotor Current (LRC). *Inrush current* is the high current drawn by a motor during its acceleration period. Inrush current begins when the motor is turned ON and continues until it reaches rated speed. High inrush current decreases as the motor accelerates. *Locked rotor current (LRC)* is the highest level of inrush current, which occurs the moment the motor is turned ON. OCPD's must be set above the LRC of a motor to prevent the OCPD from opening the circuit to the motor.

Apparent LRC is the locked rotor current without considering power factor or efficiency. *True LRC* is the locked rotor current with power factor and efficiency considered. See Applications. Apparent LRC is the most widely used because the power factor of a motor varies based on load.

The LRC is usually from four to eight times the motor's FLC. LRC also exists whenever the shaft of a running motor is stopped. The code letter on the motor nameplate is used to determine locked rotor current in kVA per horsepower. Code letters from A through V are listed in NEC® Table 430-7(b). Code letters at the beginning of the alphabet indicate low starting current. Code letters at the end of the alphabet indicate high starting current. See Figure 5-6.

LRC/CODE LETTERS

Code Letter	kVA per HP W/ Locked Rotor
A	0–3.14
B	3.15–3.54
C	3.55–3.99
D	4.0–4.49
E	4.5–4.99
F	5.0–5.59
G	5.6–6.29
H	6.3–7.09
J	7.1–7.99
K	8.0–8.99
L	9.0–9.99
M	10.0–11.19
N	11.2–12.49
P	12.5–13.99
R	14.0–15.99
S	16.0–17.99
T	18.0–19.99
U	20.0–22.39
V	22.4 and up

LOW STARTING CURRENT

HIGH STARTING CURRENT

TYPICAL CODE LETTERS — FULL-VOLTAGE STARTING

Code Letter		F	G	H	J	K	L
Horsepower	3ϕ	15 up	1-7½	5	3	2-1½	1
	1ϕ	—	5	3	2-1½	1-¾	½

$$1\phi: LRC = \frac{1000 \times HP \times kVA/HP}{V}$$

$$3\phi: LRC = \frac{1000 \times HP \times kVA/HP}{V \times \sqrt{3}}$$

kVA/HP = code letter

Figure 5-6. The code letter on a motor nameplate is used to determine locked rotor current (LRC).

NEC® Table 430-151 lists the LRC of motors with code letters A through H for motors starting and running under normal conditions. Table 430-152 lists code letters to select the percentage for determining the proper size OCPD.

The apparent LRC of a 1ϕ motor can be calculated from the code letter by applying the formula:

$$LRC = \frac{1000 \times HP \times kVA/HP}{V}$$

where

LRC = locked rotor current (in amps)

1000 = multiplier for kilo

HP = horsepower

kVA/HP = kilovolt amps per horsepower

V = volts

For example, what is the maximum apparent LRC of a ¾ HP, 115 V motor with code letter L?

$$LRC = \frac{1000 \times HP \times kVA/HP}{V}$$

$$LRC = \frac{1000 \times .75 \times 9.99}{115}$$

$$LRC = \frac{7492.5}{115}$$

LRC = **65.15 A**

The apparent LRC of a 3ϕ motor can be calculated from the code letter by applying the formula:

$$LRC = \frac{1000 \times HP \times kVA/HP}{V \times \sqrt{3}}$$

where

LRC = locked rotor current (in amps)

1000 = multiplier for kilo

HP = horsepower

kVA/HP = kilovolt amps per horsepower

V = volts

$\sqrt{3} = 1.73$

For example, what is the maximum apparent LRC of an 8 HP, 230 V, 3ϕ motor with code letter G?

$$LRC = \frac{1000 \times HP \times kVA/HP}{V \times \sqrt{3}}$$

$$LRC = \frac{1000 \times 8 \times 6.29}{398}$$

$$LRC = \frac{50,320}{398}$$

LRC = **126.43 A**

Note: When 3ϕ problems are calculated, the following values may be substituted to eliminate one mathematical step:

For 208 V × 1.732, use 360
For 230 V × 1.732, use 398
For 240 V × 1.732, use 416
For 440 V × 1.732, use 762
For 460 V × 1.732, use 797
For 480 V × 1.732, use 831

Full-Load Current (FLC). Power must be drawn from the power lines to keep a motor running. *Full-load current (FLC)* is the current level required to produce full-load torque on the motor shaft at rated speed. See Figure 5-7. FLC is listed on the motor nameplate.

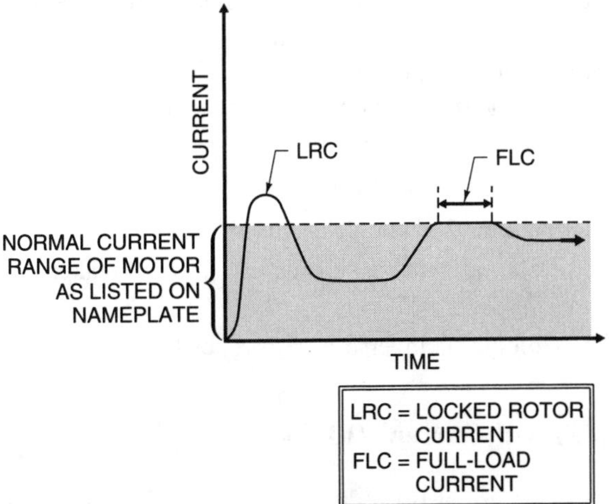

Figure 5-7. Full-load current (FLC) is the current required to produce full-load torque on the motor shaft at rated speed.

Motor Service Factor. Some motors are designed to develop more than their rated (nameplate) horsepower without causing damage to the motor. The *motor service factor* is a safety margin for motor overloads. For example, a motor with a service factor of 1.15 indicates that the motor can operate at 115% of the FLC rating without damaging the motor insulation.

To find the maximum horsepower that a motor can develop, multiply the horsepower of the motor by the service factor. For example, a 10 HP motor with a service factor of 1.25 can safely develop 12.5 HP (10 HP × 1.25 = 12.5 HP). Typical service factors are 1, 1.15, 1.25, and 1.35.

A motor with a service factor of 1 has no built-in margin of safety. A motor with a service factor of 1.35 has the highest margin of safety. The service factor of a motor is listed on the motor nameplate. See Figure 5-8.

FINDING MAXIMUM HORSEPOWER

What is the maximum horsepower of the motor?

1. $HP_{max} = HP \times SF$.   20 x 1.15 = 23

HP_{max} = **23 HP**

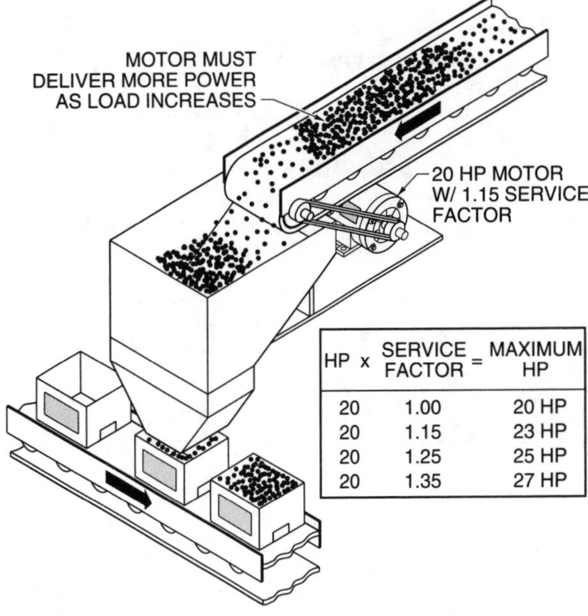

HP x	SERVICE FACTOR =	MAXIMUM HP
20	1.00	20 HP
20	1.15	23 HP
20	1.25	25 HP
20	1.35	27 HP

Figure 5-8. Motor service factor is a safety margin for motor overloads.

Ambient Temperature. *Ambient temperature* is the temperature of the air around a piece of equipment. The ambient temperature for a motor is the temperature of the air outside the motor, not the temperature of the air inside the motor. All motors are subject to an ambient temperature limit. The common ambient temperature limit is 40°C (104°F). The ambient temperature limit is listed on the motor nameplate.

Temperature Rise. Current passing through the windings of a motor increase the motor temperature. *Temperature rise* is the difference between the winding temperature of a running motor and the ambient temperature. The temperature rise produced at FLC is not harmful, provided the ambient temperature does not exceed the ambient temperature limit of the motor. The *permissible temperature rise* is the difference between the ambient temperature and the motor's listed maximum ambient temperature. See Figure 5-9.

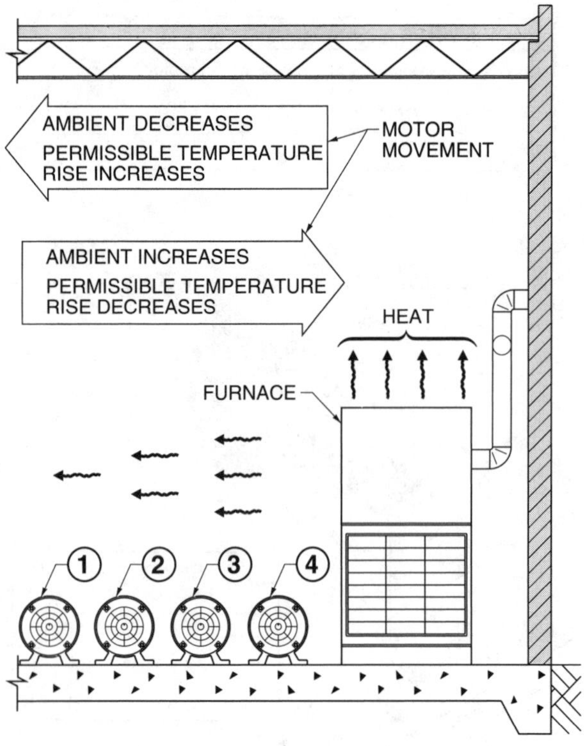

AMBIENT TEMPERATURE	LISTED MOTOR TEMPERATURE RISE	PERMISSIBLE TEMPERATURE RISE
MOTOR 1 = 25°C (77°F)	40°C	15°C (59°F)*
MOTOR 2 = 30°C (86°F)	40°C	10°C (50°F)
MOTOR 3 = 35°C (95°F)	40°C	5°C (41°F)
MOTOR 4 = 40°C (104°F)	40°C	0°C (32°F)**

* Least motor cooling required
** Most motor cooling required

Figure 5-9. The permissible temperature rise is the difference between the ambient temperature and the motor's listed maximum ambient rating.

MOTOR STARTING PROTECTION

The function of an OCPD is to protect the branch-circuit conductors, control equipment, and motor from a short circuit or ground. The OCPD must clear this type of fault, but must not open the circuit as a result of the normal momentary inrush current of a motor starting. The most commonly used OCPD's are fuses and circuit breakers.

OCPD's are installed in the combination starter, safety switch, or fuse panel. The OCPD is located before the motor starter. The OCPD will automatically activate if there is a problem when the motor is started. This will turn the motor OFF. The motor is manually restarted by changing the fuses or resetting the CB's.

Standard Sizes of Fuses and CB's

NEC® 240-6 lists standard ampere ratings of fuses and fixed-trip CB's as follows:

15, 20, 25, 30, 35, 40, 45,
50, 60, 70, 80, 90, 100, 110,
125, 150, 175, 200, 225,
250, 300, 350, 400, 450,
500, 600, 700, 800,
1000, 1200, 1600,
2000, 2500, 3000, 4000, 5000, 6000

Maximum Branch-Circuit and Short-Circuit Rating

NEC® Table 430-152 is used to select the OCPD for motors. It shows the maximum rating or setting of the motor branch-circuit, short-circuit, and ground-fault protection devices. OCPD selection is made from one of four columns:

Column 1: Nontime-delay fuses (NTDF)
Column 2: Time-delay fuses (TDF)
Column 3: Instantaneous trip circuit breaker (ITCB)
Column 4: Inverse time breaker (ITB)

Full-Load Current (FLC)

Full-load current (FLC) is generally listed on the motor nameplate. NEC® Tables 430-147, 430-148, 430-149, and 430-150 are also used to find the FLC in amperes for the DC; 1ϕ, AC; 2ϕ, AC; and 3ϕ, AC motors. For example, per Table 430-147, the FLC of a ⅓ HP, 240 V, DC motor is 2.0 A. See *NFPA 70 National Electrical Code®*. See Figure 5-10.

FLC TABLES			
Table	**Motor**	**HP**	**Voltages***
430-147	DC	¼–200	90, 120, 180, 240, 500, 550
430-148	1ϕ, AC	⅙–10	115, 200, 208, 230
430-149	2ϕ, AC	½–200	115, 230, 460, 575, 2300
430-150	3ϕ, AC	½–200	115, 200, 208, 230, 460, 575, 2300

* Voltage ranges are permitted (e.g., a range of 110–120 V is permitted for 110 V, 115 V, or 120 V).

Figure 5-10. NEC® tables may be used to find a motor's FLC.

Selecting Starting Protection

The current and code letter of the motor are used when selecting starting protection. The FLC and code letter are usually listed on the motor nameplate. Tables 430-147, 430-148, 430-149, and 430-150 for FLC values are also used. Table 430-152 lists the maximum rating of the motor starting protection device. Dual-element (time-delay) fuses and inverse time breakers are typically used as the protection device. Use the appropriate "No code letter" row in Table 430-152 for motors without a listed code letter. See Figure 5-11.

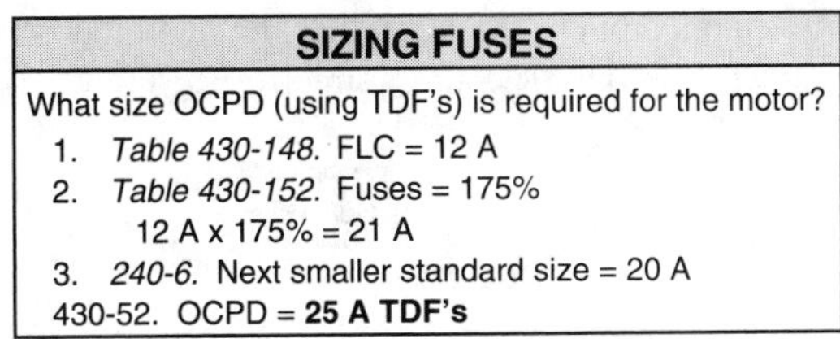

SIZING FUSES

What size OCPD (using TDF's) is required for the motor?

1. *Table 430-148.* FLC = 12 A
2. *Table 430-152.* Fuses = 175%
   12 A x 175% = 21 A
3. *240-6.* Next smaller standard size = 20 A

430-52. OCPD = **25 A TDF's**

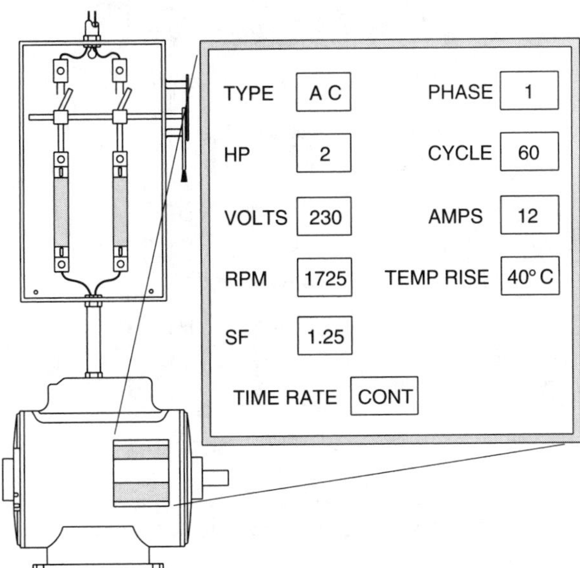

Figure 5-11. Table 430-152 may be used when the motor nameplate does not include a code letter.

Troubleshooting Starting Protection Devices

Starting protection devices protect the motor when starting and if a short circuit exists. Fuses and CB's are located in safety switches, combination starters, motor control centers, and power panels. In typical industrial applications, fuses or CB's are located in combination starters and safety switches for single-motor applications. Motor control centers are used when several motors are grouped together. Power panels are generally used for small motor applications, such as those in dwellings.

Safety Switches. A typical safety switch with fuses consists of a switch and protection devices mounted inside an enclosure and operated from the outside. Safety switches are used for connecting and disconnecting power to the circuit, in addition to providing protection. They are not used to house the motor starter or control circuit. See Figure 5-12.

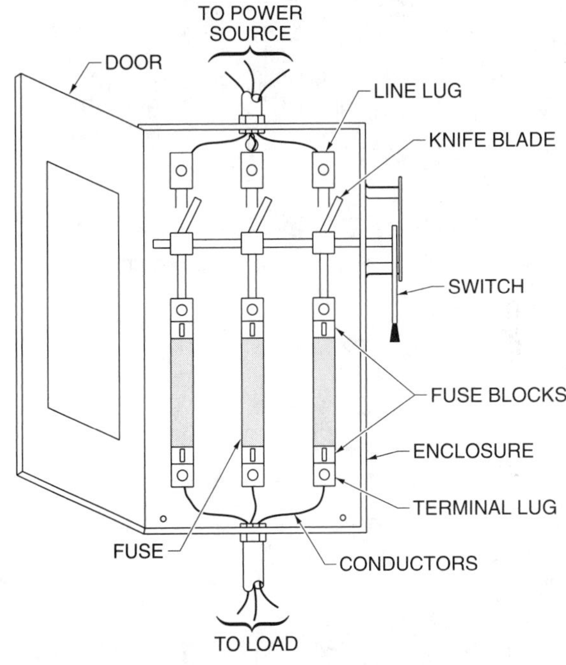

Figure 5-12. Safety switches connect and disconnect power and provide protection.

Safety switches usually have lever knife blade switching arrangements to make and break circuits. Knife blades are capable of switching very high currents. The safety switch is located before the fuses so that no power is applied to the fuses when the switch is opened.

Safety switches used to protect motors shall be located within sight of the motor controller and motor without applying exceptions to the NEC®. Safety switches shall be installed to disconnect both the motor and motor control circuit.

Combination Starters. A typical combination starter combines the parts of a safety switch with the motor starter. Room is also provided for additional control devices, such as timers and relays. Combination starters use fuses or CB's. See Figure 5-13.

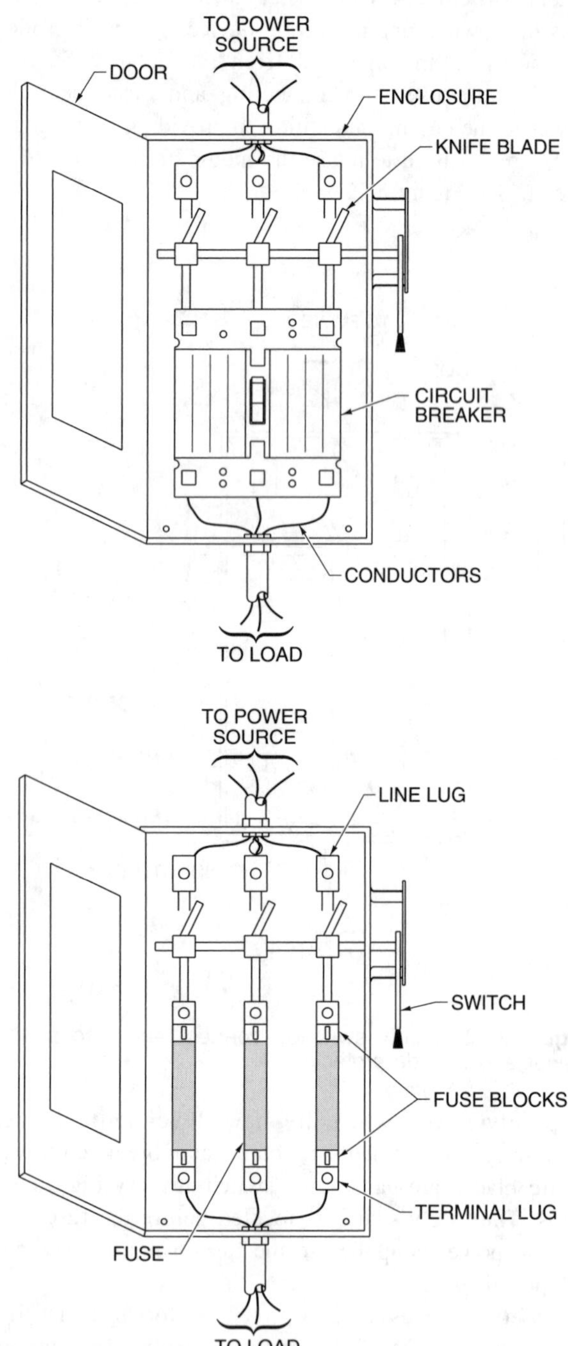

Figure 5-13. Combination starters use fuses or CB's.

A combination starter with fuses is less expensive than a combination starter with CB's. However, there are advantages to both types. The combination starter with fuses requires different size fuses for each different size motor used. When fuses blow, they must be replaced.

The combination starter with CB's uses an adjustable CB. The CB can be adjusted (set) for a range of currents. This allows the same unit to be used for many different size motors. When CB's are tripped, they can be reset.

The type of combination starter used depends on the application. In general, if the motor to be controlled remains the same, the combination starter with fuses is used. If different size motors are to be controlled, the combination starter with CB's is used.

Motor Control Centers. A typical motor control center combines individual control units into standard modular structures, which are joined together for convenience. Motor control centers provide a central location for troubleshooting and servicing motor control circuits. See Figure 5-14.

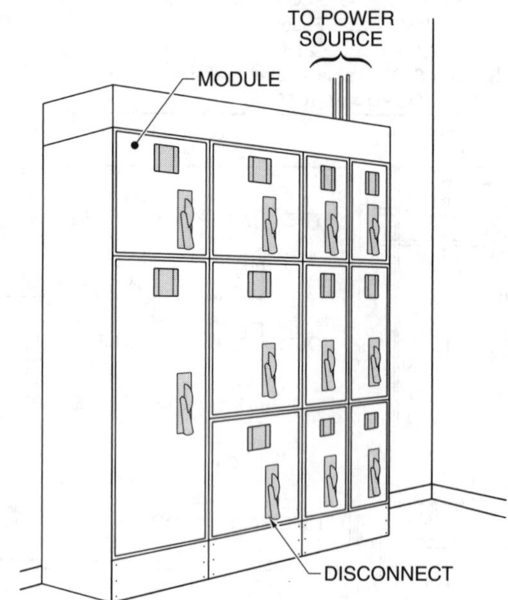

Figure 5-14. Motor control centers provide a central location for troubleshooting and servicing motor control circuits.

Motor control centers are usually supplied with power from a panelboard or switchboard. If a motor develops an overcurrent problem, the OCPD in the motor control center should operate. However, if the overcurrent is in the incoming power supply, such as a lightning strike, the switchboard OCPD should operate.

Power Panels. Power panels house the fuses or CB's that protect general lighting and appliance circuits. They provide a compact and convenient place for troubleshooting circuits that have failed. Generally, the only motors that are connected to circuits in power panels are those used in appliances, such as furnaces and refrigerators. See Figure 5-15.

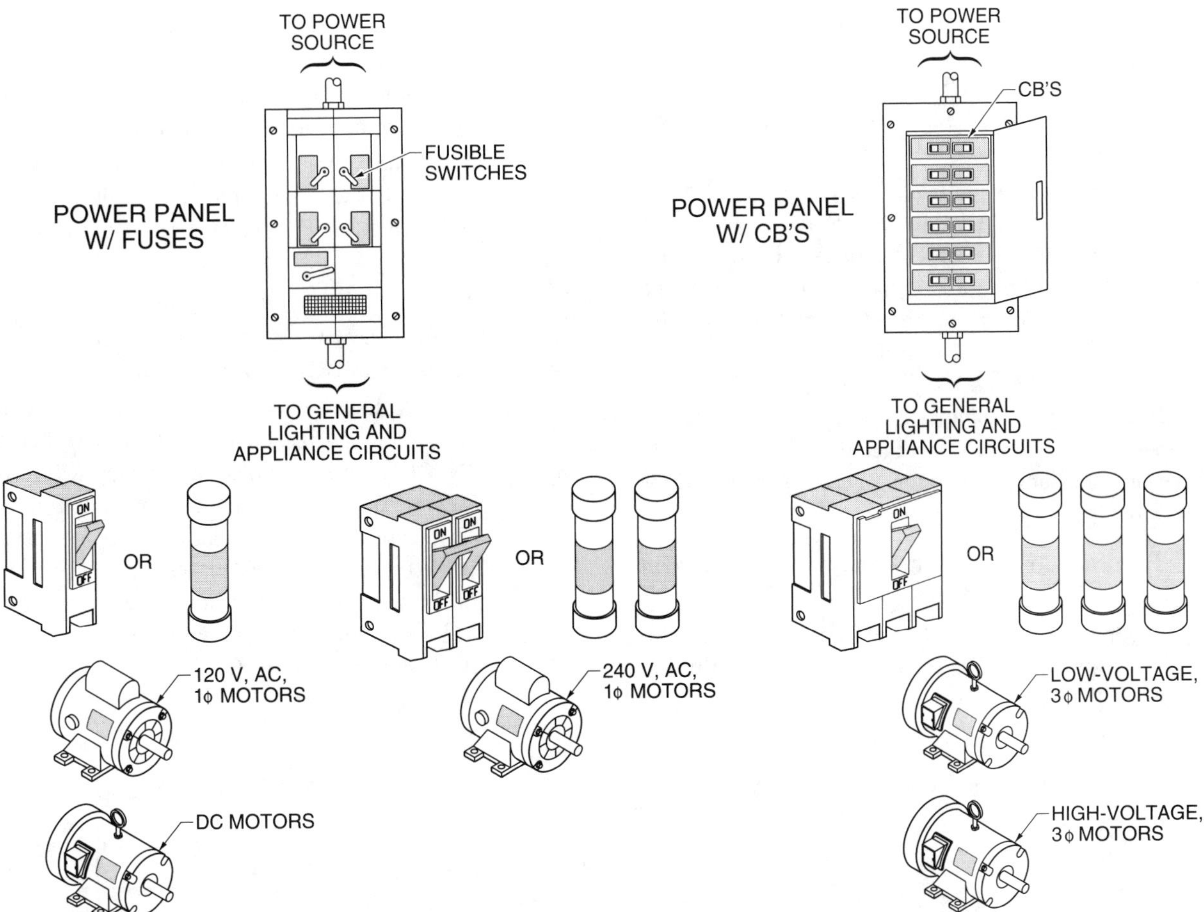

Figure 5-15. Power panels house the fuses or CB's that protect general lighting and appliance circuits.

Fuses. A multimeter with appropriate scales is used to test fuses. See Figure 5-16. When troubleshooting fuses, the following steps should be taken:

1. Turn the handle of the safety switch or combination starter OFF.
2. Open the door of the safety switch or combination starter. The operating handle must be capable of opening the switch. If it is not, replace the switch.
3. Check the enclosure and interior parts for deformation, displacement of parts, and burning. Such damage may indicate a dead short, fire, or lighting strike. Deformation requires replacement of that part or the complete device. Any indication of arcing damage or overheating, such as discoloration or melting of insulation, requires replacement of the damaged part(s).
4. Check the voltage between each pair of power leads with a voltmeter. Incoming voltage should be within 10% of the voltage rating of the motor. If it is not within 10%, a secondary problem has been found. This secondary problem may be the reason the fuses have blown.
5. If voltage is present and at the correct level, test the enclosure for grounding. To test for grounding, connect one side of the voltmeter to an unpainted metal part of the enclosure, and touch the other side to each of the incoming power leads. A voltage difference is indicated if the enclosure is grounded. The line-to-ground voltage will probably not equal the line-to-line voltage reading taken in Step 4.
6. Turn the handle of the safety switch or combination starter ON to test the fuses. One side of the voltmeter is connected to one side 'of an incoming power line at the top of one fuse. The other side of the voltmeter is connected to the bottom of each of the remaining fuses. A voltage reading indicates the fuse is good. If no voltage reading is obtained, the fuse is opened and no

voltage passes through. This fuse must be replaced (not at this time). Repeat this procedure for each fuse. When testing the last fuse, the voltmeter must be moved to a second incoming power line.

7. Turn the handle of the safety switch or combination starter OFF to replace the fuses. Use a fuse puller to remove bad fuses. Replace all bad fuses with the correct type and size replacement. Close the door on the safety switch or combination starter and turn the circuit ON.

Circuit Breakers. A multimeter with appropriate scales is used to test circuit breakers. See Figure 5-17. Circuit breakers perform the same function as fuses and are tested the same way.

1. Turn the handle of the safety switch or combination starter OFF.
2. Open the door of the safety switch or combination starter. The operating handle must be capable of opening the switch. If it is not, replace the switch.
3. Check the enclosure and interior parts for deformation, displacement of parts, and burning.
4. Check the voltage between each pair of power leads with a voltmeter. Incoming voltage should be within 10% of the voltage rating of the motor.
5. If voltage is present and at the correct level, test the enclosure for grounding.
6. Examine the CB. It will be in one of three positions, ON, TRIPPED, or OFF.
7. If no evidence of damage is present, reset the CB by moving the handle to OFF and then to ON. CB's must be cooled before they will reset. They are designed so they cannot be held in the ON position if an overload or short is present. If resetting the CB does not restore power, check for the voltage of the reset CB. Refer to Fuses, Step 6. If a faulty CB is found, replace it. Never try to service a faulty CB.

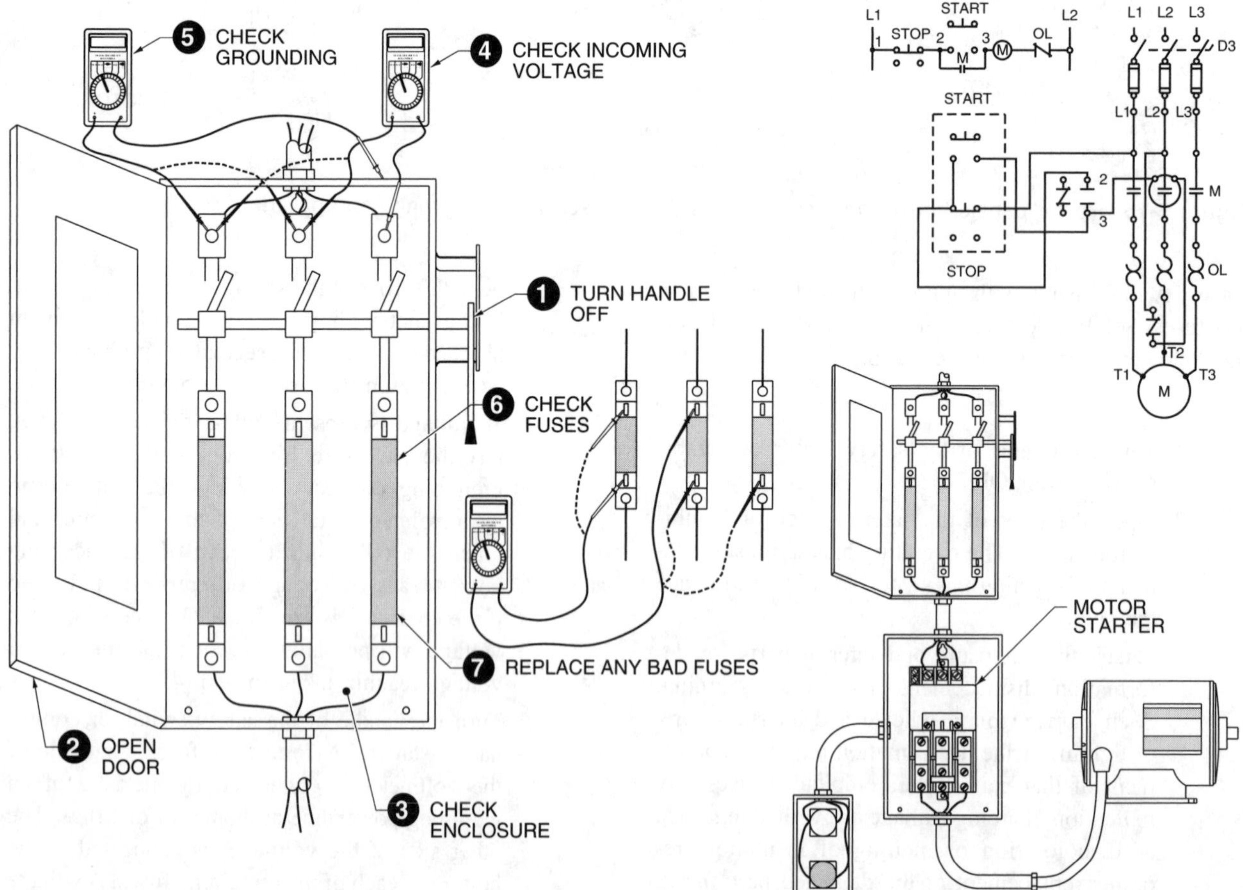

Figure 5-16. Check the enclosure, voltage between power leads, and line-to-ground voltage when troubleshooting fuses.

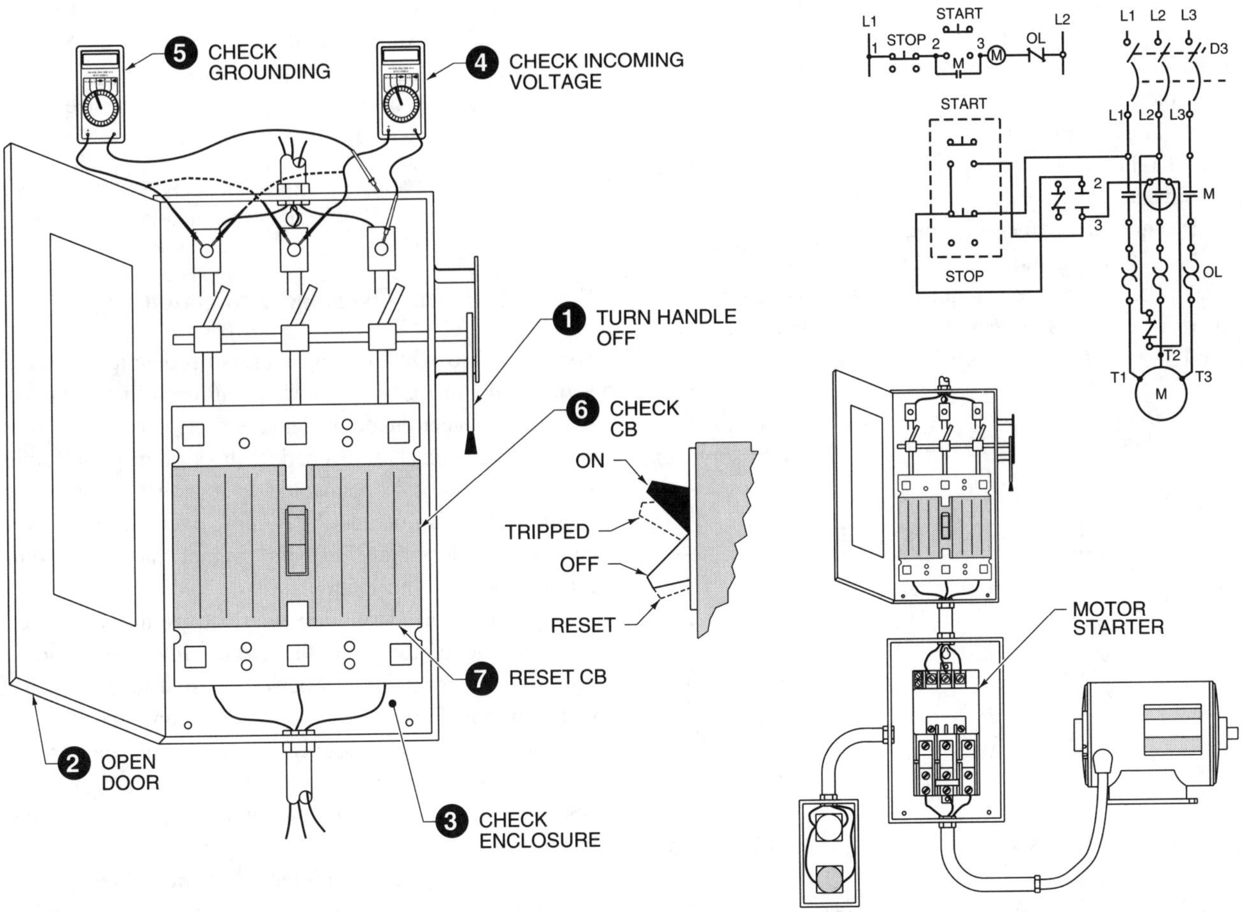

Figure 5-17. Check the enclosure, voltage between power leads, and line-to-ground voltage when troubleshooting CB's.

MOTOR RUNNING PROTECTION

The motor starter is used to turn a motor ON or OFF. It also protects the motor while running. See Figure 5-18. When a motor is started, a higher-than-normal inrush current is drawn from the power lines. Typically, inrush current is several times higher than normal full-load current. As the motor begins to rotate, the starting current reduces to the normal full-load current.

After a motor has started and has accelerated to its rated speed, the motor draws enough current from the power lines to remain running. The amount of current a motor draws from the power lines while running is primarily dependent upon the connected load. FLC is drawn when the motor is connected to the maximum load the motor is designed to drive. The FLC is listed on the motor nameplate.

The load a motor can turn is based on the motor design. If a motor is connected to an easy-to-turn load, the motor draws less than FLC. If a motor is connected to a hard-to-turn load, the motor draws more than FLC. If a motor is not connected to a load, the motor draws only the amount of current required to keep the shaft rotating at the rated rpm.

The running protection device is typically a heater, which has to be installed into the manual or magnetic motor starter. One heater is required for each hot power line. A *hot power line* is any power line that is not

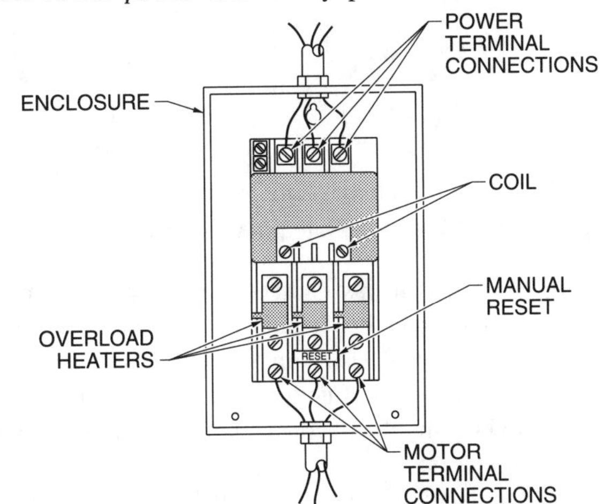

Figure 5-18. The motor starter turns a motor OFF or ON.

grounded. For all DC motors, the positive line is not grounded and the negative line is grounded. One heater in the positive power line is required when controlling a DC motor.

One line is the hot line, and the other is the neutral line for all 1ϕ, 115 V, AC motors. The neutral line is connected to ground at the service panel. One heater in the hot power line is required when controlling a 1ϕ, 115 V, AC motor. For 1ϕ, 230 V, AC motors, both lines are hot. One heater in each hot power line is required when controlling a 1ϕ, 230 V, AC motor. One heater in each power line is required for all 3ϕ motors. See Figure 5-19.

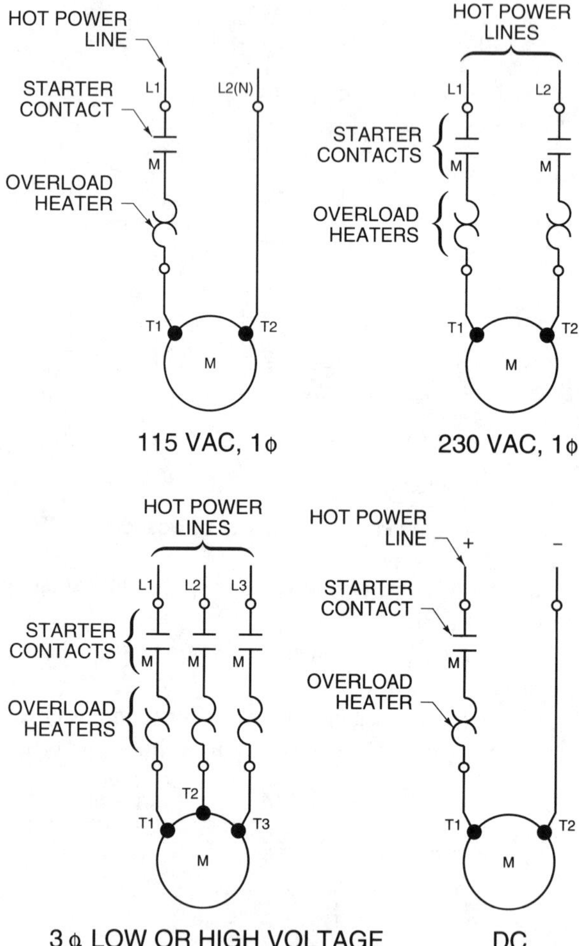

Figure 5-19. One heater is required for each hot power line.

Using Manufacturer's Charts. The proper size protection device can be calculated or manufacturer's charts can be used. Using manufacturer's charts is a fast and simple way to find information. See Appendix. The following should be considered when using manufacturer's charts:

- Manufacturer's charts are usually based upon that manufacturer's equipment only.
- Sizes in manufacturer's charts may be different than calculated values based on the NEC®. The NEC® provides minimum requirements. Manufacturer's charts often oversize equipment and undersize protection devices as a margin of safety.
- Manufacturers typically list the most common sizes in their charts. Certain sizes may require calculation.

Sizing Running Overload Protection

Using FLC to size running overload protection protects a motor up to maximum current allowed. The running overload protection device disconnects the motor only when the current has reached its maximum permissible level. If a motor is connected to a load that does not require full motor power, the running overload protection can be rated less than FLC, but greater than the current required to turn the load.

A properly sized running overload protection device removes the motor from the circuit if an overload is present for a long enough period of time to do damage to the motor. For example, overloads may occur when the motor vents are clogged from dirt or lint, or the motor bearings begin to lock. When this happens, excessive heat builds up in the windings, damaging the insulation.

The running overload protection device is set to open the circuit at 115% or 125% of the motor's FLC to protect from overloads. See Figure 5-20. The percentage above FLC depends on two factors per NEC® 430-32:

Service factor listed on the motor nameplate.

Motors with a marked service factor not less than 1.15 = 125%

Temperature rise listed on the motor nameplate.

Motors with a marked temperature rise not over 40°C = 125%

All other motors......................115%

Selecting Running Protection

An overload in a motor raises the temperature of the windings. A running overload protection device that is too large allows a larger increase in temperature, which may damage the windings. A running overload protection device that is too small turns the motor OFF during a normal increase in current as the motor is loaded. The ideal running overload protection for a motor is a device that can sense motor current and open the circuit slightly before FLC is exceeded long enough to heat the motor to the point of insulation damage.

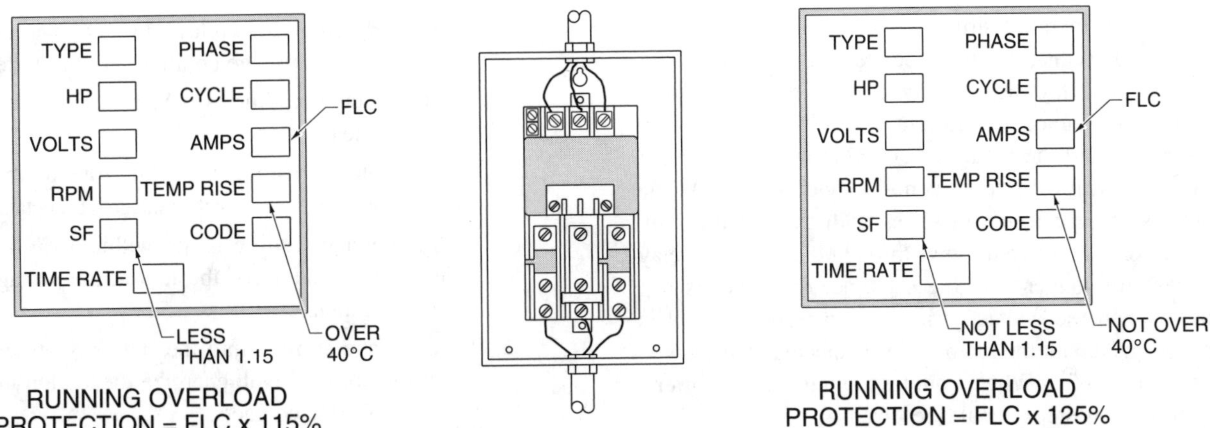

Figure 5-20. The running overload protection device is set to open the circuit at 115% or 125% of the motor's FLC to protect from overloads.

Overload relays are the most common device used to detect an overload. Overload relays can be a separate device, but are usually a part of the manual or magnetic motor starter unit. The overload relay is designed to permit a normal overcurrent during the accelerating period of the motor, but to clear an overload above FLC that exists for too long of a time period. An overload relay can be reset after an overload and will withstand repeated trip and reset cycles without need of replacement.

An overload relay has a current-sensing unit connected in the power line leading to the motor. This sensing unit directly or indirectly disconnects the motor during overloads. Heaters are installed in the starter to protect from overloads. Manufacturer's charts are used to determine the proper type and size heaters. See Appendix.

Troubleshooting Running Protection Devices

Motor starters are used to start, stop, and provide running protection for motors. Motor starters are manually or magnetically controlled. See Figure 5-21. They include overload relays that are used to detect excessive current passing through the motor.

The overload relays in a motor starter are time-delay devices that allow temporary overloads without disconnecting the motor. If an overload is present for longer than the preset time, the overload relays trip and disconnect the motor from the circuit. Overload relays on manual starters can be reset after tripping by pressing the stop button and then the start button, or by pressing the reset button on units that have one. On magnetic starters set for manual reset, the overloads are reset by pressing the reset button next to the overload contact. On magnetic starters set for automatic reset, the overloads reset automatically after the unit has cooled.

Overload relays are electromagnetic or thermal. An electromagnetic overload relay operates on the principle that, as the level of current in a circuit increases, so does the strength of the magnetic field produced by that current flow. When the level of current in the circuit reaches the preset value, the increased magnetic field opens a set of contacts.

A thermal overload relay operates on the principle that, as the level of current in a circuit increases, so does the temperature across a heating element. When the level of current in the circuit reaches the preset value, the increased temperature opens a set of contacts. The increased temperature opens the contacts

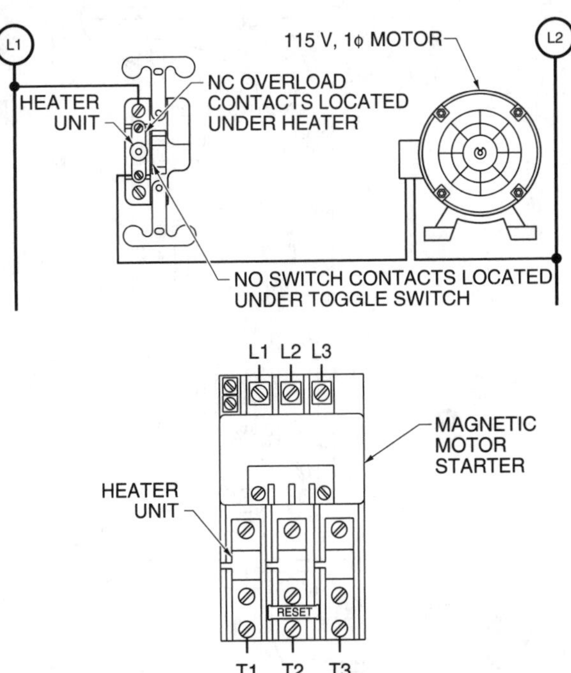

Figure 5-21. Motor starters are manually or magnetically controlled.

through a bimetallic strip or by melting an alloy that activates a mechanism that operates the contacts.

Overload relays are connected in series with the motor. The same amount of current passes through the overload relays and the motor. Overload relays are designed to operate with their contacts normally closed (NC). The contacts are connected in series with the starting coil. When excessive current flows through the overload relay element for longer than the set time, the contacts trip open. When the contacts trip open, the starting coil is de-energized, and the motor is disconnected from power. See Figure 5-22. When troubleshooting motor starters, the following steps should be taken:

1. Inspect the motor starter and overload assembly. Service or replace motor starters showing heat damage, arcing, or wear. Replace motor starters showing burning.
2. Reset overload relays if there is no visual indication of damage. Replace overload relays if there is visual indication of damage.
3. Observe the motor starter for several minutes if the motor starts after resetting the overload relays. If an overload problem still exists, the overload relays will trip open again.
4. If resetting the overload relays does not start the motor, check the voltage coming into the starter.

   If the voltage reading is 0 V, check circuit voltage ahead of the starter.

   If the voltage reading is within 10% of the voltage rating of the motor, the voltage is acceptable.

   If the voltage reading is not within 10% of the voltage reading of the motor, the voltage is not acceptable.
5. If the voltage coming into the starter is present and at the correct level, energize the starter and check the starter contacts.

   If voltage reading is acceptable, the starter contacts are good.

   If there is no voltage reading, open the starter, turn the power OFF, and replace the contacts.
6. If voltage is coming out of the starter contacts, check the overload relays.

   If the voltage reading is 0 V, turn the power OFF and replace the overload relays.

   If the voltage reading is acceptable and the motor is not operating, the problem is downstream from the starter.

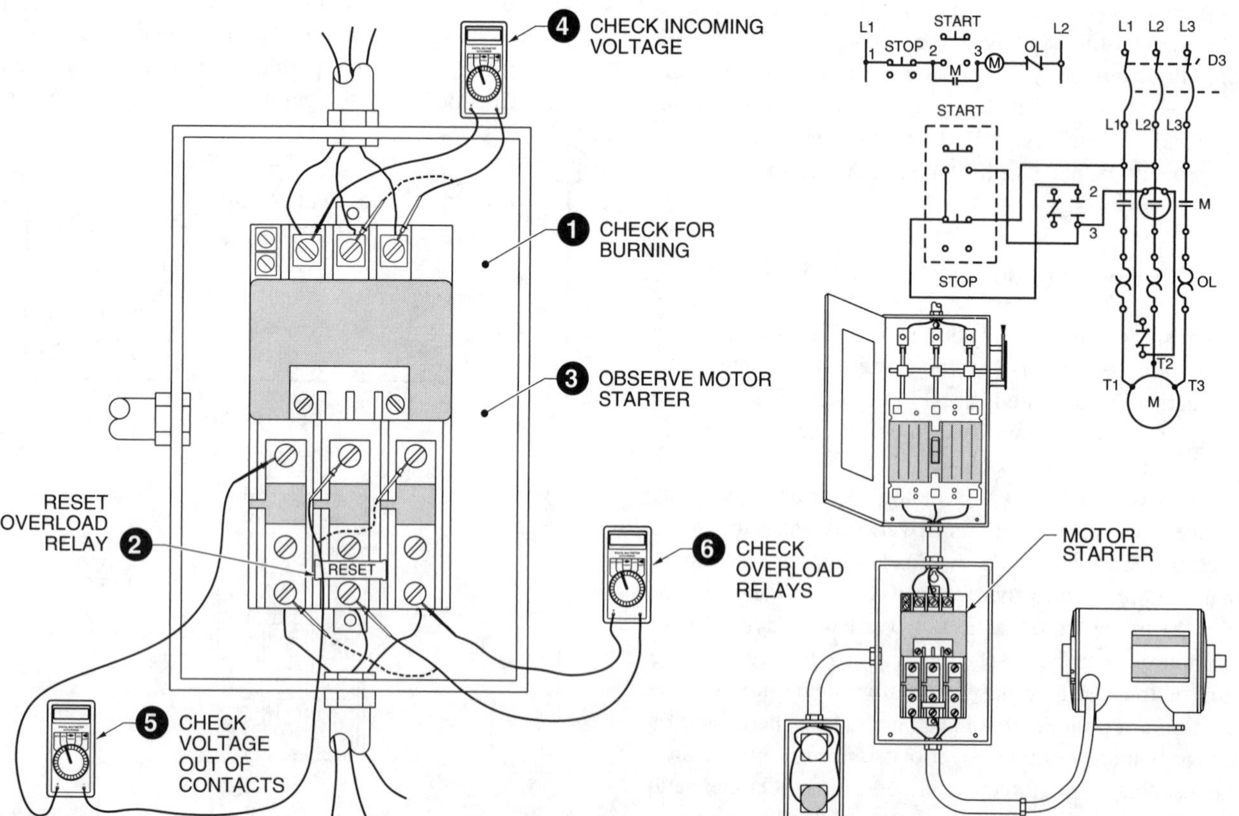

Figure 5-22. Check for heat damage, circuit voltage, and voltage through overloads when troubleshooting motor starters.

chapter 5

MOTOR PROTECTION

APPLICATIONS

START STOP 1 2 3 M OL

Application — Determining Locked Rotor Current

Apparent LRC

Locked rotor current (LRC) is the highest level of inrush current, which occurs the moment a motor is turned ON. The code letter on the motor nameplate is used to determine locked rotor current in kVA per horsepower. See LRC/Code Letters. *Apparent LRC* is the locked rotor current of a motor without considering power factor or efficiency. The apparent LRC of a 1ϕ motor is calculated from the code letter by applying the formula:

$$LRC = \frac{1000 \times HP \times kVA/HP}{V}$$

where

LRC = locked rotor current (A)
1000 = multiplier for kilo
HP = horsepower
kVA/HP = kilovolt amps per horsepower
V = volts

LRC/CODE LETTERS	
Code Letter	kVA per HP W/ Locked Rotor
A	0–3.14
B	3.15–3.54
C	3.55–3.99
D	4.0–4.49
E	4.5–4.99
F	5.0–5.59
G	5.6–6.29
H	6.3–7.09
J	7.1–7.99
K	8.0–8.99
L	9.0–9.99
M	10.0–11.19
N	11.2–12.49
P	12.5–13.99
R	14.0–15.99
S	16.0–17.99
T	18.0–19.99
U	20.0–22.39
V	22.4 and up

Example: Finding Apparent LRC — 1ϕ Motor

A 2 HP, 115 V, 1ϕ motor has a code letter J. Find the motor's apparent LRC.

$$LRC = \frac{1000 \times HP \times kVA/HP}{V}$$

$$LRC = \frac{1000 \times 2 \times 7.99}{115}$$

$$LRC = \frac{15,980}{115}$$

$$LRC = \mathbf{138.96\ A}$$

Example: Finding Apparent LRC — 3ϕ Motor

To calculate apparent LRC of a 3ϕ motor, apply the formula:

$$LRC = \frac{1000 \times HP \times kVA/HP}{V \times \sqrt{3}}$$

A 5 HP, 230 V, 3ϕ motor has a code letter M. Find the motor's apparent LRC.

$$LRC = \frac{1000 \times HP \times kVA/HP}{V \times \sqrt{3}}$$

$$LRC = \frac{1000 \times 5 \times 11.19}{398}$$

$$LRC = \frac{55,950}{398}$$

$$LRC = \mathbf{140.58\ A}$$

True LRC

In a pure resistive load, voltage and current are in phase. When voltage and current are in phase, they pass their zero points simultaneously and all power delivered to a load is used. *True LRC* is locked rotor current of a motor with the power factor and efficiency considered.

TYPICAL MOTOR POWER FACTORS

HP	Speed (rpm)	Power Factor at		
		½ load	¾ load	full load
0–5	1800	.72	.82	.84
5.01–20	1800	.74	.84	.86
20.1–100	1800	.79	.86	.89
100.1–300	1800	.81	.88	.91

All motors produce some phase difference between voltage and current. The phase difference reduces the useable power at the motor. *Power factor* is the ratio of the power used by a motor to the power not used. A poor power factor increases the operating cost of a motor.

A motor's power factor depends on the size of the motor and the amount of load on the motor. Large motors have a better power factor than small motors. Motors that are fully loaded have a better power factor than partially loaded motors. See Typical Motor Power Factors.

All motors convert electrical energy to mechanical energy. Motor efficiency is a measure of how effectively a motor converts electrical energy to mechanical energy. See Typical Motor Efficiencies in Appendix. The efficiency of a motor is found by applying the formula:

$$E_{ff} = \frac{P_{out}}{P_{in}}$$

where

E_{ff} = motor efficiency (percentage)

P_{out} = output power (in watts)

P_{in} = input power (in watts)

The power lost in a motor is converted to heat that is dissipated by the motor frame. Large motors are more efficient than small motors. Motors that are fully loaded are more efficient than partially loaded motors.

To calculate true LRC of a 1ϕ motor, apply the formula:

$$LRC = \frac{1000 \times HP \times kVA/HP}{V \times PF \times E_{ff}}$$

where

LRC = locked rotor current (in amps)

1000 = multiplier for kilo

HP = horsepower

kVA/HP = kilovolt amps per horsepower

V = volts

PF = power factor

E_{ff} = motor efficiency

Example: Finding True LRC — 1ϕ Motor

A .5 HP, 115 V, 1ϕ motor with a power factor of .80 and an efficiency of .84 has a code letter F. Find the motor's true LRC.

$$LRC = \frac{1000 \times HP \times kVA/HP}{V \times PF \times E_{ff}}$$

$$LRC = \frac{1000 \times .5 \times 5.59}{115 \times .80 \times .84}$$

$$LRC = \frac{2795}{77.28}$$

LRC = **36.17 A**

To calculate true LRC of a 3φ motor, apply the formula:

$$LRC = \frac{1000 \times HP \times kVA/HP}{V \times \sqrt{3} \times PF \times E_{ff}}$$

Example: Finding True LRC — 3φ Motor

An 8 HP, 230 V, 3φ motor with a power factor of .85 and an efficiency of .86 has a code letter H. Find the motor's true LRC.

$$LRC = \frac{1000 \times HP \times kVA/HP}{V \times \sqrt{3} \times PF \times E_{ff}}$$

$$LRC = \frac{1000 \times 8 \times 7.09}{398 \times .85 \times .86}$$

$$LRC = \frac{56{,}720}{290.94}$$

LRC = **194.95 A**

Application — Sizing Motor Overcurrent Protection Devices

The size of a motor's running overcurrent protection device (OCPD) is based on the motor's code letter, FLC, and the type of OCPD used. *Motor FLC* is the current level required to produce full-load torque on the motor shaft at rated speed. Motor FLC is listed on a motor nameplate. NEC® Tables 430-147–430-150 are used to determine the motor FLC if it is not listed on the motor nameplate. The size of an OCPD is dependent on the type of OCPD used. See Overcurrent Protection Devices in Appendix. To calculate the maximum OCPD of a motor, apply the formula:

$OCPD = FLC \times R_M$

where

FLC = full-load current (from motor nameplate or NEC® Tables 430-147–430-150)

R_M = maximum rating of OCPD (from Overcurrent Protection Devices in Appendix)

Example: Sizing Motor OCPD

Determine the NTDF size for a 1φ, 15 A rated motor.

$OCPD = FLC \times R_M$

$OCPD = 15 \times 300\%$

$OCPD$ = **45 A**

Application — Selecting Overload Heaters

Manufacturers provide overload heater selections with the motor starter. The heater number is found by matching the FLC to the size of the motor starter used. For example, a #56 heater is used with a 13.9 A rated motor and a Size 1 starter. See Heater Selections in Appendix.

Motor overload heaters are sized using standard values of 115% or 125% of the motor's FLC. When using manufacturer overload heater selections, the manufacturer usually has factored in the percentage above FLC. If the manufacturer has not factored in the percentage above FLC, a standard value of 115% or 125% of the motor's FLC is used to select an overload heater. If the motor is not marked, 115% is used. The overload heater current rating is found by applying the formula:

overload heater current rating = $FLC \times 1.15$ or *overload heater current rating* = $FLC \times 1.25$

Application — Ambient Temperature Compensation with Overloads

Thermal overloads are heat sensing devices that provide a means of monitoring the current drawn by a motor. Thermal overloads trip when the heat generated by motor windings approaches a harmful level. Because thermal overloads are temperature dependent, ambient temperature must be accounted for in applications where the ambient temperature varies above or below the standard rating temperature of 104°F. If the ambient temperature of the motor is different than that of the overloads, the overloads can cause nuisance tripping or motor burnout.

For example, if nontemperature-compensated overloads are used for a well pump motor that is at a different temperature than the surface-mounted overloads, the overloads are adjusted for the difference in temperature. Graphs show temperature adjustments for different ambient temperatures. See Heater Ambient Temperature Correction.

To find the overload trip current using an ambient temperature correction, apply the procedure:

1. Determine ambient temperature.

2. Find the rated current (%) for the ambient temperature on the graph.

3. Multiply the full-load current (from motor nameplate) by the rated current.

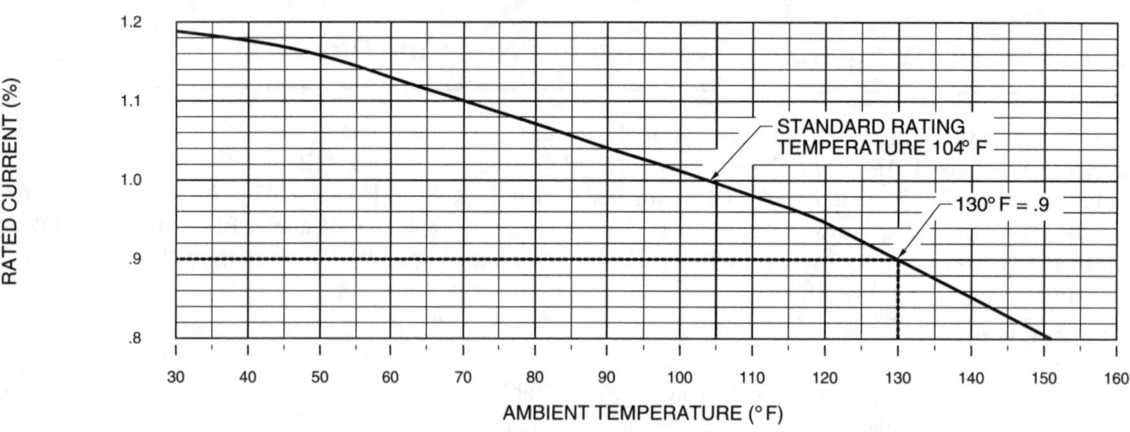

HEATER AMBIENT TEMPERATURE CORRECTION

Example: Finding Overload Trip Current

A motor has a full-load current of 25 A. The ambient temperature is 130°F. Find the overload trip current.

1. Determine ambient temperature.
Ambient temperature is 130°F.

2. Find the rated current (%) for the ambient temperature on the graph.
At 130°F, the rated current is .9 (from graph).

3. Multiply the full-load current (from motor nameplate) by the rated current.
Overload trip current = 25 × .9
Overload trip current = **22.5 A**

Application — Determining Overload Trip Time

Overload heaters are designed to trip and disconnect the motor from the power lines when an overload condition occurs. The overload trip time depends on the extent of the overload. The higher the overload, the faster the trip time. Manufacturers provide heater overload trip characteristics. See Heater Trip Characteristics in Appendix.

For example, if a motor is overloaded 600%, the overloads trip in 15.5 seconds (from Heater Trip Characteristics).

Name ______________________ Date ______________

MOTOR PROTECTION

chapter 5
ACTIVITIES

Activity 5-1. Determining Locked Rotor Current

Determine apparent and true LRC for each motor. Each motor has Code Letter F.

1. A 3 HP, 115 V, 1φ, 34 A rated motor with an efficiency of 88.5% is ½ loaded.

__________ **A.** Apparent LRC = ________ A.

__________ **B.** True LRC = ________ A.

2. A 10 HP, 230 V, 3φ, 50 A rated motor with an efficiency of 90.3% is ½ loaded.

__________ **A.** Apparent LRC = ________ A.

__________ **B.** True LRC = ________ A.

3. A 200 HP, 460 V, 3φ, 240 A rated motor with an efficiency of 96.1% is ¾ loaded.

__________ **A.** Apparent LRC = ________ A.

__________ **B.** True LRC = ________ A.

4. A 75 HP, 230 V, 3φ, 192 A rated motor with an efficiency of 95.0% is fully loaded.

__________ **A.** Apparent LRC = ________ A.

__________ **B.** True LRC = ________ A.

5. A 3 HP, 115 V, 1φ, 34 A rated motor with an efficiency of 80.8% is ½ loaded.

__________ **A.** Apparent LRC = ________ A.

__________ **B.** True LRC = ________ A.

6. A 10 HP, 230 V, 3φ, 50 A rated motor with an efficiency of 85.0% is ½ loaded.

__________ **A.** Apparent LRC = ________ A.

__________ **B.** True LRC = ________ A.

7. A 200 HP, 460 V, 3φ, 240 A rated motor with an efficiency of 92.3% is ¾ loaded.

__________ **A.** Apparent LRC = ________ A.

__________ **B.** True LRC = ________ A.

8. A 75 HP, 230 V, 3φ, 192 A rated motor with an efficiency of 90.8% is fully loaded.

__________ **A.** Apparent LRC = ________ A.

__________ **B.** True LRC = ________ A.

Activity 5-2. Sizing Motor Overcurrent Protection Devices

Determine the size of the OCPD for each motor using the motor nameplates. Select a standard size fuse or breaker for the application. *Note:* Select the next smallest size of standard fuse or breaker.

TYPE	AC	PHASE	1
HP	3/4	CYCLE	60
VOLTS	115	AMPS	13.8
RPM	1725	TEMP RISE	40° C
SF	1.0	CODE	D
TIME RATE	CONT		

FULL-VOLTAGE START

1. An NTDF is used as the OCPD.

_________ **A.** The calculated OCPD size is ________ A.

_________ **B.** The standard size fuse used for the application is ________ A.

_________ **C.** The required number of fuses is ________ .

TYPE	AC	PHASE	3
HP	60	CYCLE	60
VOLTS	460	AMPS	77
RPM	1150	TEMP RISE	50° C
SF	1.25	CODE	H
TIME RATE	CONT		

RESISTOR START

2. An NTDF is used as the OCPD.

_________ **A.** The calculated OCPD size is ________ A.

_________ **B.** The standard size fuse used for the application is ________ A.

_________ **C.** The required number of fuses is ________ .

TYPE	DC COMPOUND		
HP	3	CYCLE	60
VOLTS	240	AMPS	12.2
RPM	1725	TEMP RISE	40° C
SF	1.15		
TIME RATE	CONT		

FULL-VOLTAGE START

3. A TDF is used as the OCPD.

_________ **A.** The calculated OCPD size is ________ A.

_________ **B.** The standard size fuse used for the application is ________ A.

_________ **C.** The required number of fuses is ________ .

TYPE	AC	PHASE	3
HP	75	CYCLE	60
VOLTS	460	AMPS	96
RPM	900	TEMP RISE	50° C
SF	1.35	CODE	F
TIME RATE	CONT		

RESISTOR START

4. A TDF is used as the OCPD.

_________ **A.** The calculated OCPD size is ________ A.

_________ **B.** The standard size fuse used for the application is ________ A.

_________ **C.** The required number of fuses is ________ .

5. An ITCB is used as the OCPD.

_____________ **A.** The calculated OCPD size is _________ A.

_____________ **B.** The standard size breaker used for the application is _________ A.

_____________ **C.** The required number of breaker units is _________ .

TYPE	AC	PHASE	1
HP	7.5	CYCLE	60
VOLTS	230	AMPS	40
RPM	1725	TEMP RISE	40° C
SF	1	CODE	D
TIME RATE	CONT		

FULL-VOLTAGE START

6. An ITCB is used as the OCPD.

_____________ **A.** The calculated OCPD size is _________ A.

_____________ **B.** The standard size breaker used for the application is _________ A.

_____________ **C.** The required number of breaker units is _________ .

TYPE	AC	PHASE	3
HP	25	CYCLE	60
VOLTS	460	AMPS	34
RPM	1150	TEMP RISE	45° C
SF	1.25	CODE	G
TIME RATE	CONT		

RESISTOR START

7. An ITB is used as the OCPD.

_____________ **A.** The calculated OCPD size is _________ A.

_____________ **B.** The standard size breaker used for the application is _________ A.

_____________ **C.** The required number of breaker units is _________ .

TYPE	AC	PHASE	1
HP	$\frac{1}{4}$	CYCLE	60
VOLTS	115	AMPS	6
RPM	900	TEMP RISE	40° C
SF	1.35	CODE	F
TIME RATE	CONT		

FULL-VOLTAGE START

8. An ITB is used as the OCPD.

_____________ **A.** The calculated OCPD size is _________ A.

_____________ **B.** The standard size breaker used for the application is _________ A.

_____________ **C.** The required number of breaker units is _________ .

TYPE	AC	PHASE	3
HP	40	CYCLE	60
VOLTS	460	AMPS	52
RPM	1725	TEMP RISE	50° C
SF	1.25	CODE	F
TIME RATE	CONT		

RESISTOR START

Activity 5-3. Selecting Overload Heaters

Using the motor nameplates, determine the current rating of the overload heater and the heater number for each motor. *Note:* Select the next smallest standard size heater.

1. A Size 0 starter is used.

_______ **A.** The overload heater current rating is _______ A.

_______ **B.** The heater number is _______.

TYPE	AC	PHASE	1
HP	$\frac{3}{4}$	CYCLE	60
VOLTS	115	AMPS	13.8
RPM	1725	TEMP RISE	40° C
SF	1.0	CODE	D
TIME RATE	CONT		

FULL-VOLTAGE START

2. A Size 4 starter is used.

_______ **A.** The overload heater current rating is _______ A.

_______ **B.** The heater number is _______.

TYPE	AC	PHASE	3
HP	60	CYCLE	60
VOLTS	460	AMPS	77
RPM	1150	TEMP RISE	40° C
SF	1.25	CODE	H
TIME RATE	CONT		

RESISTOR START

3. A Size 1 starter is used.

_______ **A.** The overload heater current rating is _______ A.

_______ **B.** The heater number is _______.

TYPE	DC COMPOUND		
HP	3	CYCLE	60
VOLTS	240	AMPS	12.2
RPM	1725	TEMP RISE	55° C
SF	1.35		
TIME RATE	INT		

FULL-VOLTAGE START

4. A Size 4 starter is used.

_______ **A.** The overload heater current rating is _______ A.

_______ **B.** The heater number is _______.

TYPE	AC	PHASE	3
HP	75	CYCLE	60
VOLTS	460	AMPS	96
RPM	900	TEMP RISE	40° C
SF	1.15	CODE	F
TIME RATE	CONT		

RESISTOR START

5. A Size 3 starter is used.

__________ **A.** The overload heater current rating is __________ A.

__________ **B.** The heater number is __________.

TYPE	AC	PHASE	1
HP	7.5	CYCLE	60
VOLTS	230	AMPS	40
RPM	1725	TEMP RISE	40° C
SF	1.0	CODE	D
TIME RATE	CONT		

FULL-VOLTAGE START

6. A Size 3 starter is used.

__________ **A.** The overload heater current rating is __________ A.

__________ **B.** The heater number is __________.

TYPE	AC	PHASE	3
HP	25	CYCLE	60
VOLTS	460	AMPS	34
RPM	1725	TEMP RISE	50° C
SF	1.25	CODE	G
TIME RATE	CONT		

RESISTOR START

7. A Size 0 starter is used.

__________ **A.** The overload heater current rating is __________ A.

__________ **B.** The heater number is __________.

TYPE	AC	PHASE	1
HP	$\frac{1}{4}$	CYCLE	60
VOLTS	115	AMPS	5.8
RPM	900	TEMP RISE	40° C
SF	1.15	CODE	F
TIME RATE	INT		

FULL-VOLTAGE START

8. A Size 3 starter is used.

__________ **A.** The overload heater current rating is __________ A.

__________ **B.** The heater number is __________.

TYPE	AC	PHASE	3
HP	40	CYCLE	60
VOLTS	460	AMPS	52
RPM	1150	TEMP RISE	45° C
SF	1.35	CODE	F
TIME RATE	CONT		

RESISTOR START

Activity 5-4. Ambient Temperature Compensation with Overloads

State the overload trip current for each motor installation using Heater Ambient Temperature Correction in Appendix. *Note:* Each motor is installed in a standard enclosure.

_______ **1.** A 27 A rated motor is installed in a 35°F ambient temperature location. The overload trip current is _______ A.

_______ **2.** A 52 A rated motor is installed in a 100°F ambient temperature location. The overload trip current is _______ A.

_______ **3.** A 180 A rated motor is installed in a 95°F ambient temperature location. The overload trip current is _______ A.

_______ **4.** A 477 A rated motor is installed in a 115°F ambient temperature location. The overload trip current is _______ A.

_______ **5.** A .5 A rated motor is installed in a 150°F ambient temperature location. The overload trip current is _______ A.

Activity 5-5. Determining Overload Trip Time

Answer the questions using Heater Trip Characteristics in Appendix.

_______ **1.** If a motor draws 1000% of rated current, the overloads trip in _______ seconds.

_______ **2.** If a motor draws 800% of rated current, the overloads trip in _______ seconds.

_______ **3.** If a motor draws 600% of rated current, the overloads trip in _______ seconds.

_______ **4.** If a motor draws 450% of rated current, the overloads trip in _______ seconds.

_______ **5.** If a motor draws 75% of rated current, the overloads trip in _______ seconds.

Activity 5-6. Troubleshooting Motor Starting Protection Devices

1. Connect Meter 1 so that the meter checks the incoming supply voltage from L1 and L2. Connect Meter 2 so that the meter checks the incoming supply voltage from L2 and L3.

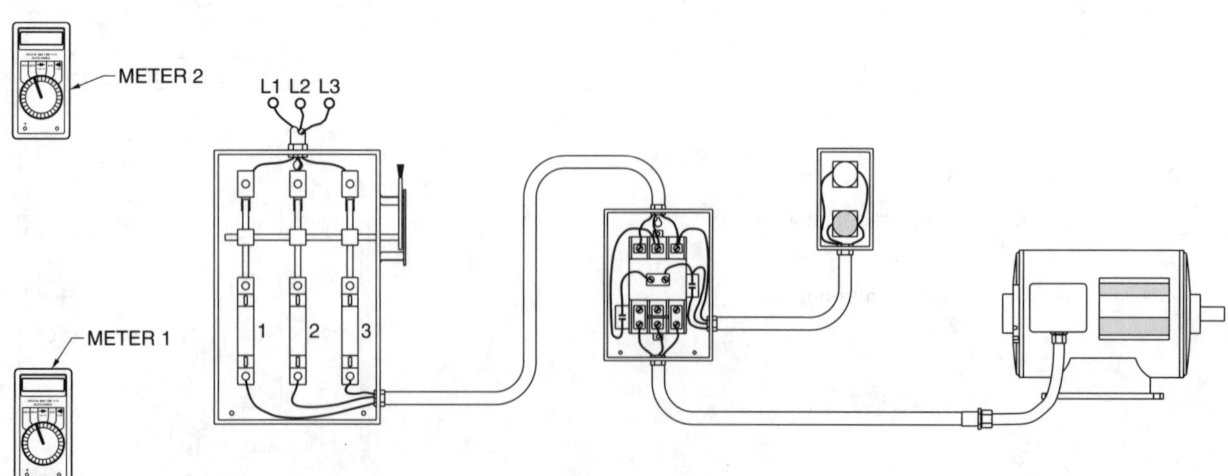

2. Connect Meter 1 so that the meter checks Fuse 1 and the output of the disconnect switch. Connect Meter 2 so that the meter checks Fuse 2 and the output of the disconnect switch.

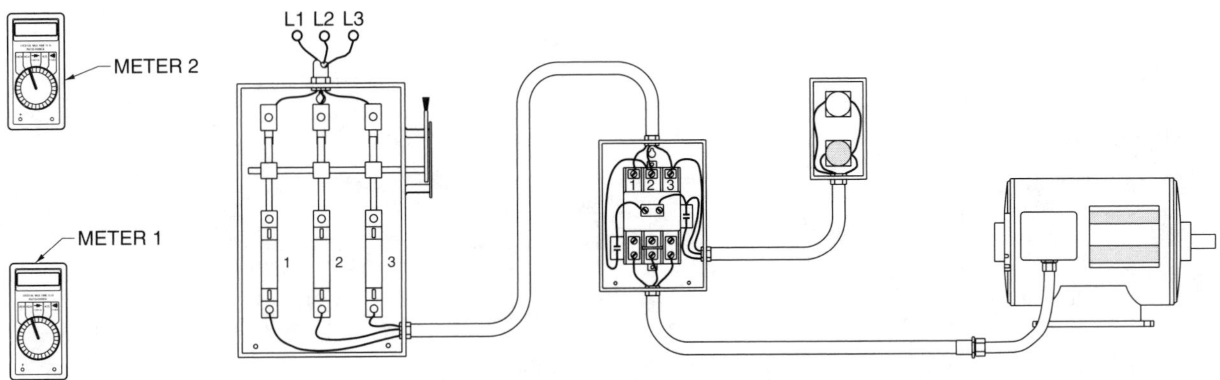

Activity 5-7. Motor Starter Troubleshooting

1. Connect Meter 1 so that the meter checks the incoming supply voltage from L1 and L3. Connect Meter 2 so that the meter checks the incoming supply voltage from L2 and L3.

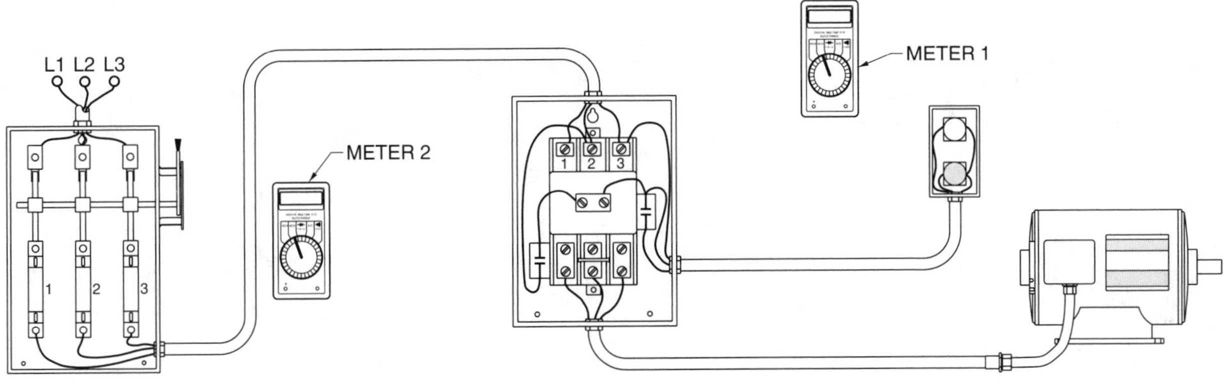

2. Connect Meter 1 so that the meter checks Starting Contact 1. Connect Meter 2 so that the meter checks Starting Contact 2.

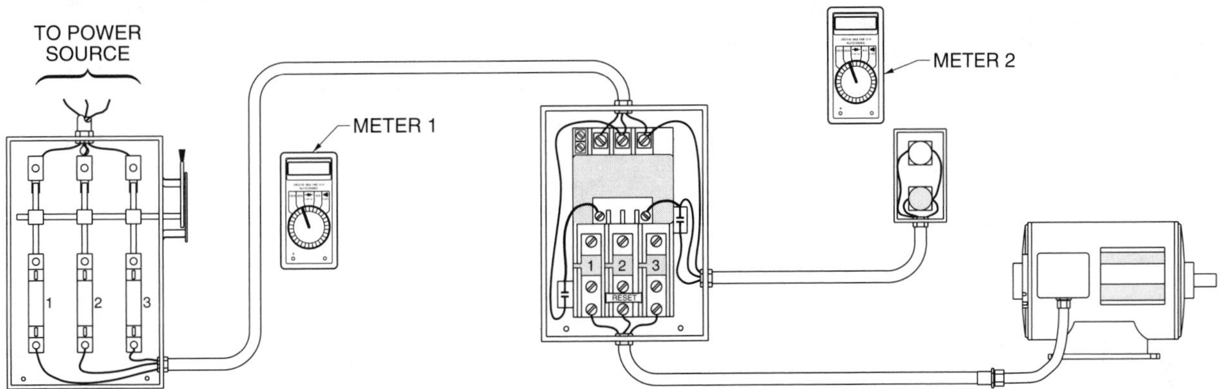

3. Connect Meter 1 so that the meter checks Heater 1 and Starting Contact 1. Connect Meter 2 so that the meter checks Heater 2 and Starting Contact 2.

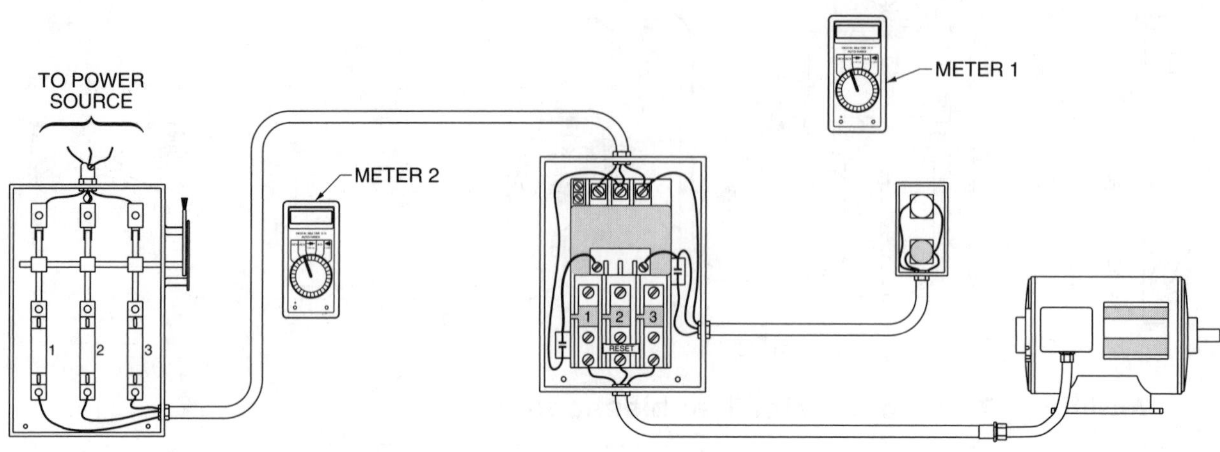

4. Connect Meter 1 so that the meter checks the voltage of L1 and L2 at the motor. Connect Meter 2 so that the meter checks the voltage of L2 and L3 at the motor.

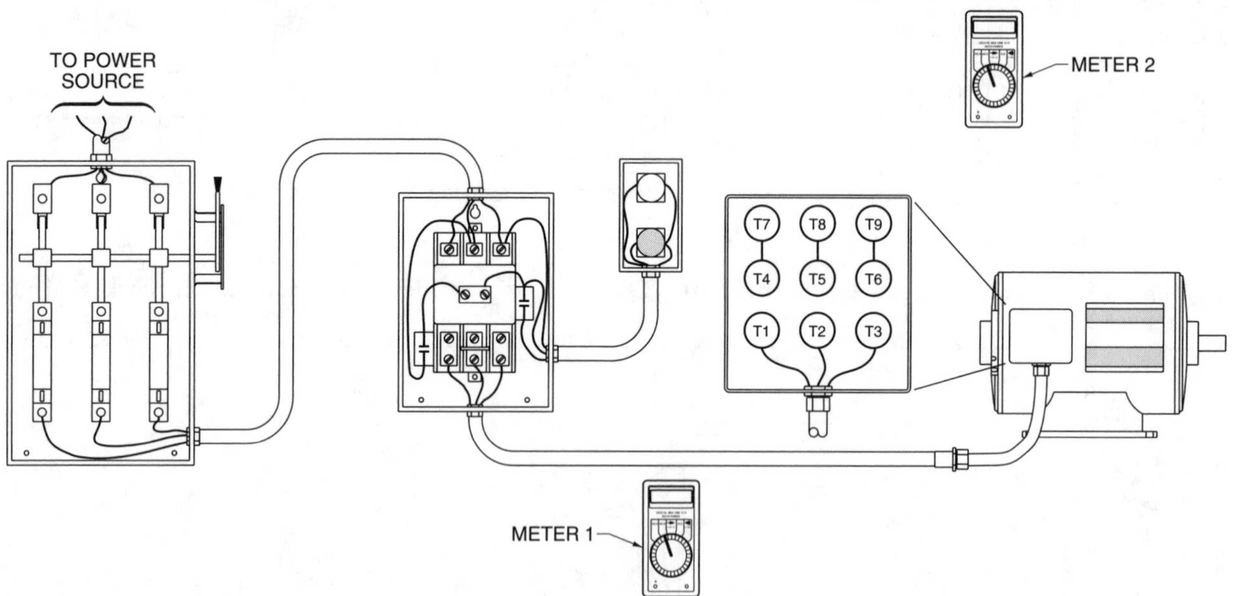

Activity 5-8. Control Circuit Modification

1. Redraw the line diagram so that the fan motor is automatically controlled by a temperature switch.

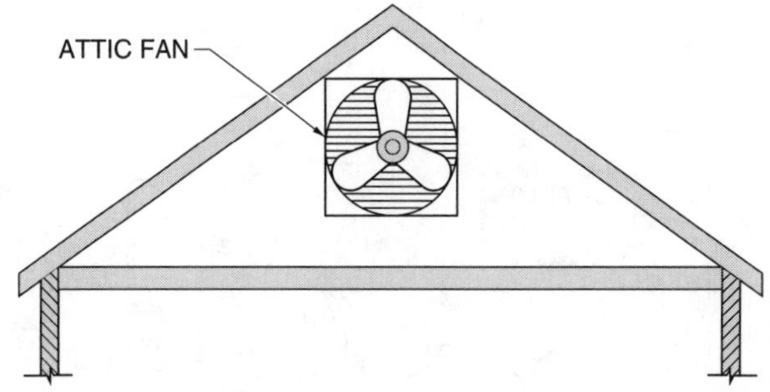

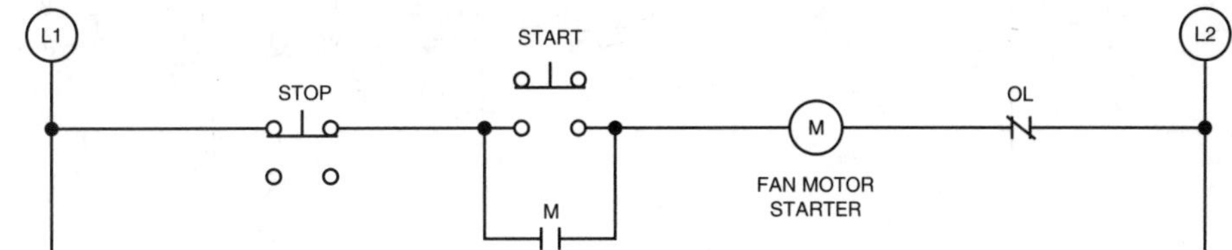

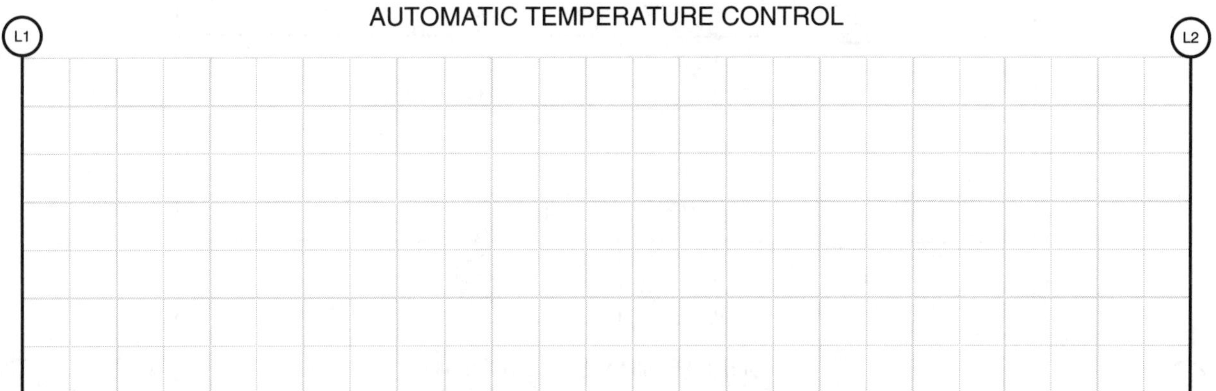

2. Redraw the line diagram so that the temperature switch controls a control relay coil. Draw the circuit so that the relay contacts control the fan motor. Include a red pilot light to indicate that the motor is ON and a green pilot light to indicate that the motor is OFF. Use the relay contacts to control the pilot lights.

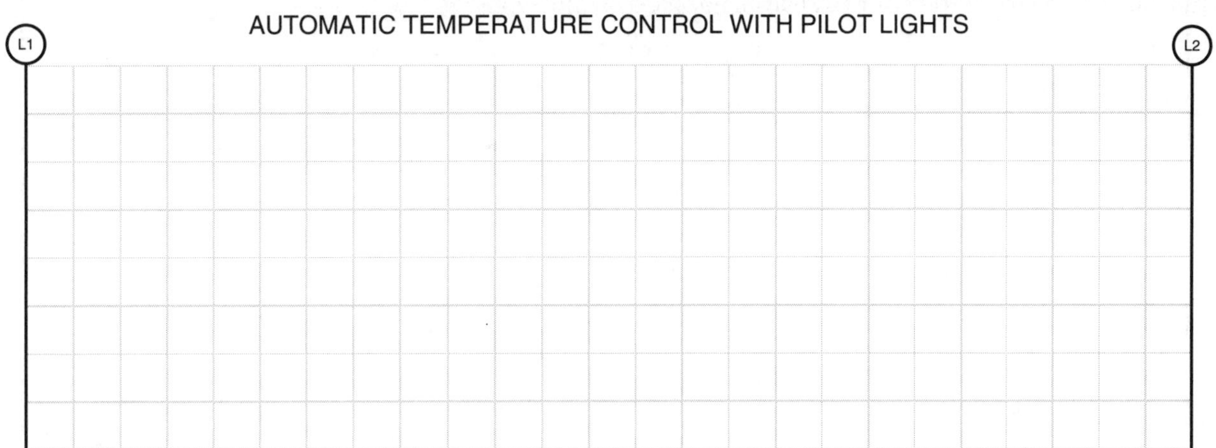

3. Redraw the line diagram so that Pump Motor 2 cannot be started unless Pump Motor 1 is ON. Include an emergency stop pushbutton and an override pushbutton for Motor 2. The emergency stop pushbutton turns OFF both motors and the override pushbutton turns ON Pump Motor 2 even if Pump Motor 1 is OFF.

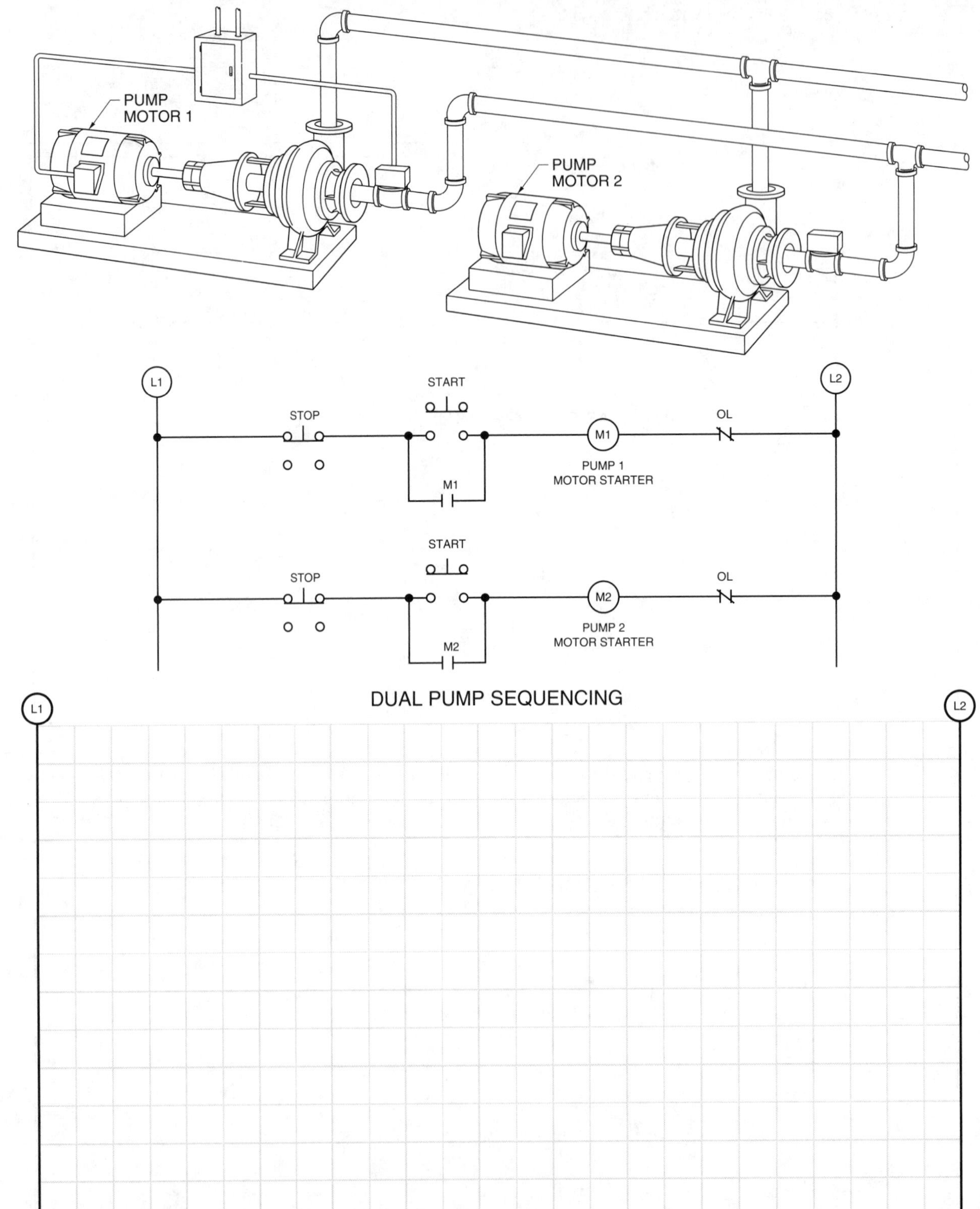

Name ______________________ Date ____________

chapter 5

MOTOR PROTECTION

TRADE TEST

Completion

______ **1.** A(n) ________ occurs when the load connected to the motor exceeds the full-load torque rating of the motor.

______ **2.** The motor ________ is a safety margin for motor overloads.

______ **3.** ________ temperature is the temperature of the air around a piece of equipment.

______ **4.** Motor starters are manually or ________ controlled.

______ **5.** The $\sqrt{3}$ equals ________.

______ **6.** ________ LRC is the locked rotor current with power factor and efficiency considered.

______ **7.** A(n) ________ with appropriate scales is used to test fuses.

______ **8.** A(n) ________ circuit occurs when current does not follow its designed path.

______ **9.** Overloads are usually between one and ________ times the normal current level of the circuit.

______ **10.** The LRC is usually from four to ________ times the motor's FLC.

______ **11.** The common ambient temperature limit for motors is ________°C.

______ **12.** The most commonly used ________ are fuses and circuit breakers.

______ **13.** A typical combination starter combines the parts of a(n) ________ with the motor starter.

______ **14.** ________ panels house the fuses or CB's that protect general lighting and appliance circuits.

______ **15.** The three positions of a CB are ON, ________, or OFF.

True-False

T F **1.** An overcurrent may be an overload current or a short-circuit current.

T F **2.** Fault current may return to ground or the power source.

T F **3.** OCPD's must be set below the LRC of a motor to prevent the OCPD from opening the circuit to the motor.

T F **4.** A combination starter with CB's is less expensive than a combination starter with fuses.

T F **5.** A hot power line is any power line that is not grounded.

T F **6.** Overloads occur in most circuits at modest levels.

T F **7.** High inrush current increases as the motor accelerates.

T F **8.** The motor starter also protects a motor while it is running.

T F **9.** One heater is required to protect 3ϕ motors.

T F **10.** An overload in a motor decreases the temperature of the windings.

Multiple Choice

________ **1.** Current equals ________.

A. voltage times resistance
B. voltage divided by resistance
C. resistance divided by voltage
D. resistance plus voltage

________ **2.** A 10 HP motor with a service factor of 1.25 can safely develop ________ HP.

A. 8.75
B. 10
C. 11.25
D. 12.5

________ **3.** NEC® Table 430-150 deals with ________ motors.

A. DC, ¼–200 HP
B. 1φ, AC, ⅙–10 HP
C. 2φ, AC, ½–200 HP
D. 3φ, AC, ½–200 HP

________ **4.** Temperature rise is the difference between the ambient temperature and the ________ temperature of a running motor.

A. listed maximum
B. winding
C. both A and B
D. neither A nor B

________ **5.** NEC® 240-6 lists standard ampere ratings of fuses and fixed-trip CB's at every 5A from 15A through ________A.

A. 25
B. 45
C. 75
D. 95

________ **6.** The incoming voltage to a CB should be within ________% of the voltage rating of the motor.

A. 10
B. 15
C. 25
D. 40

________ **7.** The running overload protection device is set to open the circuit at ________% or ________% of the motor's FLC.

A. 100; 115
B. 115; 125
C. 125; 140
D. 140; 150

________ **8.** A thermal overload relay operates on the principle that as the level of current increases, the temperature across the heating element ________.

A. is not affected
B. fluctuates
C. increases
D. decreases

________ **9.** The function of an OCPD is to protect the ________ from a short circuit or ground.

A. branch-circuit conductors
B. control equipment
C. motor
D. A, B, and C

________ **10.** Generally, safety switches used to protect motors shall be ________.

A. located within sight of the motor controller
B. installed to disconnect the motor and motor control circuit
C. both A and B
D. neither A nor B

Problems

For problems 1 through 6, indicate the OCPD's required per the motor nameplates.

A = 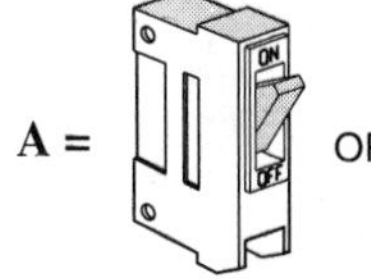 OR

B = 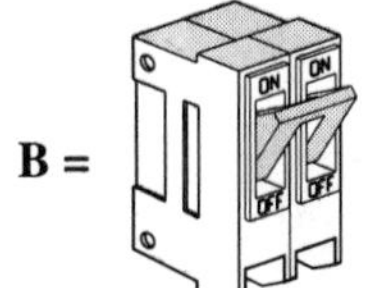 OR 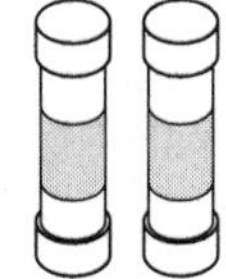

C = OR

______ **1.**

TYPE	AC	PHASE	1
HP	$\frac{3}{4}$	CYCLE	60
VOLTS	115	AMPS	13.8
RPM	1150	TEMP RISE	40° C
SF	1.25	CODE	F
TIME RATE	INT		

______ **2.**

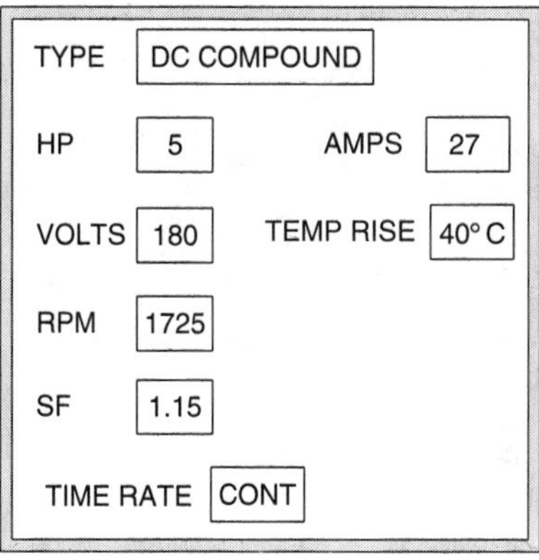

TYPE	DC COMPOUND		
HP	5	AMPS	27
VOLTS	180	TEMP RISE	40° C
RPM	1725		
SF	1.15		
TIME RATE	CONT		

______ **3.**

TYPE	AC	PHASE	3
HP	200	CYCLE	60
VOLTS	460	AMPS	240
RPM	1725	TEMP RISE	40° C
SF	1.25	CODE	F
TIME RATE	CONT		

______ **4.**

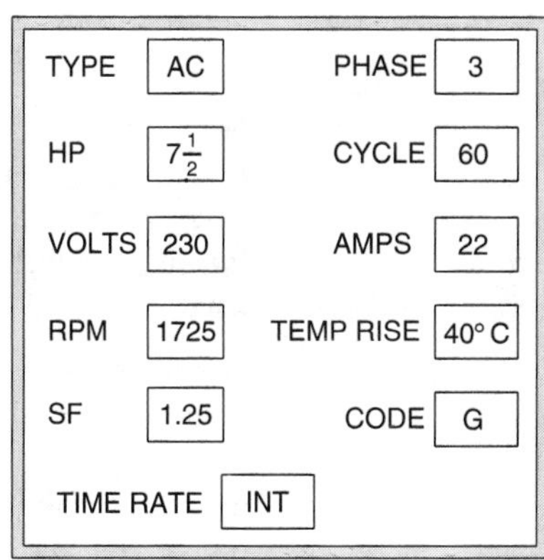

TYPE	AC	PHASE	3
HP	$7\frac{1}{2}$	CYCLE	60
VOLTS	230	AMPS	22
RPM	1725	TEMP RISE	40° C
SF	1.25	CODE	G
TIME RATE	INT		

______ **5.**

TYPE	AC	PHASE	1
HP	$1\frac{1}{2}$	CYCLE	60
VOLTS	230	AMPS	10
RPM	1725	TEMP RISE	40° C
SF	1.35	CODE	D
TIME RATE	CONT		

______ **6.**

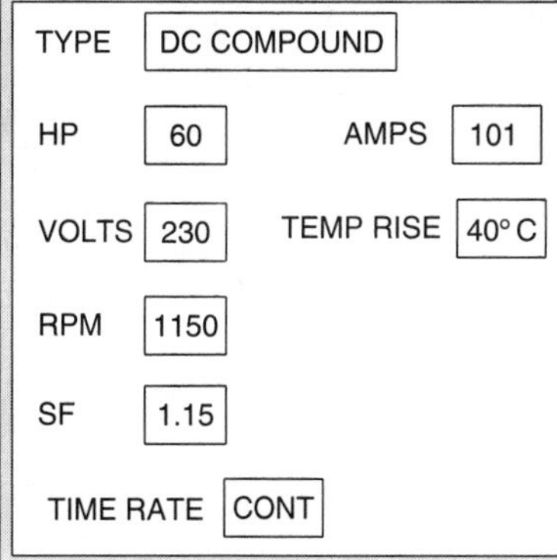

TYPE	DC COMPOUND		
HP	60	AMPS	101
VOLTS	230	TEMP RISE	40° C
RPM	1150		
SF	1.15		
TIME RATE	CONT		

For problems 7 through 14, give the test points to which the voltmeter should be connected.

_______ **7.** A voltmeter is connected to test points _______ and _______ when testing L1 and L2 for incoming power to the fuse panel.

_______ **8.** A voltmeter is connected to test points 5 and _______ or _______ when testing to determine if Fuse 1 is good.

_______ **9.** A voltmeter is connected to test points _______ and _______ when testing to determine if Fuses 2 and 3 are good.

_______ **10.** A voltmeter is connected to test points 1 or 2 and test point _______ to test the enclosure for grounding.

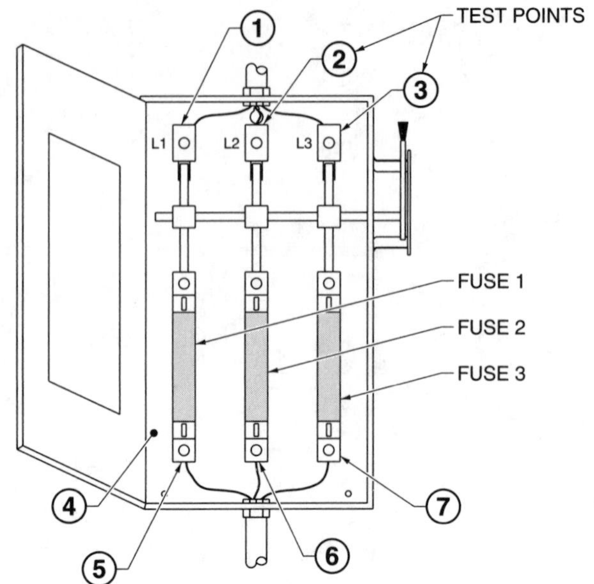

FUSE PANEL

_______ **11.** A voltmeter is connected to test points _______ and _______ when testing L2 and L3 for incoming power to the breaker panel.

_______ **12.** A voltmeter is connected to test points _______, _______, and _______ when testing to determine if the CB is delivering output voltage.

_______ **13.** A voltmeter is connected to test points 9 and _______ when testing to determine if the disconnect switch is delivering output voltage on L3.

_______ **14.** A voltmeter is connected to test points 8 or 9 and test point _______ to test the enclosure for grounding.

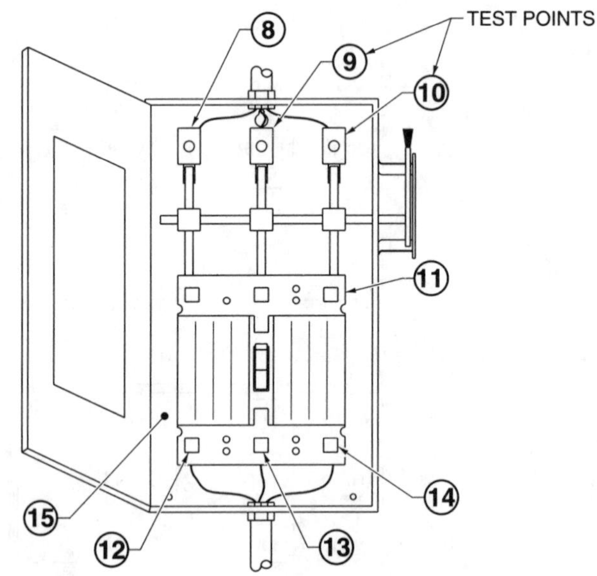

BREAKER PANEL

For problems 15 through 18, refer to the 50 HP motor.

__________ **15.** When using a TDF, the calculated OCPD size for the motor is _________ A.

__________ **16.** The calculated current value used to select the OCPD for the motor is _________ A.

__________ **17.** The overload heater current rating is _________ A.

__________ **18.** If a Size 3 starter is used, the heater number is _________.

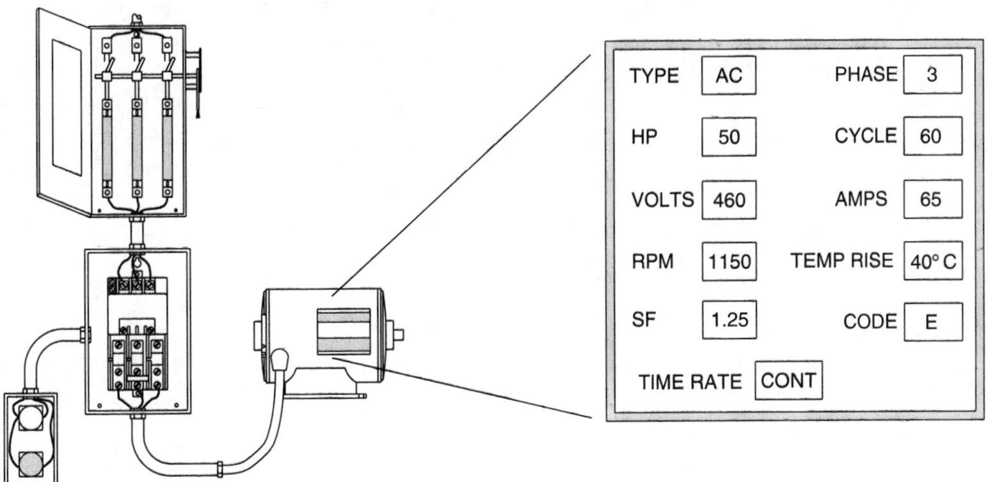

For problems 19 through 22, refer to the 20 HP motor.

__________ **19.** When using an ITB, the calculated OCPD size for the motor is _________ A.

__________ **20.** The calculated current value used to select the OCPD for the motor is _________ A.

__________ **21.** The overload heater current rating is _________ A.

__________ **22.** If a Size 3 starter is used, the heater number is _________.

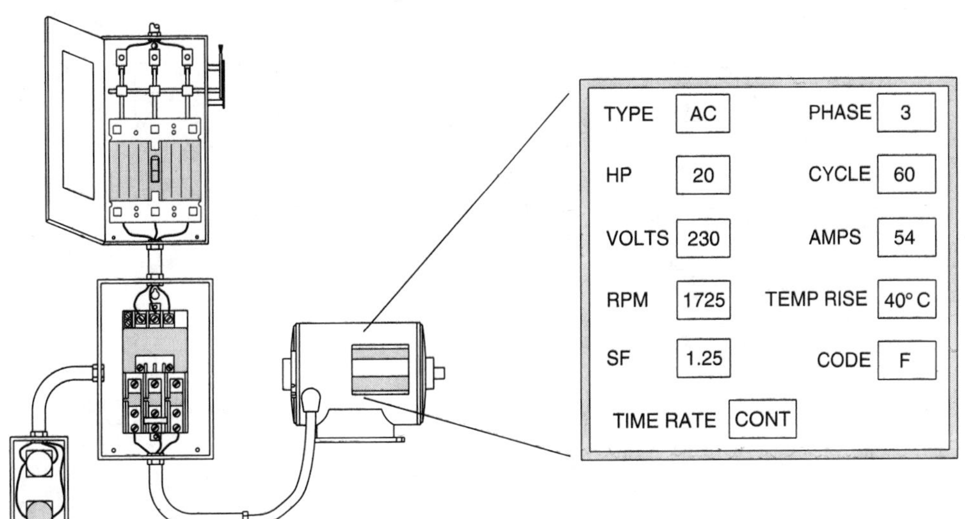

For problems 23 through 26, use LRC/Code Letters to determine the maximum apparent LRC of the motors.

LRC/CODE LETTERS	
Code Letter	**kVA per HP W/ Locked Rotor**
A	0–3.14
B	3.15–3.54
C	3.55–3.99
D	4.0–4.49
E	4.5–4.99
F	5.0–5.59
G	5.6–6.29
H	6.3–7.09
J	7.1–7.99
K	8.0–8.99
L	9.0–9.99
M	10.0–11.19
N	11.2–12.49
P	12.5–13.99
R	14.0–15.99
S	16.0–17.99
T	18.0–19.99
U	20.0–22.39
V	22.4 and up

__________ **23.** The maximum apparent LRC is ________ A.

TYPE	AC	PHASE	1
HP	7.5	CYCLE	60
VOLTS	230	AMPS	40
RPM	1725	TEMP RISE	40° C
SF	1.25	CODE	D
TIME RATE	CONT		

__________ **24.** The maximum apparent LRC is ________ A.

TYPE	AC	PHASE	3
HP	25	CYCLE	60
VOLTS	460	AMPS	34
RPM	1725	TEMP RISE	40° C
SF	1.25	CODE	G
TIME RATE	CONT		

__________ **25.** The maximum apparent LRC is ________ A.

TYPE	AC	PHASE	1
HP	$\frac{1}{4}$	CYCLE	60
VOLTS	115	AMPS	5.8
RPM	1725	TEMP RISE	40° C
SF	1.25	CODE	F
TIME RATE	CONT		

__________ **26.** The maximum apparent LRC is ________ A.

TYPE	AC	PHASE	3
HP	40	CYCLE	60
VOLTS	230	AMPS	104
RPM	1725	TEMP RISE	40° C
SF	1.35	CODE	H
TIME RATE	CONT		

For problems 27 through 32, state the permissible temperature rise for Motors 1, 2, and 3. The listed temperature rise for each motor is 40°C.

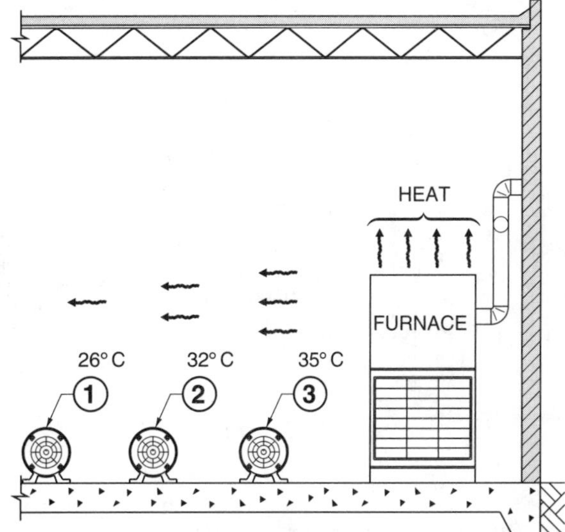

_______________ **27.** The permissible temperature rise for Motor 1 is _________ °C.

_______________ **28.** The permissible temperature rise for Motor 1 is _________ °F.

_______________ **29.** The permissible temperature rise for Motor 2 is _________ °C.

_______________ **30.** The permissible temperature rise for Motor 2 is _________ °F.

_______________ **31.** The permissible temperature rise for Motor 3 is _________ °C.

_______________ **32.** The permissible temperature rise for Motor 3 is _________ °F.

33. Connect Meter 1 so that the meter checks the power coming into the circuit. Connect Meter 2 so that the meter checks Fuses 1 and 2.

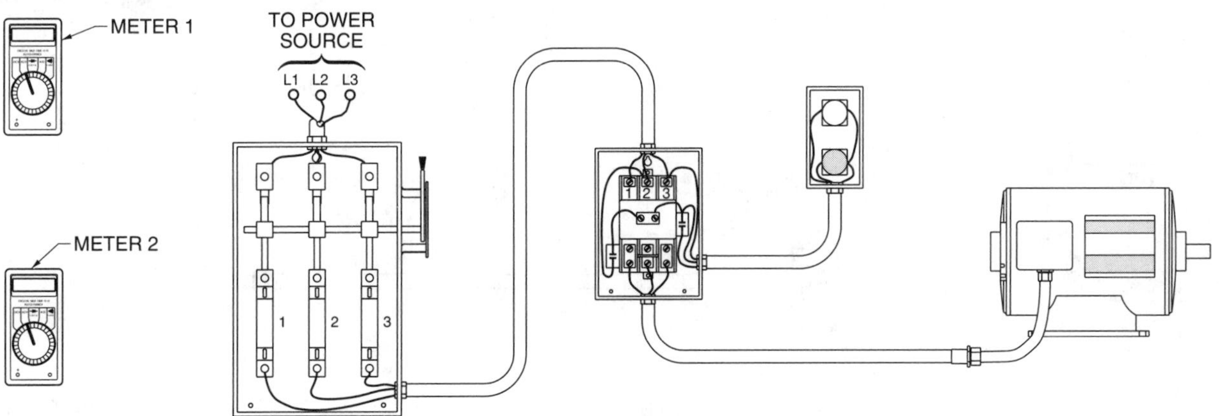

34. Connect Meter 1 so that the meter checks the incoming supply voltage to the motor starter. Connect Meter 2 so that the meter checks the power out of the motor starter.

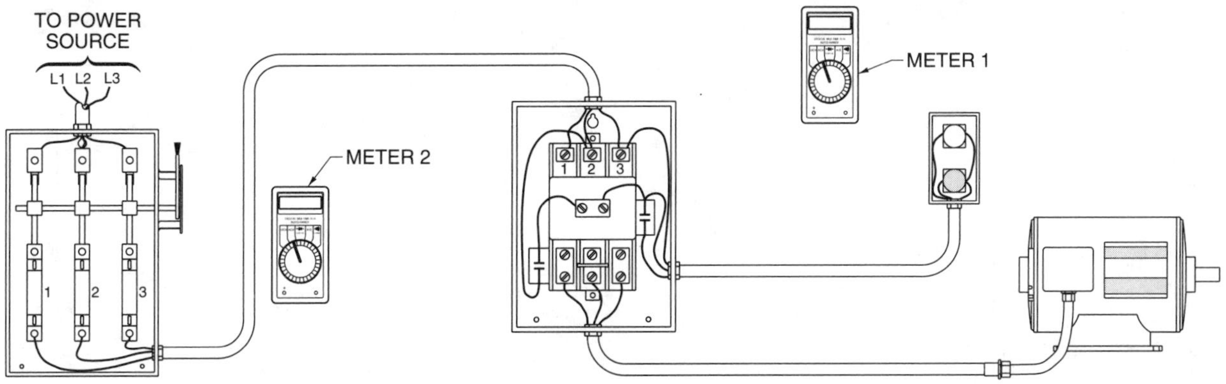

35. Connect Meter 1 so that the meter checks for a voltage drop across the heater monitoring L1. Connect Meter 2 so that the meter checks Starting Contact 3 and the heater monitoring L3.

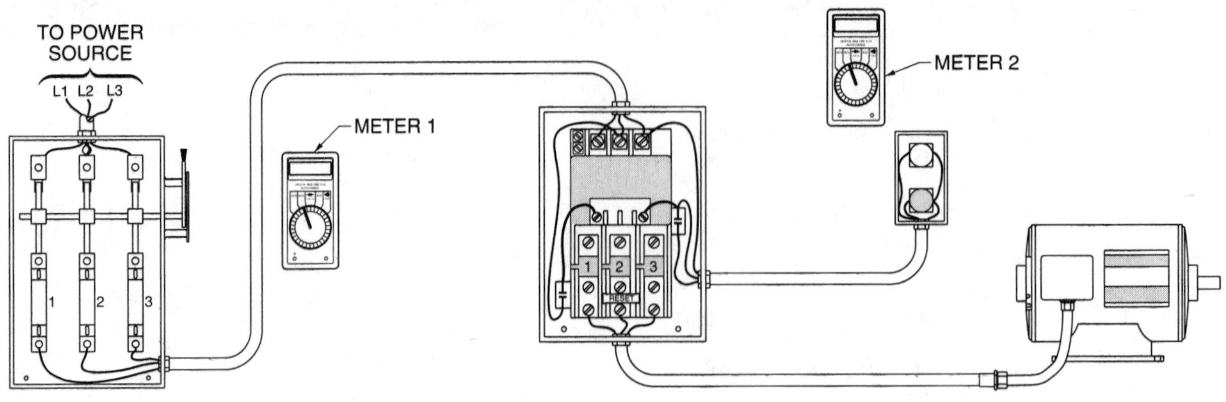

36. Connect Meter 1 so that the meter checks the voltage of L1 and L2 out of the circuit breaker. Connect Meter 2 so that the meter checks the voltage at the motor.

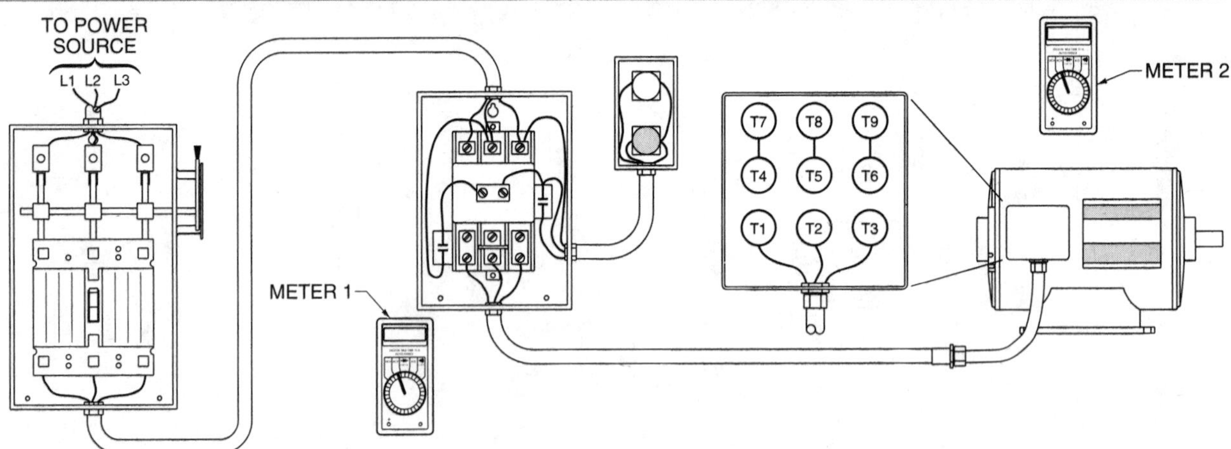

37. Connect Meter 1 so that the meter checks the power coming into the circuit and to the motor for L1. Connect Meter 2 so that the meter checks the voltage through Starter Contact 1.

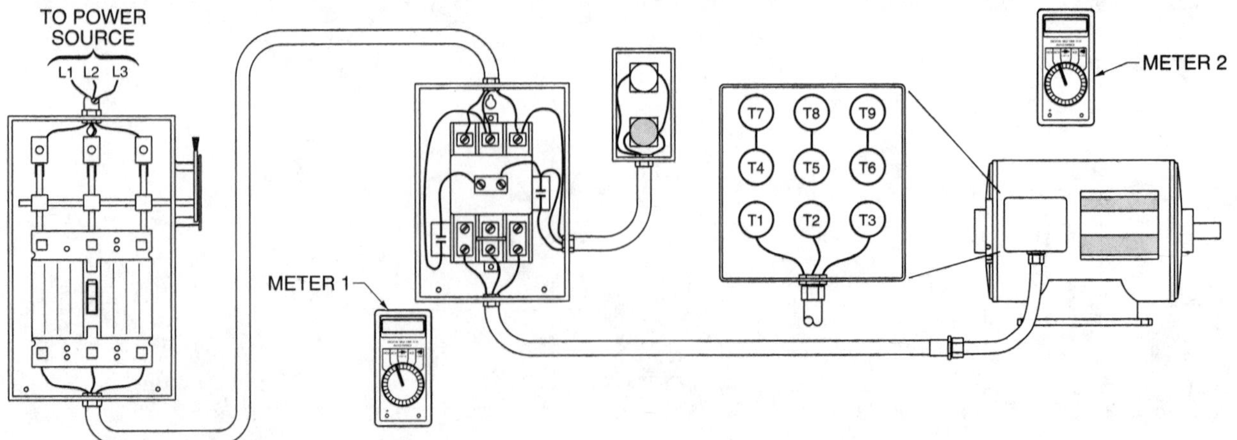

chapter 6

MOTOR FAILURE

Motor failure occurs for a variety of reasons. More motors fail due to overheating than any other reason. A motor properly selected and sized to the load to be driven is a very reliable machine and can provide long service when properly maintained and serviced.

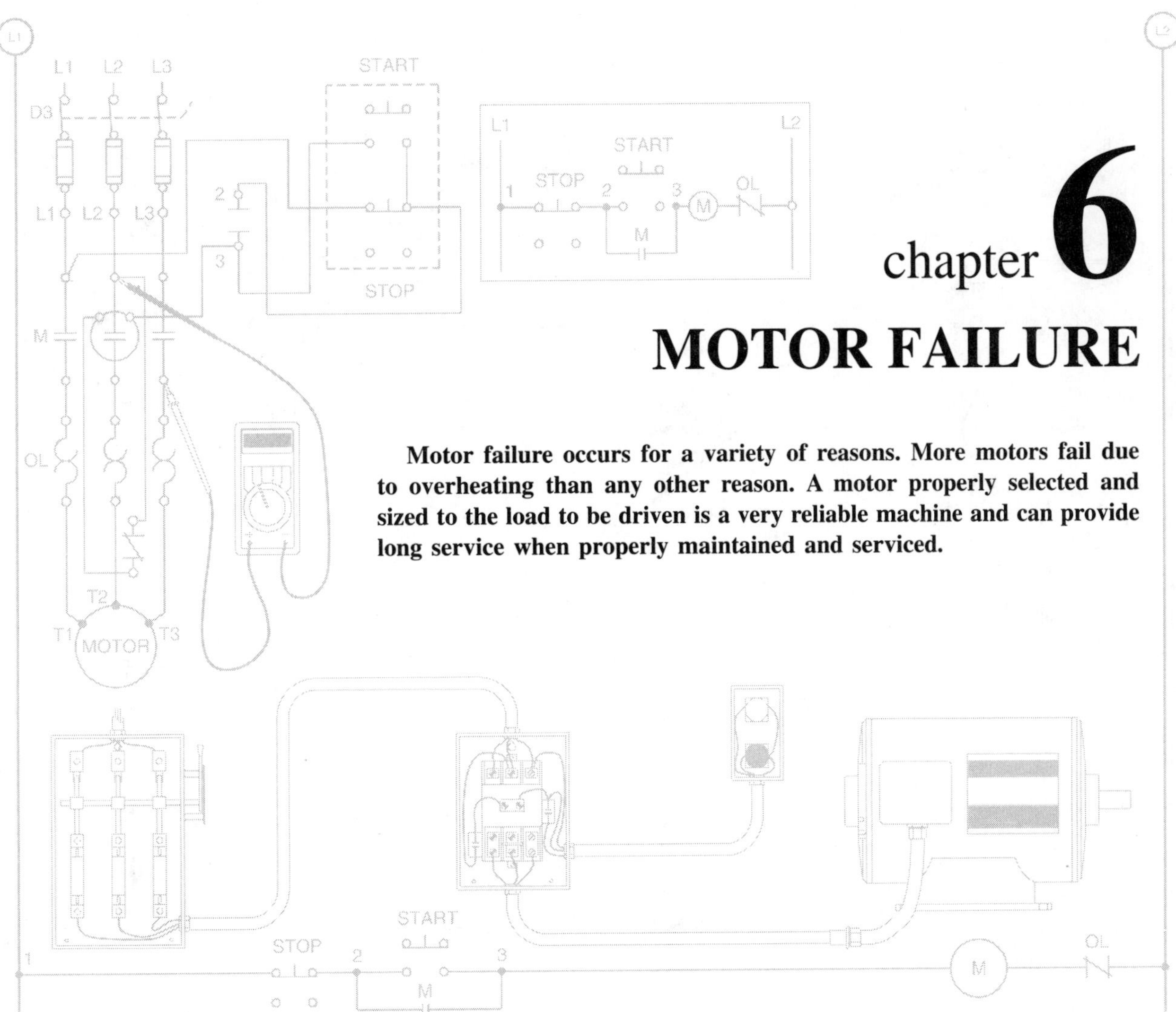

MOTOR FAILURE

Electric motors are highly effective and reliable drivers of machinery and other loads. However, motors do fail at times. Motor manufacturers have found that overloading is the number one cause of motor failure. Thirty percent of all motors fail due to overloading. A motor is overloaded anytime it is required to deliver more power than it was designed for. The most common type of overloading is placing too large of a load on the motor.

Other types of motor failure include single phasing, contaminants, old age, bearing failure, rotor failure, etc. Miscellaneous motor failures account for 9% of all motor failures. Misaligned sheaves is a common cause of miscellaneous motor failures. See Figure 6-1.

Motor failure occurs due to overheating, phase unbalance, voltage unbalance, single phasing, surge voltages, poor ventilation, lack of lubrication, overloads, over cycling, excessive moisture, improper belt tension, misalignment and vibration, loose connections, pests, etc. Incorrect motor selection for the application and motor defects can also cause motor failure.

Heat

Excessive heat is a major cause of motor failure and a sign of other motor problems. Heat destroys motor insulation. When motor insulation is destroyed, the windings are shorted, and the motor is no longer functional.

As the heat in a motor increases beyond the temperature rating of the insulation, the life of the insulation is shortened. The higher the temperature, the sooner the insulation will fail. The temperature rating of motor insulation is listed as the insulation class. The insulation class is given in celsius (centigrade) (°C) and/or Fahrenheit (°F). The motor nameplate typically lists the insulation class of the motor. See Figure 6-2.

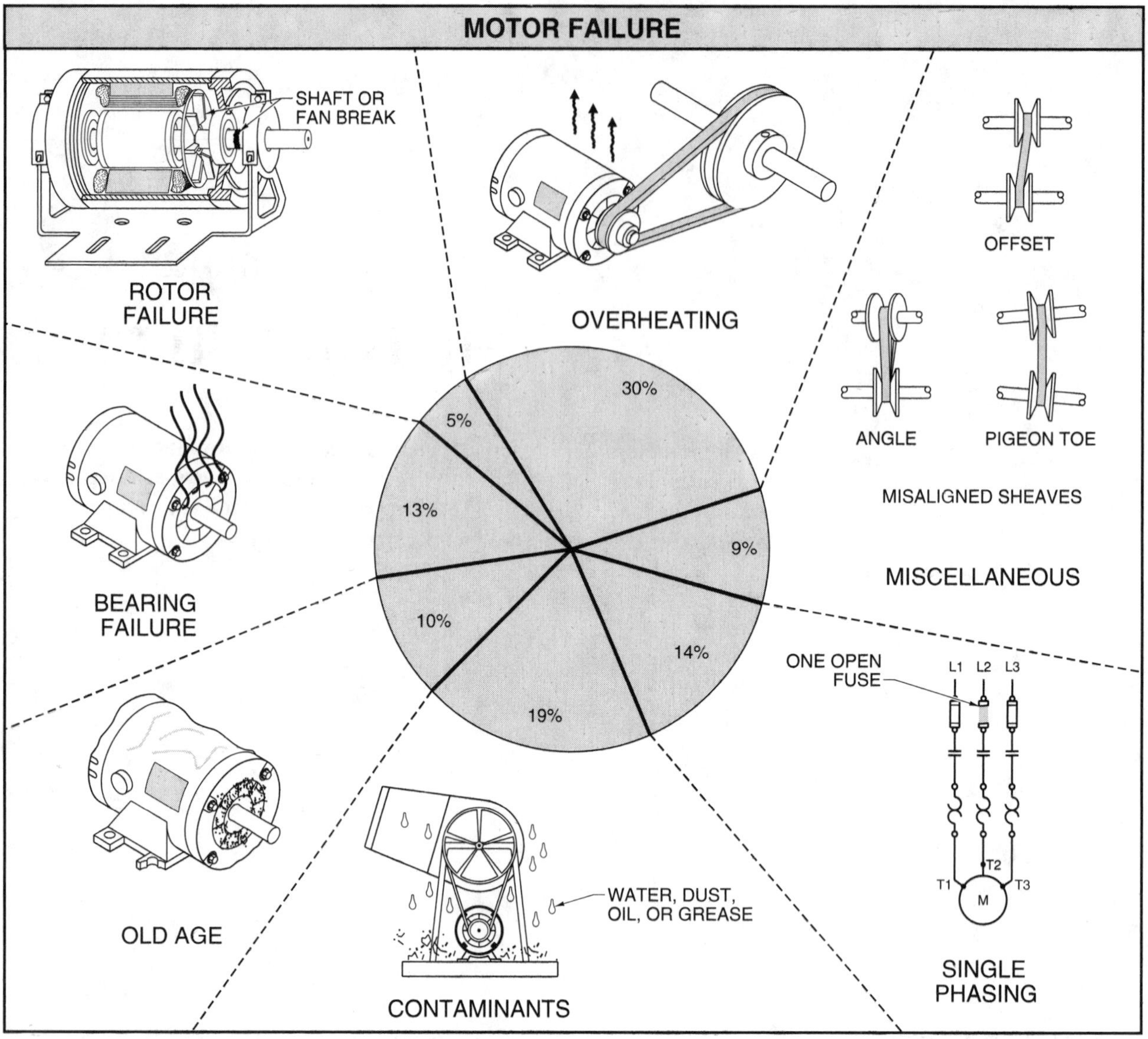

Figure 6-1. Overloading is the leading cause of motor failure.

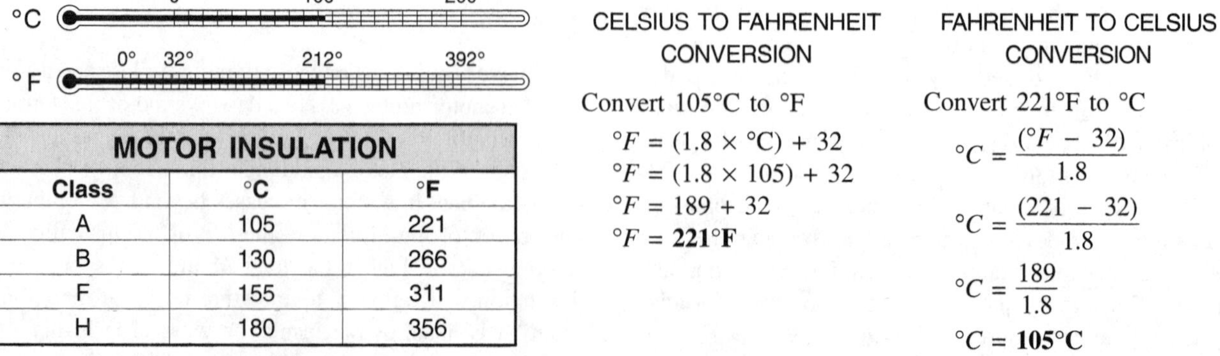

MOTOR INSULATION		
Class	**°C**	**°F**
A	105	221
B	130	266
F	155	311
H	180	356

CELSIUS TO FAHRENHEIT CONVERSION

Convert 105°C to °F

$$°F = (1.8 \times °C) + 32$$
$$°F = (1.8 \times 105) + 32$$
$$°F = 189 + 32$$
$$°F = \mathbf{221°F}$$

FAHRENHEIT TO CELSIUS CONVERSION

Convert 221°F to °C

$$°C = \frac{(°F - 32)}{1.8}$$
$$°C = \frac{(221 - 32)}{1.8}$$
$$°C = \frac{189}{1.8}$$
$$°C = \mathbf{105°C}$$

Figure 6-2. The insulation class of motors is given in °C and/or °F.

Heat buildup in a motor can be caused by several factors, such as:

- Incorrect motor type or size for the application
- Improper cooling, usually from dirt buildup
- Excessive load, usually from improper use
- Excessive friction, usually from misalignment or vibration
- Electrical problems, typically voltage unbalance, phase loss, or surge voltages

Phase Unbalance

Phase unbalance is the unbalance that occurs when lines are out-of-phase. Phase unbalance of a 3ϕ power system occurs when 1ϕ loads are applied, causing one or two of the lines to carry more or less of the load. The loads of 3ϕ power systems are balanced by the electricians during installation. However, as additional 1ϕ loads are added to the system, an unbalance begins to occur. This unbalance causes the 3ϕ lines to move out-of-phase, and are consequently no longer 120 electrical degrees apart.

Phase unbalance causes 3ϕ motors to run at temperatures higher than their listed ratings. The greater the phase unbalance, the greater the temperature rise. These high temperatures produce insulation breakdown and other related problems. See Figure 6-3.

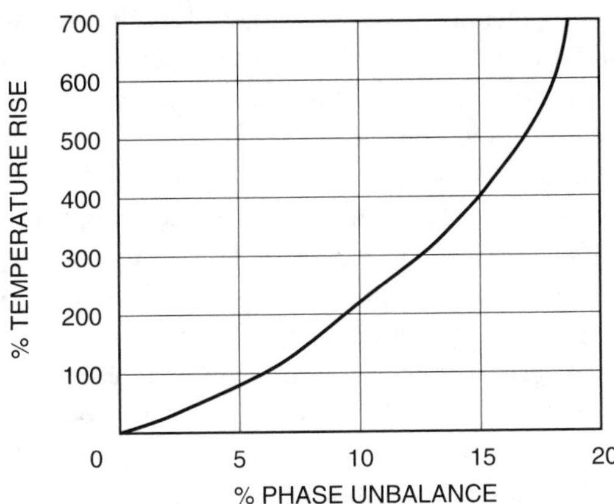

Figure 6-3. As phase unbalance increases, the motor temperature increases.

Three-phase motors cannot deliver their rated horsepower when a system is unbalanced. For example, a phase unbalance of 3% can cause a motor to work at only 90% of its rated power, requiring the motor to be derated for any given application. See Figure 6-4.

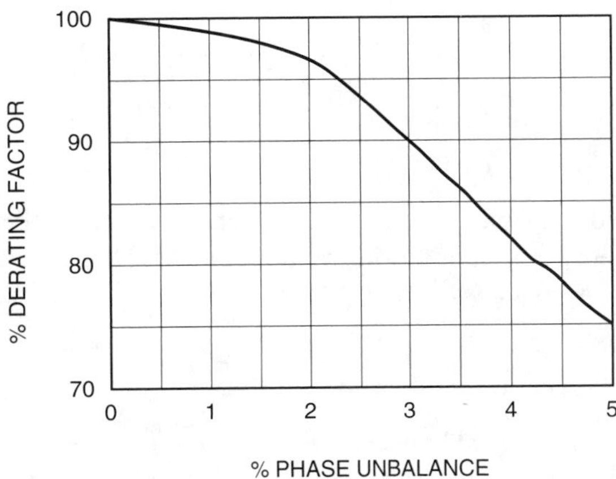

Figure 6-4. Motors with a phase unbalance require derating.

Voltage Unbalance

Voltage unbalance is the unbalance that occurs when the voltages at the motor terminals are not equal. This voltage unbalance can range from as little as a few millivolts to full voltage loss on one line. If the voltage is not balanced, one winding will overheat, causing thermal deterioration of that winding. The voltage unbalance results in a current unbalance.

Voltage should be checked for voltage unbalance periodically and during all service calls. Whenever more than 2% voltage unbalance is measured, always:

- Check the surrounding power system for excessive loads connected to one line.
- Notify the power company.
- If the voltage unbalance cannot be corrected, adjust the load or motor rating by reducing the load on the motor or oversizing the motor.

Voltage unbalance is measured by taking a voltage reading between each of the incoming power lines. The readings are taken from L1 to L2, L1 to L3, and L2 to L3. The voltages are (1.) added together and (2.) divided by 3 to find the voltage average (3.). The voltage deviation is found by subtracting the voltage average from the voltage with the largest deviation. Using these figures, voltage unbalance is found by (4.) applying the formula:

$$V_u = \frac{V_d}{V_a} \times 100$$

where

V_u = voltage unbalance (%)
V_d = voltage deviation (V)
V_a = voltage average (V)
100 = constant

For example, what is the voltage unbalance of a feeder system with the following voltage readings?

L1 to L2 = 442 V
L1 to L3 = 474 V
L2 to L3 = 456 V

Step 1. Add voltages.

$$442\text{ V} + 474\text{ V} + 456\text{ V} = 1372\text{ V}$$

Step 2. Find V_a.

$$V_a = \frac{V}{3}$$

$$V_a = \frac{1372\text{ V}}{3} = 457\text{ V}$$

Step 3. Find V_d.

$$V_d = V - V_a$$

$$V_d = 474 - 457$$

$$V_d = 17\text{ V}$$

Step 4. Find V_u.

$$V_u = \frac{V_d}{V_a} \times 100$$

$$V_u = \frac{17}{457} \times 100 = \mathbf{3.72\%}$$

The troubleshooter can observe the blackening of one or two of the stator windings, which occurs when a motor has failed due to voltage unbalance. See Figure 6-5. If a large unbalance exists on one winding, it is darkened the most. If the unbalance is divided over two windings, they are both darkened. The winding that had the largest unbalance is the darkest.

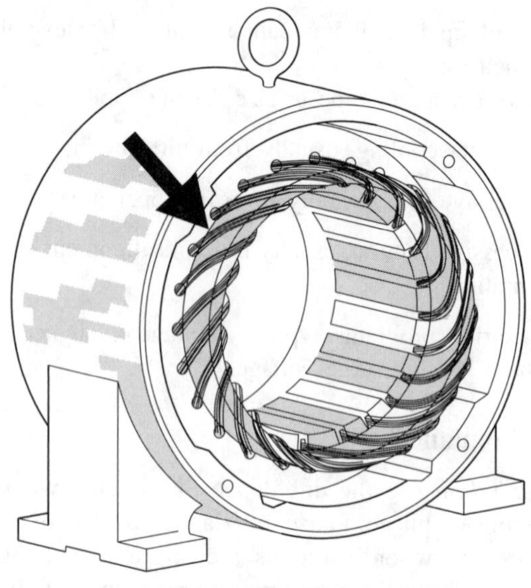

Figure 6-5. Voltage unbalance causes blackening of one or two of the stator windings.

Single Phasing

When one of the 3ϕ lines leading to a 3ϕ motor no longer delivers voltage to the motor, the motor will single phase. *Single phasing* is the operation of a motor designed to operate on three phases operating on only two phases because one phase is lost. It is the maximum condition of voltage unbalance. Single phasing occurs when one phase opens on either the primary or secondary power distribution system. This can happen when one fuse blows, there is a mechanical failure within the switching equipment, or lightning takes out one of the lines.

A 3ϕ phase motor running on 2ϕ will continue to run in most applications. Therefore, single phasing can go undetected on most systems for a long enough time to burn out a motor. When single phasing, the motor will draw all its current from two of the lines.

Measuring the voltage at the motor will not usually detect a single phasing condition. The open winding in the motor generates a voltage almost equal to the phase voltage that was lost. In this case, the open winding acts as the secondary of a transformer, and the two windings connected to power act as the primary.

Single phasing can be reduced by using the proper size dual-element fuse and by using the correct heater sizes. In motor circuits, or other types of circuits in which a single phasing condition can not be allowed to exist for even a short period of time, an electronic phase-loss monitor is used to detect phase loss. When a phase loss is detected, the monitor activates a set of contacts to drop out the starter coil.

The troubleshooter can observe the blackening of one of the 3ϕ windings, which occurs when a motor has failed due to single phasing. See Figure 6-6. The coil that experienced the voltage loss will indicate obvious and fast damage, which includes the blowing out of the insulation on the one winding.

Single phasing is distinguished from voltage unbalance by the severity of the damage. Voltage unbalance causes less blackening (but usually over more coils) and little or no distortion. Single phasing causes severe burning and distortion to one phase coil.

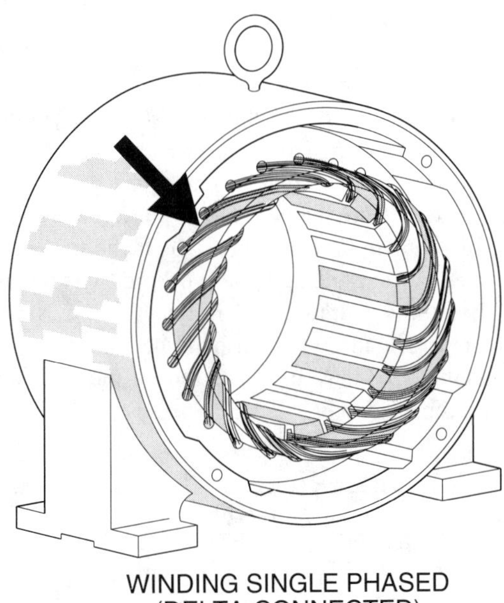

Figure 6-6. Single phasing causes severe burning and distortion to one phase coil.

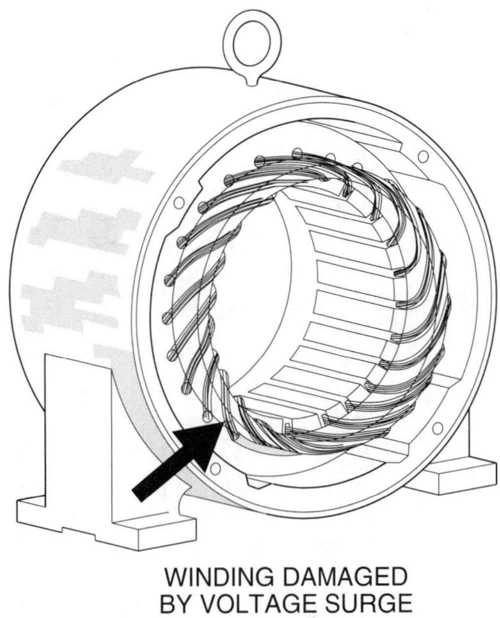

Figure 6-7. Voltage surge causes burning and opening of the first few turns of the windings.

Surge Voltages

Surge voltage is any higher-than-normal voltage that temporarily exists on one or more of the power lines. Lightning is a major cause of large surge voltages. A lightning surge on the power lines comes from a direct hit or induced voltage. The lightning energy moves in both directions on the power lines, much like a rapidly moving wave. This traveling surge causes a large voltage rise in an extremely short period of time. The large voltage is impressed on the first few turns of the motor windings, destroying the insulation and burning out the motor.

The troubleshooter can observe the burning and opening of the first few turns of the windings, which occur when a motor has failed due to a voltage surge. See Figure 6-7. The rest of the windings appear normal, with little or no damage.

Lighting arresters with the proper voltage rating and connection to an excellent ground assure maximum protection. Surge protectors are also available. These are placed on the equipment or throughout the distribution system.

Voltage surges can also occur from normal switching of higher-rated power circuits. These are of much less magnitude than lightning strikes and usually do not cause any problems in motors. A surge protector should be used on circuits with computer equipment to provide protection to sensitive electronic components.

Improper Ventilation

All motors produce heat as they convert electrical energy to mechanical energy. This heat must be removed or it will destroy the motor insulation, and consequently the motor. Motors are designed with air passages that permit a free flow of air over and through the motor. This air flow removes the heat from the motor. Anything that restricts air flow through the motor causes the motor to operate at a higher temperature than it is designed for. Air flow may be restricted by the accumulation of dirt, dust, lint, grass, pests, rust, etc. If the motor becomes coated with oil from leaking seals or from over lubrication, air flow is restricted much faster. See Figure 6-8.

Overheating can also occur if the motor is placed in an enclosed area. When a motor is installed in a location that does not permit the heated air to escape, the motor will overheat due to the recirculation of the heated air. Vents can be added at the top and bottom of the enclosed area to allow a natural flow of heated air.

Overloads

An *overload* is the application of too much load to a motor. Motors attempt to drive the connected load when the power is ON. The larger the load, the more power required. All motors have a limit to the load they can drive. For example, a 5 HP, 460 V, 3ϕ motor should draw no more than 7.6 A. See NEC® Table 430-150.

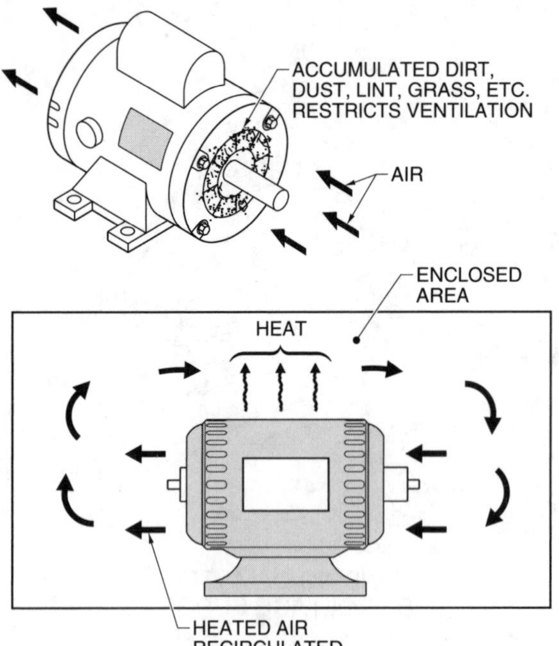

Figure 6-8. Improper ventilation causes overheating of motors.

Overloads should not harm a properly protected motor. Any overload that is present longer than the built-in time delay of the protection device will be detected and removed. Properly sized heaters in the motor starter assure that an overload is removed before any damage is done. See Figure 6-9.

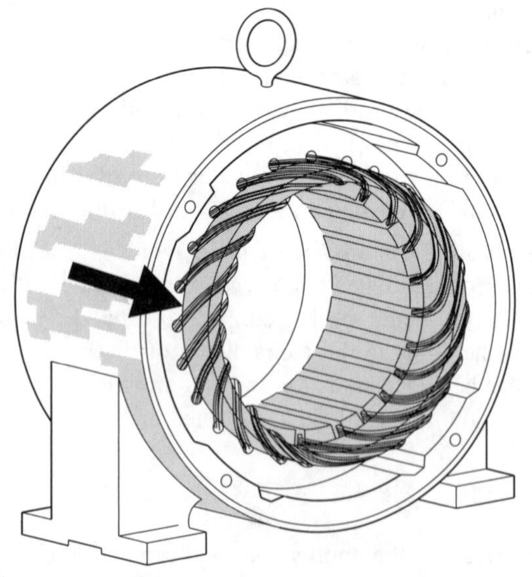

Figure 6-9. Overloading causes an even blackening of all windings.

The troubleshooter can observe the even blackening of all motor windings, which occurs when a motor has failed due to overloading. The even blackening is caused by the slow destruction of the motor over a long period of time. There is no obvious damage to the insulation, and there are no isolated areas of damage.

Current readings are taken at the motor to determine an overload problem. See Figure 6-10. If the motor is drawing rated current, the motor is working to its maximum. If the motor is drawing more than rated current, the motor is overloaded. If overloads become a problem, the motor size may be increased or the load on the motor decreased.

RATED CURRENT OF MOTOR	METER READING		
	MOTOR UNDERLOADED	MOTOR FULLY LOADED	MOTOR OVERLOADED
20 A	12 A	20 A	22 A
↑ NAMEPLATE LISTED VALUE	↑ 0 TO 95% OF LISTED VALUE	↑ 95 TO 105% OF LISTED VALUE	↑ 105% + OF LISTED VALUE

DIGITAL MULTIMETER AUTO-RANGE

TO POWER SOURCE

Figure 6-10. Current readings are taken at the motor to determine an overload problem.

Over Cycling

Over cycling a motor is the process of turning a motor ON and OFF repeatedly. See Figure 6-11. Motor starting current is usually five to six times the full-load running current of the motor. Most motors are not designed to start more than ten times per hour. Over cycling occurs when a motor is at its operating temperature and still cycles ON and OFF. This will further increase the temperature of the motor, destroying the motor insulation. Totally enclosed motors can better withstand over cycling than open motors, because they can hold heat longer.

The following procedure should be followed when a motor application requires a motor to be cycled often:

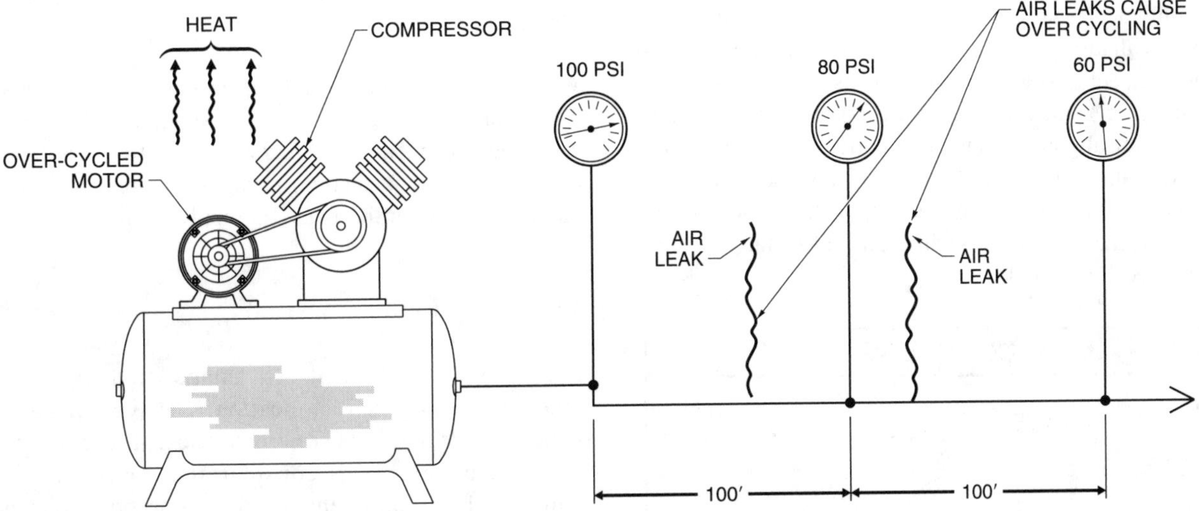

Figure 6-11. Over cycling occurs when a motor is repeatedly turned ON and OFF.

- Use a motor with a 50°C rise, instead of the standard 40°C.
- Use a motor with a 1.25 or 1.35 service factor, instead of a 1.00 or 1.15.
- Provide additional cooling by forcing air over the motor.

Moisture

Moisture causes metal parts to rust and motor coil insulation to lose some of its insulating properties. A motor cools when it is turned OFF. This causes air (with its moisture) to be sucked into the motor. Motors that operate every day will heat enough to remove any moisture inside the motor. Moisture is usually a problem for a motor that is seldom operated, or is shut down for a period of time.

Any motor that is not operated on a regular basis should contain a heating element to keep the motor dry. If adding a heating element is not practical, a maintenance schedule calling for short operation of motors that are seldom used should be developed. This schedule should also consider new motor installations, since in some plants, motors may be installed some time in advance of the plant startup.

Improper Belt Tension

Belt drives provide a quiet, compact, and durable form of power transmission and are widely used in industrial applications. A belt must be tight enough not to slip, but not so tight as to overload the motor bearings.

Belt tension is usually checked by placing a straightedge from sheave to sheave and measuring the amount of deflection at the midpoint, or by using a tension tester. Belt deflection should equal $\frac{1}{64}''$ per inch of span. For example, if the span between the center of the drive pulley and the center of the driven pulley is 16″, the belt deflection is $\frac{1}{4}''$ ($16 \times \frac{1}{64}'' = \frac{1}{4}''$). If the belt tension requires adjustment, it is usually accomplished by moving the drive component away from or closer to the driven component. This reduces or increases deflection. See Figure 6-12.

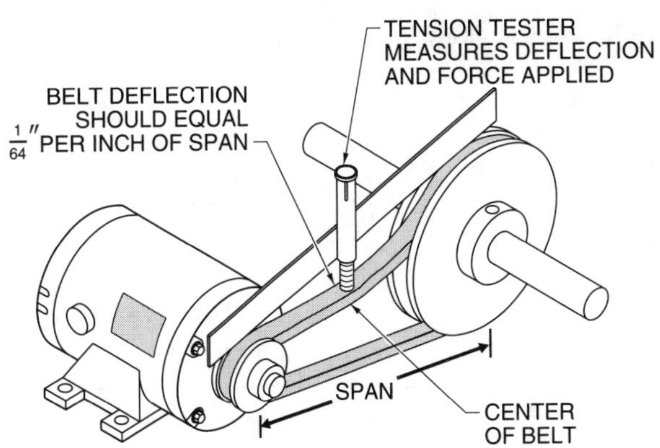

Figure 6-12. Belt tension is usually checked by measuring deflection.

Misalignment and Vibration

Misalignment of the motor and driven load is a major cause of motor failure. If the motor and driven load are misaligned, premature failure of the motor bearings, load, or both may occur.

Equipment shafts should be properly aligned on all new installations and checked during periodic maintenance inspections. Misalignment is usually corrected by placing shims under the feet of the motor or driven equipment. If misalignment cannot be corrected, a coupler designed to allow some misalignment can be used. Couplers that can be used in misaligned applications include the rubber-in-shear, flexible spring, and all-metal flex link types. See Figure 6-13.

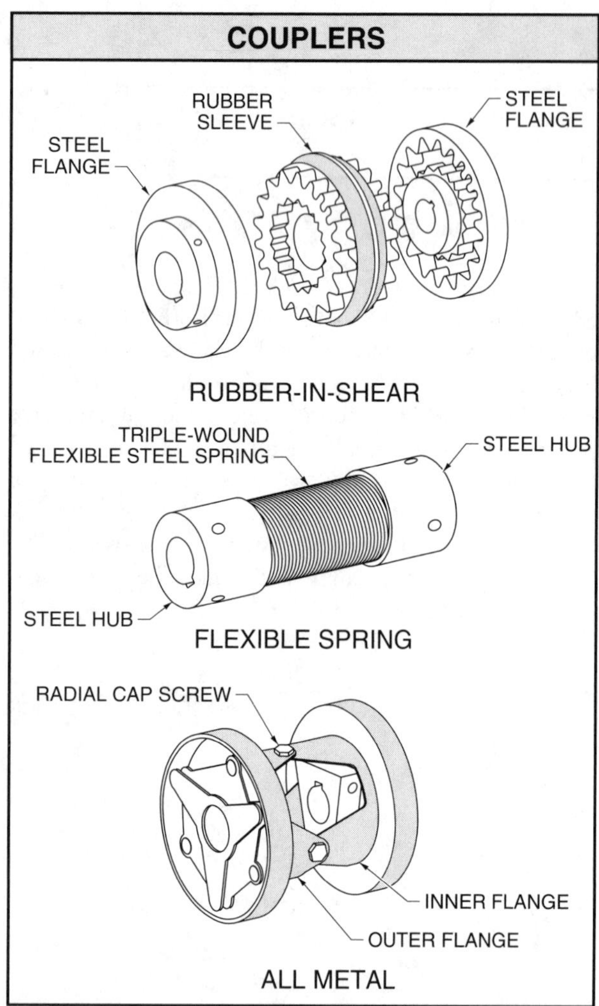

Figure 6-13. Couplers compensate for misalignment of the motor and driven load.

Loose Connections. All motors produce vibration as they rotate. This vibration can loosen mechanical and electrical connections. Loose mechanical connections generally cause noise and can be easily detected. Loose electrical connections do not cause noise, but do cause a voltage drop to the motor and excess heat. Always check mechanical and electrical connections when troubleshooting a motor.

Pests

A motor that is turned OFF remains warm for some time. This warmth can attract insects, snakes, and rodents. These pests can damage a motor by restricting ventilation or corroding the insulation. In high-pest areas, a special zip-seal jacket can be placed around the motor.

Incorrect Motor

Each motor type has its advantages and disadvantages. For any given application, one type of motor generally offers the best performance. If a motor has a recurring problem, consider the application in which it is used. A change of motor type may be required for better service.

Motor Defect

As with any machine, a motor can fail due to a motor defect or motor damage. A *motor defect* is an imperfection created during the manufacture of the motor that impairs its use. If it impairs initial motor operation, the defect is usually caught by the manufacturer. If the defect manifests itself after the motor has been in operation for some time, the troubleshooter determines that the problem is a defect in the motor. Motors with defects should be replaced, and the manufacturer should be notified.

The troubleshooter can observe the effect when a motor has failed due to a defect, which is usually confined to a small area of the motor. See Figure 6-14. Typical defects that may occur in a motor include windings grounded in the slot, windings grounded at the edge of the slot, windings shorted phase-to-phase, and shorted connections.

Motor damage is any damage that occurs to a properly manufactured motor. The damage may occur before or during installation and during operation. A sound maintenance schedule and proper operation of a motor minimize the occurrence of motor damage.

GENERAL MOTOR MAINTENANCE

Maintenance can help prevent motor problems from occurring. A motor that is well-maintained and used in an application for which it is suited can have a long service life. Maintenance can be performed as needed or as part of a routine scheduled maintenance program.

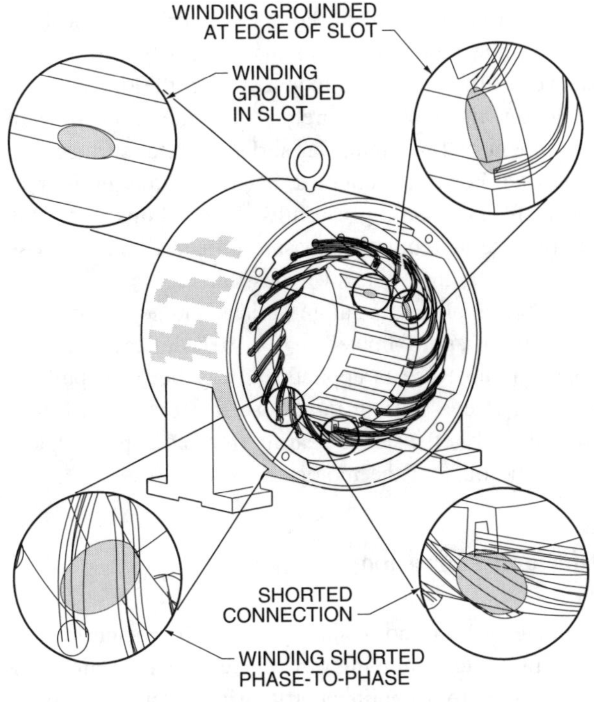

Figure 6-14. A defect is an imperfection that impairs use.

Water-Soaked Motors

Motors may become water soaked from flooding, broken water pipes, or lack of proper protection. Generally, water alone does not damage a motor if it is serviced shortly after soaking. Servicing includes a thorough cleaning, drying, and testing.

Cleaning. The following steps should be followed to clean a motor:

1. Disconnect the motor circuit. Make sure all power is OFF.
2. Disconnect the motor from the motor circuit.
3. Clean with a stiff brush and water. Water pressure should not exceed 25 psi. Water temperature should not exceed 200°F.
4. Apply approved cleaning solvent. Allow the cleaning solvent sufficient time to work per manufacturer's recommendations. Rinse cleaning solvent with a high-pressure hose (See Step 3).

Drying. After the motor has been cleaned, it must be thoroughly dried before any power is applied. Motors may be slow-dried or force-dried. Slow-drying a motor is better than force-drying. The motor can be slow-dried by placing it in a warm room or in the sun for two to four days.

Motors can be force-dried by heating or by applying low voltage. To force-dry a motor by heating, apply 150°F to 200°F heat for approximately 18 to 30 hours, depending upon the motor type and temperature. To force-dry a motor by applying low voltage, apply approximately 10% of the rated voltage to the motor for two to four hours to dry the coils.

Always check the resistance of a motor before reapplying power. The motor insulation is checked to make sure it has the proper resistance value. A megger® or ohmmeter can be used to test the resistance of the insulation, but a megger® is preferred. Although a motor may operate satisfactorily with a reading of less than one megohm, a resistance of one megohm or more is recommended as the minimum resistance. Additional drying, or running the motor for a short time, will increase resistance.

Check for signs of spitting or smoking when restarting the motor. Spitting indicates moisture in the motor. Smoking indicates an insulation breakdown. In either case, turn the power OFF, and completely dry and retest the motor.

Lubrication

Motors are lubricated at the factory to provide long operation under normal service conditions without relubrication. Excessive and frequent lubrication can damage a motor. The time period between lubrications depends upon the motor's service conditions, its ambient temperature, and its environment.

Always follow lubrication instructions provided with the motor. These instructions are usually listed on the nameplate or terminal box cover. Alternately, there may be separate instructions furnished with the motor. If lubrication instructions are not available, relubricate sleeve bearings and ball bearings per a schedule. See Figure 6-15.

Sleeve Bearings. For normal operation, add electric motor oil (or SAE #10 or #20 non-detergent oil) after three years. For heavy-duty operation, relubricate once a year. For light operation, relubricate every four years.

Ball Bearings. Ball bearings are designed for many years of operation without relubricating. The schedule for relubricating ball bearings varies from 1 to 10 years, depending upon the service conditions, ambient temperature, and environment. When relubricating, use standard, long-life ball-bearing grease.

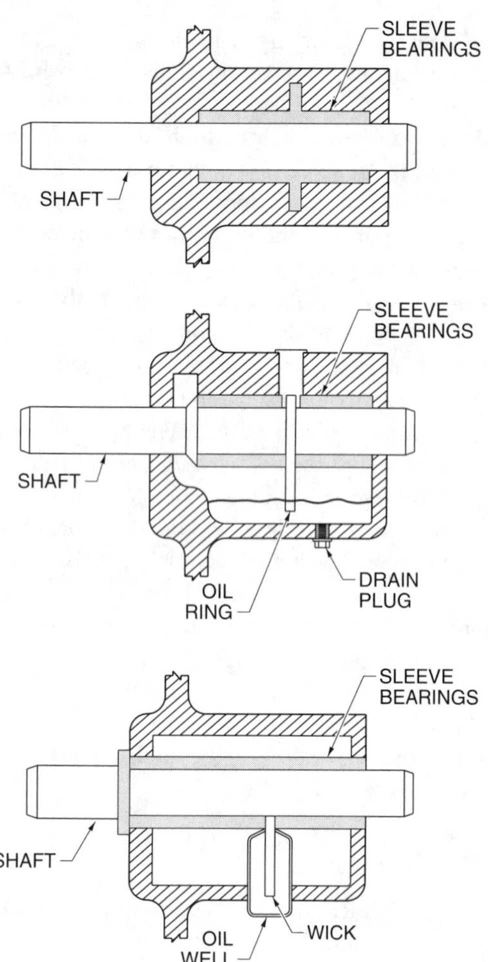

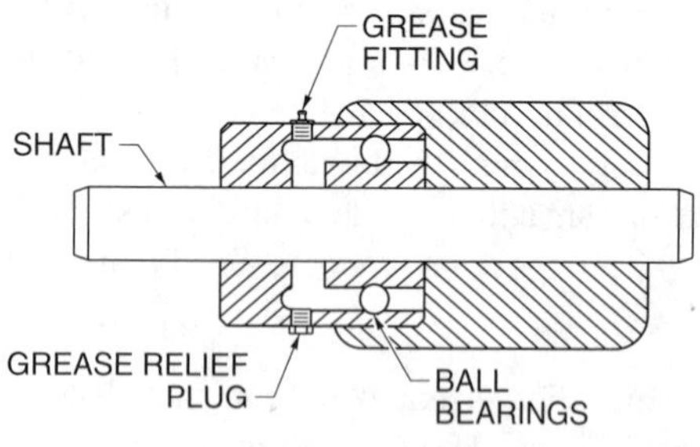

Figure 6-15. Proper lubrication is required for long motor life.

Mounting/Remounting

Motors other than dripproof types can usually be mounted in any position or at any angle. Dripproof motors must be mounted in the normal horizontal position to meet the requirements of the enclosure. Motor with sleeve bearings must be mounted with the oil cap up.

Mount the motor securely to the mounting base of equipment or to a rigid, flat surface. Metal surfaces are preferred. For direct-coupled installations, align the motor shaft and coupling carefully. Place shims under the motor base as required to assure proper alignment. Use flexible couplings whenever possible.

In belt applications, align pulleys and adjust belt tension so that approximately ½″ of belt deflection occurs when thumb force is applied midway between pulleys. Position sleeve-bearing motors so that the belt is away from the oil in the sleeve bearing (located approximately under the oiler of the motor).

Dirt and Corrosion

Remove dirt and corrosion by brushing, vacuuming, or blowing. After removing obvious dirt, feel for air being discharged from cooling ports on the motor. If the air flow is weak, the internal air passages may be clogged.

Check for signs of corrosion. As time passes, small amounts of corrosion are normal. Larger amounts of corrosion may indicate a problem. After removing corrosion, use corrosion-resistant, high-temperature paint to repaint the motor.

Heat, Noise, and Vibration

Touch the motor frame and bearings lightly to determine if there is excessive heat or vibration. Listen closely for any abnormal noise. Problems with heat are usually due to improper ventilation, excessive motor cycling, or overloads. Vibration and noise are caused by misalignment and loose parts. Tighten all mountings connecting the motor and motor load. If excessive vibration remains, realign the motor.

Scheduled Maintenance

A maintenance schedule is essential to the satisfactory operation of electric motors. The frequency of scheduled maintenance on motors varies. Motor maintenance checklists for scheduled semiannual and annual maintenance provide a record of maintenance performed. A motor repair record provides a record of motor repairs. See Appendix.

MOTOR FAILURE

Application — Belt Drive Problems

When using a belt drive for a horizontal application, belt sag should be on top. Maximum belt contact is made with the drive pulley when the taut part of the belt is on the bottom. Whenever possible, align pulley centers on the same horizontal plane. See Horizontal Pulley Drive.

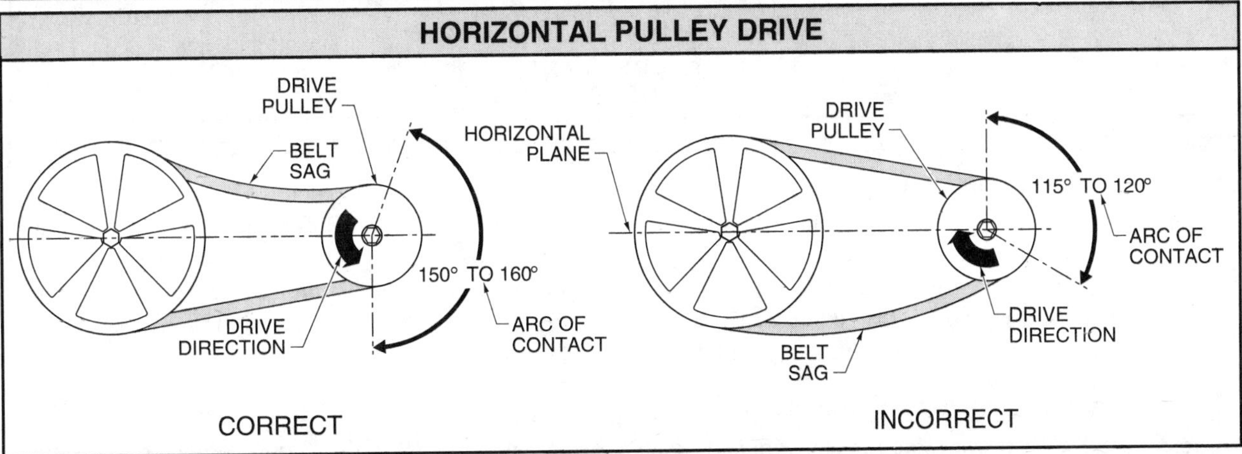

Vertical belt drives cause more problems than horizontal belt drives. If an application requires a vertical belt drive, mount the drive pulley on top. Maximum belt contact is made with the drive pulley when the taut part of the belt is pulling up. See Vertical Pulley Drive. Whenever possible, align pulley centers on the same vertical plane. If the pulley centers cannot be aligned on the same vertical plane, an angle of 45° or less between the pulley centers and the vertical plane is permissible.

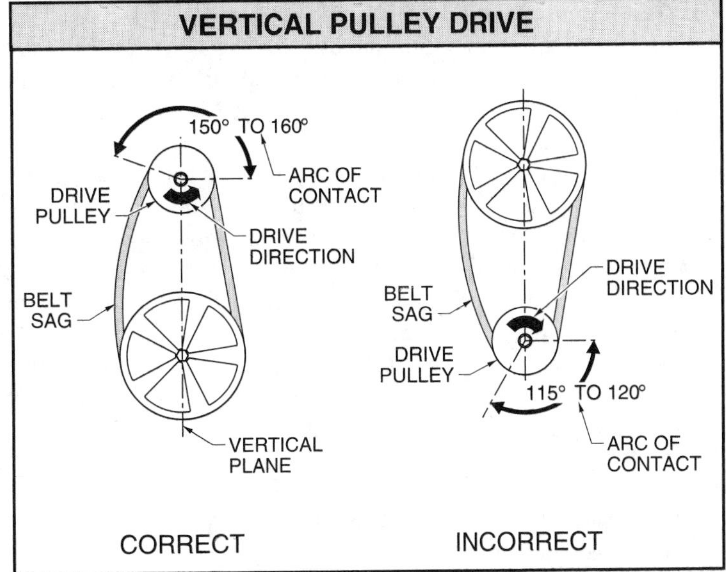

Application — Three-Phase Motor Failure

Three-phase motors can fail or be damaged if problems occur in the incoming 3ϕ power supply. Common problems that occur in 3ϕ power circuits include improper phase sequence, phase unbalance, phase loss, and phase angle error. See Three-Phase Problems.

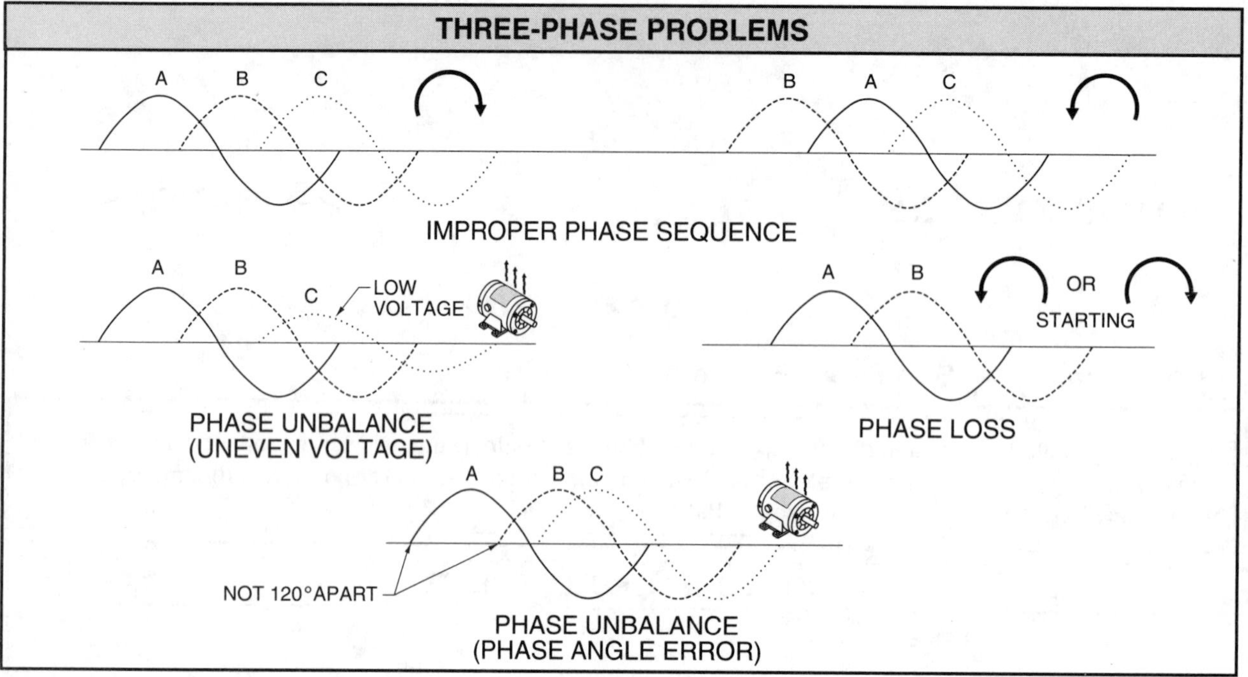

Improper Phase Sequence

Changing the sequence of any two phases (phase reversal) in a 3ϕ motor control circuit reverses the motor rotation. Reversing motor rotation can cause damage to driven machinery or injury to personnel. Phase reversal can occur when modifications are made to a power distribution system, or when maintenance is performed on electrical conductors or switching equipment. The NEC® requires phase reversal protection on all personnel transportation equipment, such as moving walkways, escalators, and ski lifts.

Phase Unbalance (Uneven Voltage)

Unbalance of a 3ϕ power circuit occurs when 1ϕ loads are unevenly applied to the circuit. When 1ϕ loads are unevenly applied, one power line carries more of the load. A phase unbalance causes 3ϕ motors to run at temperatures above their normal ratings. A 3ϕ motor operating in an unbalanced circuit cannot deliver its rated horsepower. In new 3ϕ power circuit installations, careful attention is given to balancing loads.

Phase Loss

The complete loss of one phase in a power circuit (single phasing) is an extreme case of phase unbalance. A phase loss causes a motor to start in the opposite direction of rotation and also causes the motor to overheat. When one phase is lost prior to starting the motor, the motor can start in either direction when the two other phase voltages are applied. If the two good phase voltages cannot supply enough power to start the motor, the motor's temperature increases rapidly. If the two good phases can supply enough power to start the motor, the motor's temperature increases over a longer time period. In both cases, the increased temperature can burn out a motor. Since a motor can start in the reverse direction when one phase is lost, damage to driven machinery or injury to personnel is possible. Lightning, fallen tree branches, or a blown fuse can take out an incoming power line, which leads to phase loss.

Phase Unbalance (Phase Angle Error)

In a 3ϕ power circuit, each phase is 120 electrical degrees apart. The phase angle changes if a circuit is unbalanced, or if a heavy inductive or capacitive load is placed on one or two of the power lines. When the phase angle changes, a phase angle error occurs. A phase angle error causes 3ϕ motors to run at temperatures above their normal ratings. A 3ϕ motor operating in a circuit with a phase angle error cannot deliver its rated horsepower.

Application — Measuring Voltage Unbalance

A motor runs at higher-than-normal temperatures when a voltage unbalance occurs. It is difficult to detect voltage unbalance in large motors because measuring the voltage at the motor leads does not easily show an open winding, as the open winding in the motor generates a voltage nearly equal to the line voltage lost. The generated voltage is high when the motor is not loaded and low when the motor is fully loaded. The larger the motor, the higher the generated voltage. It is easier to detect voltage unbalance when the motor is fully loaded because voltage unbalance decreases as the motor load increases.

Application — Monitoring Power Problems

A power monitor is added to a circuit to prevent a problematic power supply from damaging a motor. The power monitor is connected in the motor power supply lines, and the monitor contacts are connected in the motor control circuit. The power monitor contacts are connected so that they stop the motor if a power problem occurs. Power monitors are added to a power distribution system to protect a motor from improper phase sequence, phase loss, phase unbalance, phase angle error, and excessive voltage or undervoltage.

A power monitor is connected as close to a motor as possible because a power monitor detects a problem only if the problem is ahead of the monitor in the circuit. If a power monitor is connected directly to the motor terminals, the monitor detects the normal stopped condition of the motor as a power loss.

Improper Phase Sequence or Phase Loss

A power monitor can be used to detect improper phase sequence or phase loss. See Model A Power Monitor. The relay operates if all three voltages are present. The relay drops out if any one or more of the phases lose voltage. The relay operates if the phases are in the correct sequence (L1 to Pin 5, L2 to Pin 6, and L3 to Pin 7). The relay drops out if any two phases are reversed.

MODEL A POWER MONITOR

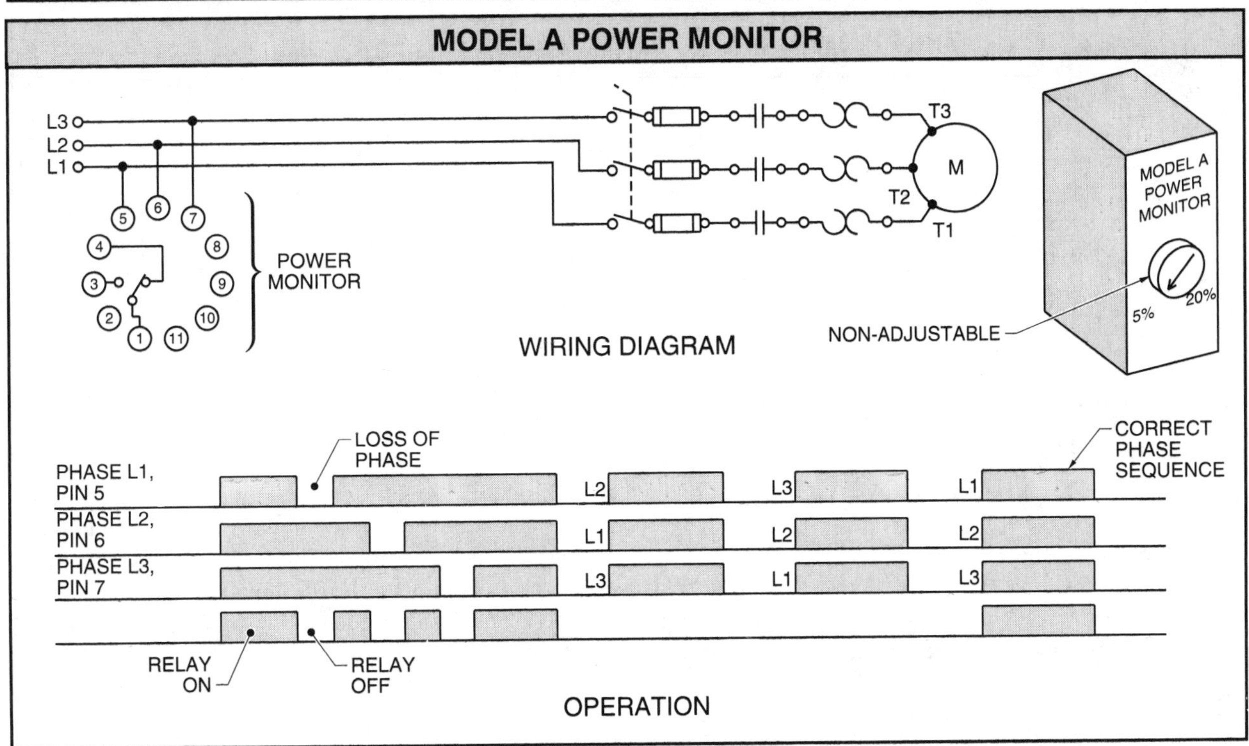

Phase Angle Error

A power monitor can be used to detect a phase angle error. See Model B Power Monitor. The power monitor is set at a designated phase angle error (usually 5% to 20%). The power monitor is set at the lowest percentage without causing nuisance tripping. The relay operates as long as all three phases are within the set phase angle error. The relay drops out if any phase is out of phase by more than the phase angle error.

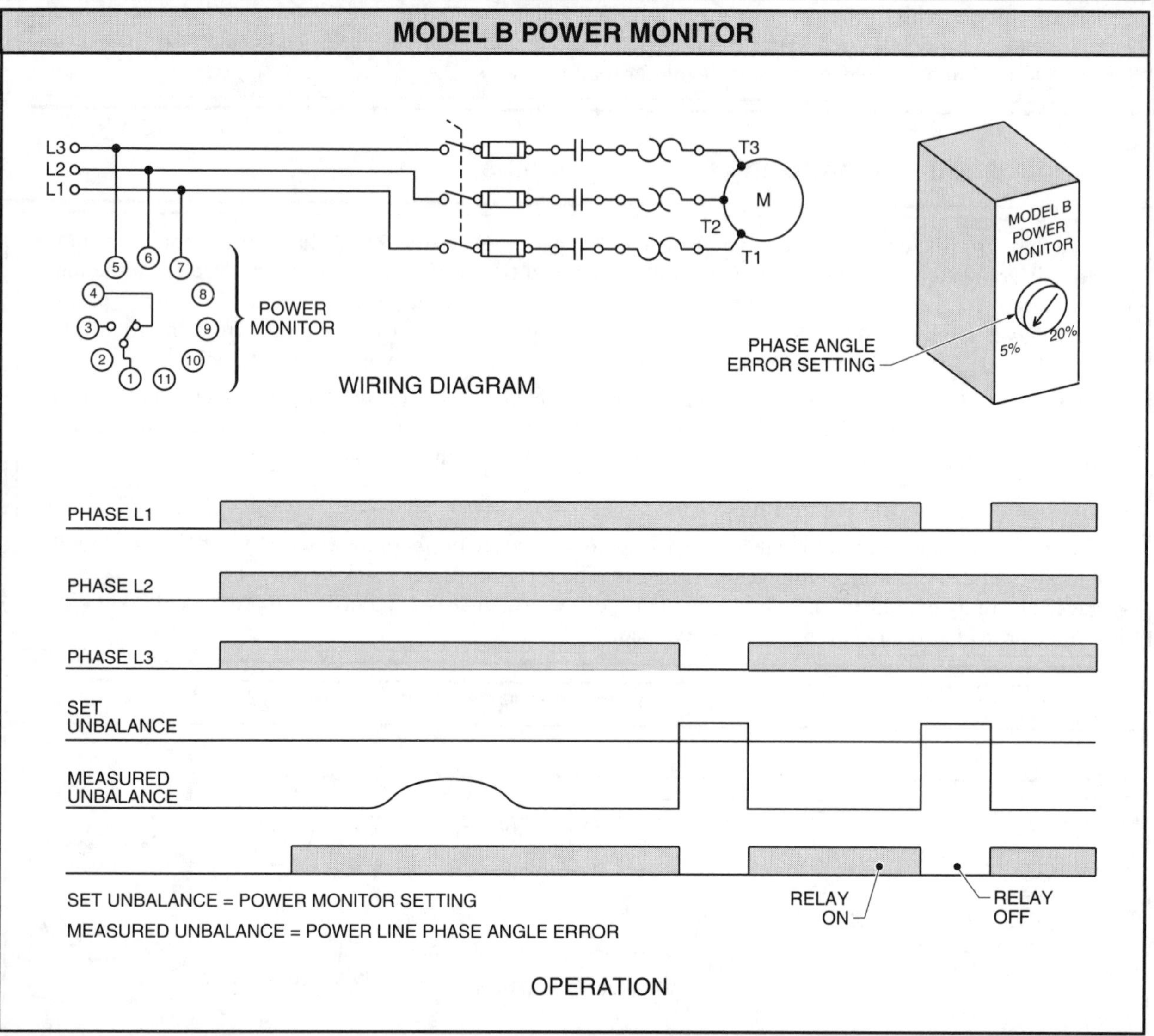

Phase Unbalance

A power monitor can be used to detect phase unbalance. See Model C Power Monitor. The power monitor is set to an upper limit (usually 10% higher than the rated voltage) and a lower limit (usually 10% lower than the rated voltage). The relay operates if the phase voltages are within the set limits. The relay drops out if the voltage on any one or more phases varies above or below the set limits. When the voltage applied to a motor is less than the motor's rated voltage, the motor develops less than its rated horsepower. When the voltage applied to the motor is greater than the motor's rated voltage, the motor develops greater than its rated horsepower at a much higher temperature. Do not overset the power monitor settings unless necessary for handling large voltage fluctuations.

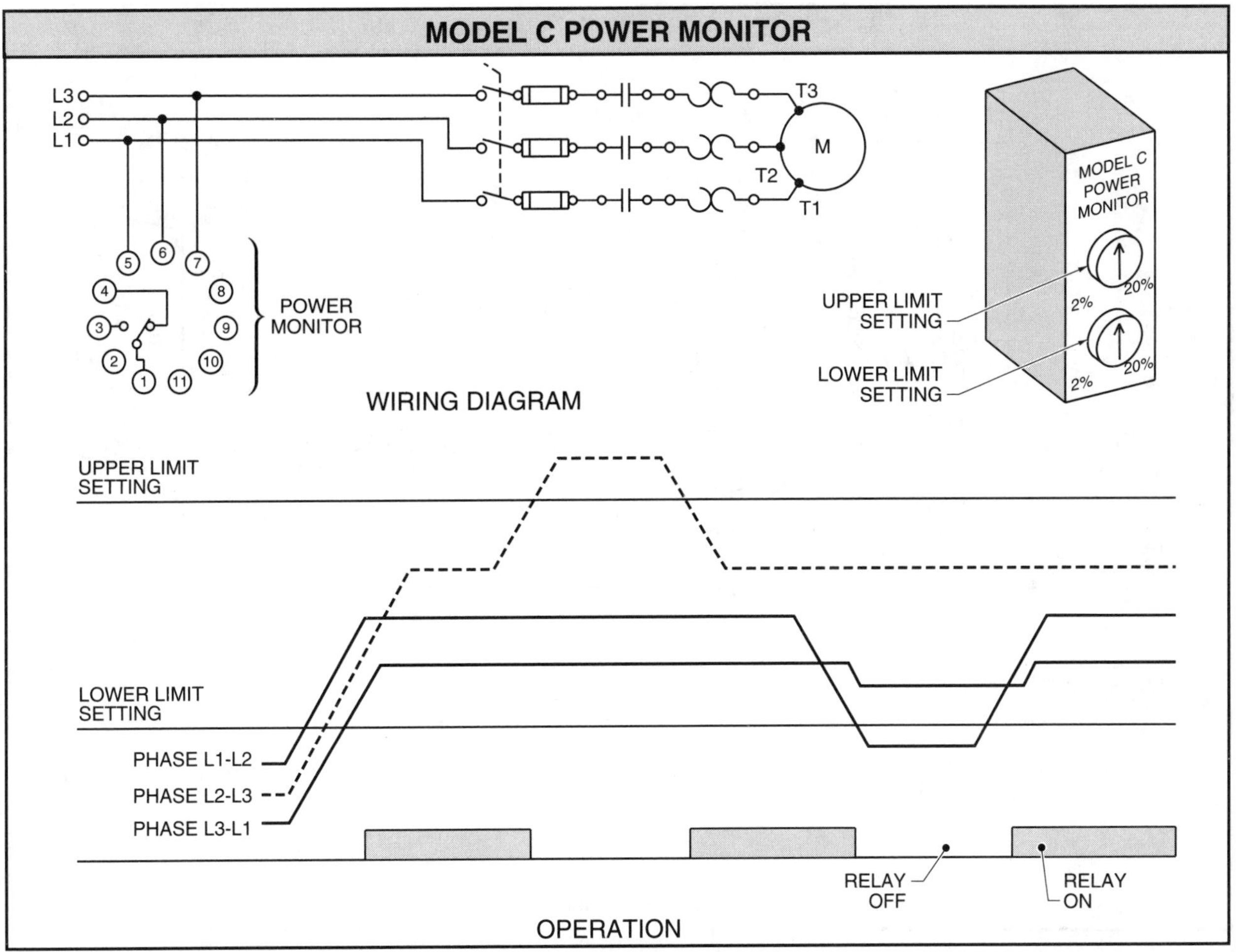

Excessive Voltage or Undervoltage

A power monitor can be used to detect excessive voltage or undervoltage on a 1ϕ or DC power supply. See Model D1 and D2 Power Monitors. The power monitor is set to an upper limit (usually 10% higher than the rated voltage) and a lower limit (usually 10% lower than the rated voltage). For example, on an incoming power voltage of 210 V, the power monitor is set for an upper limit of 231 V (210 V + 10% (21 V) = 231 V) and a lower limit of 189 V (210 V – 10% (21 V) = 189 V). The relay operates if the power line voltage is within the set limits. The relay drops out if the voltage varies above or below the set limits.

When connecting the power monitor's contacts in the control circuit, the contacts are typically connected to perform a stop function. To perform a stop function, the normally open contacts, now held closed, are connected in series with the stop pushbutton. If the stop pushbutton or the power monitor contacts are activated, the circuit opens and the motor stops. The power monitor's normally closed contacts, now held open, can be connected to sound an alarm if a problem is detected.

Combination Monitoring

Several power monitors are typically used together to detect potential problems. A phase-sequence, phase-angle-error, and phase-unbalance power monitor can each be added to detect problems in a 3ϕ power supply. An excessive-voltage or undervoltage power monitor can each be added to the control circuit to detect a problem in the single phase or DC supply voltage. A low voltage in the control circuit causes motor starters, relays, and solenoids to drop out. Too high of a voltage can cause the circuit to overheat and damage the components.

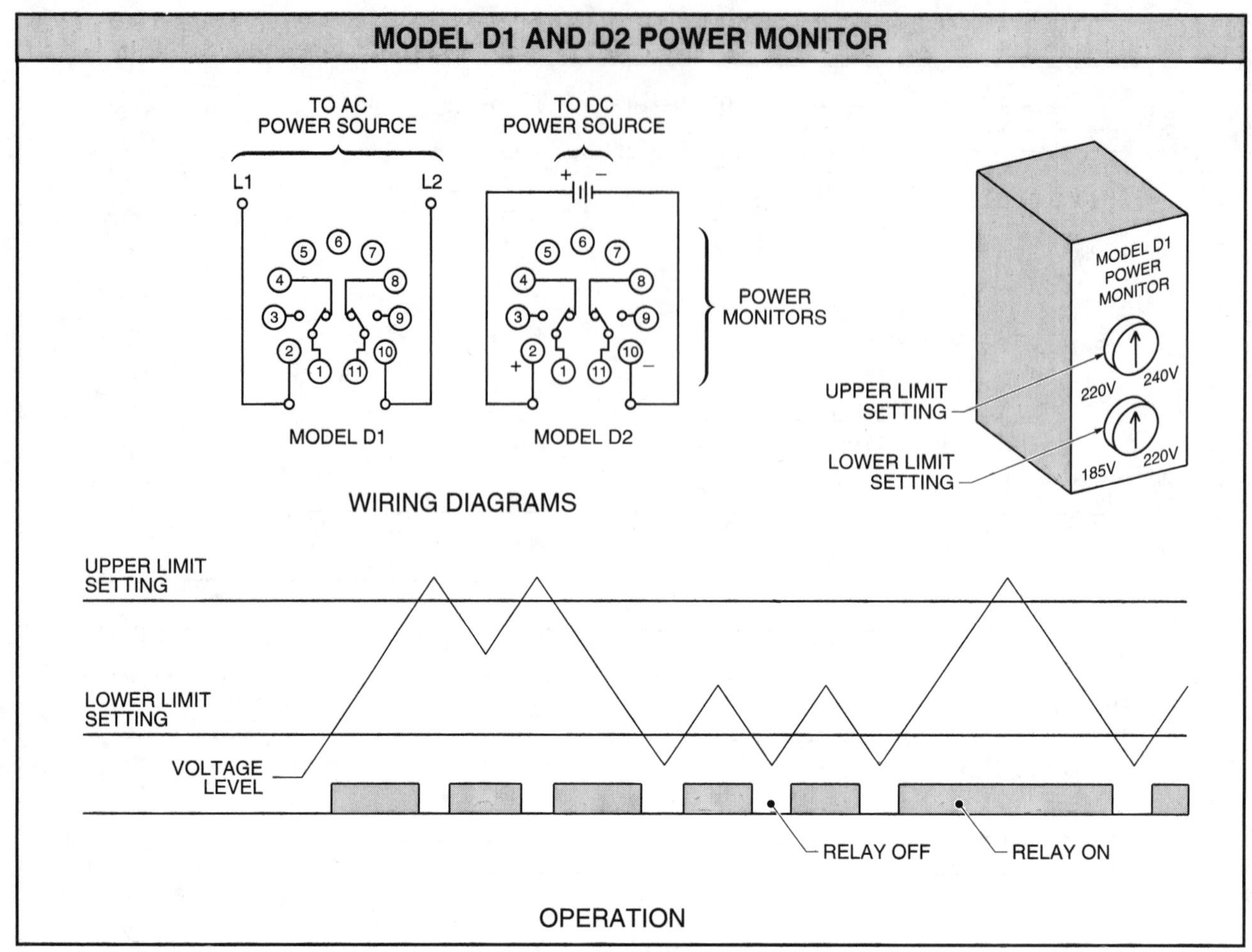

POWER MONITOR CHARACTERISTICS

Power Monitor	Power Type			Monitor Detects							
	3ϕ	1ϕ	DC	Proper phase sequence	Phase loss	Phase angle error	Phase unbalance (3ϕ)	Excessive voltage (1ϕ)	Undervoltage (1ϕ)	Excessive voltage (DC)	Undervoltage (DC)
Model A	X			X	X						
Model B	X					X					
Model C	X						X				
Model D1		X						X	X		
Model D2			X							X	X

Name ______________________________ Date ________________

chapter 6

MOTOR FAILURE

ACTIVITIES

Activity 6-1. Belt Drive Problems

Identify the belt drive problems.

__________ 1. Excessive belt tension

__________ 2. Misaligned pulleys

__________ 3. Mechanical interference

__________ 4. Loose pulley

__________ 5. Incorrect mounting

__________ 6. Overloaded drive

__________ 7. Contamination on belt

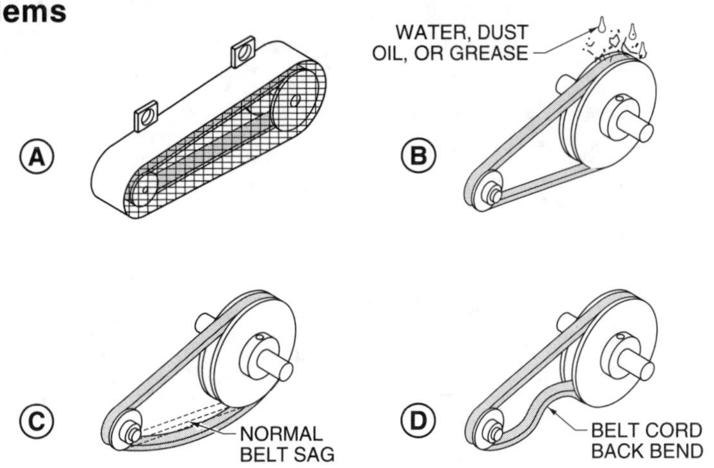

A

B

WATER, DUST OIL, OR GREASE

C

NORMAL BELT SAG

D

BELT CORD BACK BEND

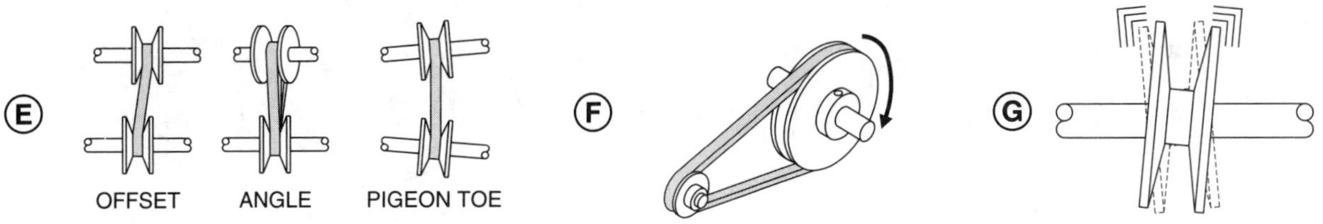

E

OFFSET

ANGLE

PIGEON TOE

F

G

Activity 6-2. Three-Phase Motor Failure

State the problem with the power supply and the effect it has on the motor.

__________ 1. The problem is ________.

__________ 2. The effect on the motor is ________.

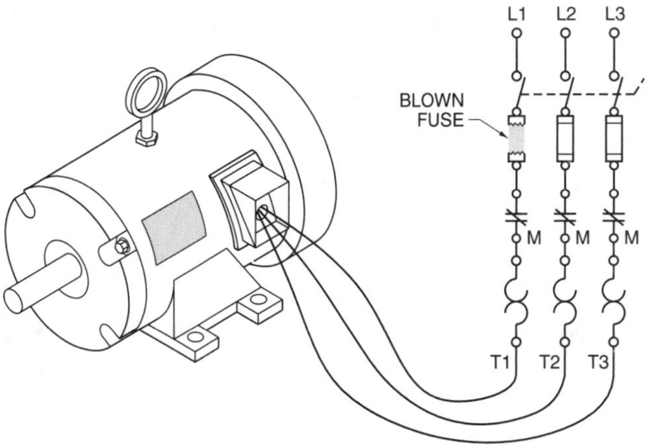

L1 L2 L3

BLOWN FUSE

M M M

T1 T2 T3

_____________ **3.** The problem is _________.

_____________ **4.** The effect on the motor is _________.

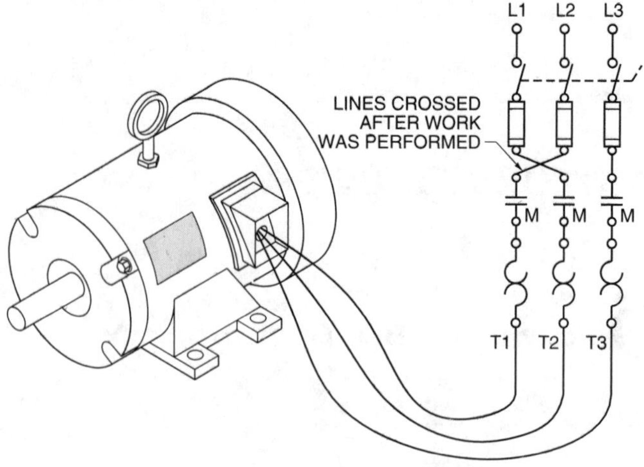

_____________ **5.** The problem is _________.

_____________ **6.** The effect on the motor is _________.

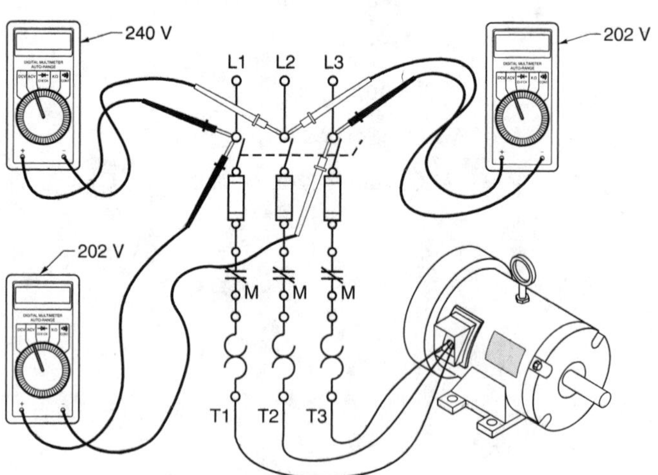

_____________ **7.** The problem is _________.

_____________ **8.** The effect on the motor is _________.

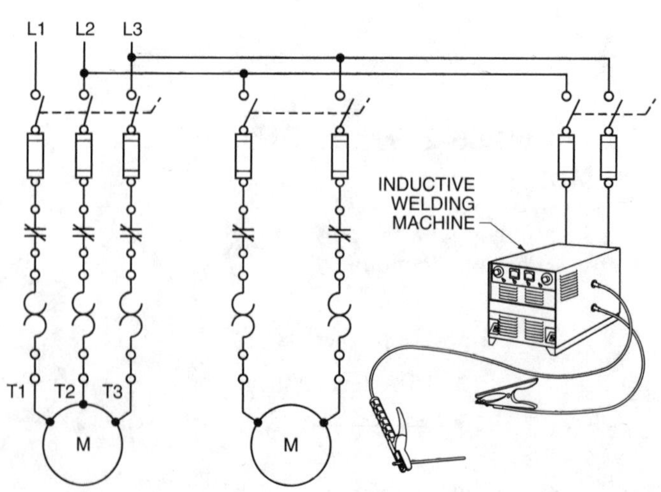

❍ Activity 6-3. Measuring Voltage Unbalance

Each motor has lost power in one incoming power line. State the percentage of voltage unbalance. Identify the motor phase that is not connected to the power line.

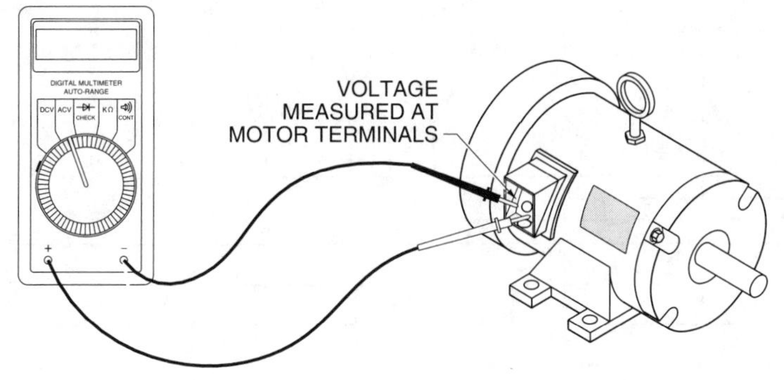

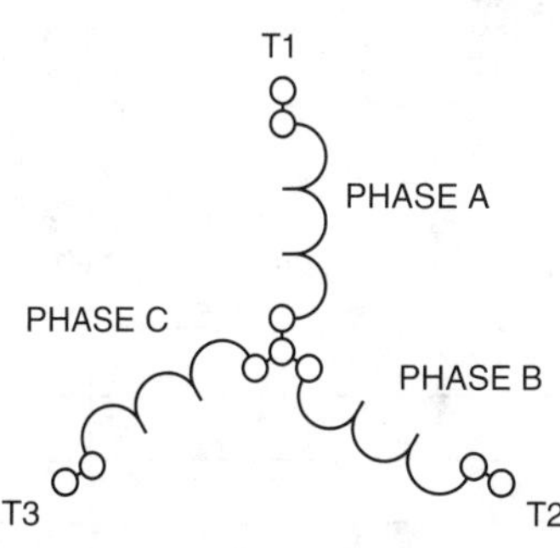

1 HP INDUCTION MOTOR			
Motor Loaded	**Voltage Readings**		
	L1–L2	L1–L3	L2–L3
¼	480	423	402
½	480	406	400
¾	480	377	395
fully	480	365	392

_____ **1.** Voltage unbalance when the motor is ¼ loaded is _____%.

_____ **2.** Voltage unbalance when the motor is ½ loaded is _____%.

_____ **3.** Voltage unbalance when the motor is ¾ loaded is _____%.

_____ **4.** Voltage unbalance when the motor is fully loaded is _____%.

_____ **5.** Phase _____ has no power.

15 HP INDUCTION MOTOR			
Motor Loaded	**Voltage Readings**		
	L1–L2	L1–L3	L2–L3
¼	440	480	439
½	430	480	436
¾	428	480	426
fully	413	480	414

_____ **6.** Voltage unbalance when the motor is ¼ loaded is _____%.

_____ **7.** Voltage unbalance when the motor is ½ loaded is _____%.

_____ **8.** Voltage unbalance when the motor is ¾ loaded is _____%.

_____ **9.** Voltage unbalance when the motor is fully loaded is _____%.

_____ **10.** Phase _____ has no power.

125 HP INDUCTION MOTOR			
Motor Loaded	**Voltage Readings**		
	L1–L2	L1–L3	L2–L3
¼	437	452	480
½	430	460	480
¾	409	448	480
fully	327	439	480

_____ **11.** Voltage unbalance when the motor is ¼ loaded is _____%.

_____ **12.** Voltage unbalance when the motor is ½ loaded is _____%.

_____ **13.** Voltage unbalance when the motor is ¾ loaded is _____%.

_____ **14.** Voltage unbalance when the motor is fully loaded is _____%.

_____ **15.** Phase _____ has no power.

Activity 6-4. Monitoring Power Problems

1. Connect the Model A power monitor in the power circuit to detect improper phase sequence. Redraw the line diagram to include the power monitor contacts in the control circuit so that the motor is turned OFF if a problem occurs.

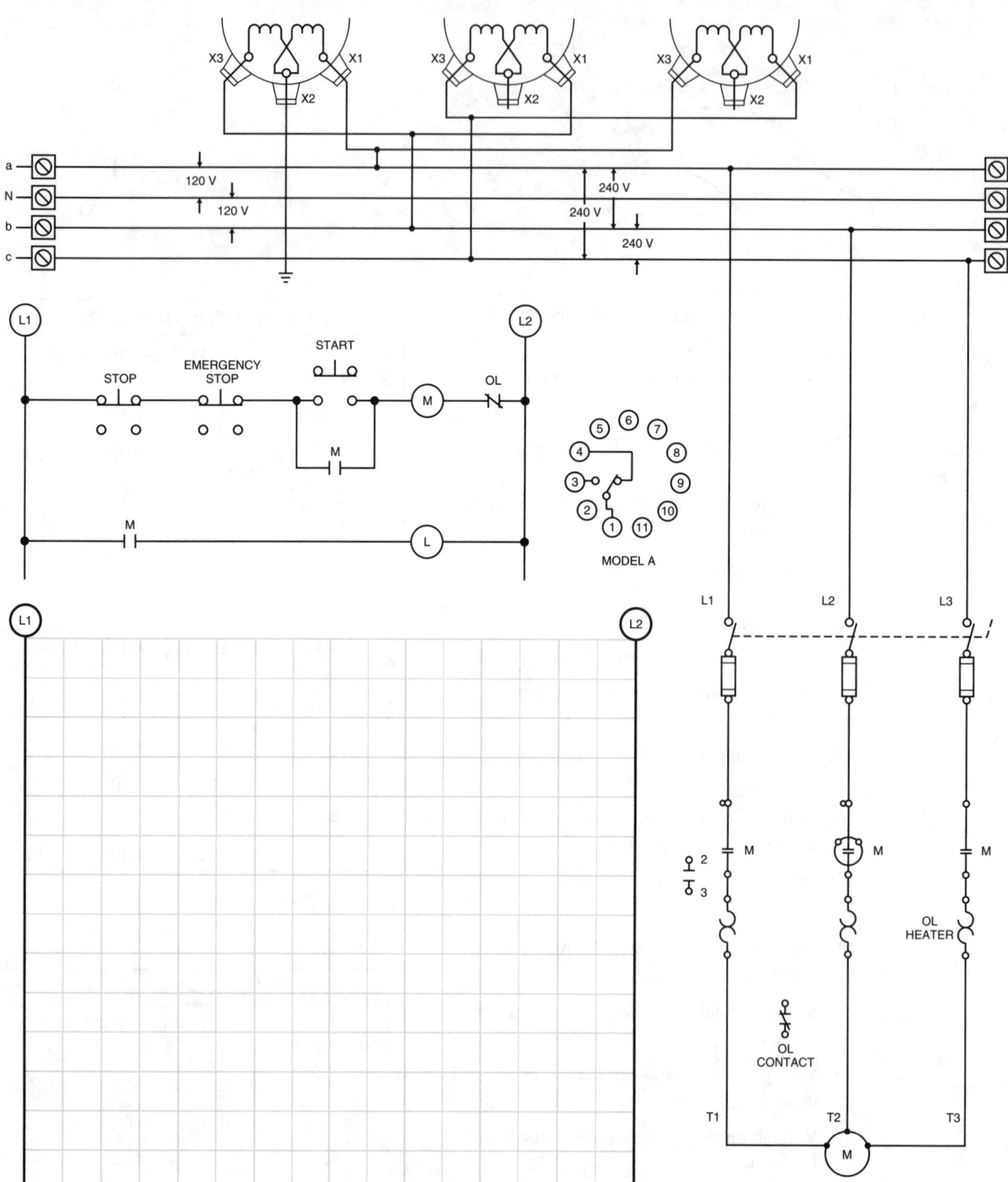

2. Connect the Model B power monitor in the power circuit to detect for phase angle error. Redraw the line diagram to include the power monitor contacts in the control circuit so that the motor is turned OFF if a problem occurs and a warning light turns ON when a phase angle error occurs.

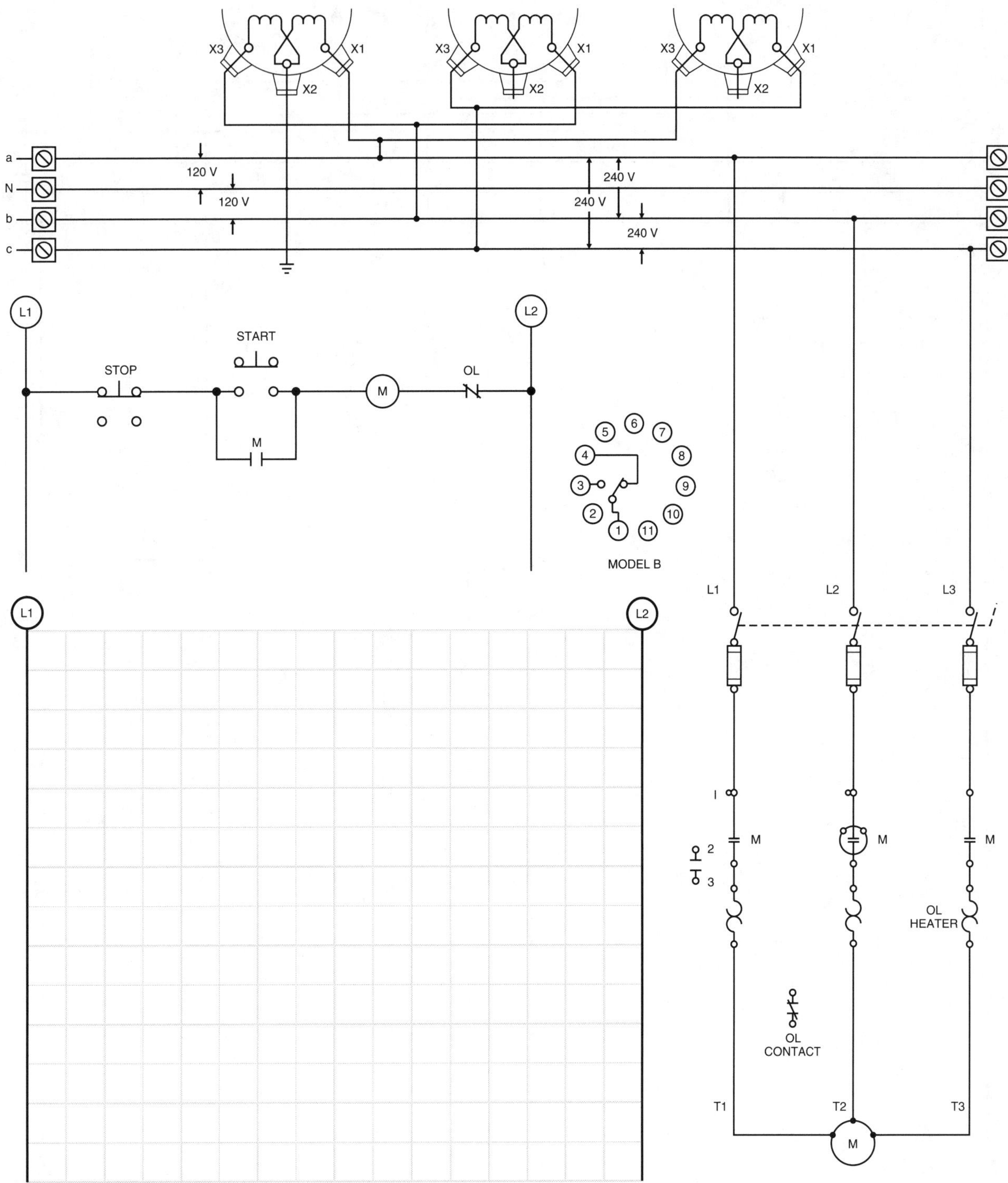

3. Connect the Model C power monitor in the power circuit to detect for phase unbalance. Redraw the line diagram to include the power monitor contacts in the control circuit so that the monitor turns both motors OFF if a problem occurs.

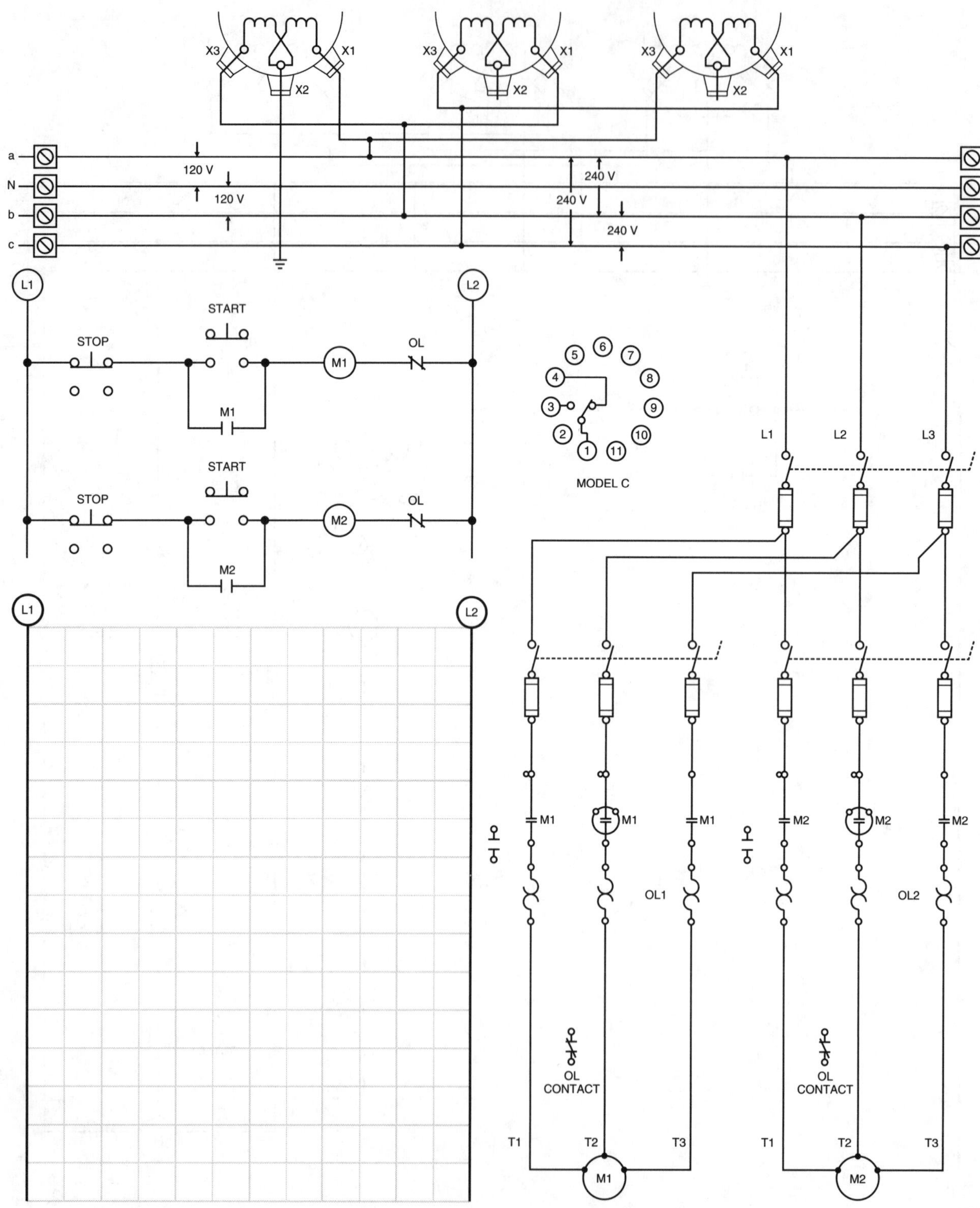

4. Connect the Model D2 power monitor in the power circuit to detect for an improper voltage level. Redraw the line diagram to include the power monitor contacts in the control circuit so that the motor is turned OFF if a problem occurs.

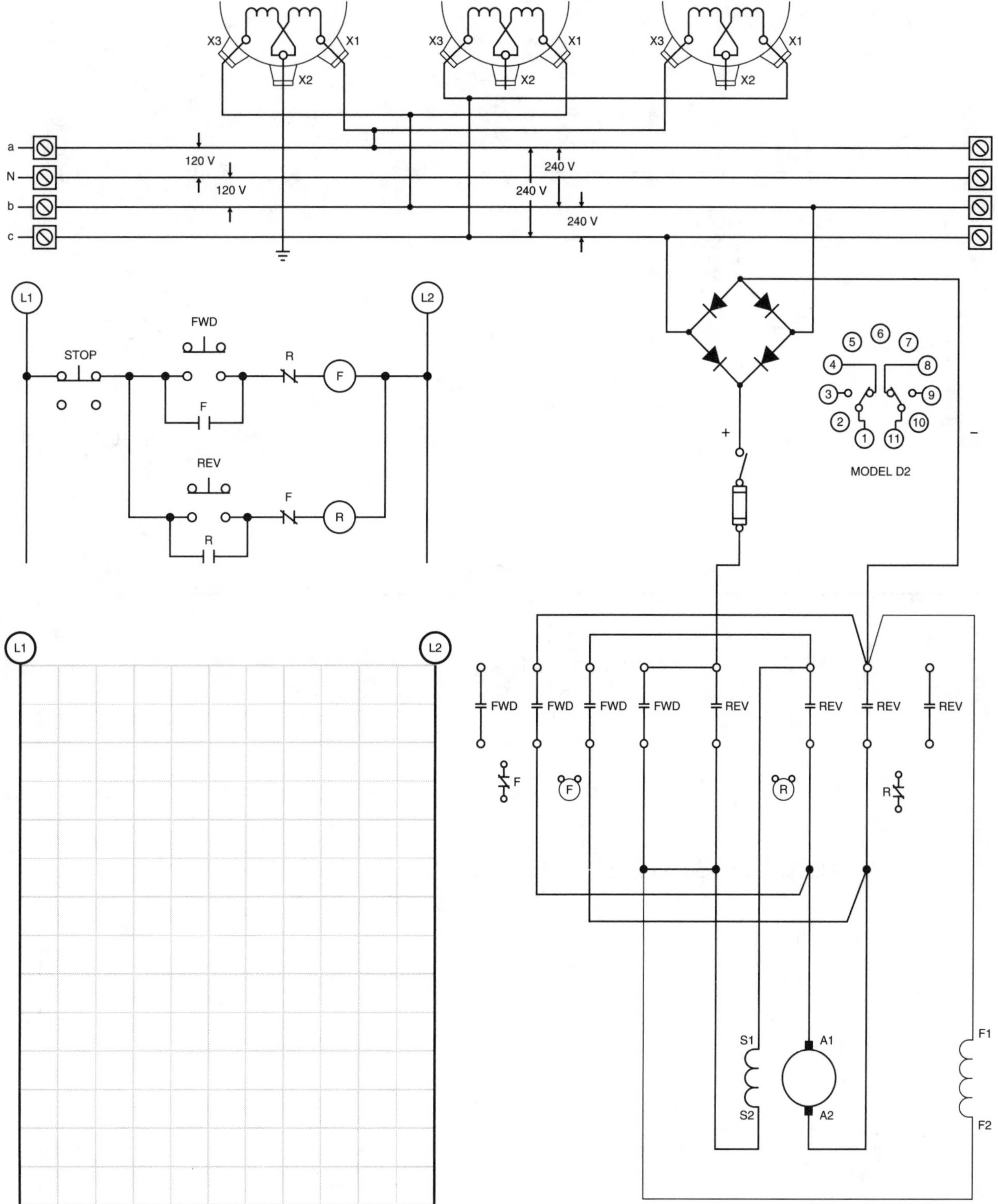

5. Connect the Model A, B, and C power monitors in the power circuit to detect a problem in the 3ϕ supply voltage. Draw the line diagram to include the Model A, B, and C power monitor contacts in the control circuit so that the motor is turned OFF if a problem occurs. Connect the Model D1 power monitor to detect a problem in the control voltage power supply. Add the power monitor contacts in the circuit so that the starter coil does not receive power unless the voltage is within the set limits.

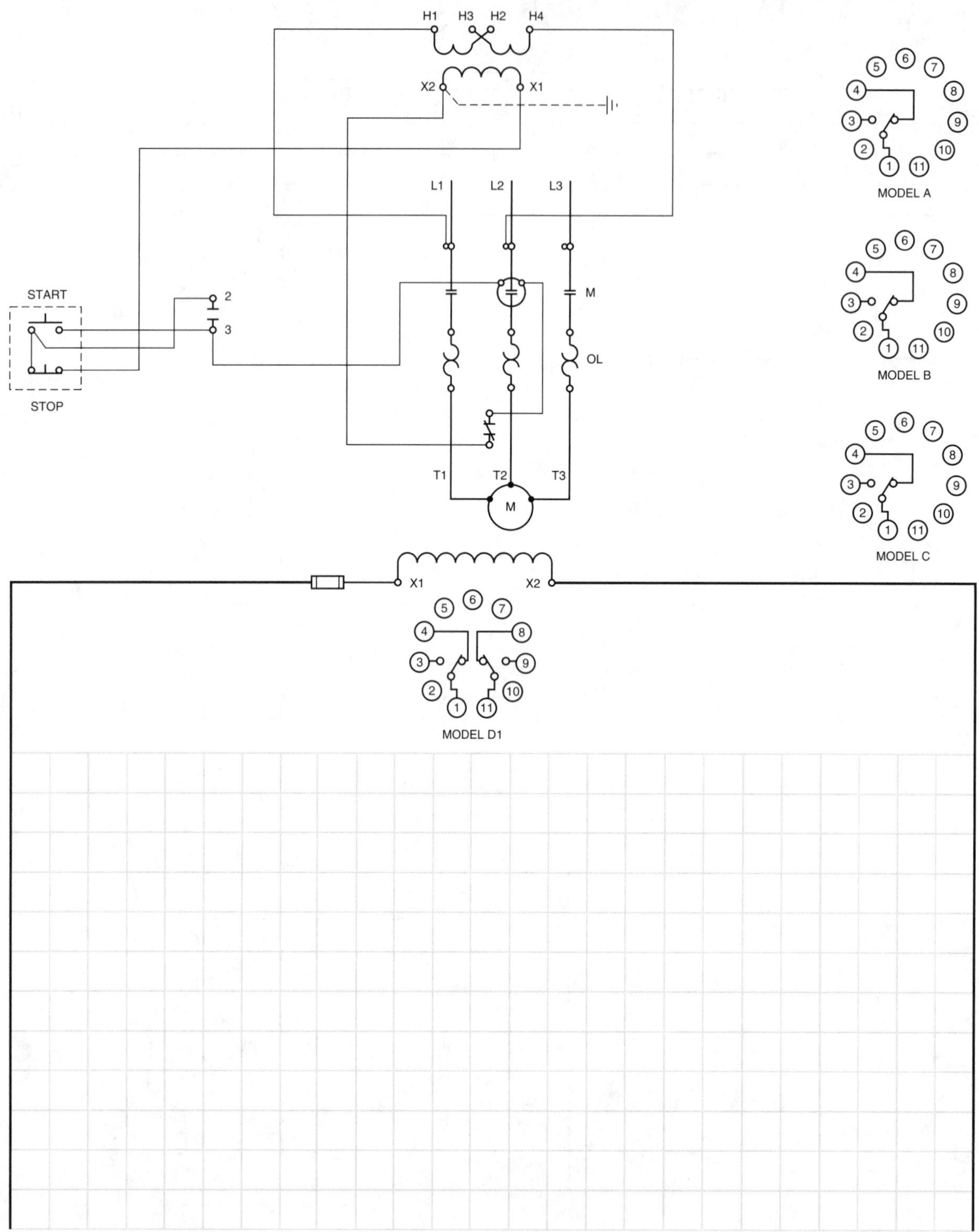

Activity 6-5. Control Circuit Modification

1. Redraw the line diagram adding a two-position selector switch which determines if the circuit operates in the run or jog mode. In the jog position, the motor turns ON in the slow speed only after a jog pushbutton is pressed. In the run position, the fast and slow pushbuttons control the motor speed.

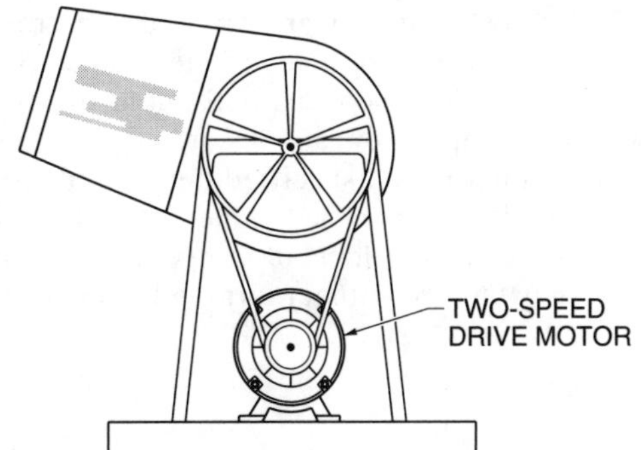

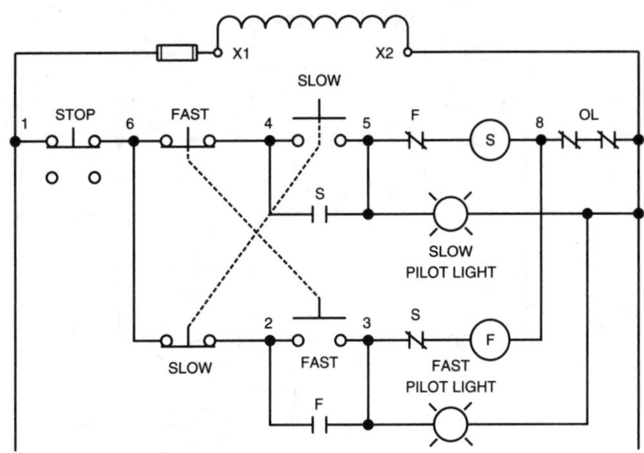

TWO-SPEED MOTOR CONTROL

2. Redraw the line diagram so that a control relay coil is controlled by a level and temperature switch. Add the relay contact in the control circuit so that the pump motor cannot start unless the level of the product is at a specified height and the temperature is at a specified value. Once the pump motor is started, the level or temperature of the product may change without turning the motor OFF.

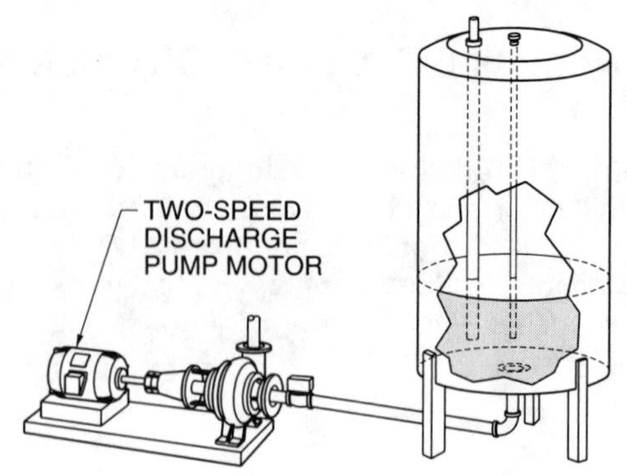

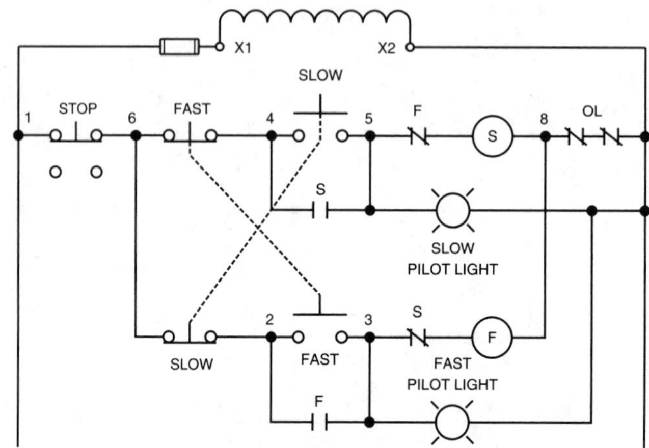

DISCHARGE PUMP MOTOR PROTECTION

Name ______________________ Date ____________

chapter 6

MOTOR FAILURE

TRADE TEST

Completion

______ **1.** More motors fail due to ______ than any other reason.

______ **2.** ______ unbalance is the unbalance that occurs when lines are out-of-phase.

______ **3.** Single phasing is the maximum condition of ______.

______ **4.** All motors produce ______ as they convert electrical energy to mechanical energy.

______ **5.** A(n) ______ is the application of too much load to a motor.

______ **6.** ______ causes metal parts to rust and motor coil insulation to lose some of its insulating properties.

______ **7.** The ______ of a belt is measured from the center of the drive pulley to the center of the driven pulley.

______ **8.** ______ is usually corrected by placing shims under the feet of the motor or driven equipment.

______ **9.** A motor ______ is an imperfection created during the manufacture of the motor that impairs its use.

______ **10.** Motor ______ is any damage that occurs to a properly manufactured motor.

______ **11.** Water used to clean a motor should not exceed ______°F.

______ **12.** For normal operation, electric motor oil should be added to sleeve bearings of motors after ______ years.

______ **13.** For normal operation, motor ball bearings should be lubricated after ______ years.

______ **14.** Motors other than ______ types can usually be mounted in any position.

______ **15.** The belt should deflect approximately ______″ when thumb force is applied midway between pulleys.

True-False

T F **1.** Excessive heat is a major cause of motor failure.

T F **2.** The insulation class of motors is given in °C and/or °F.

T F **3.** As phase balance increases, motor temperature decreases.

T F **4.** Motors with a voltage unbalance require derating.

T F **5.** Voltage unbalance causes blackening of all stator windings.

T F **6.** Single phasing causes severe burning and distortion to two or more phase coils.

T F **7.** Over cycling occurs when a motor is repeatedly turned ON or OFF.

T F **8.** Belt tension is usually checked by measuring deflection.

T F **9.** Couplers compensate for misalignment of the motor and driven load.

T F **10.** To force dry a motor, heat is applied for approximately 18 to 30 hours.

Multiple Choice

_____ **1.** Whenever more than _____% voltage unbalance is measured, the power company should be notified.

A. 2
B. 4
C. 6
D. 8

_____ **2.** When one of the 3ϕ lines of a motor no longer delivers voltage to the motor, the motor will _____.

A. not operate
B. operate on one phase
C. operate on two phases
D. not be affected

_____ **3.** Surge voltage is _____ voltage.

A. higher-than-normal, temporary
B. higher-than-normal, permanent
C. lower-than-normal, temporary
D. lower-than-normal, permanent

_____ **4.** If a motor is drawing rated current, it is _____.

A. barely working
B. working in its lower mid-range
C. working in its upper mid-range
D. working to its maximum

_____ **5.** Motor starting current is usually _____ times the full-load running current of the motor.

A. two to three
B. three to four
C. four to five
D. five to six

_____ **6.** When a motor application requires that the motor be cycled often, _____.

A. use a 50°C rise motor
B. use a 1.25 or 1.35 service factor motor
C. provide additional cooling
D. A, B, and C

_____ **7.** When cleaning a motor with water, the water pressure should not exceed _____ psi.

A. 10
B. 15
C. 20
D. 25

_____ **8.** Single phasing can be reduced by using the _____.

A. proper size dual-element fuse
B. correct heater sizes
C. both A and B
D. neither A nor B

_____ **9.** When a motor has failed due to overloading, _____.

A. all motor windings will be blackened evenly
B. there will be obvious damage to the insulation
C. there will be isolated areas of damage
D. A, B, and C

_____ **10.** Belt deflection should equal _____″ per inch of span.

A. 1/64
B. 1/16
C. 1/4
D. neither A, B, nor C

Problems

State the proper direction of rotation for the drive (smaller) pulleys in problems 1 through 6.

________ **1.**

________ **2.**

________ **3.**

________ **4.**

________ **5.**

________ **6.**

Identify the type of misaligned sheaves in problems 7 through 9.

________ **7.** Offset

________ **8.** Angle

________ **9.** Pigeon toe

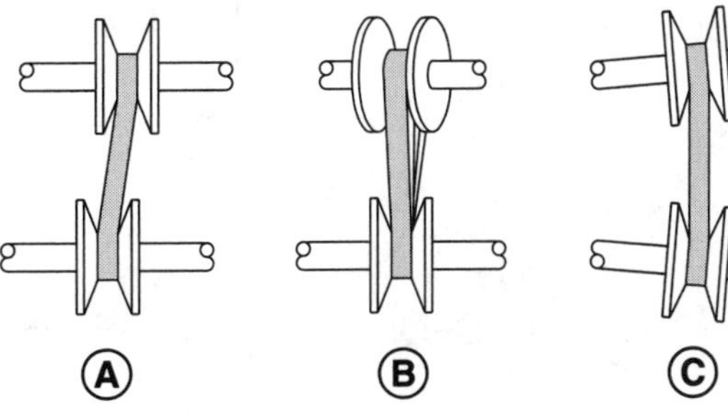

For problems 10 through 13, state the problem caused by the disruption.

______ **10.** The first few turns of the windings are burnt and and opened.

______ **11.** All windings are burnt.

______ **12.** One-third of the windings are burnt.

______ **13.** Two-thirds of the windings are burnt.

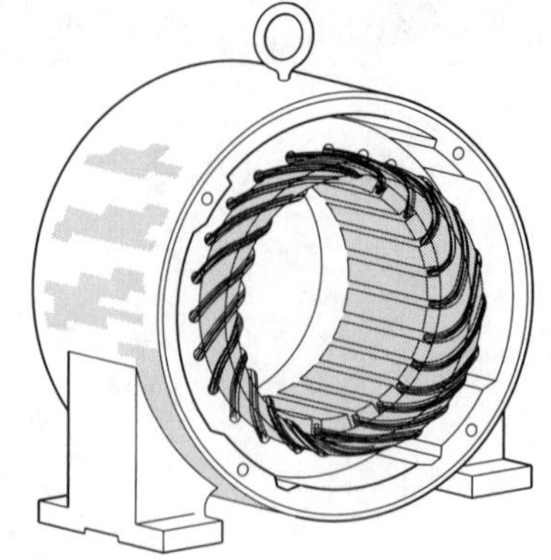

For problems 14 through 20, state the problem based on the motor drawings and/or meter readings.

______ **14.** The 25 HP motor is ________ .

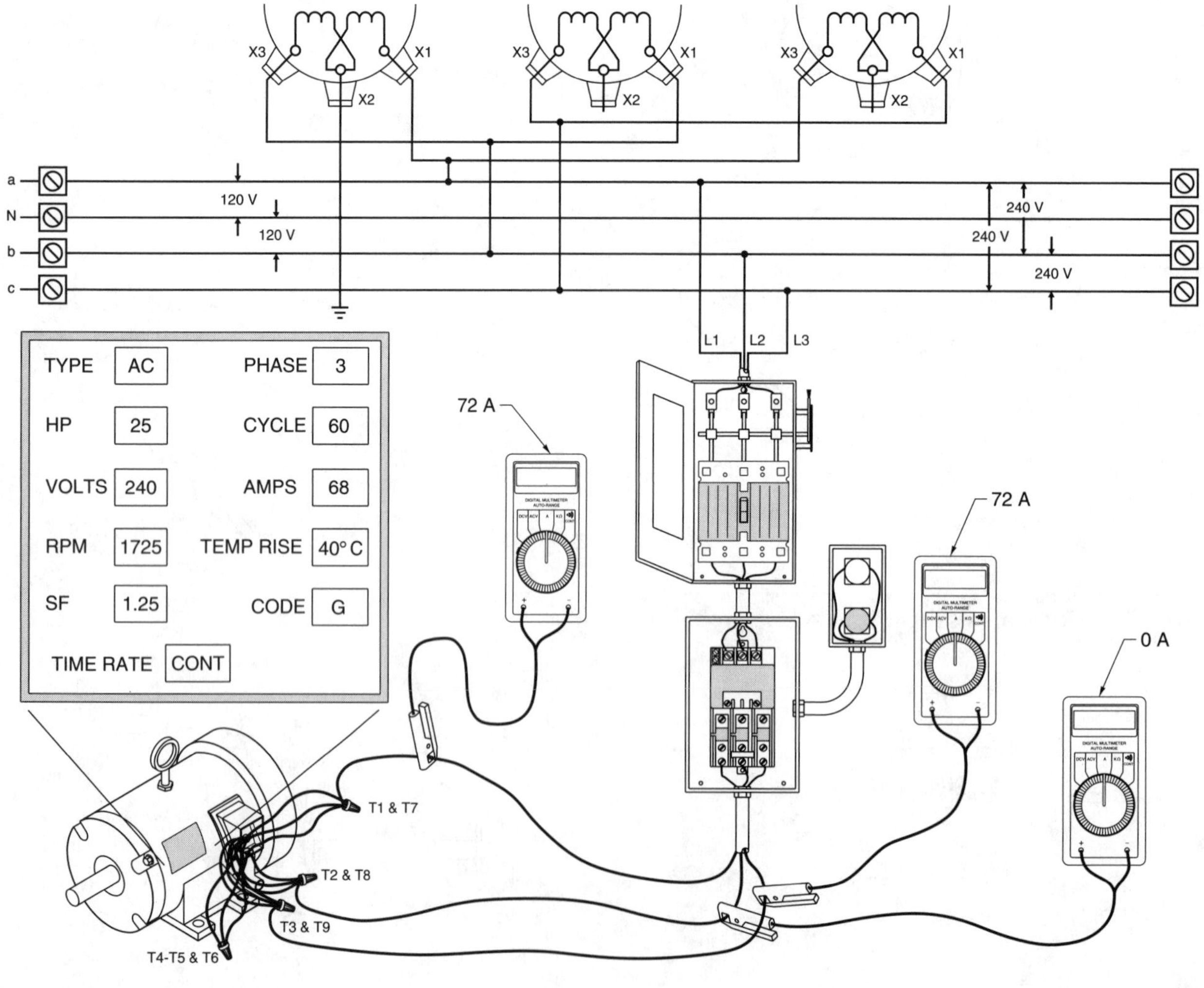

X3 X1 X2 X3 X1 X2 X3 X1 X2

a N b c

120 V 120 V 240 V 240 V 240 V

L1 L2 L3

TYPE	AC	PHASE	3
HP	25	CYCLE	60
VOLTS	240	AMPS	68
RPM	1725	TEMP RISE	40° C
SF	1.25	CODE	G
TIME RATE	CONT		

72 A

72 A

0 A

T1 & T7

T2 & T8

T3 & T9

T4-T5 & T6

__________ **15.** The 15 HP motor has a(n) ________ .

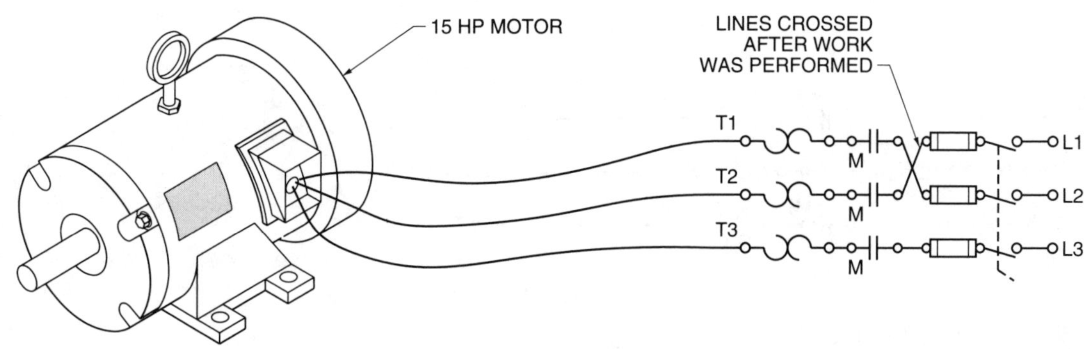

__________ **16.** The 20 HP motor has a(n) ________ .

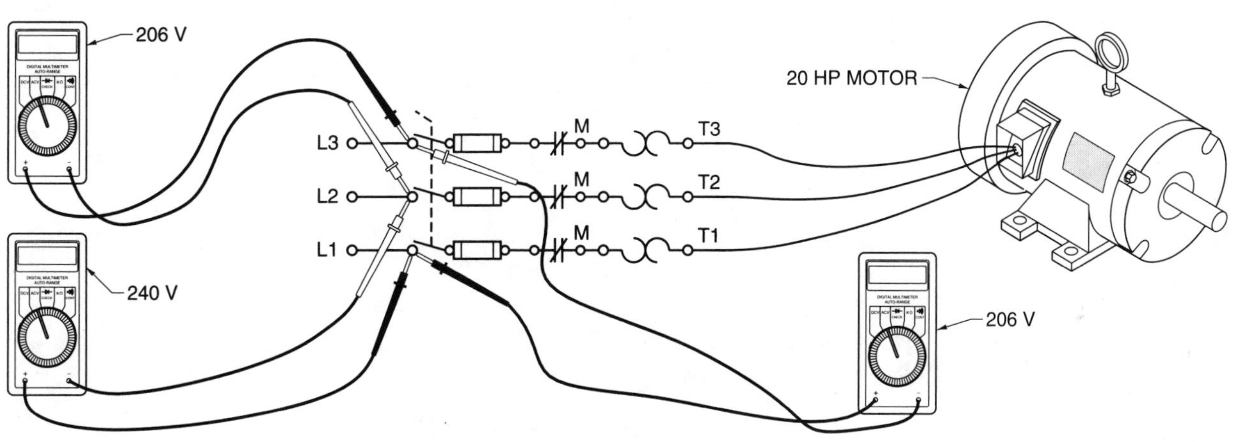

__________ **17.** The 30 HP motor has a(n) ________ .

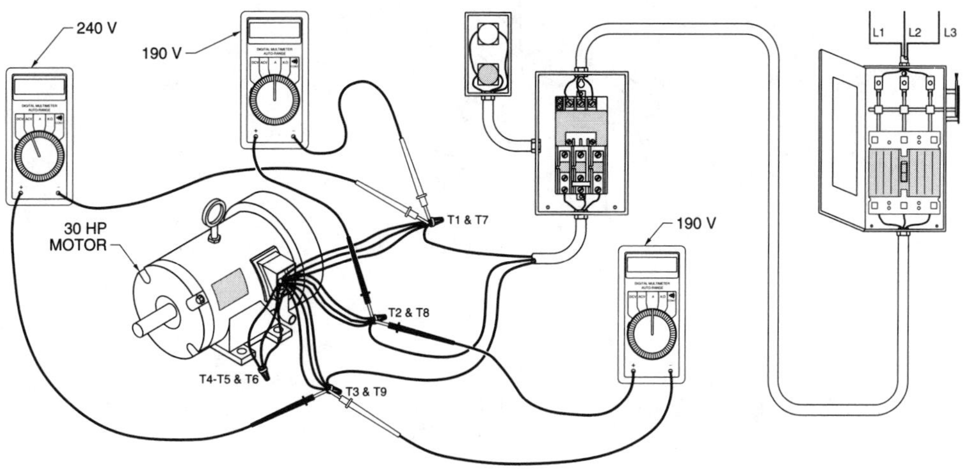

_________ **18.** The 10 HP motor has a(n) _________ .

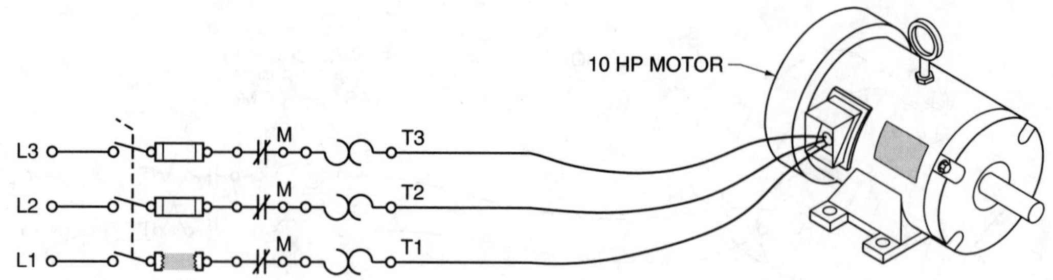

_________ **19.** The belt tension is too _________.

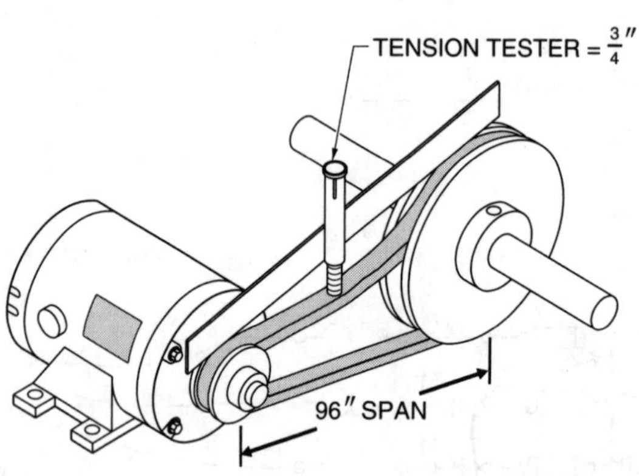

_________ **20.** The belt tension is _________.

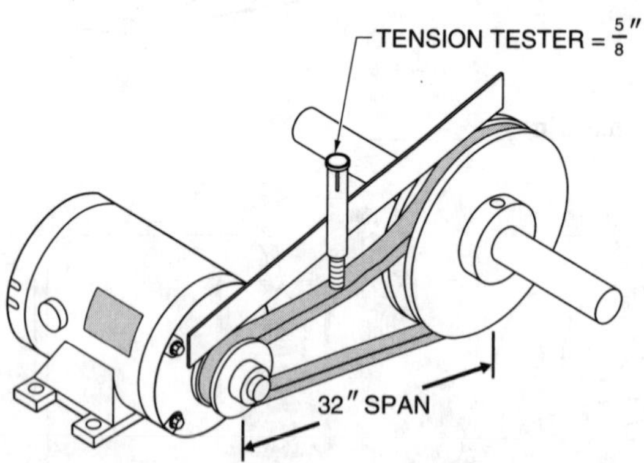

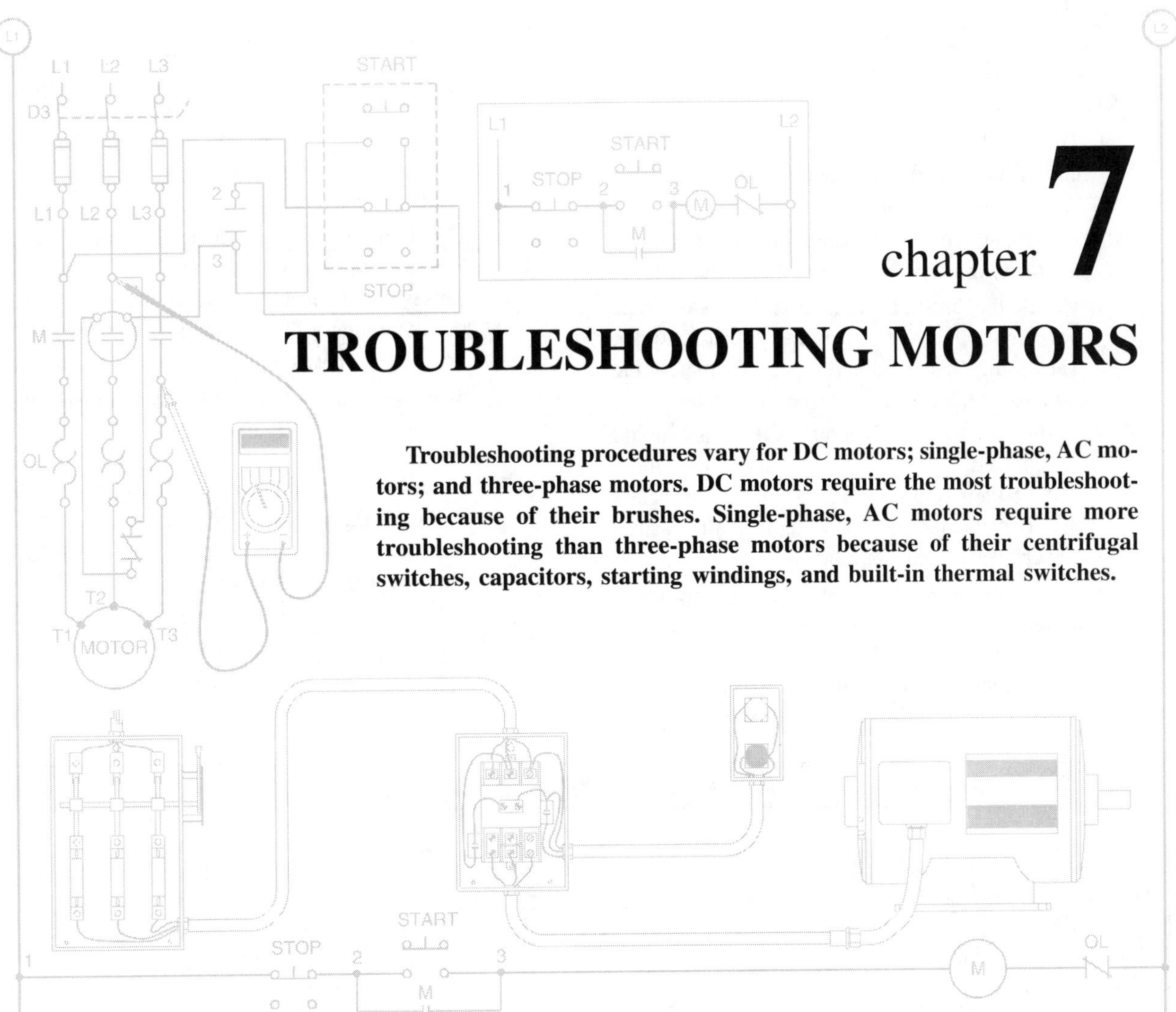

chapter 7 TROUBLESHOOTING MOTORS

Troubleshooting procedures vary for DC motors; single-phase, AC motors; and three-phase motors. DC motors require the most troubleshooting because of their brushes. Single-phase, AC motors require more troubleshooting than three-phase motors because of their centrifugal switches, capacitors, starting windings, and built-in thermal switches.

DIRECT CURRENT MOTORS

Direct current motors are used in applications that require very high torque. See Appendix. To produce the high torque, the outside power supply is connected to both the armature and field. A commutator and brushes are used to supply power to the rotating field. Because of their brushes, DC motors generally require more repair than motors that do not use brushes. The brushes should be checked first when troubleshooting DC motors.

Brushes wear faster than any other component of a DC motor. They ride on the fast-moving commutator. When two moving surfaces must touch each other, bearings and lubrication are generally used to reduce friction. However, no lubrication can be used between the moving brushes and commutator because the brushes must carry current from the armature. Sparking occurs as the current passes from the commutator to the brushes. Sparking causes heat, and heat causes burning and wear of electric parts.

Troubleshooting Direct Current Motors

The brushes and commutator are subject to wear. The brushes are designed to wear as the motor ages. It is much easier and less expensive to replace worn brushes than to service or replace a worn commutator. Most DC motors are designed so that the brushes and the commutator can be inspected without disassembling the motor. Some motors require disassembly for close inspection of the brushes and commutator.

If the motor is still operable, observe the brushes as the motor is operating. The brushes should be riding on the commutator smoothly, with little or no sparking. There should be no brush noise, such as chattering. Brush sparking, chattering, or a rough commutator indicates service is required.

Troubleshooting Brushes. The condition of the brushes and their holders is extremely important for good motor operation. The brushes should be checked every time the motor is serviced. See Figure 7-1. To troubleshoot brushes, apply the following procedure:

1. Turn the handle of the safety switch or combination starter OFF. Lock out and tag the starting mechanism per company policy.
2. Using a voltmeter, measure the voltage at the motor terminals to make sure the power is OFF.
3. Check the brush movement and tension. The brushes should move freely in the brush holder. The spring tension should be approximately the same on each brush. Remove the brushes.
4. Check the length of the brushes. Brushes should be replaced when they have worn down to about half of their original size. If any brush is less than half its original length, replace all brushes. Never replace only one brush.

   Brush compositions include high-grade carbon, electrographite, natural graphite, and carbon graphite. Each composition has its advantages or disadvantages. Always replace brushes with brushes of the same composition. Check manufacturer's recommendations for type of brushes to use.
5. Check the position of the brush holder in relationship to the commutator. The brush holder should be $1/16''$ to $1/8''$ from the commutator. If the brush holder is closer, the commutator may be damaged. If the brush holder is too far away, the brush may break.
6. Check for proper brush pressure. Brush pressure is critical to proper operation. Too little pressure causes the brushes to arc excessively and groove the commutator. Too much pressure causes the brushes to chatter and wear faster than normal.

   Brush pressure varies with the composition of the brush. It is usually about 1.5 to 5 psi of surface area. If the original spring is in good condition, it should provide the proper pressure. If the spring is not in good condition, replace with one of the same type. Brush pressure is checked using a brush-pressure tester. Follow the manufacturer's procedures.

   When checking brush pressure, remove the endbell on the side in which the commutator is located. Pull back on the gauge, noting the

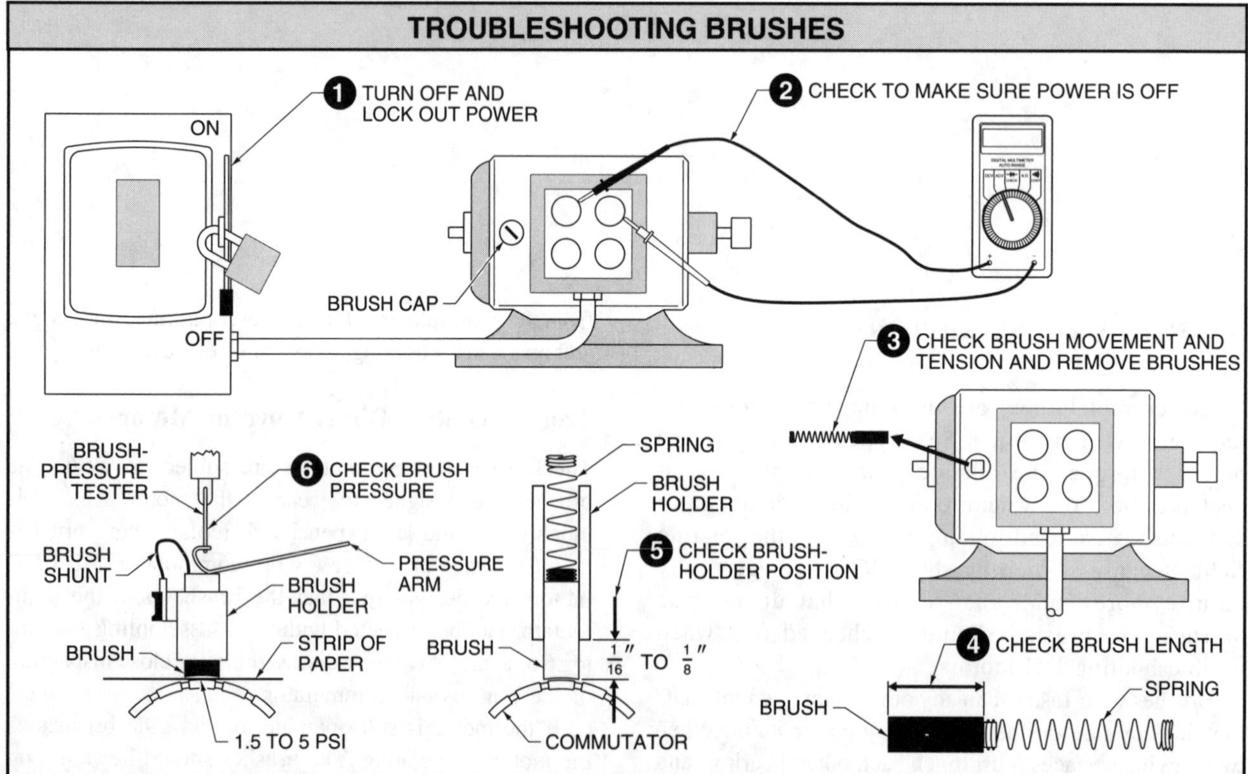

Figure 7-1. Troubleshoot brushes by checking brush movement and length.

pressure at which the piece of paper is free to move. Divide this reading by the contact area of the brush to get actual brush pressure in psi. Check the measured pressure to make sure it falls within the manufacturer's listed range.

Troubleshooting Commutators. Brushes wear faster than the commutator. However, after the brushes have been changed once or twice, the commutator usually needs servicing. Any marking on the commutator, such as grooves or ruts, or discolorations other than a polished, brown color where the brushes ride, indicate a problem. See Figure 7-2. To troubleshoot commutators, apply the following procedure:

1. Make a visual check of the commutator. The commutator should be smooth and concentric. A uniform dark copper oxide carbon film should be present on the surface of the commutator. This naturally occurring film acts like a lubricant by prolonging the life of the brushes and reducing wear on the commutator surface.
2. Check the mica insulation between the commutator segments. The mica insulation separates and insulates each commutator segment. It should be undercut (lowered below the surface) approximately 1/32″ to 1/16″, depending upon the size of the motor. The larger the motor, the deeper the undercut. Replace or service the commutator if the mica is raised.

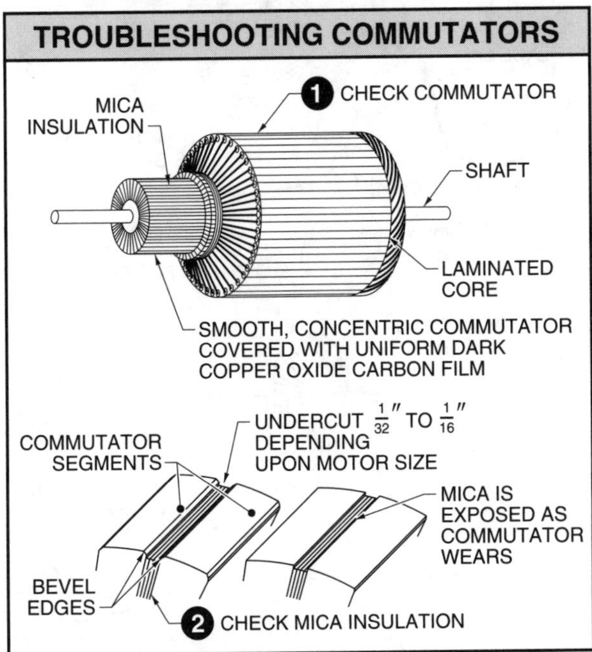

Figure 7-2. Troubleshoot commutators by checking film, segments, and mica.

Troubleshooting for Grounded, Open, or Short Circuits. The DC motor can be tested for a grounded, open, or short circuit by using a test light. A *grounded circuit* is a circuit in which current leaves it normal path and travels to the frame of the motor. It is caused when insulation breaks down or is damaged and touches the metal frame of the motor.

An *open circuit* is a circuit that no longer provides a path for current to flow. It is caused when a wire or connection has physically moved apart from another wire or connection.

A *short circuit* is a circuit in which current takes a shortcut around the normal path of current flow. It is caused when the insulation of two wires from different parts of the circuit touch. Shorts are usually a result of insulation breakdown.

A test light is preferred for a quick check of the motor. The test light gives good results for obvious problems. Additional testing equipment, such as ohmmeters and megohmmeters, are required for less obvious problems. For example, a megohmmeter is used to test for insulation breakdown. See Applications. See Figure 7-3. To troubleshoot for a grounded circuit, open circuit, or short circuit, apply the following procedure:

1. To test for a grounded circuit, connect one lead of the test light to the frame of the motor. Touch the other test light lead from one motor lead to the other. If the test light turns ON, a grounded circuit is present. Service and repair the motor.
2. To test for an open circuit, connect the two test light leads to the motor field and armature circuits as follows:

COMPOUND MOTORS	SHUNT MOTORS	SERIES MOTORS
A1 to A2	A1 to A2	A1 to A2
F1 to F2	F1 to F2	S1 to S2
S1 to S2		

   If the test light turns ON, the circuits are complete. If the test light does not turn ON, the circuit is open. Service and repair the motor.
3. To test for a short circuit between windings, connect the two test-light leads to the motor field and armature circuits as follows:

COMPOUND MOTORS	SHUNT MOTORS	SERIES MOTORS
A1 to F1, A2 to F2	A1 to F1	A1 to S1
A1 to F2, A2 to S1	A1 to F2	A1 to S2
A1 to S1, A2 to S2	A2 to F1	A2 to S1
A1 to S2, F1 to S1	A2 to F2	A2 to S2
A2 to F1, F1 to S2		

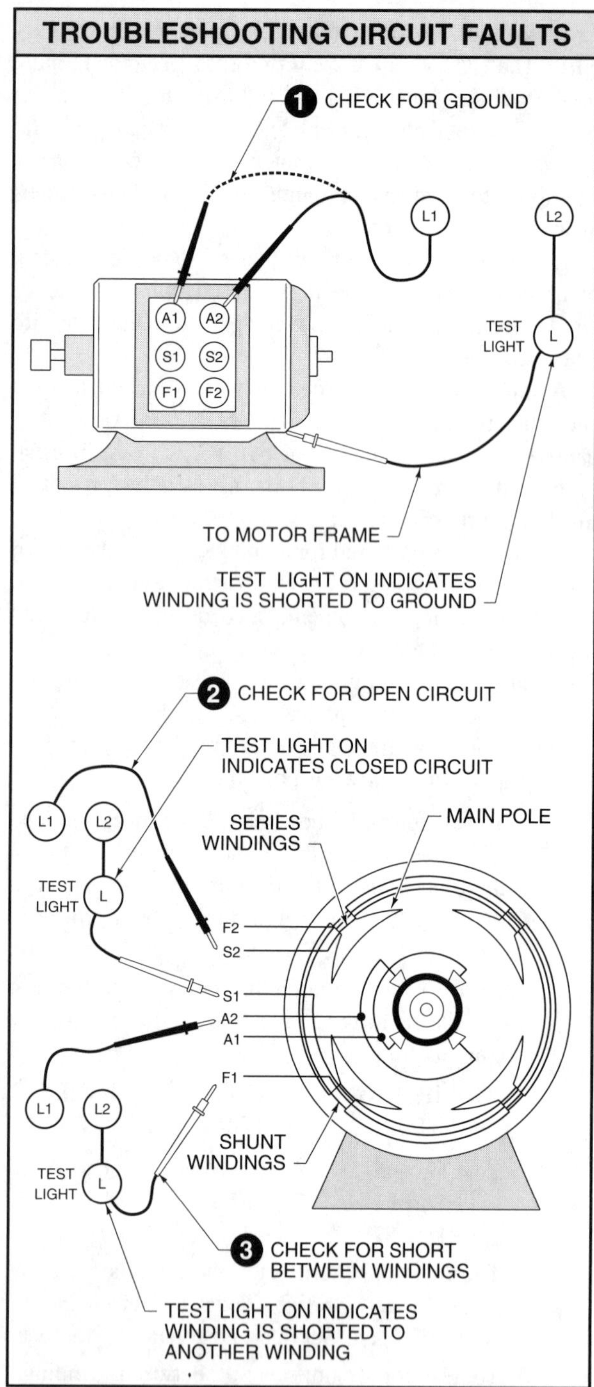

Figure 7-3. Troubleshoot for grounded, open, or short circuits with a test light.

If the test light turns ON, the circuit is shorted. If the test light does not turn ON, the circuit is not shorted. Service and repair the motor.

Troubleshooting for Grounded or Shorted Commutator Windings. A commutator is grounded whenever one or more of its segments (bars) make contact with the iron core of the commutator. An armature winding is also grounded whenever one or more windings makes contact with the iron core. See Figure 7-4. To troubleshoot for a grounded commutator or armature winding, apply the following procedure:

1. To test for a commutator segment grounded to the shaft, connect one lead of the test light to the shaft. Touch the other test lead to each commutator segment. The test light will turn ON if voltage passes through the commutator segments. If the test light turns ON, the commutator or the winding is grounded. Service and repair the commutator.
2. To test for a short between adjacent commutator segments, connect one test lead to a commutator segment. Touch the other test leads to each adjacent commutator segment. The test light will turn ON if voltage passes through the commutator segments. If the test light turns ON, the adjacent segments are shorted. Service and repair the commutator. There should also be no sparking or arcing between any segments. This would indicate a partial short. Service and repair the commutator.

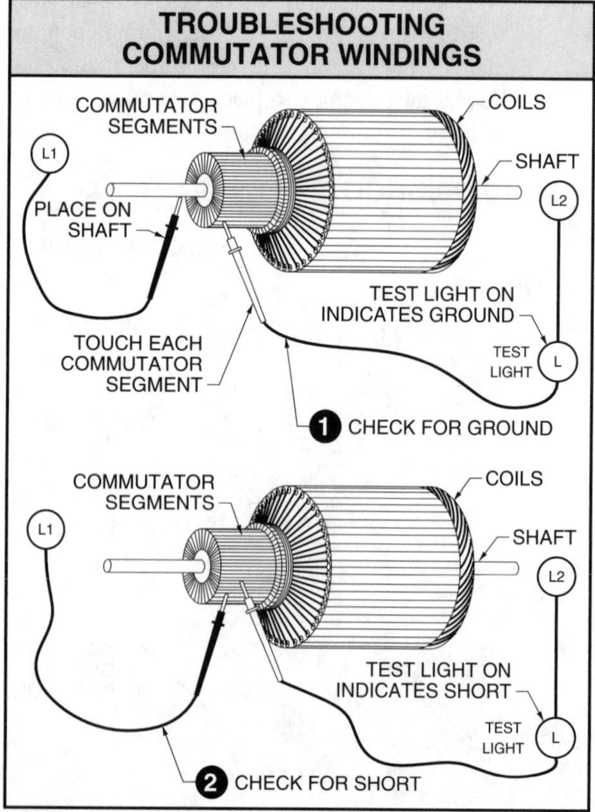

Figure 7-4. Troubleshoot for grounded or shorted commutator windings with a test light.

SINGLE-PHASE MOTORS

Most problems with 1ϕ motors involve the centrifugal switch, thermal switch, or capacitor(s). If the problem is in the centrifugal switch, thermal switch, or capacitor, the motor is usually serviced and repaired. However, if the motor is more than 10 years old and less than 1 HP, the motor is usually replaced. If the motor is less than 1⁄8 HP, it is almost always replaced.

Troubleshooting Shaded-Pole Motors

The shaded-pole motor has very low starting torque. It is generally limited to approximately 1⁄20 HP and used for applications, such as small fans and timing devices. Shaded-pole motors that fail are usually replaced. However, the reason for the motor failure should be found, if possible. If the motor failed due to a jammed load, etc., replacing the motor will not solve the problem. See Figure 7-5. To troubleshoot a shaded-pole motor, apply the following procedure:

1. Turn power to motor OFF. Visually inspect the motor. Replace the motor if it is burned, the shaft is jammed, or if there is any sign of damage.
2. The only electric circuit that can be tested without taking the motor apart is the stator winding. With an ohmmeter, measure the resistance of the stator winding. Set the ohmmeter to the lowest scale for taking the reading. If the ohmmeter indicates an infinity reading, the winding is open. Replace the motor. If the ohmmeter indicates a zero reading, the winding is shorted. Replace the motor. If the ohmmeter indicates a low-resistance reading, the winding may still be good. Check the winding with a megohmmeter before replacing. See Applications.

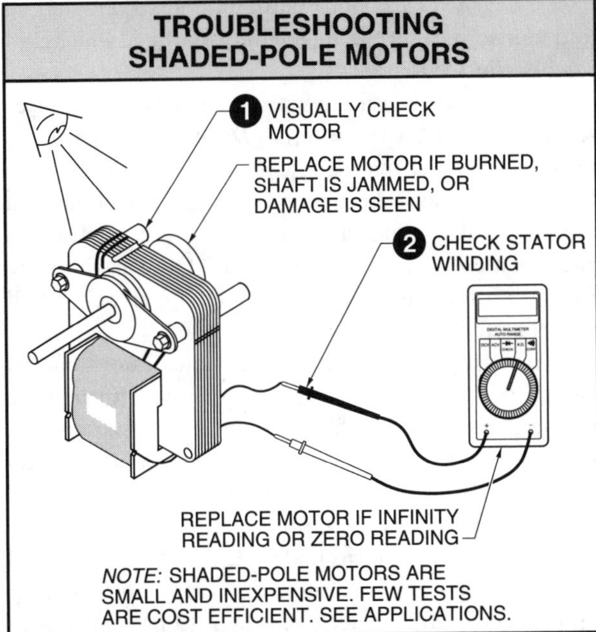

Figure 7-5. Troubleshoot shaded-pole motors with an ohmmeter.

Troubleshooting Split-Phase Motors

The split-phase motor has a starting and running winding. The starting winding is automatically removed by a centrifugal switch as the motor accelerates. Some split-phase motors also include a thermal switch that automatically turns the motor OFF when it overheats. Thermal switches may have a manual reset or automatic reset. Caution should be taken with any motor that has an automatic reset, as the motor can automatically restart at any time. See Figure 7-6. To troubleshoot a split-phase motor, apply the following procedure:

1. Turn power to motor OFF. Visually inspect the motor. Replace the motor if it is burned, the shaft is jammed, or if there is any sign of damage.
2. Check to determine if the motor is controlled by a thermal switch. If the thermal switch is manual, reset the thermal switch and turn motor ON.
3. If the motor does not start, use a voltmeter to check for voltage at the motor terminals. The voltage should be within 10% of the motor's listed voltage. If the voltage is not correct, troubleshoot the circuit leading to the motor. If the voltage is correct, turn power to motor OFF so the motor can be tested.
4. Turn the handle of the safety switch or combination starter OFF. Lock out and tag the starting mechanism per company policy.
5. With power OFF, connect the ohmmeter to the same motor terminals the incoming power leads were disconnected from. The ohmmeter will read the resistance of the starting and running windings. Since the windings are in parallel, their combined resistance is less than the resistance of either winding alone. If the meter reads zero, a short is present. If the meter reads infinity, an open circuit is present and the motor should be replaced. *Note:* The motor size is too small for a repair to be cost efficient.
6. Visually inspect the centrifugal switch for signs of burning or broken springs. If any obvious signs of problems are present, service or replace the switch. If not, check the switch using an ohmmeter.

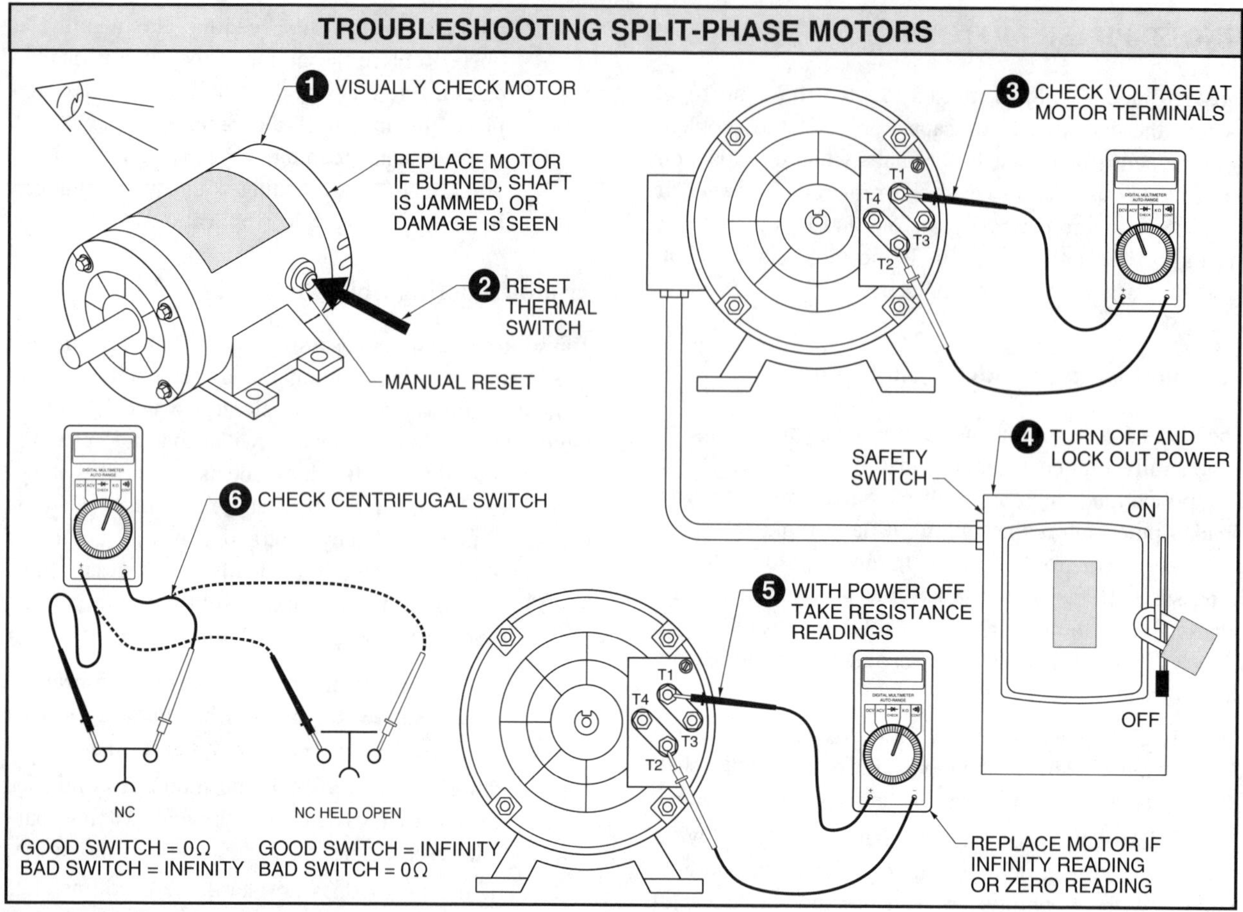

Figure 7-6. Troubleshoot split-phase motors with an ohmmeter.

Manually operate the centrifugal switch. (The endbell on the switch side may have to be removed.) If the motor is good, the resistance on the ohmmeter will decrease. If the resistance does not change, a problem exists. Continue checking to determine the problem.

Troubleshooting Capacitor Motors

A capacitor motor is a split-phase motor with the addition of one or two capacitors. Capacitors give the motor more starting and/or running torque. Troubleshooting capacitor motors is similar to troubleshooting split-phase motors. The only additional device to be considered is the capacitor.

Capacitors have a limited life and are often the problem in capacitor motors. Capacitors may have a short circuit, an open circuit, or may deteriorate to the point that they must be replaced. Deterioration can also change the value of a capacitor, which can cause additional problems. When a capacitor short-circuits, the winding in the motor may burn out. When a capacitor deteriorates or opens, the motor has poor starting torque. Poor starting torque may prevent the motor from starting, which will usually trip the overloads.

All capacitors are made with two conducting surfaces separated by dielectric material. *Dielectric material* is a medium in which an electric field is maintained with little or no outside energy supply. It is the type of material used to insulate conducting surfaces of a capacitor. Capacitors are either oil or electrolytic. Oil capacitors are filled with oil and sealed in a metal container. The oil serves as the dielectric material.

More motors use electrolytic capacitors than oil capacitors. Electrolytic capacitors are formed by winding two sheets of aluminum foil separated by pieces of thin paper impregnated with an electrolyte. An *electrolyte* is a conducting medium in which the current flow occurs by ion migration. The electrolyte is used as the dielectric material. The aluminum foil and electrolyte are encased in a cardboard or aluminum cover. A vent hole is provided to prevent a possible explosion in the event the capacitor is shorted or overheated.

AC capacitors are used with capacitor motors. Capacitors that are designed to be connected to AC have no polarity. See Figure 7-7. To troubleshoot a capacitor motor, apply the following procedure:

1. Turn the handle of the safety switch or combination starter OFF. Lock out and tag the starting mechanism per company policy.
2. Using a voltmeter, measure the voltage at the motor terminals to make sure the power is OFF.
3. Capacitors are located on the outside frame of the motor. Remove the cover of the capacitor. **Caution:** A good capacitor will hold a charge, even when power is removed.
4. Visually check the capacitor for leakage, cracks, or bulges. Replace the capacitor if present.
5. Remove the capacitor from the circuit and discharge it. To safely discharge a capacitor, place a 20,000 SL, 2 W resistor across the terminals for five seconds.
6. After the capacitor is discharged, connect the ohmmeter leads to the capacitor terminals. The ohmmeter will indicate the general condition of the capacitor. A capacitor is either good, shorted, or open.

- Good Capacitor. The needle will swing to zero resistance and slowly move across the scale to infinity. When the needle reaches the halfway point, remove one of the leads and wait 30 seconds. When the lead is reconnected, the needle should swing back to the halfway point and continue to infinity. This shows the capacitor can hold a charge. If the needle swings back to zero resistance, the capacitor can not hold a charge and must be replaced.
- Shorted Capacitor. The needle will swing to zero and not move. The capacitor is bad and must be replaced.
- Open Capacitor. The needle will not move from infinity. The capacitor is bad and must be replaced.

THREE-PHASE MOTORS

Three-phase motors have less components that may malfunction than other motor types. Therefore, 3ϕ motors usually operate for many years without any problems.

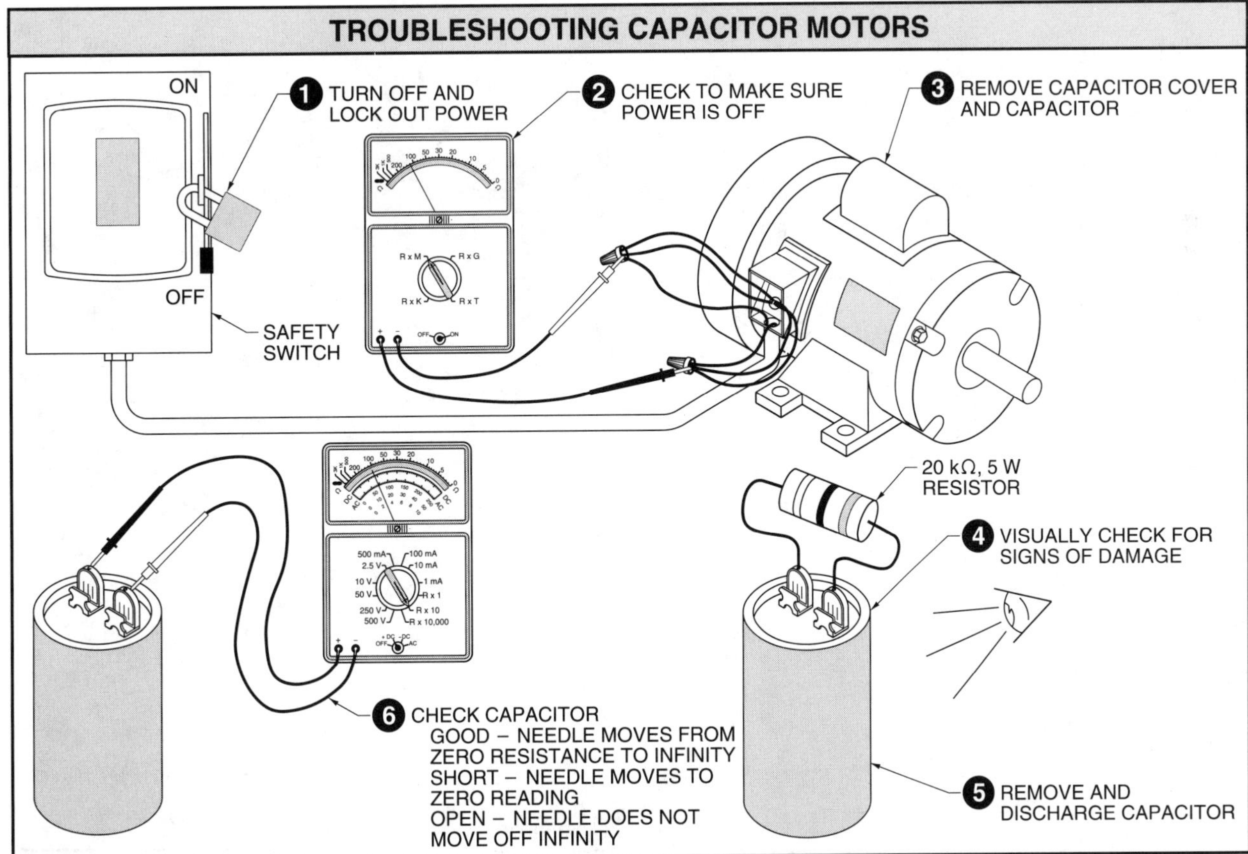

Figure 7-7. Troubleshoot capacitors with an ohmmeter and a resistor.

If a 3ϕ motor is the problem, the motor is serviced or replaced. Servicing usually requires that the motor be sent to a motor repair shop for rewinding. If the motor is less than 1 HP and more than five years old, it is replaced. If the motor is more than 1 HP, but less than 5 HP, it may be serviced or replaced. If the motor is more than 5 HP, it is usually serviced.

Troubleshooting Three-Phase Motors

The extent of troubleshooting a 3ϕ motor is dependent upon the motor's application. If the motor is used in an application that is critical to the operation or production, testing is usually limited to checking the voltage at the motor. If the voltage is present and correct, the motor is assumed to be the problem. Unless it is very large, the motor is usually replaced at this time so production can be resumed. If time is not a critical factor, further tests can be made in order to determine the exact problem. See Figure 7-8. To troubleshoot a three-phase motor, apply the following procedure:

1. Using a voltmeter, measure the voltage at the motor terminals. If the voltage is present and at the correct level on all three phases, the motor must be checked. If the voltage is not present on all three phases, the incoming power supply must be checked.
2. If voltage is present but the motor is not operating, turn the handle of the safety switch or combination starter OFF. Lock out and tag the starting mechanism per company policy.
3. Disconnect the motor from the load.
4. After the load is disconnected, turn power ON to try restarting the motor. If the motor starts, check the load.

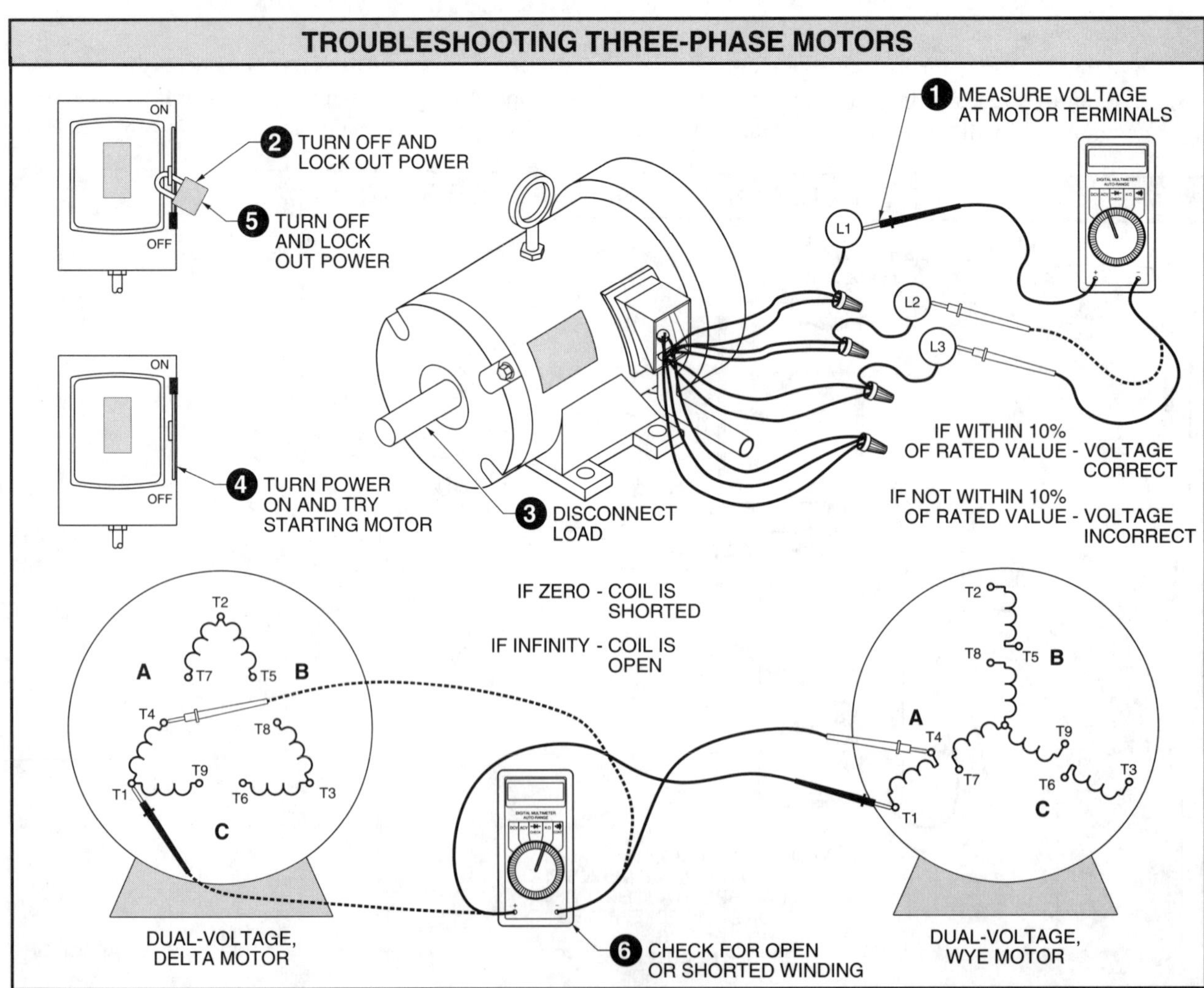

Figure 7-8. Troubleshoot three-phase motors with an ohmmeter.

5. If the motor does not start, turn it OFF and lock out the power.
6. With an ohmmeter, check the motor windings for any opens or shorts. Take a resistance reading of the T1-T4 coil. This coil must have a resistance reading. If the reading is zero, the coil is shorted. If the reading is infinity, the coil is opened. Since the coil winding is made of wire only, the resistance is low. However, there is resistance on a good coil winding. The larger the motor, the smaller the resistance reading.

   After the resistance of one coil has been found, the basic electrical laws of series and parallel circuits are applied. When measuring the resistance of two coils in series, the total resistance is twice the resistance of one coil. When measuring the resistance of two coils in parallel, the total resistance is one half the resistance of one coil.

TROUBLESHOOTING GUIDES

Troubleshooting guides for motors state a problem, its possible cause(s), and corrective actions(s) that may be taken. These easy-to-reference guides, while general in nature, may be used to quickly determine potential problems and possible courses of action. See Figure 7-9.

TROUBLESHOOTING GUIDE FOR SHADED-POLE MOTORS		
Problem	**Possible Cause**	**Corrective Action**
Motor will not start.	Blown fuse or open CB	Test the OCPD. If voltage is present at the input, but not the output of the OCPD, the fuse is blown or the CB is open. Check the rating of the OCPD. It should be at least 125% of the motor's FLC.
	Motor overload on starter tripped.	Allow overloads to cool. Reset overloads. If reset overloads do not start the motor, test the starter.
	Low or no voltage applied to motor	Check the voltage at the motor terminals. The voltage must be present and within 10% of the motor nameplate voltage. If voltage is present at the motor but the motor is not operating, remove the motor from the load the motor is driving. Reapply power to the motor. If the motor runs, the problem is with the load. If the motor does not run, the problem is with the motor. Replace or service the motor.
	Open control circuit between incoming power and motor	Check for cleanliness, tightness, and breaks. Use a voltmeter to test the circuit starting with the incoming power and moving to the motor terminals. Voltage generally stops at the problem area.
Fuse, CB, or overloads retrip after service.	Excessive load	If the motor is loaded to excess or jammed, the circuit OCPD will open. Disconnect the load from the motor. If the motor now runs properly, check the load. If the motor does not run and the fuse or CB opens, the problem is with the motor or control circuit. Remove the motor from the control circuit and connect it directly to the power source. If the motor runs properly, the problem is in the control circuit. Check the control circuit. If the motor opens the fuse or CB again, the problem is in the motor. Replace or service the motor.
Excessive noise db db	Unbalanced motor or load	An unbalanced motor or load causes vibration, which causes noise. Realign the motor and load. Check for excessive end play or loose parts. If the shaft is bent, replace the rotor or motor.
	Dry or worn bearings	Dry or worn bearings cause noise. The bearings may be dry due to dirty oil, oil not reaching the shaft, or motor overheating. Oil the bearings as recommended. If noise remains, replace the bearings or the motor.
	Excessive grease	Ball bearings that have excessive grease may cause the bearings to overheat. Overheated bearings cause noise. Remove any excess grease.

Figure 7-9. Troubleshooting guides are used to determine problems and possible courses of action.

TROUBLESHOOTING GUIDE FOR SPLIT-PHASE MOTORS		
Problem	**Possible Cause**	**Corrective Action**
Motor will not start.	Thermal cutout switch is open.	Reset the thermal switch. **Caution:** Resetting the thermal switch may automatically start the motor.
	Blown fuse or open CB	Test the OCPD. If voltage is present at the input, but not the output of the OCPD, the fuse is blown or the CB is open. Check the rating of the OCPD. It should be at least 125% of the motor's FLC.
	Motor overload on starter tripped.	Allow overloads to cool. Reset overloads. If reset overloads do not start the motor, test the starter.
	Low or no voltage applied to motor	Check the voltage at the motor terminals. The voltage must be present and within 10% of the motor nameplate voltage. If voltage is present at the motor but the motor is not operating, remove the motor from the load the motor is driving. Reapply power to the motor. If the motor runs, the problem is with the load. If the motor does not run, the problem is with the motor. Replace or service the motor.
	Open control circuit between incoming power and motor	Check for cleanliness, tightness, and breaks. Use a voltmeter to test the circuit starting with the incoming power and moving to the motor terminals. Voltage generally stops at the problem area.
	Starting winding not receiving power	Check the centrifugal switch to make sure it connects the starting winding when the motor is OFF.
Fuse, CB, or overloads retrip after service.	Blown fuse or open CB	Test the OCPD. If voltage is present at the input, but not the output of the OCPD, the fuse is blown or the CB is open. Check the rating of the OCPD. It should be at least 125% of the motor's FLC.
	Motor overload on starter tripped.	Allow overloads to cool. Reset overloads. If reset overloads do not start the motor, test the starter.
	Low or no voltage applied to motor	Check the voltage at the motor terminals. The voltage must be present and within 10% of the motor nameplate voltage. If voltage is present at the motor but the motor is not operating, remove the motor from the load the motor is driving. Reapply power to the motor. If the motor runs, the problem is with the load. If the motor does not run, the problem is with the motor. Replace or service the motor.
	Open control circuit between incoming power and motor	Check for cleanliness, tightness, and breaks. Use a voltmeter to test the circuit starting with the incoming power and moving to the motor terminals. Voltage generally stops at the problem area.
	Motor shaft does not turn.	Disconnect the motor from the load. If the motor shaft still does not turn, the bearings are frozen. Replace or service the motor.
Motor produces electric shock.	Broken or disconnected ground strap	Connect or replace ground strap. Test for proper ground.
	Hot power lead at motor connecting terminals is touching motor frame.	Disconnect the motor. Open the motor terminal box and check for poor connections, damaged insulation, or leads touching the frame. Service and test motor for ground.
	Motor winding shorted to frame	Remove, service, and test motor.
Motor overheats.	Starting windings are not being removed from circuit as motor accelerates.	When the motor is turned OFF, a distinct click should be heard as the centrifugal switch closes.
	Improper ventilation	Clean all ventilation openings. Vacuum or blow dirt out of motor with low-pressure, dry, compressed air.
	Motor is overloaded.	Check the load for binding. Check shaft straightness. Measure motor current under operating conditions. If the current is above the listed current rating, remove the motor. Remeasure the current under no-load conditions. If the current is excessive under load but not when unloaded, check the load. If the motor draws excessive current when disconnected, replace or service the motor.

	Dry or worn bearings	Dry or worn bearings cause noise. The bearings may be dry due to dirty oil, oil not reaching the shaft, or motor overheating. Oil the bearings as recommended. If noise remains, replace the bearings or the motor.
	Dirty bearings	Clean or replace bearings.
Excessive noise	Excessive end play	Check end play by trying to move the motor shaft in and out. Add end-play washers as required.
	Unbalanced motor or load	An unbalanced motor or load causes vibration, which causes noise. Realign the motor and load. Check for excessive end play or loose parts. If the shaft is bent, replace the rotor or motor.
	Dry or worn bearings	Dry or worn bearings cause noise. The bearings may be dry due to dirty oil, oil not reaching the shaft, or motor overheating. Oil the bearings as recommended. If noise remains, replace the bearings or the motor.
	Excessive grease	Ball bearings that have excessive grease may cause the bearings to overheat. Overheated bearings cause noise. Remove any excess grease.

TROUBLESHOOTING GUIDE FOR DIRECT CURRENT MOTORS

Problem	Possible Cause	Corrective Action
Motor will not start.	Blown fuse or open CB	Test the OCPD. If voltage is present at the input, but not the output of the OCPD, the fuse is blown or the CB is open. Check the rating of the OCPD. It should be at least 125% of the motor's FLC.
	Motor overload on starter tripped.	Allow overloads to cool. Reset overloads. If reset overloads do not start the motor, test the starter.
	No brush contact	Check brushes. Replace, if worn.
	Open control circuit between incoming power and motor	Check for cleanliness, tightness, and breaks. Use a voltmeter to test the circuit starting with the incoming power and moving to the motor terminals. Voltage generally stops at the problem area.
Fuse, CB, or overloads retrip after service.	Excessive load	If the motor is loaded to excess or is jammed, the circuit OCPD will open. Disconnect the load from the motor. If the motor now runs properly, check the load. If the motor does not run and the fuse or CB opens, the problem is with the motor or control circuit. Remove the motor from the control circuit and connect it directly to the power source. If the motor runs properly, the problem is in the control circuit. Check the control circuit. If the motor opens the fuse or CB again, the problem is in the motor. Replace or service the motor.
	Motor shaft does not turn.	Disconnect the motor from the load. If the motor shaft still does not turn, the bearings are frozen. Replace or service the motor.
Brushes chip or break.	Brush material is too weak or the wrong type for motor's duty rating.	Replace with better grade or type of brush. Consult manufacturer if problem continues.
	Brush face is overheating and losing brush bonding material.	Check for an overload on the motor. Reduce the load as required. Adjust brush holder arms.
	Brush holder is too far from commutator.	Too much space between the brush holder and the surface of the commutator allows the brush end to chip or break. Set correct space between brush holder and commutator.
	Brush tension is incorrect.	Adjust brush tension so the brush rides freely on the commutator.
Brushes spark.	Worn brushes	Replace worn brushes. Service the motor if rapid brush wear, excessive sparking, chipping, breaking, or chattering is present.
	Commutator is concentric.	Grind commutator and undercut mica. Replace commutator if necessary.
	Excessive vibration	Balance armature. Check brushes. They should be riding freely.
Rapid brush wear	Wrong brush material, type, or grade	Replace with brushes recommended by manufacturer.
	Incorrect brush tension	Adjust brush tension so the brush rides freely on the commutator.

Motor overheats.	Improper ventilation	Clean all ventilation openings. Vacuum or blow dirt out of motor with low-pressure, dry, compressed air.
	Motor is overloaded.	Check the load for binding. Check shaft straightness. Measure motor current under operating conditions. If the current is above the listed current rating, remove the motor. Remeasure the current under no-load conditions. If the current is excessive under load but not when unloaded, check the load. If the motor draws excessive current when disconnected, replace or service the motor.

TROUBLESHOOTING GUIDE FOR THREE-PHASE MOTORS

Problem	Possible Cause	Corrective Action
Motor will not start.	Wrong motor connections	Most 3ϕ motors are dual-voltage. Check for proper motor connections.
	Blown fuse or open CB	Test the OCPD. If voltage is present at the input, but not the output of the OCPD, the fuse is blown or the CB is open. Check the rating of the OCPD. It should be at least 125% of the motor's FLC.
	Motor overload on starter tripped.	Allow overloads to cool. Reset overloads. If reset overloads do not start the motor, test the starter.
	Low or no voltage applied to motor	Check the voltage at the motor terminals. The voltage must be present and within 10% of the motor nameplate voltage. If voltage is present at the motor but the motor is not operating, remove the motor from the load the motor is driving. Reapply power to the motor. If the motor runs, the problem is with the load. If the motor does not run, the problem is with the motor. Replace or service the motor.
	Open control circuit between incoming power and motor	Check for cleanliness, tightness, and breaks. Use a voltmeter to test the circuit starting with the incoming power and moving to the motor terminals. Voltage generally stops at the problem area.
Fuse, CB, or overloads retrip after service.	Power not applied to all three lines	Measure voltage at each power line. Correct any power supply problems.
	Blown fuse or open CB	Test the OCPD. If voltage is present at the input, but not the output of the OCPD, the fuse is blown or the CB is open. Check the rating of the OCPD. It should be at least 125% of the motor's FLC.
	Motor overload on starter tripped.	Allow overloads to cool. Reset overloads. If reset overloads do not start the motor, test the starter.
	Low or no voltage applied to motor	Check the voltage at the motor terminals. The voltage must be present and within 10% of the motor nameplate voltage. If voltage is present at the motor but the motor is not operating, remove the motor from the load the motor is driving. Reapply power to the motor. If the motor runs, the problem is with the load. If the motor does not run, the problem is with the motor. Replace or service the motor.
	Open control circuit between incoming power and motor	Check for cleanliness, tightness, and breaks. Use a voltmeter to test the circuit starting with the incoming power and moving to the motor terminals. Voltage generally stops at the problem area.
	Motor shaft does not turn.	Disconnect the motor from the load. If the motor shaft still does not turn, the bearings are frozen. Replace or service the motor.
Motor overheats.	Motor is single phasing.	Check each of the 3ϕ power lines for correct voltage.
	Improper ventilation	Clean all ventilation openings. Vacuum or blow dirt out of motor with low-pressure, dry, compressed air.
	Motor is overloaded.	Check the load for binding. Check shaft straightness. Measure motor current under operating conditions. If the current is above the listed current rating, remove the motor. Remeasure the current under no-load conditions. If the current is excessive under load but not when unloaded, check the load. If the motor draws excessive current when disconnected, replace or service the motor.

Application — Megohmmeter Use

A megohmmeter is a device that detects motor insulation deterioration before the motor fails. A *megohmmeter* is an ohmmeter capable of measuring very high resistances by using high voltages. Typical megohmmeter test voltages range from 50 V to 5000 V. A megohmmeter is used to perform motor insulation tests to prevent electrical shock and other causes of motor insulation failure, which include excessive moisture, dirt, heat, cold, corrosive vapors or solids, vibration, and aging.

A megohmmeter measures the resistance of different windings, or it measures the resistance from a winding to ground. An ohmmeter measures the resistance of common windings and components in a motor circuit. See Ohmmeter and Megohmmeter Connections.

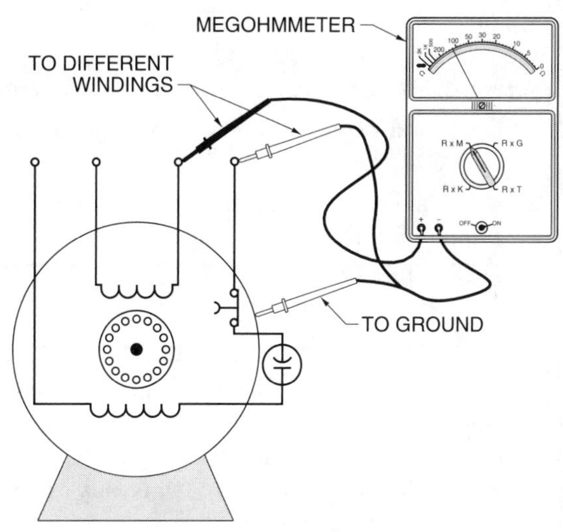

MEGOHMMETER CONNECTIONS

Several megohmmeter readings should be taken over a long period of time because the resistance of good insulation varies greatly. Megohmmeter readings are typically taken when the motor is installed and semiannually thereafter. A motor is in need of service if the megohmmeter reading is below the minimum acceptable resistance. See Recommended Minimum Resistance.

RECOMMENDED MINIMUM RESISTANCE*	
Minimum Acceptable Resistance	**Motor Voltage Rating (from nameplate)**
100,000 Ω	Less than 208
200,000 Ω	208–240
300,000 Ω	240–600
1 MΩ	600–1000
2 MΩ	1000–2400
3 MΩ	2400–5000

* values for motor windings at 40°C

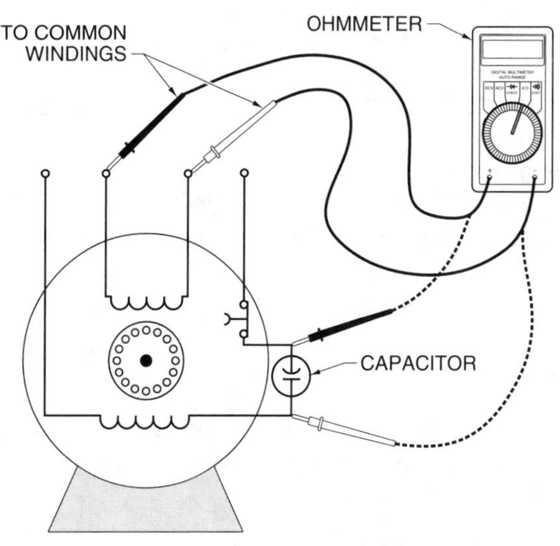

OHMMETER CONNECTIONS

Note: A motor with good insulation may have readings of 10 to 100 times the minimum acceptable resistance. If the resistance reading is less than the minimum value, service the motor.

Caution: A megohmmeter uses very high voltage for testing (up to 5000 V). Avoid touching the meter leads to the motor frame. Always follow the manufacturer's recommended procedures and safety rules. After performing insulation tests with a megohmmeter, connect the motor windings to ground through a 1000 Ω, 2 W resistor. The winding should be connected for 10 times the motor testing time in order to discharge the energy stored in the insulation.

Application — Insulation Spot Test

An *insulation spot test* checks motor insulation over the life of the motor. An insulation spot test is taken when the motor is placed in service and every six months thereafter. The test should also be taken after a motor is serviced. To perform an insulation spot test, apply the procedure:

1. Connect a megohmmeter to measure the resistance of each winding lead to ground. Record the readings after 60 seconds.
2. If a reading does not meet the minimum acceptable resistance, service the motor. See Recommended Minimum Resistance on page 211.
3. If all readings are above the minimum acceptable resistance, record the lowest meter reading on an insulation spot test graph. The lowest reading is used because a motor is only as good as its weakest point.
4. Discharge the motor windings.
5. Repeat Steps 1 through 3 every six months.
6. Interpret results. See Insulation Spot Test Graph.

Point A represents the motor insulation condition when the motor was placed in service. Point B represents the effects of aging, contamination, etc., on the motor insulation. Point C represents motor insulation failure. Point D represents motor insulation condition after being rewound.

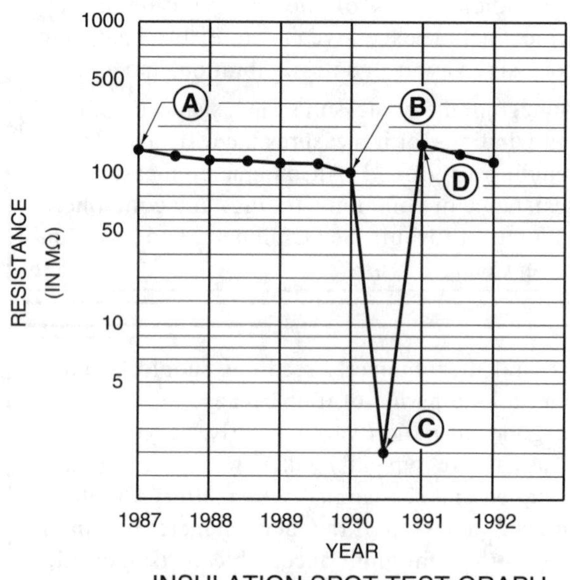

INSULATION SPOT TEST GRAPH

Application — Dielectric Absorption Test

A *dielectric absorption test* checks the absorption characteristics of humid or contaminated insulation. The test is performed over a 10-minute period. To perform a dielectric absorption test, apply the procedure:

1. Connect a megohmmeter to measure the resistance of each winding lead to ground. If a reading does not meet the minimum acceptable resistance, service the motor.
2. If all readings are above the minimum acceptable resistance, record the lowest meter reading on a dielectric absorption test graph. Record the readings every 10 seconds for the first minute and every minute thereafter for 10 minutes.

3. Discharge the motor windings.
4. Interpret the results. See Dielectric Absorption Test Graph.

The slope of the curve shows the condition of the insulation. Good insulation (Curve A) shows a continual increase in resistance. Moist or cracked insulation (Curve B) shows a relatively constant resistance.

A polarization index is obtained by dividing the value of the 10-minute reading by the value of the 1-minute reading. The polarization index is an indication of the condition of the insulation. A low polarization index indicates excessive moisture or contamination. See Minimum Acceptable Polarization Index Values.

For example, if the 1-minute reading of Class B insulation is 80 MΩ and the 10-minute reading is 90 MΩ, the polarization index is 1.125 (90 MΩ ÷ 80 MΩ = 1.125). The insulation contains excessive moisture or contamination.

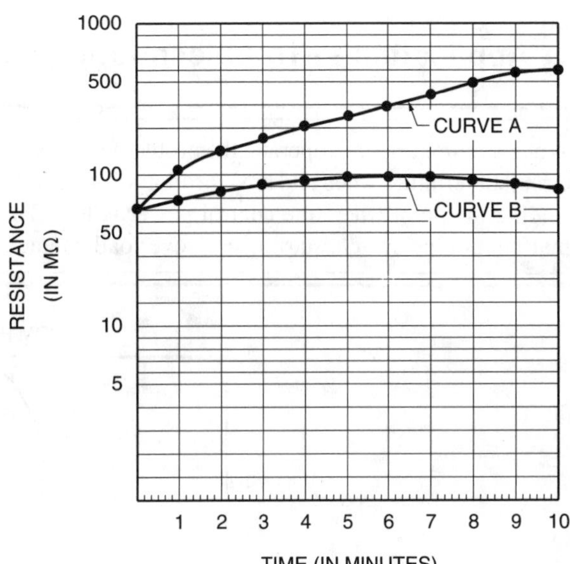

DIELECTRIC ABSORPTION TEST GRAPH

MINIMUM ACCEPTABLE POLARIZATION INDEX VALUES

Insulation	Value
Class A	1.5
Class B	2.0
Class C	2.0

Application — Insulation Step Voltage Test

An *insulation step voltage test* creates electrical stress on internal insulation cracks to reveal aging or damage not found during other motor insulation tests. The insulation step voltage test is performed only after an insulation spot test. To perform an insulation step voltage test, apply the procedure:

1. Set the megohmmeter to 500 V and connect to measure the resistance of each winding lead to ground. Take each resistance reading after 60 seconds.
2. Record the lowest reading.
3. Place the meter leads on the winding that has the lowest reading.
4. Set the megohmmeter on increments of 500 V starting at 1000 V and ending at 5000 V. Record each reading after 60 seconds.
5. Discharge the motor windings.
6. Interpret the results. See Insulation Step Voltage Test Graph.

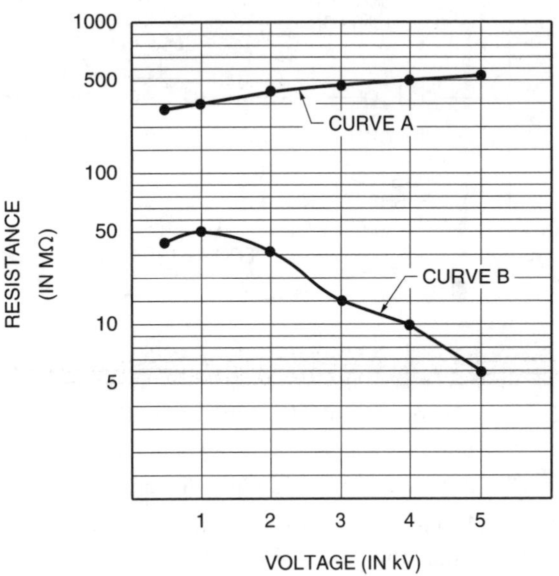

INSULATION STEP VOLTAGE TEST GRAPH

The resistance of good insulation that is thoroughly dry (Curve A) remains approximately the same at different voltage levels. The resistance of deteriorated insulation (Curve B) decreases substantially at different voltage levels.

Application — Troubleshooting a Motor Control Circuit

When a motor does not operate, the problem may be in the fuses, motor, or motor control circuit. The motor control circuit determines when and how the motor is turned ON and OFF. Troubleshooting a motor control circuit requires finding the point where the control power is lost. The point where the control power is lost typically indicates a malfunctioning switch, starting coil, overload contact, or other component. See Control Circuit.

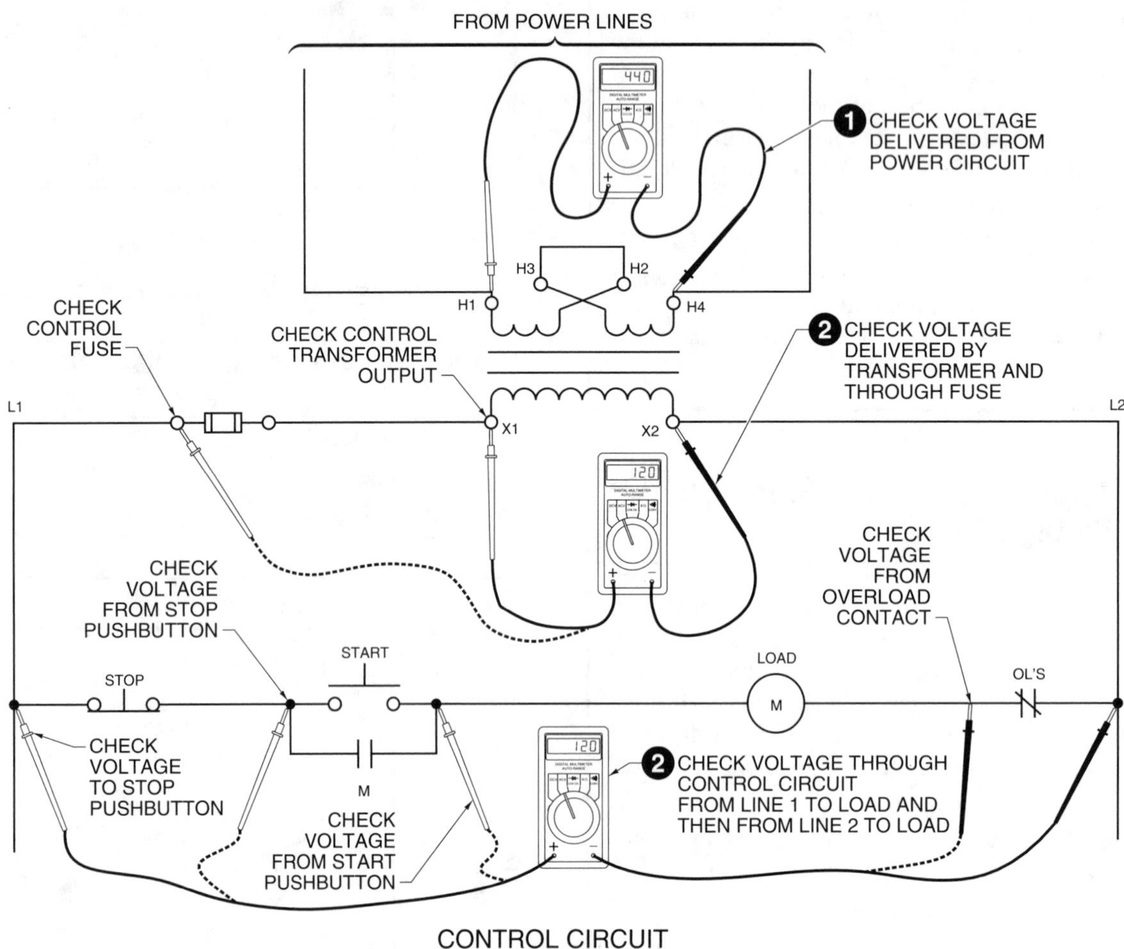

CONTROL CIRCUIT

To troubleshoot a control circuit, apply the procedure:

1. Check the voltage delivered from the power circuit. All control circuits receive voltage from a power circuit. Check the voltage coming from the power circuit to make sure that voltage is present and at the correct level.
2. Check the voltage delivered through the control transformer. Most control circuits operate at a voltage lower than the power circuit. A control transformer reduces the voltage to the control circuit. Most control transformers have a fuse on the secondary side, or a fuse is added on the primary side. Check that the correct voltage is delivered by the transformer and that voltage is delivered through the fuse.
3. Check the voltage through the control circuit. Check the voltage through the control circuit by starting at Line 1 and Line 2. If the correct voltage is between Line 1 and Line 2, move one lead of the voltmeter through the control circuit. Start with Line 1 and move to the load in the control circuit. When a device does not pass the voltage as required, replace or service that device.

Name________________________ Date____________

chapter **7**

TROUBLESHOOTING MOTORS

ACTIVITIES

Activity 7-1. Megohmmeter Use

1. Connect Megohmmeter 1 to measure the resistance between the starting winding and the running winding. Connect Megohmmeter 2 to measure the resistance between the starting winding and ground.

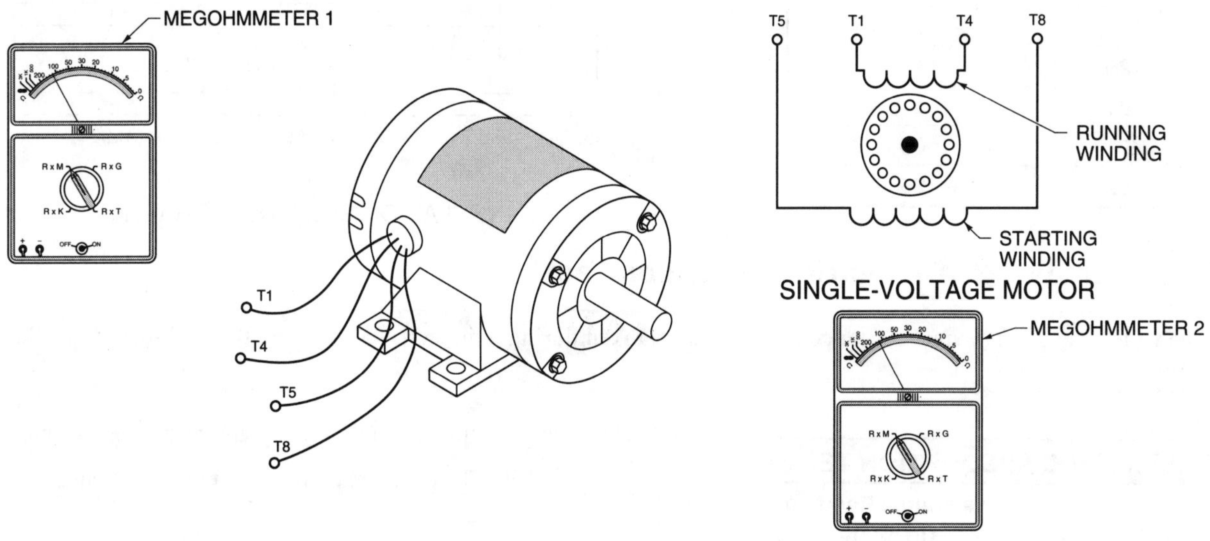

2. Connect Megohmmeter 1 to measure the resistance between the shunt field and ground. Connect Megohmmeter 2 to measure the resistance between the armature and ground.

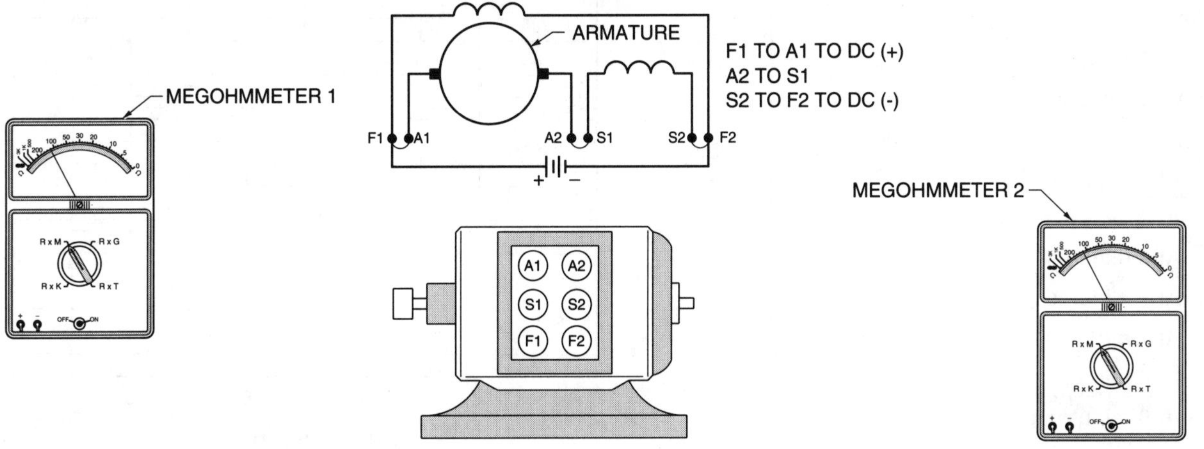

Activity 7-2. Insulation Spot Test

A 120 VAC, split-phase motor was placed in service in January, 1987. Semiannual resistance readings were taken. Develop the insulation spot test graph from the readings. Mark the point at which the motor requires service.

INSULATION SPOT TEST	
Test Taken	Resistance Reading (in MΩ)
1/87	90
7/87	87
1/88	84
7/88	82
1/89	75
7/89	12
1/90	11
7/90	9
1/91	2
7/91	.09
1/92	.05

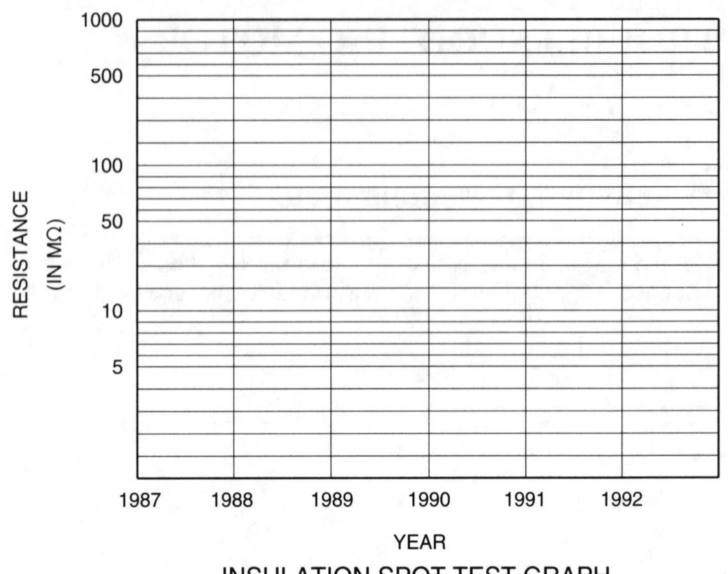

INSULATION SPOT TEST GRAPH

Activity 7-3. Dielectric Absorption Test

The following semiannual resistance readings were taken during a dielectric absorption test at 240 V with Class A insulation.

DIELECTRIC ABSORPTION TEST	
Test Taken	Resistance Reading (in MΩ)
At 10 seconds	100
At 20 seconds	101
At 30 seconds	102
At 40 seconds	104
At 50 seconds	106
At 60 seconds	109
At 2 minutes	200
At 3 minutes	250
At 4 minutes	325
At 5 minutes	350
At 6 minutes	375
At 7 minutes	425
At 8 minutes	450
At 9 minutes	475
At 10 minutes	480

1. Develop the dielectric absorption test graph from the readings.

_______________ **2.** The polarization index of the insulation is __________.

_______________ **3.** Is the motor insulation good or bad?

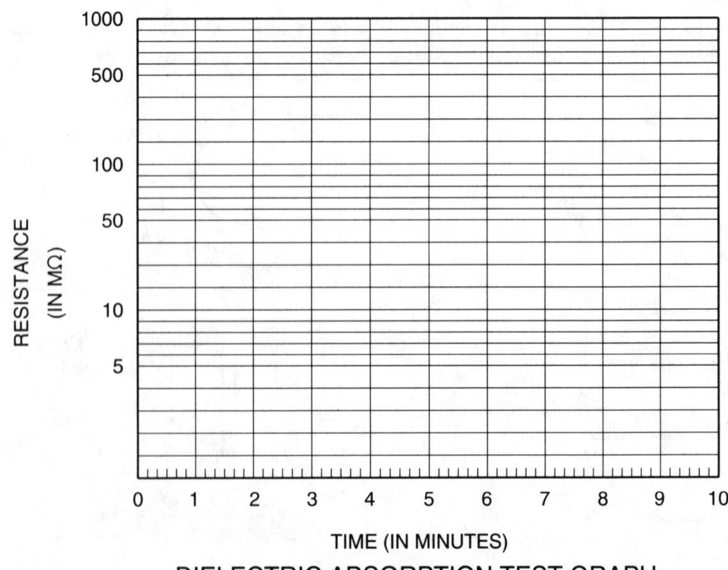

DIELECTRIC ABSORPTION TEST GRAPH

Activity 7-4. Insulation Step Voltage Test

The following resistance readings were taken during an insulation step voltage test.

1. Develop the insulation step voltage graph from the readings.

__________ **2.** Is the motor insulation good or bad?

INSULATION STEP VOLTAGE TEST	
Applied Voltage (in volts)	**Resistance Reading (in MΩ)**
500	100
1000	125
1500	200
2000	225
2500	175
3000	90
3500	75
4000	60
4500	10
5000	6

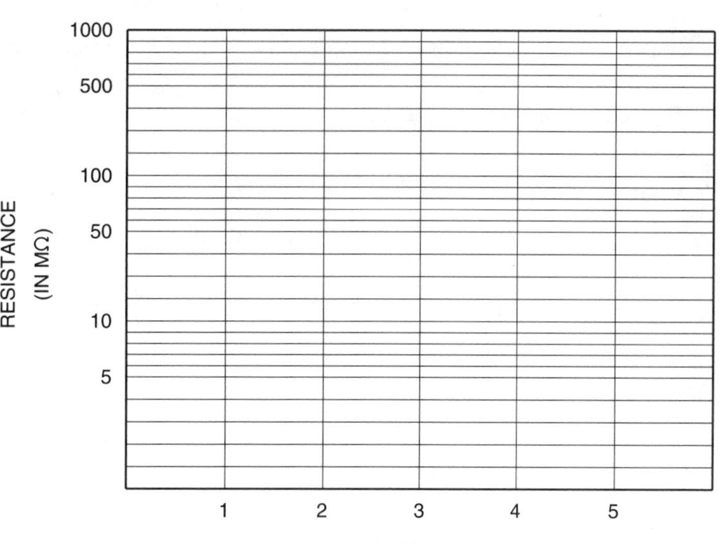

INSULATION STEP VOLTAGE TEST GRAPH

Activity 7-5. Troubleshooting a Motor Control Circuit

1. A start/stop pushbutton station has a pilot light that indicates when the motor is running. When the start pushbutton is pressed, the motor starts but the pilot light does not light. Connect Meter 1 to test the primary voltage delivered to the transformer. Connect Meter 2 to test the voltage output of the transformer and fuse. Connect Meter 3 to test the pilot light.

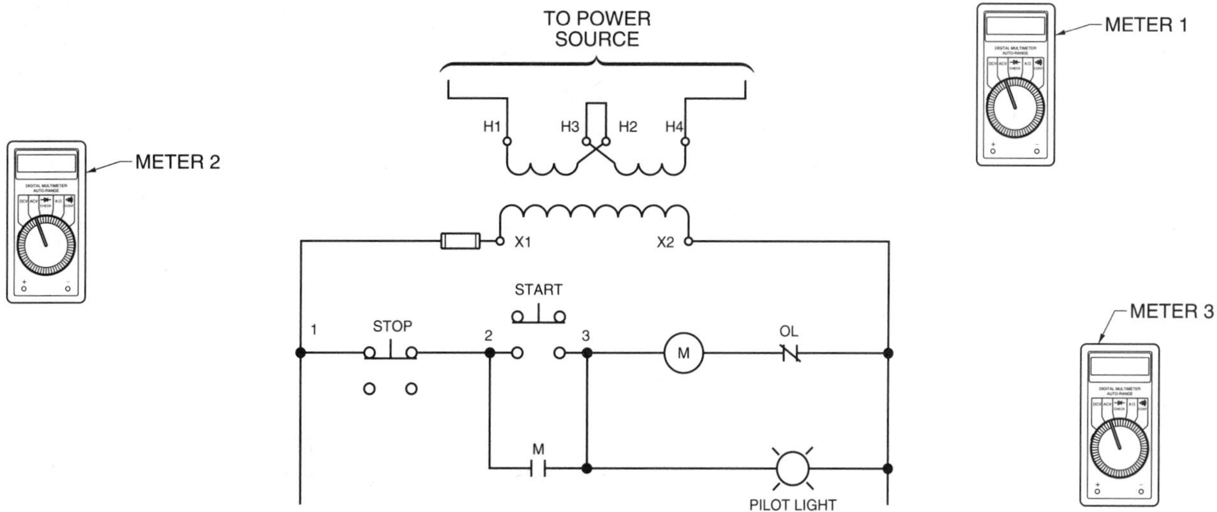

2. Multiple pushbutton stations control a single motor starter. Start Pushbutton 1 starts the motor and the stop pushbuttons stop the motor. Start Pushbutton 2 does not start the motor. Connect Meter 1 to test the voltage output of Start Pushbutton 2. Connect Meter 2 to test the voltage output of the stop pushbuttons.

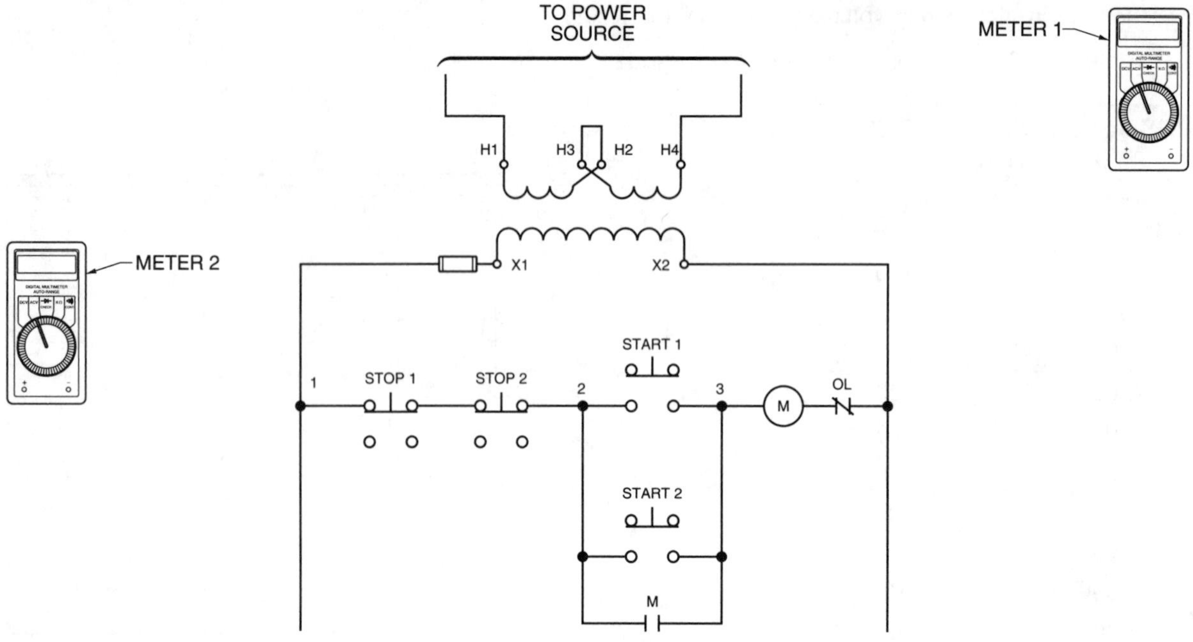

3. A start/stop/jog pushbutton station controls a motor starter. The jog pushbutton starts the motor. The start pushbutton does not start the motor. Connect Meter 1 to test the voltage output of the start pushbutton. Connect Meter 2 to measure the voltage at the starter coil and the overload contact.

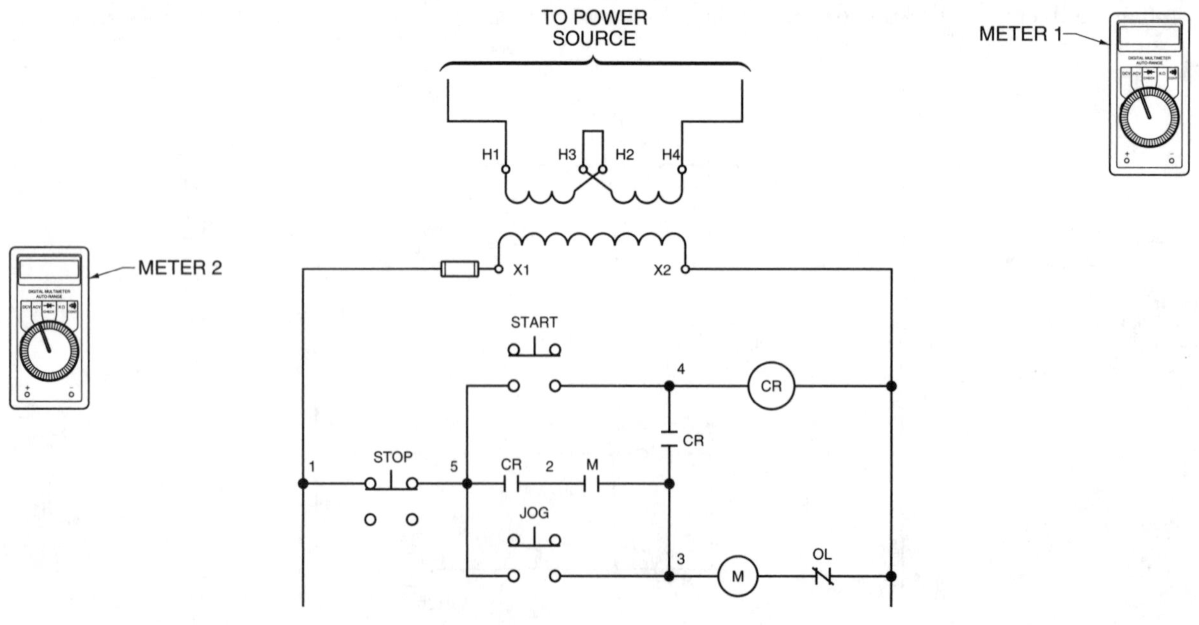

4. Individual start/stop pushbutton stations control individual motor starters. The Master Stop Pushbutton controls both motors. Connect Meter 1 to test for power at Motor Starter 1. Connect Meter 2 to test if the overload contact of Motor Starter 2 closes before the pushbuttons are pressed.

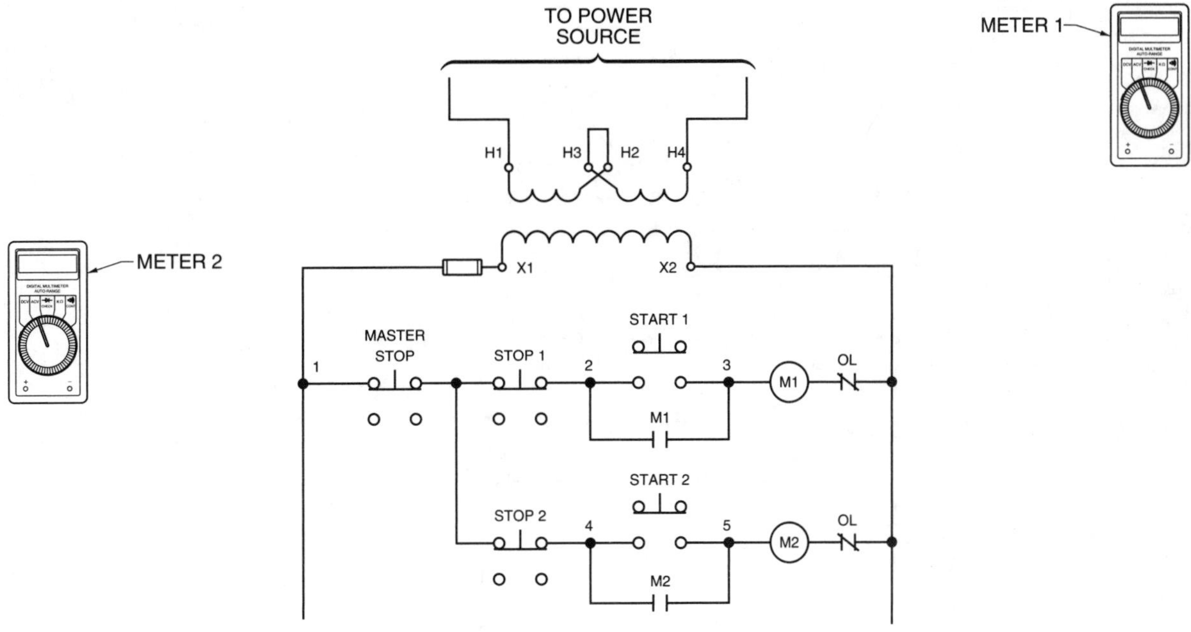

5. A forward/reverse/stop pushbutton station has pilot lights to indicate the direction of motor rotation. Connect Meter 1 to measure the voltage at the forward pilot light. Connect Meter 2 to measure the voltage output from the forward pushbutton contacts that stop the motor from running in reverse.

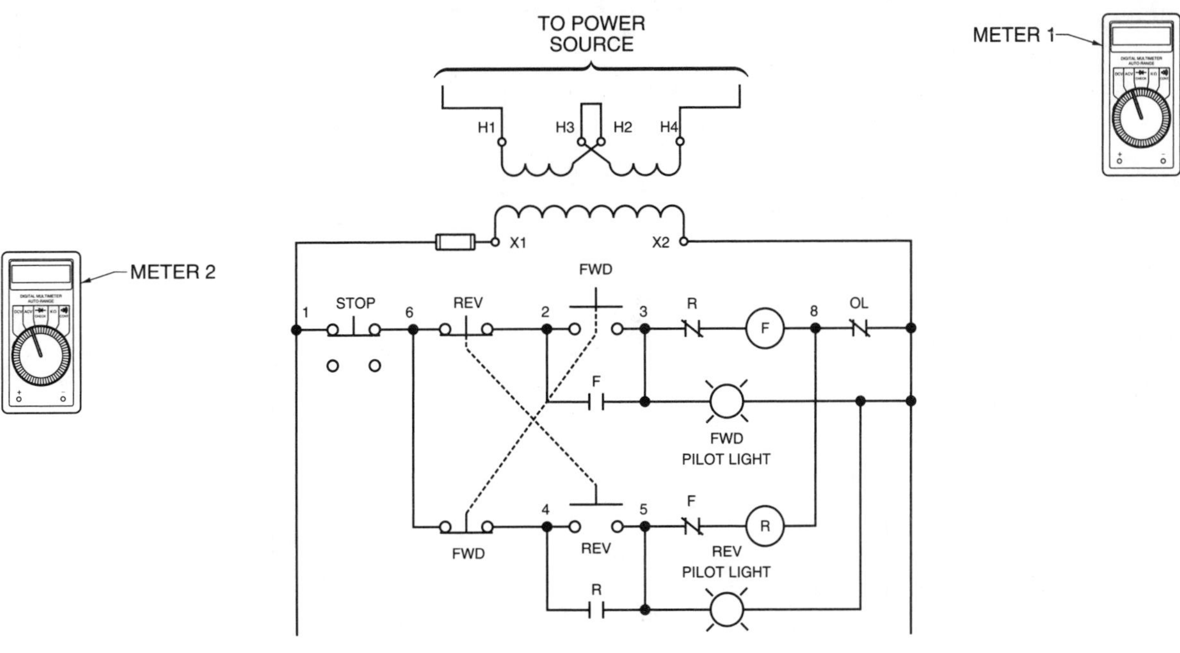

6. A slow/fast/stop pushbutton station has pilot lights to indicate the motor's operating speed. Connect Meter 1 to test for voltage at the starter coil that controls the motor operating at slow speed. Connect Meter 2 to test for the voltage output from the Fast Pushbutton.

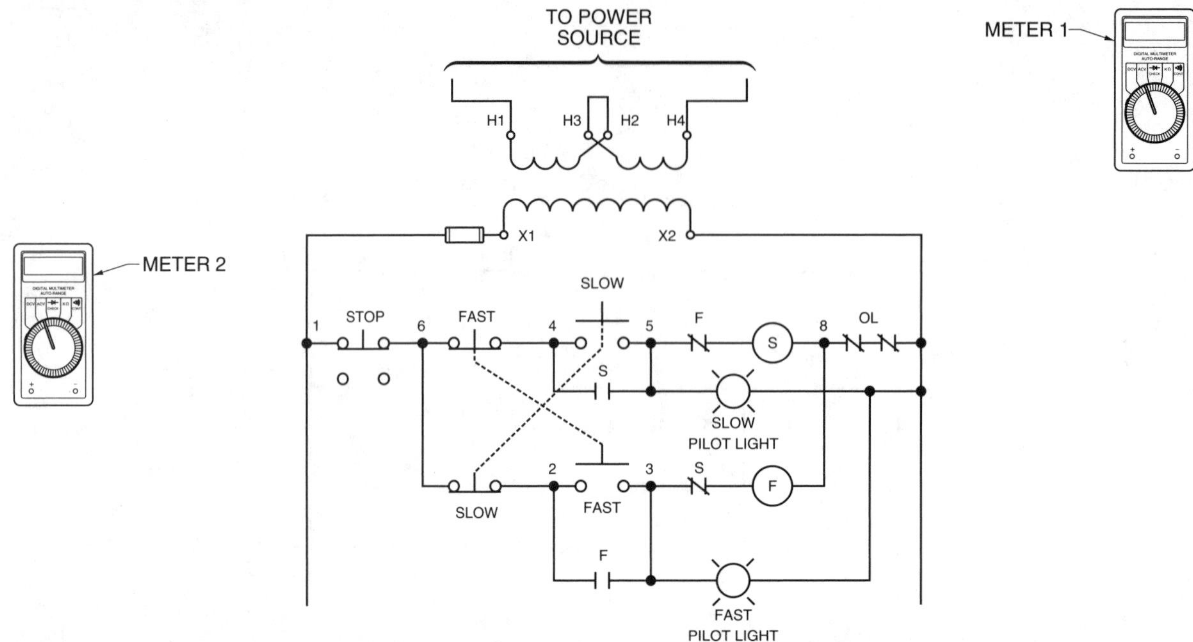

7. A start/stop pushbutton station has a pilot light to indicate when a motor is running. A push-to-test pushbutton is used to test the operation of the pilot light at any given time without affecting the operation of the motor. When the start pushbutton is pressed, the pilot light turns ON and the motor does not start. When the start pushbutton is released, the pilot light turns OFF. When the push-to-test pushbutton is pressed, the pilot light turns ON. Connect Meter 1 to test for voltage at the motor starter when the start pushbutton is pressed. Connect Meter 2 to test for an open overload contact.

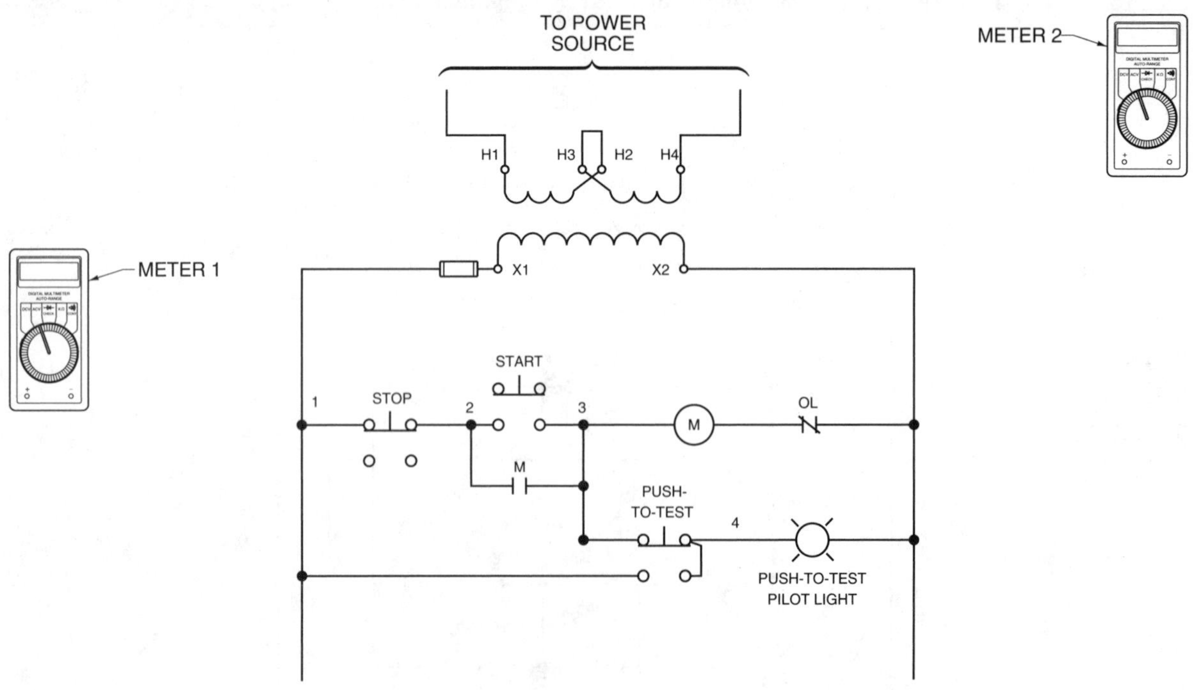

Activity 7-6. Control Circuit Modification

1. Redraw the line diagram so that the compressor motor speed automatically changes from slow to fast after the motor has run in slow speed for 5 minutes. Add a start pushbutton to start the motor and a stop pushbutton to stop the motor. Add a timer coil and timer contacts to change speeds.

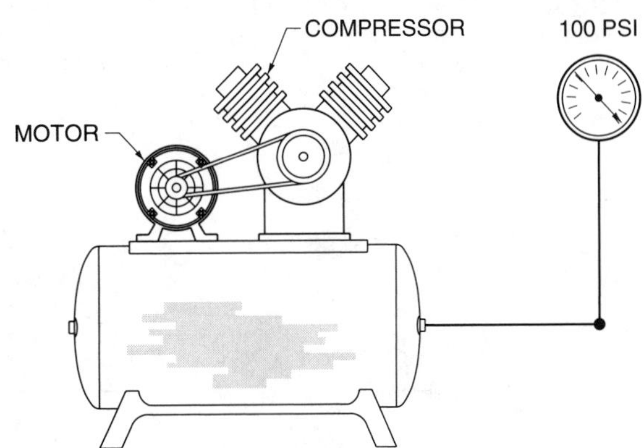

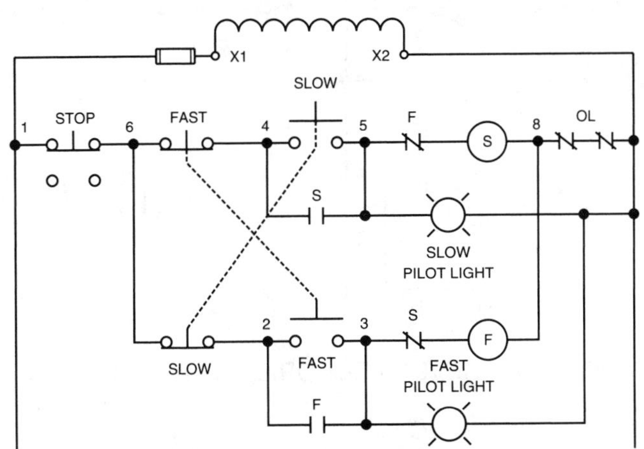

COMPRESSOR MOTOR TIME CONTROL

2. Redraw the line diagram by combining the two circuits so that the motor runs in the forward slow or fast speeds and in the reverse slow speed. The motor cannot run in the reverse fast speed.

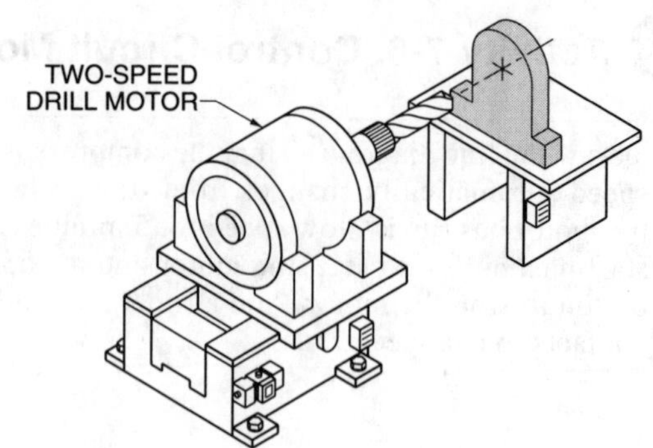

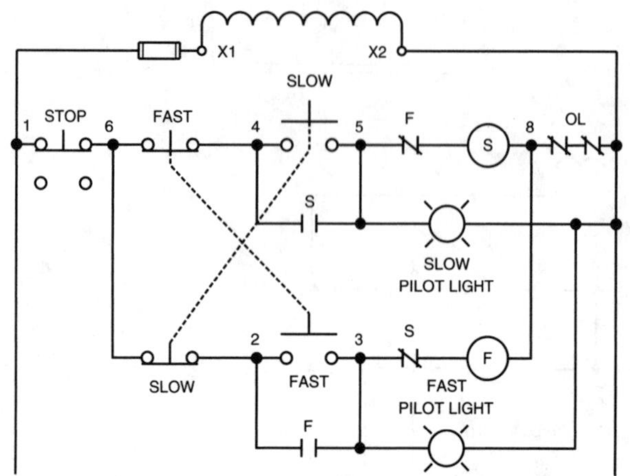

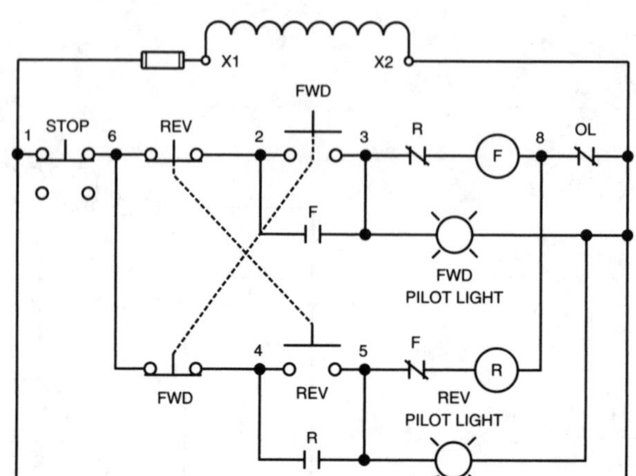

TWO-SPEED REVERSIBLE DRILL MOTOR CONTROL

Name ______________________ Date ______________

chapter **7**

TROUBLESHOOTING MOTORS

TRADE TEST

Completion

______ **1.** DC motors are used in applications that require very ______ torque.

______ **2.** ______ wear faster than any other component of a DC motor.

______ **3.** The ohmmeter needle will swing to zero and not move if a capacitor is ______.

______ **4.** The ohmmeter needle will swing to zero and slowly move to infinity if the capacitor is ______.

______ **5.** A malfunctioning DC motor of ______ HP or more is usually serviced.

______ **6.** The brush holder of a DC motor should be $1/16''$ to ______$''$ from the commutator.

______ **7.** Any discolorations on a commutator other than a polished, ______ color indicate a problem.

______ **8.** A(n) ______ circuit is a circuit in which current takes a shortcut around the normal path of current flow.

______ **9.** The starting winding of a split-phase motor is removed by a(n) ______ switch as the motor accelerates.

______ **10.** ______ material is a medium in which an electric field is maintained with little or no outside energy supply.

______ **11.** A(n) ______ is a conducting medium in which the current flow occurs by ion migration.

______ **12.** A capacitor may be discharged by placing a 20,000 SL, 2 W resistor across the terminals for ______ seconds.

______ **13.** Before troubleshooting electric motors, the starting mechanism should be locked out and ______.

______ **14.** An OCPD should be at least ______% of a motor's FLC.

______ **15.** When a split-phase motor is turned OFF, a distinct ______ should be heard.

True-False

T F **1.** Shaded-pole motors that fail are usually replaced.

T F **2.** The brushes of DC motors should be replaced when they have worn down to half their original size.

T F **3.** A megohmmeter may be used to test for insulation breakdown.

T F **4.** When a capacitor is open, the motor has good starting torque.

T F **5.** A good capacitor will hold a charge even when power is removed.

T F **6.** Overloads should be reset before cooling.

T F **7.** Overheated bearings may cause motor noise.

T F **8.** The brushes of a DC motor should be lubricated on a scheduled basis.

T F **9.** A commutator should be smooth and concentric.

T F **10.** An armature winding is grounded whenever one or more windings make contact with the iron core.

Multiple Choice

__________ **1.** When troubleshooting DC motor brushes, the brush ________ should be checked.

A. tension
B. movement
C. length
D. A, B, and C

__________ **2.** The brush pressure of a DC motor should be approximately 1.5 to ________ psi of surface area.

A. 2
B. 3
C. 4
D. 5

__________ **3.** Mica insulation should be approximately ________ below the commutator segments.

A. 1/64″ to 1/32″
B. 1/32″ to 1/16″
C. 1/16″ to 1/8″
D. neither A, B, nor C

__________ **4.** A(n) ________ circuit is a circuit that no longer provides a path for current to flow.

A. short
B. closed
C. open
D. full

__________ **5.** A shaded-pole motor has ________ starting torque.

A. very low
B. medium
C. very high
D. variable

__________ **6.** A split-phase motor has a ________ winding.

A. starting
B. running
C. both A and B
D. neither A nor B

__________ **7.** When troubleshooting a 3ϕ motor, if the check for open or shorted windings reads ________, the coil is shorted.

A. infinity
B. zero
C. either A or B
D. neither A nor B

__________ **8.** A(n) ________ circuit is a circuit in which current leaves its normal path and travels to the frame of the motor.

A. open
B. closed
C. grounded
D. full

__________ **9.** A voltmeter check of a split-phase motor should show voltage within ________% of the motor's listed voltage.

A. 2.5
B. 5
C. 7.5
D. 10

__________ **10.** AC capacitors are ________.

A. used with capacitor motors
B. designed to have no polarity
C. both A and B
D. neither A nor B

Problems

A 3ϕ, delta-connected, dual-voltage motor is checked with an ohmmeter. Determine the motor problem based on the meter readings.

Connections	Ω
T1 to T4	20
T1 to T9	20
T4 to T9	40
T2 to T5	20
T2 to T7	20
T5 to T7	40
T3 to T6	20
T3 to T8	infinity
T6 to T8	infinity

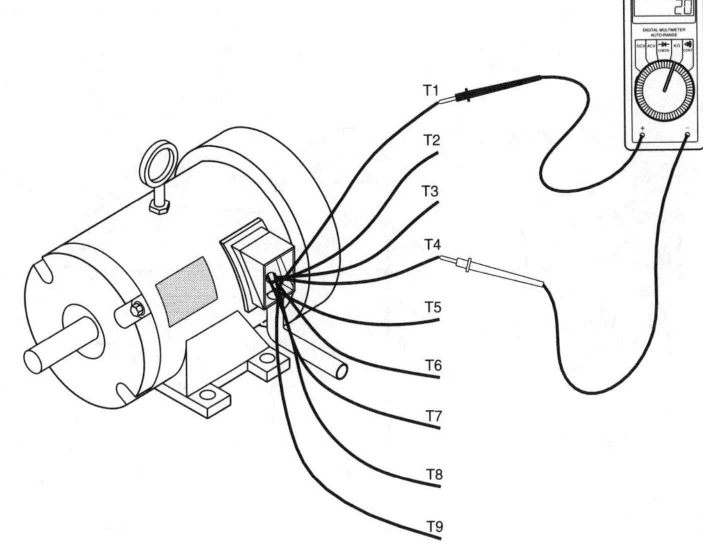

_______ **1.** The motor problem is a(n) _______.

A 3ϕ, wye-connected, dual-voltage motor is checked with an ohmmeter. Determine the motor problem based on the meter readings.

Connections	Ω
T1 to T4	15
T2 to T5	15
T3 to T6	15
T7 to T8	0
T8 to T9	30
T9 to T7	0

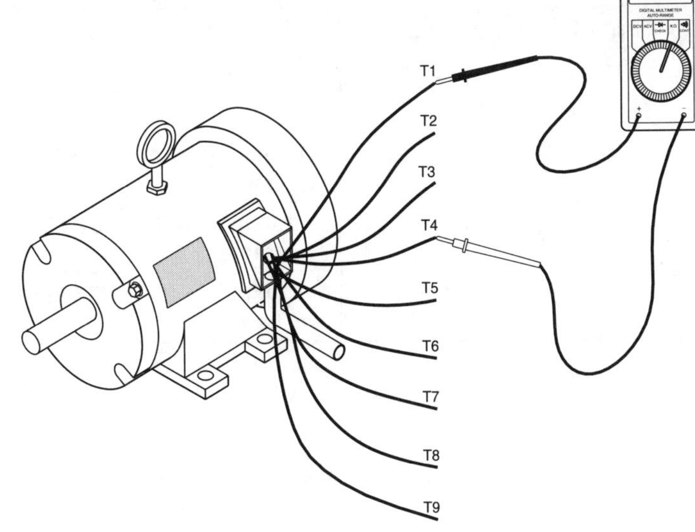

_______ **2.** The motor problem is a(n) _______.

Determine the malfunctioning component using the forward/reversing/stop circuit and the meter readings. *Note:* The machine operator reports that the motor operates in the reverse direction only. When the forward pushbutton is pressed, the forward pilot light turns ON and Meter A, Meter B, and Meter C read 115 V.

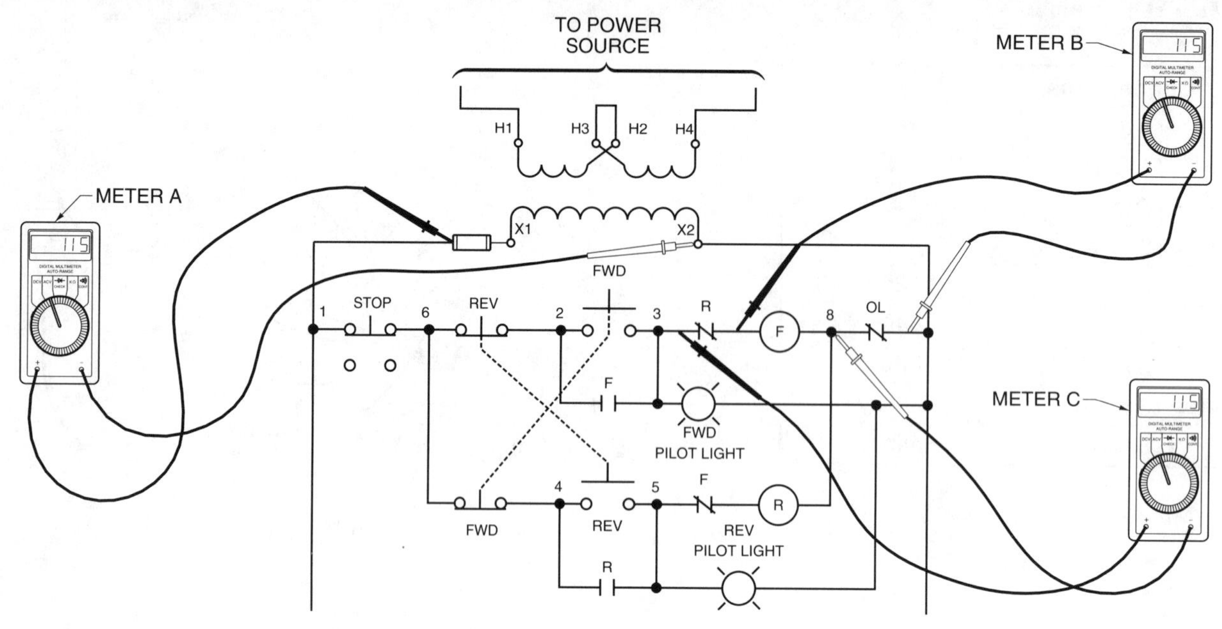

_________ **3.** The problem is a(n) _________.

A motor is checked with an ohmmeter and megohmmeter. Determine the motor problem based on the meter readings.

Ohmmeter Readings		**Megohmmeter Readings**	
Connections	Ω	Connections	Ω
A1 to A2	10 Ω	S1 to F1	85 MΩ
F1 to F2	60 Ω	S1 to A1	98 MΩ
S1 to S2	5 Ω	A1 to F1	115 MΩ
—	—	A1 to motor frame	105 MΩ
—	—	F1 to motor frame	82 MΩ
—	—	S1 to motor frame	75 kΩ

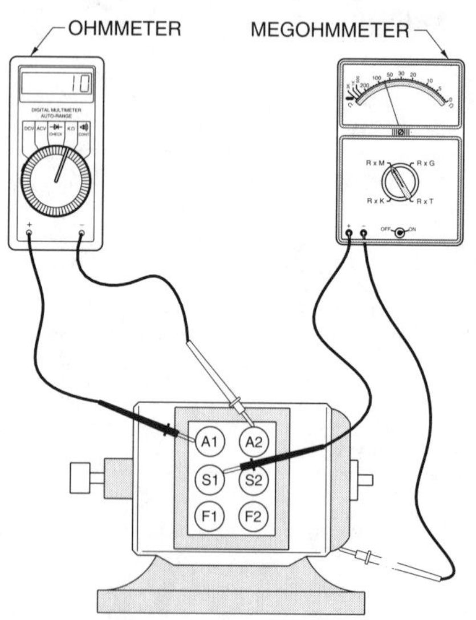

_________ **4.** The motor problem is a(n) _________.

5. Connect Multimeter 1 to check voltage delivered from power circuit. Connect Multimeter 2 to check the control fuse.

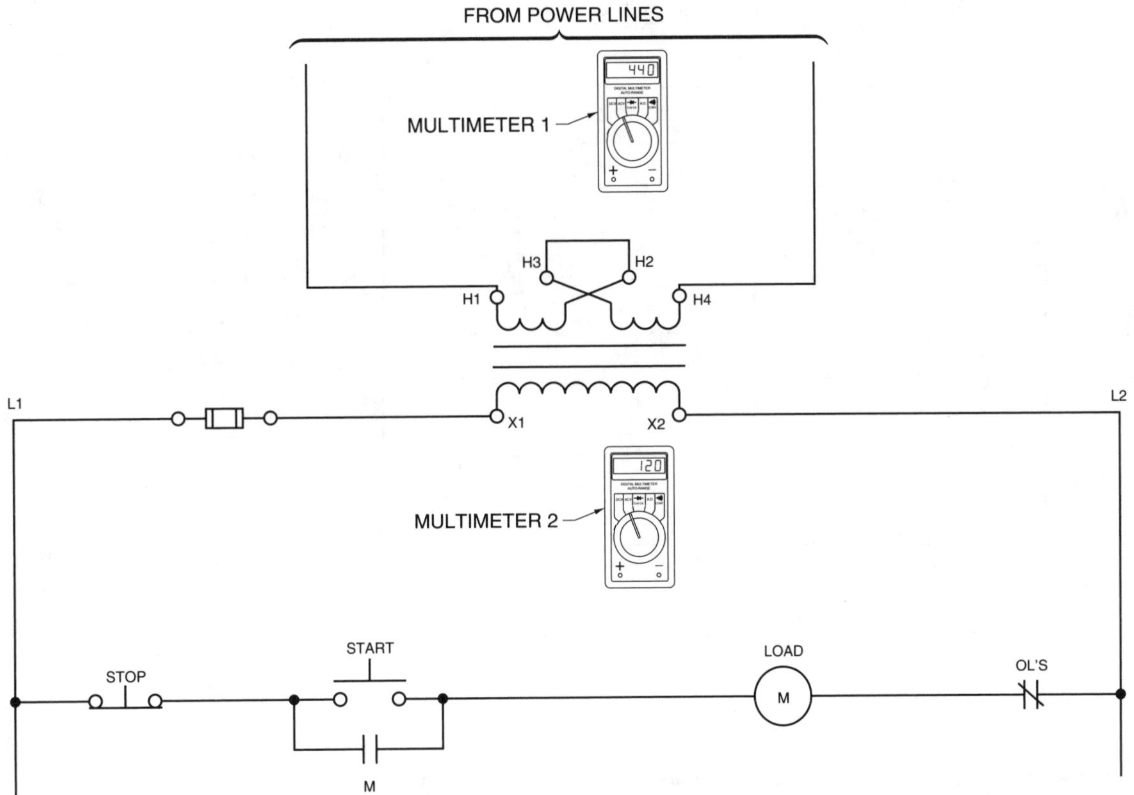

A 230 VAC, 3ϕ motor was placed in service in January, 1988. Semiannual resistance readings were taken.

6. Develop the insulation spot test graph from the readings. Mark the point at which the motor requires service.

INSULATION SPOT TEST	
Test Taken	**Resistance Reading (in MΩ)**
1/88	200
7/88	150
1/89	119
7/89	98
1/90	93
7/90	87
1/91	80
7/91	76
1/92	74
7/92	2
1/93	.7

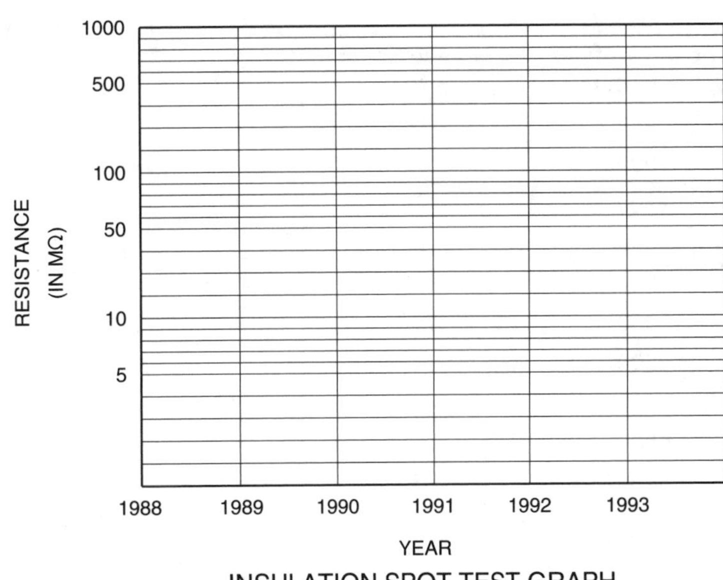

INSULATION SPOT TEST GRAPH

Semiannual resistance readings were taken during a dielectric absorption test.

7. Develop the dielectric absorption test graph from the readings.

__________ **8.** Is the motor insulation good or bad?

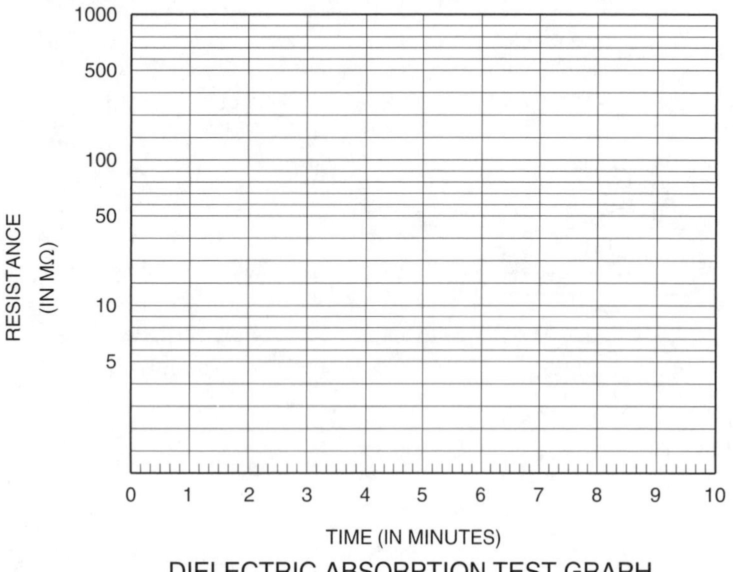

DIELECTRIC ABSORPTION TEST GRAPH

DIELECTRIC ABSORPTION TEST	
Test Taken	**Resistance Reading (in MΩ)**
At 10 seconds	310
At 20 seconds	312
At 30 seconds	313
At 40 seconds	315
At 50 seconds	320
At 60 seconds	330
At 2 minutes	350
At 3 minutes	367
At 4 minutes	372
At 5 minutes	377
At 6 minutes	383
At 7 minutes	396
At 8 minutes	390
At 9 minutes	381
At 10 minutes	372

Resistance readings were taken during an insulation step voltage test.

9. Develop the insulation step voltage test graph from the readings.

__________ **10.** Is the motor insulation good or bad?

INSULATION STEP VOLTAGE TEST	
Applied Voltage (in volts)	**Resistance Reading (in MΩ)**
500	117
1000	200
1500	176
2000	100
2500	88
3000	79
3500	74
4000	62
4500	45
5000	18

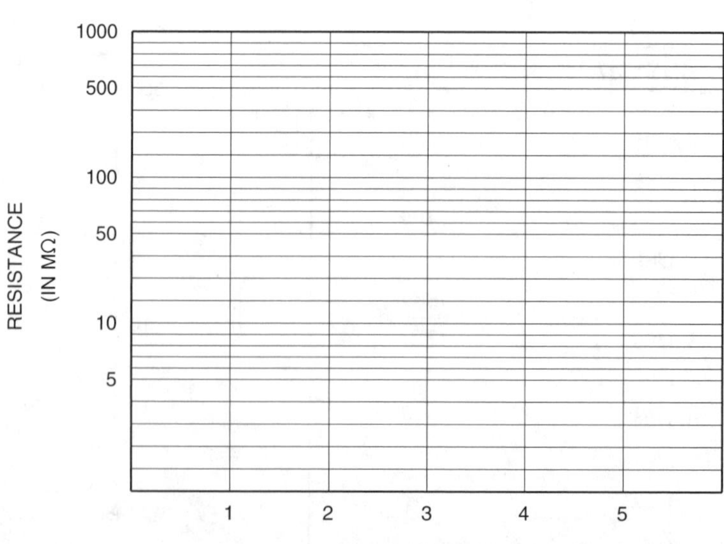

INSULATION STEP VOLTAGE TEST GRAPH

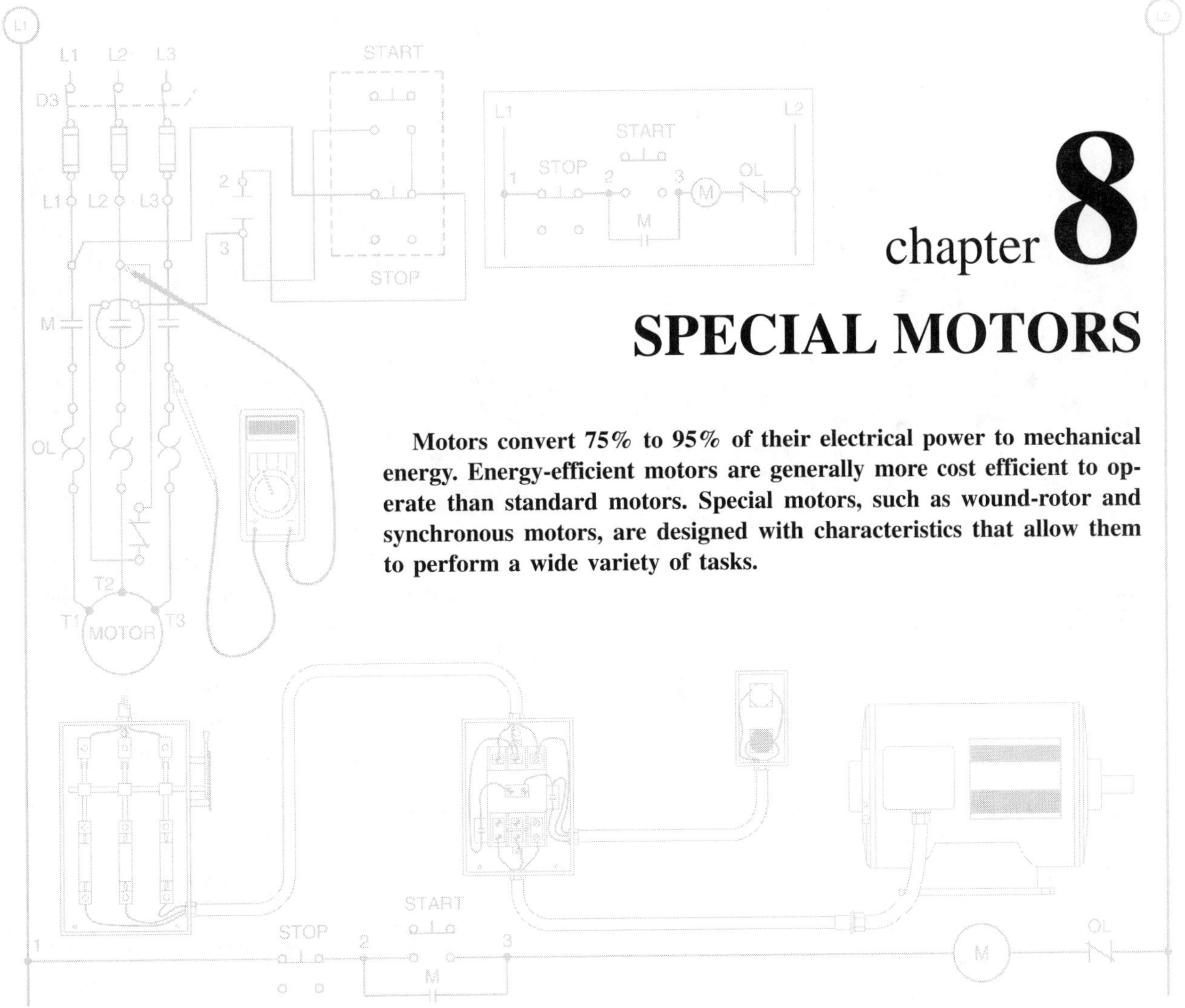

chapter 8

SPECIAL MOTORS

Motors convert 75% to 95% of their electrical power to mechanical energy. Energy-efficient motors are generally more cost efficient to operate than standard motors. Special motors, such as wound-rotor and synchronous motors, are designed with characteristics that allow them to perform a wide variety of tasks.

ENERGY-EFFICIENT MOTORS

Motors perform work by converting electrical energy to mechanical energy. Depending upon the motor size and design, motors typically convert between 75% and 95% of their electrical power to usable mechanical energy. The mechanical energy is used to produce work. The balance of the electrical power is lost. Lost power adds to the cost of electricity, but performs no work. See Figure 8-1.

Motor Efficiency

Motor efficiency is the measure of the effectiveness with which a motor converts electrical energy to mechanical energy. Improvements in motor efficiency can be achieved only by reducing power losses in the motor. Power losses in a motor are a result of energy losses in the stator core, stator windings, bearings, and the rotor. Power losses are considered the cost of converting electrical energy into mechanical energy. Power losses are always present to some degree. See Figure 8-2.

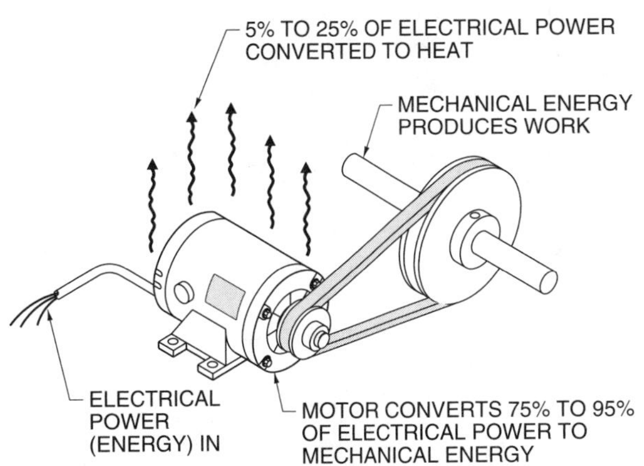

Figure 8-1. Motors typically convert 75% to 95% of their electrical power to mechanical energy.

FINDING MOTOR EFFICIENCY

What is the efficiency of the motor?

1. $E_{ff} = \frac{P_{out}}{P_{in}}$
2. $E_{ff} = \frac{40}{42} = .952$

E_{ff} = **95%**

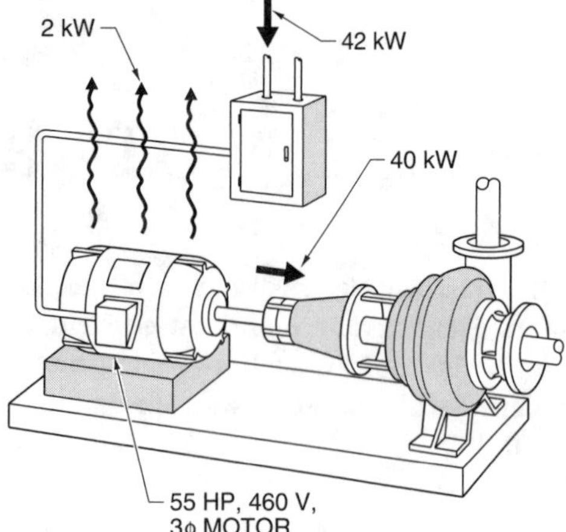

Figure 8-2. Motor efficiency is the measure of the effectiveness with which a motor converts electrical energy to mechanical energy.

When input and output power is known, efficiency is found by applying the formula:

$$E_{ff} = \frac{P_{out}}{P_{in}}$$

where

E_{ff} = efficiency (%)

P_{out} = output power (W)

P_{in} = input power (W)

For example, a motor delivers 37.5 kW of power and draws 41.5 kW of power from the power lines. What is the efficiency of the motor?

$$E_{ff} = \frac{P_{out}}{P_{in}}$$

$$E_{ff} = \frac{37{,}500}{41{,}500} = .9036$$

$$E_{ff} = \mathbf{90.4\%}$$

When horsepower and power loss are known, efficiency is found by applying the formula:

$$E_{ff} = \frac{746 \times HP}{746 \times HP + W_l}$$

where

E_{ff} = efficiency (%)

746 = constant

HP = horsepower

W_l = watts lost

For example, a 40 HP motor has a power loss of 2200 W. What is the efficiency of the motor?

$$E_{ff} = \frac{746 \times HP}{746 \times HP + W_l}$$

$$E_{ff} = \frac{746 \times 40}{746 \times 40 + 2200}$$

$$E_{ff} = \frac{29{,}840}{32{,}040} = .9313$$

$$E_{ff} = \mathbf{93.1\%}$$

Power Consumed

Motors consume power as they convert electrical energy to mechanical energy. To save energy, motor manufacturers offer energy-efficient motors in addition to their standard motors. Energy-efficient motors have greater efficiency and cost less to operate than a standard motor of the same rating and type. Standard motors have an average efficiency of 83%. Energy-efficient motors have an average efficiency of 89%. Many manufacturers list the efficiency of the motor on the motor nameplate. The efficiency is also listed in motor data sheets. See Figure 8-3.

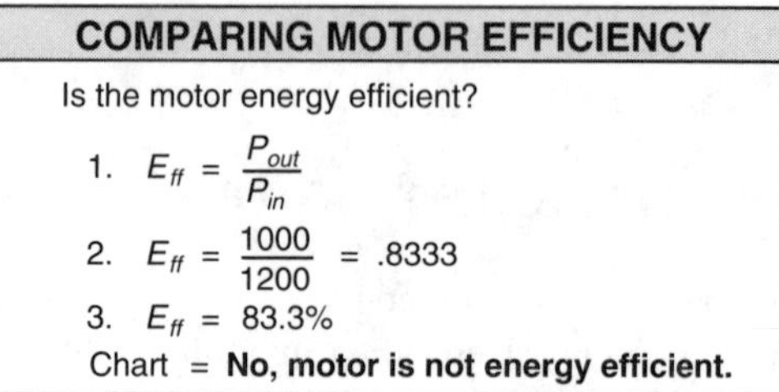

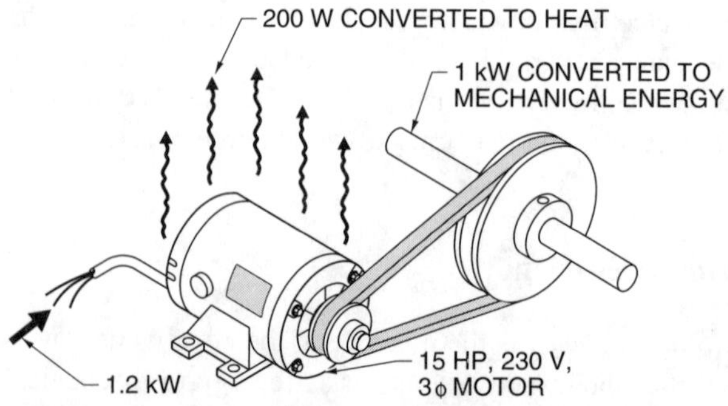

Figure 8-3. Standard motors have an average efficiency of 83%. Energy-efficient motors have an average efficiency of 89%.

Energy-efficient motors are more expensive than standard motors. An energy-efficient motor typically costs 20% more than a standard motor of the same rating and type. To find the power consumed by a motor, apply the formula:

$$P = \frac{HP \times 746}{E_{ff}}$$

where

P = power consumed (W)

HP = horsepower

746 = constant

E_{ff} = efficiency (%)

For example, how much power is consumed by a standard, 50 HP motor with an 85% efficiency rating?

$$P = \frac{HP \times 746}{E_{ff}}$$

$$P = \frac{50 \times 746}{.85}$$

$$P = \frac{37{,}300}{.85} = 43{,}882.35$$

P = **43,882.35 W**

For example, how much power is consumed by an energy-efficient, 50 HP motor with a 93.7% efficiency?

$$P = \frac{HP \times 746}{E_{ff}}$$

$$P = \frac{50 \times 746}{.937}$$

$$P = \frac{37{,}300}{.937} = 39{,}807.89$$

P = **39,807.89 W**

Operating Cost

The cost of electrical power is based on the number of kilowatt hours (kWh) of electricity consumed. The operating cost of a motor is dependent on the cost of electricity. Most power companies have several different rates. For example, the winter rate (low demand) is typically about $.085/kWh. The summer rate (high demand) is typically about $.105/kWh. Most power companies also apply a power factor (demand) charge to the power bill of industrial customers. The power factor charge typically ranges from .5% to 2.5% of the total bill. The power factor demand is applied because motors cause the current to lag behind the voltage on the power lines. This lag causes power inefficiency in the power distribution system. See Figure 8-4.

FINDING OPERATING COST

What is the operating cost of the motor at .143¢ per kWh?

1. $C_{/hr} = \frac{P_{/hr} \times C_{/KWH}}{1000}$
2. $C_{/hr} = \frac{24{,}618 \times .143}{1000}$
3. $C_{/hr} = \frac{3520.374}{1000} = 3.520$

$C_{/hr}$ = **$3.52**

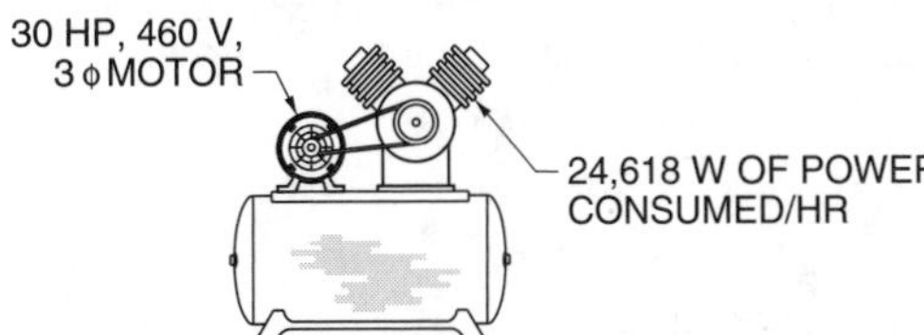

UTILITY COST*			
POWER CONSUMED	WINTER RATE	DEMAND CHARGE	
		+.5%	+2.5%
	.085	+0.590	+2.590
100 kWh	$8.50	$8.5425	$8.7125
POWER CONSUMED	SUMMER RATE	DEMAND CHARGE	
		+.5%	+2.5%
	.105	+0.590	+2.590
100 kWh	$10.50	$10.5525	$10.7625

* per kWh

Figure 8-4. The cost of electrical power is based on the number of kilowatt hours of electricity consumed.

When the power consumed and cost of electrical power are known, the operating cost of a motor is found by applying the formula:

$$C_{/hr} = \frac{P_{/hr} \times C_{/kWh}}{1000}$$

where

$C_{/hr}$ = operating cost per hour

$P_{/hr}$ = power consumed per hour

$C_{/kWh}$ = cost per kilowatt hour

1000 = constant to remove kilo

For example, what is the operating cost per hour for a standard, 50 HP motor with an 82% efficiency rating at a cost of $.10/kWh?

$$P = \frac{HP \times 746}{E_{ff}}$$

$$P = \frac{50 \times 746}{.82}$$

$$P = \frac{37{,}300}{.82} = 45{,}487.80$$

P = **45,487.80 W**

$$C_{/hr} = \frac{P_{/hr} \times C_{/kWh}}{1000}$$

$$C_{/hr} = \frac{45{,}487.80 \times .10}{1000}$$

$$C_{/hr} = \frac{4548.78}{1000} = 4.548$$

$$C_{/hr} = \mathbf{\$4.55}$$

For example, what is the operating cost per hour for an energy-efficient, 50 HP motor with a 95% efficiency rating at a cost of $.10/kWh?

$$P = \frac{HP \times 746}{E_{ff}}$$

$$P = \frac{50 \times 746}{.95}$$

$$P = \frac{37{,}300}{.95} = 39{,}263.15$$

$$P = \mathbf{39{,}263.15\ W}$$

$$C_{/hr} = \frac{P_{/hr} \times C_{/kWh}}{1000}$$

$$C_{/hr} = \frac{39{,}263 \times .10}{1000}$$

$$C_{/hr} = \frac{3926.30}{1000} = 3.926$$

$$C_{/hr} = \mathbf{\$3.93}$$

The operating cost per week (based on a 40 hour week) is found by multiplying the operating cost per hour times 40. The operating cost per year is found by multiplying the operating cost per week times 52. For example, the operating cost per week for the standard, 50 HP motor with an 82% efficiency rating is $182.00 ($4.55 × 40 = $182.00). The operating cost per year is $9464.00 ($182.00 × 52 = $9464.00).

The operating cost per week for the energy-efficient, 50 HP motor with a 95% efficiency rating is $157.20 ($3.93 × 40 = $157.20). The operating cost per year is $8174.40 ($157.20 × 52 = $8174.40).

Cost Savings

An energy-efficient motor costs more to purchase and less to operate than a standard motor. If a motor is not operated often, a standard motor is more cost efficient. If a motor is operated often, an energy-efficient motor is more cost efficient. See Figure 8-5.

To calculate the annual savings for operating an energy-efficient motor compared to a standard motor, apply the formula:

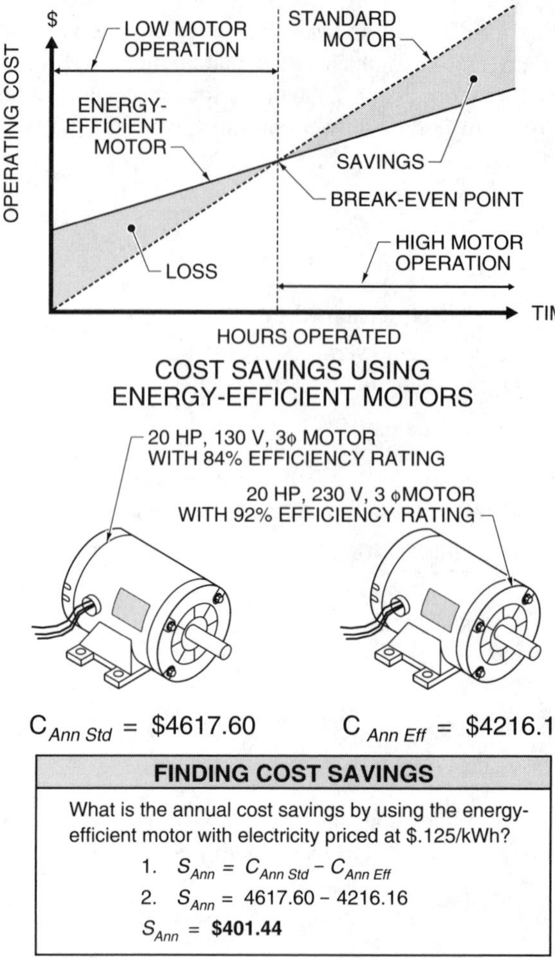

Figure 8-5. An energy-efficient motor costs less to operate than an equivalent standard motor.

$$S_{Ann} = C_{Ann\ Std} - C_{Ann\ Eff}$$

S_{Ann} = annual cost savings

$C_{Ann\ Std}$ = annual operating cost for standard motor

$C_{Ann\ Eff}$ = annual operating cost for energy-efficient motor

For example, what is the annual savings for operating the energy-efficient, 50 HP motor with a 95% efficiency rating as compared to the standard, 50 HP motor with an 82% efficiency rating?

$$S_{Ann} = C_{Ann\ Std} - C_{Ann\ Eff}$$

$$S_{Ann} = 9464.00 - 8174.40 = 1289.60$$

$$S_{Ann} = \mathbf{\$1289.60}$$

Payback Period

To find the payback period when using an energy-efficient motor, divide the price premium by the annual savings. For example, a standard, 50 HP, 3φ, open-enclosure motor costs $1700.00. An energy-efficient, 50 HP, 3φ, open-enclosure motor typically costs 20% more, or \$2,040.00 (\$1700.00 × 1.2 = \$2040.00).

The difference (price premium) in the purchase price is \$340.00 (\$2040.00 – 1700.00 = \$340.00). The payback period for the energy-efficient, 50 HP, 3ϕ, open-enclosure motor is .2636 years or 96.2 days (\$340.00 ÷ 1289.60 = .2636 years or 96.2 days).

WOUND-ROTOR MOTORS

A wound-rotor motor is a 3ϕ motor in which the rotor windings are connected to slip rings. As the motor rotates, the slip rings make contact with stationary brushes. The brushes are connected to external resistors. The resistors change the resistance of the rotor while the motor is starting and running. A higher resistance when starting produces a higher starting torque. A change in resistance when the motor is running allows the motor to operate at speeds below the motor's rated speed. Wound-rotor motors are also known as slip-ring motors.

The stator of a 3ϕ, wound-rotor motor is the same as the stator of a 3ϕ, wye-connected, induction motor. The stator windings are brought out of the motor and marked terminals T1, T2, and T3. The stator terminals are connected to the motor starter.

The rotor is made of insulated windings similar to the stator windings. The rotor is wound to have the same number of magnetic poles as the stator. The rotor windings are marked M1, M2, and M3. Rotor windings are wye-connected, with the open ends of each phase winding connected to three slip rings. See Figure 8-6.

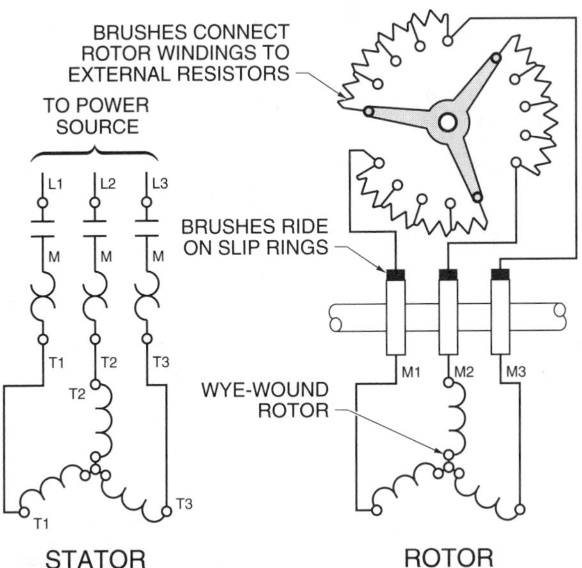

Figure 8-6. Rotor windings are wye-connected with the open ends of each phase winding connected through slip rings to external resistors.

Operating Characteristics

A wound-rotor motor is normally started with full resistance in the circuit. As the motor accelerates, resistance is gradually phased out. Resistance can be phased out either manually or automatically. When the motor reaches full speed, the slip rings are short-circuited. When all resistance is out, a wound-rotor motor has the same basic characteristics as a 3ϕ induction motor.

A high-resistance rotor develops a high starting torque at low starting current. The torque of the motor is controlled so that a maximum value of torque is provided throughout the acceleration period.

To gain the maximum starting torque, the motor is started with maximum rotor resistance, which is reduced as the motor accelerates. See Figure 8-7. Curve 1 shows the starting torque when no resistance is applied to the rotor circuit. When no resistance is applied, the motor has the same basic starting torque characteristics as an induction motor. The starting torque is about 125% of the full-load torque (FLT).

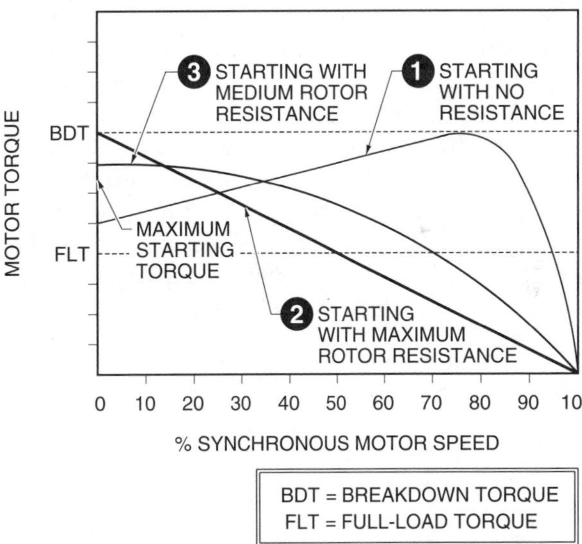

Figure 8-7. A wound-rotor motor is normally started with maximum rotor resistance.

Curve 2 shows the starting torque when maximum resistance is applied to the rotor. When maximum resistance is applied, the motor's starting torque is almost equal to the motor's breakdown torque (BDT), or about 200%.

Curve 3 shows the starting torque when medium resistance is applied to the rotor. When medium resistance is applied, the motor has less starting torque than at maximum resistance, but has a higher torque at approximately 15% to 30% of full speed.

Speed Control

Once the motor has started, resistors connected to the rotor can be used to reduce the speed of the motor. Increasing the resistance of the rotor while it is running reduces the speed of the motor. When the speed of the rotor is reduced, more voltage is induced into the windings of the rotor, due to increased slip. The higher voltage increases current flow, providing higher torque. The higher torque allows the motor to operate at a lower speed and still drive the connected load.

When the motor operates at a lower speed, the increased current causes a higher temperature in the motor. Since the motor is operating at a lower speed, normal ventilation is also reduced. Therefore, the speed of the motor is usually reduced no more than 50%.

SYNCHRONOUS MOTORS

Standard induction motors and wound-rotor motors always run at slower than synchronous speed. A synchronous motor always runs at exactly synchronous speed. Because of their speed characteristics, they are used with loads that require constant speed. Synchronous motors are used for applications for which a NEMA Class B motor is designed.

The synchronous motor has a two-part rotor. The rotor has a standard induction motor rotor section and a wound-rotor section. A synchronous motor is started as an induction motor and is accelerated to near synchronous speed, using the induction part of the rotor. At approximately 95% of synchronous speed, DC excitation is applied to the wound-rotor section, and the motor pulls into synchronous speed. See Figure 8-8.

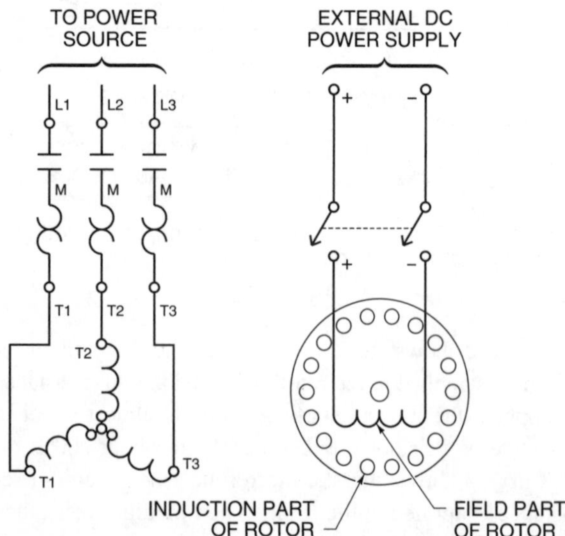

Figure 8-8. A synchronous motor is started as an induction motor with DC power supplied to the rotor to bring the motor up to synchronous speed.

Operating Principles

A magnetic field is produced when 3ϕ power is applied to the stator of the motor. The magnetic field revolves synchronously with the power supply frequency. This revolving magnetic field produces the torque that causes the rotor to rotate. The rotor starts and comes up to near synchronous speed as a standard induction motor. The motor speed remains slightly less than synchronous speed until the DC power is applied to the rotor field. See Figure 8-9.

When the DC excitation is applied to the rotor, it produces alternate north and south poles, which lock into step with the revolving field of the stator. The rotor then revolves in step or in synchronization with the supply line.

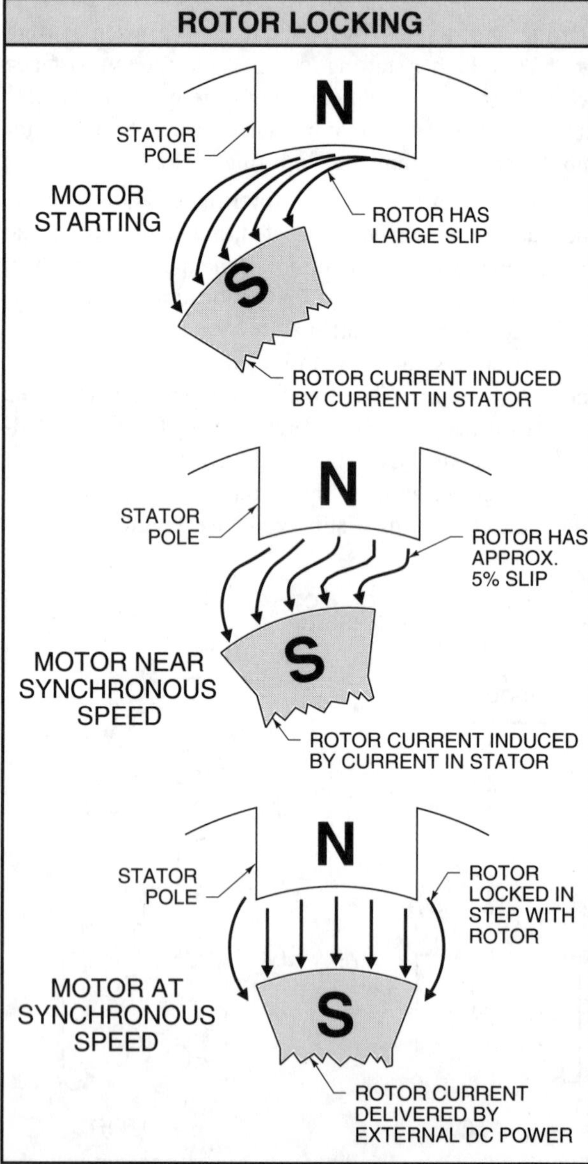

Figure 8-9. The rotor locks in step with the stator when DC power is applied.

The DC power to the motor is frequently supplied by an exciter generator mounted on the end of the synchronous motor. The integrally mounted generator is usually driven by an extension of the synchronous motor shaft. The exciter generator voltage is seldom higher than 250 V. The kW capacity of an exciter generator usually ranges from approximately 1% to 3% of the synchronous motor's rating.

Power Factor

Synchronous motors are not only used to produce mechanical power, but are also used for power factor correction. A synchronous motor usually operates with a leading power factor, which is the opposite of induction and wound-rotor motors. This leading power factor can be used to counteract the effect of the lagging power factor caused by other motor types.

A *leading power factor* is circuit current leading voltage by some angle between 0° and 90°. A *lagging power factor* is circuit current lagging behind voltage by some angle between 0° and 90°. A leading or lagging power factor causes power losses in the system, since voltage and current are not in-phase. See Figure 8-10.

The power factor of a synchronous motor is determined by the amount of current applied to the rotor. Varying the current varies the power factor of the motor. A synchronous motor can operate at unity power factor (unity), a lagging power factor (underexcited), or a leading power factor (overexcited).

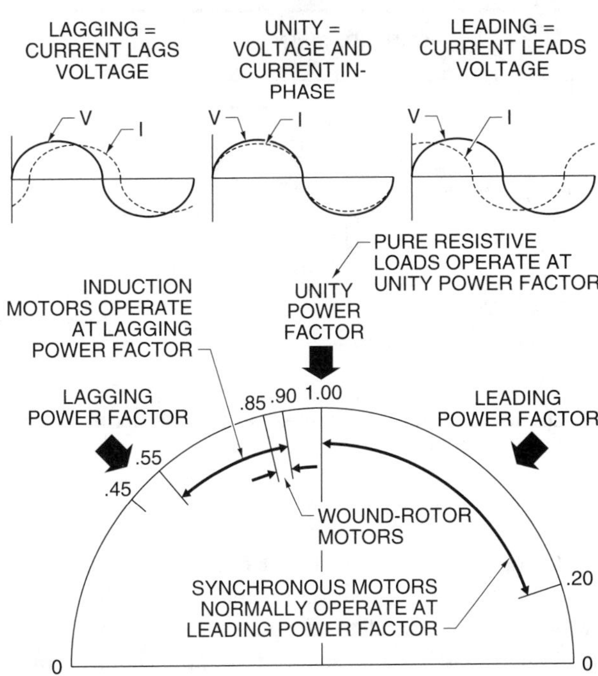

Figure 8-10. Power factor is determined by current in relation to voltage.

Unity. The alternating current is in-phase with the applied voltage. Except for normal motor losses, all of the power is delivered to the load as mechanical power. This is the most efficient operating condition of a synchronous motor.

Underexcited. With weak DC power applied to the motor, the power factor is less than unity. The current lags the applied voltage by some angle. When underexcited, the synchronous motor operates with the same type of lagging power factor as induction and wound-rotor motors. Being underexcited is not the normal operating condition of a synchronous motor.

Overexcited. With high DC power applied to the motor, the power factor is also less than unity. The current leads the applied voltage and produces a leading power factor. This is the normal operating condition of a synchronous motor, even though the motor is less efficient when not operated at unity. The leading power factor of the synchronous motor offsets the lagging power factor of other motor types. Synchronous motors typically are used in very large horsepower applications and offset many smaller lagging motor types. Being overexcited is the normal operating condition of a synchronous motor. It is not the most efficient operating condition for the motor, but it is the most efficient operating condition for the entire distribution system. See Figure 8-11.

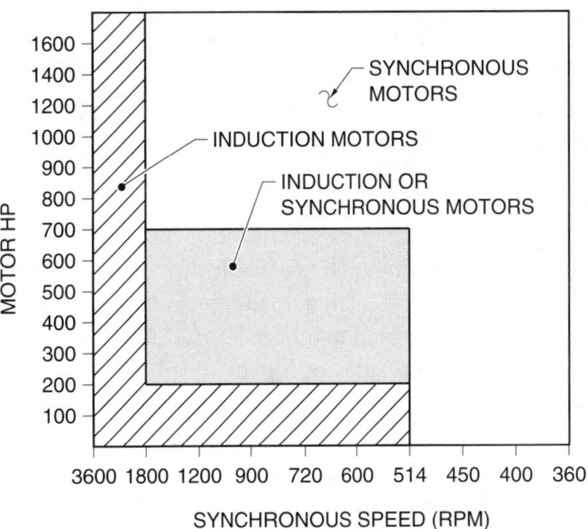

Figure 8-11. Synchronous motors are used for slower-speed applications requiring higher-horsepower motors.

STEPPING MOTORS

A *stepping motor* is a motor that divides shaft rotation into discrete distances (steps). Stepping motors are always DC motors. They are used in applications that require precise control of the position of the motor shaft. Typical applications include pen positioning, rotary and indexing table control, floppy disk control, laser positioning, and printer control. See Figure 8-12.

TYPICAL STEPPING INCREMENTS

STEPS[1]	STEP ANGLE[2]	MAXIMUM RUN RATE[3]
4	90	100
8	45	260
20	18	500
24	15	600
48	7.5	1000
72	5.0	1000
96	3.75	1000
144	2.5	1000
180	2.0	1500
200	1.8	2000
400	0.72	1000

[1] per revolution
[2] in degrees
[3] in steps per second (typical)

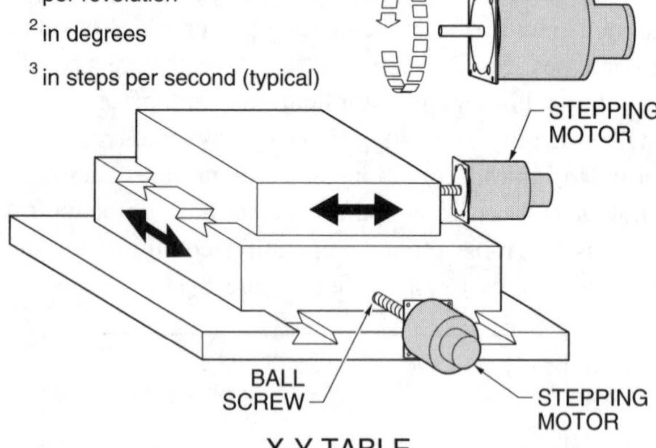

Figure 8-12. A stepping motor divides shaft rotation into discrete distances (steps).

Although stepping motors provide precise positioning, they can not operate large loads because their torque output is low compared to other motors. Stepping motors are prone to losing steps at higher speed. Motor size is relatively large for the amount of torque output.

The torque output of stepping motors typically ranges from 0.5 oz/in. for small motors to 5000 oz/in. for larger motors. Stepping motors are good for applications with a constant load. They should not be used with varying loads. Stepping motors provide good positional accuracy both at rest and while in motion. However, to hold the shaft in position, power must be maintained to the stator winding. This power causes heat in the windings and must be considered in applications requiring a load to be held in position. Using a higher rated motor and providing ventilation usually takes care of any heat problems.

Stepping motors are commercially available in a wide range of step increments. Most stepping motors used in industrial applications have 200 to 400 steps per revolution.

Operation

The shaft of a stepping motor rotates at fixed angle when it receives an electric pulse. Each input pulse produces shaft rotation through the stepping motors rated step angle. For example, if 50 pulses are applied to a 1.8° stepping motor, the shaft rotates exactly 90° ($50 \times 1.8 = 90$).

The rotor is a permanent magnet. The stator windings are electromagnets. When the control switch is closed, the stator windings are magnetized by the current flowing through the coil. See Figure 8-13. If Switch 1 is opened and Switch 2 is closed, the rotor moves a fixed interval to the next stator winding. If the switches are opened and closed in the same order (excitation sequence), the rotor continues to move.

EXCITATION SEQUENCE

SW1 SW2 SW3 SW4	SW4 SW3 SW2 SW1
CLOCKWISE ROTATION	COUNTER-CLOCKWISE ROTATION

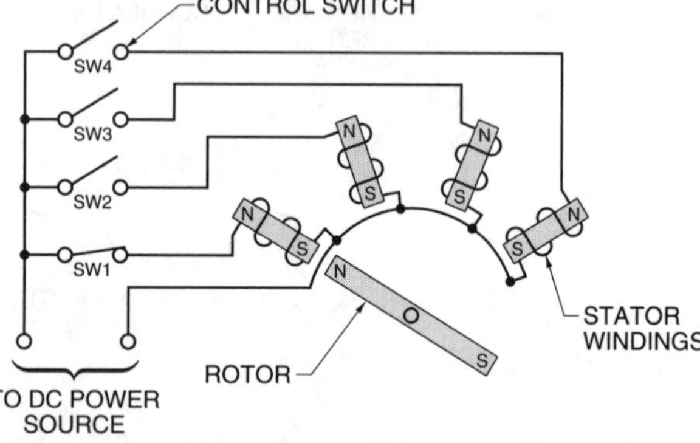

Figure 8-13. The excitation sequence determines the direction of rotation of a stepping motor.

Changing the excitation sequence to the windings reverses the direction of the motor. A stepping motor can rotate in either direction, based on the order in which the control switches are activated. Although control switches can be used to energize the stator windings, solid-state switches are used for most applications. Transistors are typical solid-state switches used to control stepping motors.

chapter 8

SPECIAL MOTORS APPLICATIONS

Application — Rheostat Control of Wound-Rotor Motor Speed

A rheostat controls the acceleration or the speed of wound-rotor motors up to 50 HP. The rotor current of a 50 HP motor can be as high as 150 A, which is the limit of most rheostats. A rheostat provides up to a 50% speed reduction when the motor is under full-load operation. The rheostat adds resistance to the rotor circuit when the motor is running. The more resistance added to the rotor circuit, the slower the motor runs. When the resistance is removed, the motor operates at synchronous speed minus the slip.

Application — Power Resistor Control of Wound-Rotor Motor Acceleration

Power resistors control the acceleration or the speed of wound-rotor motors up to 2000 HP. Power resistors are required because the rotor current of a 2000 HP motor can be as high as 1000 A. The resistors are wye-connected to match the wye-connected wound rotor. Resistors of the same value are used. The resistors in the first phase are marked R1, R2, R3, etc. The resistors in the second phase are marked R11, R12, R13, etc. The resistors in the third phase are marked R21, R22, R23, etc.

To limit the amount of starting current, the maximum resistance is added to the circuit at startup. As the motor accelerates, resistance is removed from the circuit. See Power Resistor Connections.

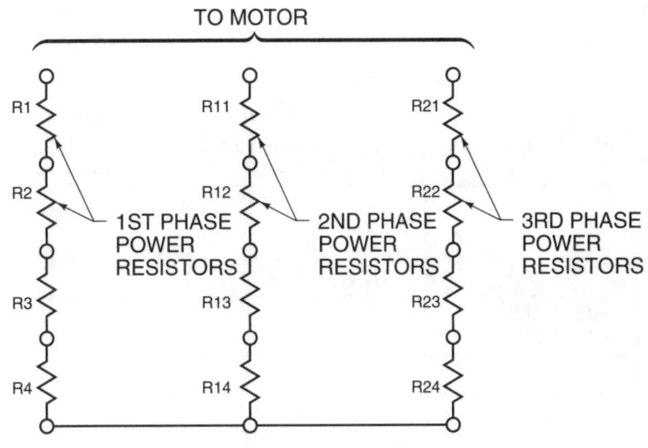

POWER RESISTOR CONNECTIONS

Application — Synchronous Motor Power Factor

When a synchronous motor is at unity power factor, the current in the stator power circuit is at a minimum level. If the current in the rotor winding is increased (overexcited), the current in the stator increases and the motor develops a leading power factor. If the current in the rotor winding is decreased (underexcited), the current in the stator increases and the motor develops a lagging power factor. To measure stator current, an AC ammeter connected to a current transformer (CT) is added to the stator power circuit. A current transformer with a typical value of 10:1 (or 100:1, depending on motor size) is used to reduce the current from the main power lines to the ammeter. To measure the rotor current, a DC ammeter connected to a DC shunt is added to the rotor power circuit. A rheostat or other resistance is used to vary the rotor current. The higher the resistance value, the lower the rotor current. The lower the resistance value, the higher the rotor current. See Measuring Stator and Rotor Current.

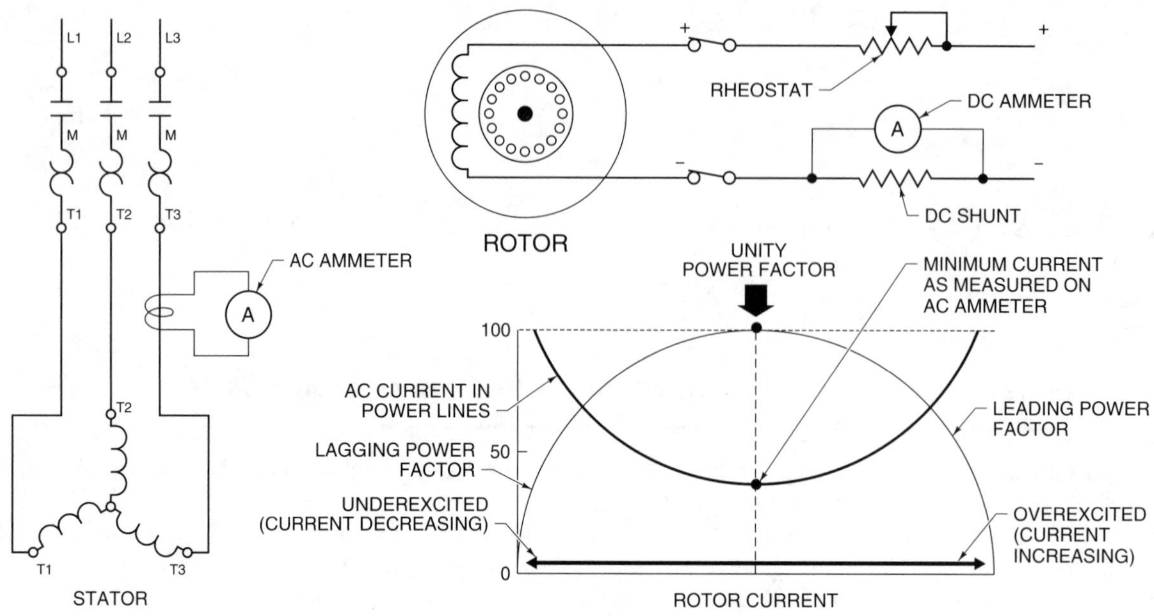

MEASURING STATOR AND ROTOR CURRENT

Application — Controlling Stepping Motor Shaft Position

Stepping motor shaft position is controlled by energizing the stator windings. Control switches apply or remove power from each stator winding. As each winding is energized, the rotor moves 30°. Initially, S_1 lines up with Stator Winding 1. When Switch 2 (SW2) is closed, the rotor rotates 30°, placing S_2 in line with Stator Winding 2. See Stepping Motor Operation.

SWITCH TABLE				
ROTATION (DEGREES)	SW1	SW2	SW3	SW4
0	X			
30		X		
60			X	
90				X
120	X			
150		X		
180			X	
210				X
240	X			
270		X		
300			X	
330				X
360	X			

X = SWITCH CLOSED

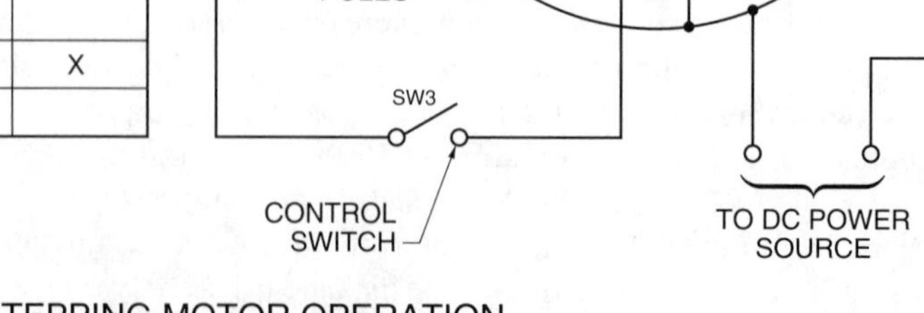

STEPPING MOTOR OPERATION

Name ______________________ Date ______________

chapter 8

SPECIAL MOTORS

ACTIVITIES

Activity 8-1. Rheostat Control of Wound-Rotor Motor Speed

The rheostat is placed in five positions for slow, fast, medium-slow, medium, and medium-fast speeds. Identify the speed for each position of the rheostat.

_______ **1.** Position A = _______ speed

_______ **2.** Position B = _______ speed

_______ **3.** Position C = _______ speed

_______ **4.** Position D = _______ speed

_______ **5.** Position E = _______ speed

_______ **6.** Starting position _______ allows for minimum starting current on the main power lines.

_______ **7.** Starting position _______ allows the motor to start as a standard induction type motor.

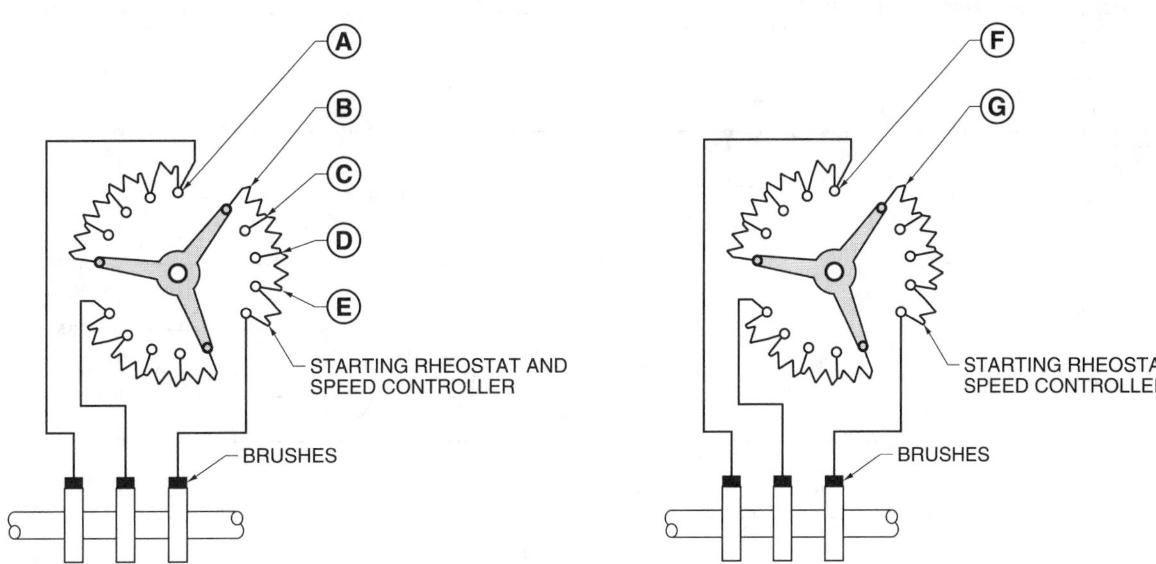

Activity 8-2. Power Resistor Control of Wound-Rotor Motor Acceleration

The motor starts with full resistance in the circuit when the start pushbutton is pressed. After 5 seconds, the resistance of the rotor circuit is reduced by ⅓. After 5 additional seconds, the resistance is reduced by ⅔. After 10 additional seconds, all resistance is removed. Contactors start the motor and control the power resistors. Three timers control the contactors that remove the power resistors from the circuit as the motor accelerates.

1. Identify the resistor numbers.

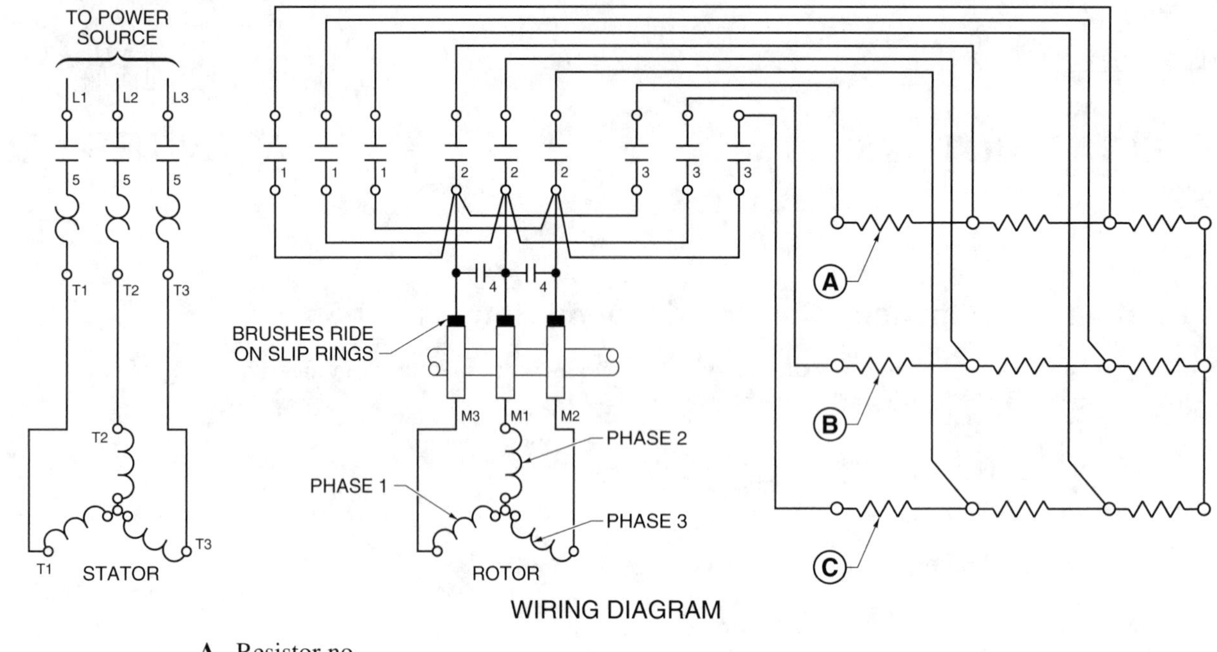

_________ **A.** Resistor no. _________

_________ **B.** Resistor no. _________

_________ **C.** Resistor no. _________

2. Using the wiring diagram, identify the contactor numbers (1, 2, 3, 4, or 5) that allow for proper circuit operation.

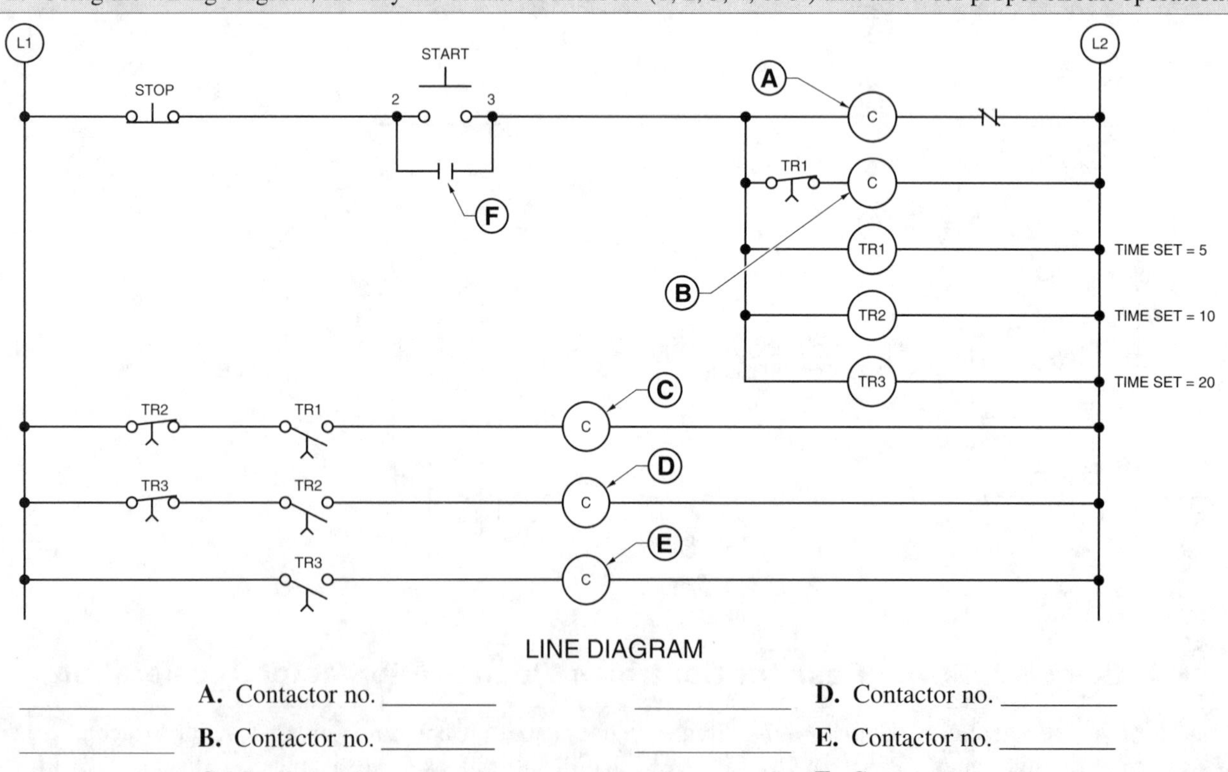

_________ **A.** Contactor no. _________

_________ **B.** Contactor no. _________

_________ **C.** Contactor no. _________

_________ **D.** Contactor no. _________

_________ **E.** Contactor no. _________

_________ **F.** Contactor no. _________

◯ Activity 8-3. Synchronous Motor Power Factor

Using the ammeter readings, draw the curve that represents the current in the stator and rotor. Mark the point at which the motor is at unity power factor. Also, mark the area representing leading and lagging power factor.

AMMETER READINGS	
Stator Current	**Rotor Current**
180	24
170	22
155	20
150	18
155	16
157	14
163	12
195	7

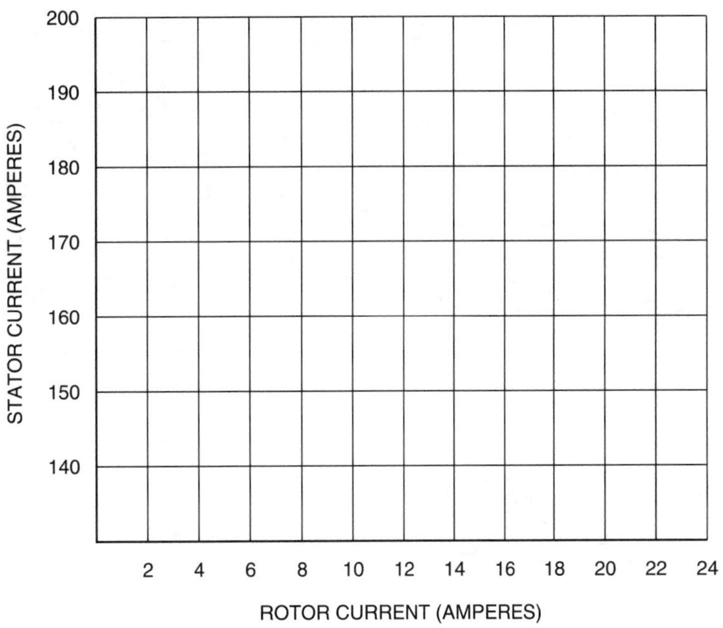

◯ Activity 8-4. Controlling Stepping Motor Shaft Position

Using the switch tables on page 242, draw the final position of the rotor.

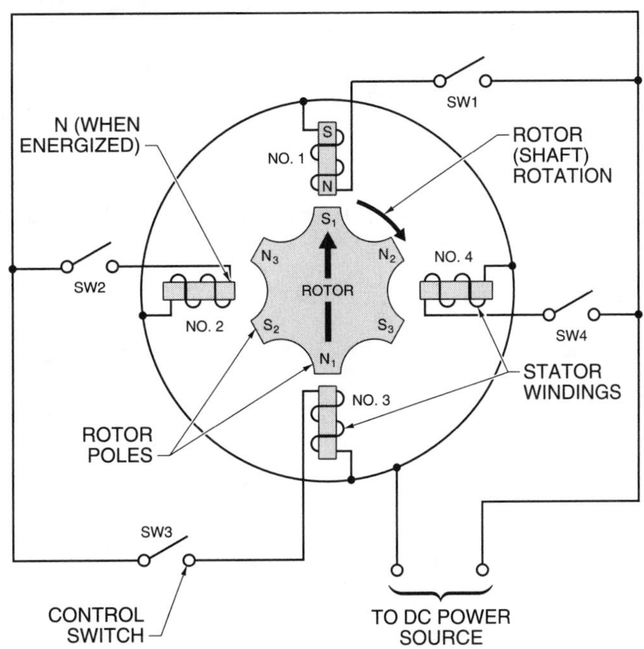

1.

SWITCH TABLE			
SW1	SW2	SW3	SW4
	X		
		X	
	X		
		X	
			X
		X	
			X
		X	
	X		
X			
	X		
X			

X = SWITCH CLOSED

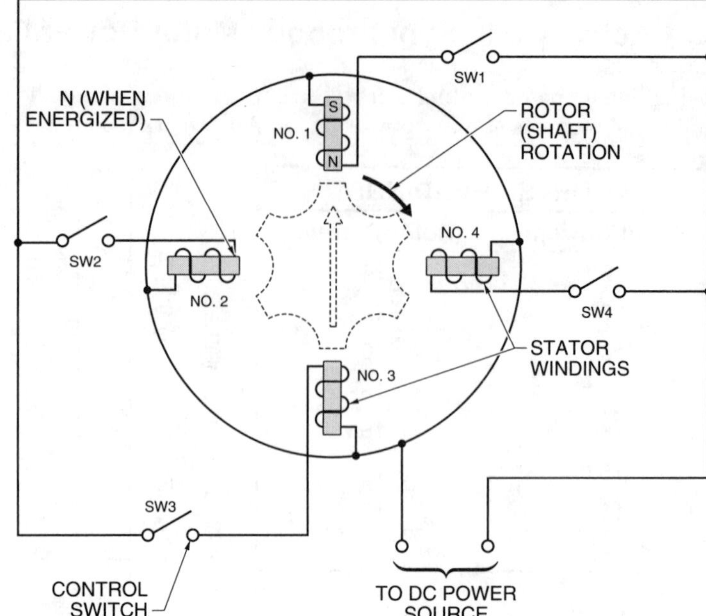

2.

SWITCH TABLE			
SW1	SW2	SW3	SW4
	X		
		X	
			X
		X	
	X		
X			
	X		
		X	
			X

X = SWITCH CLOSED

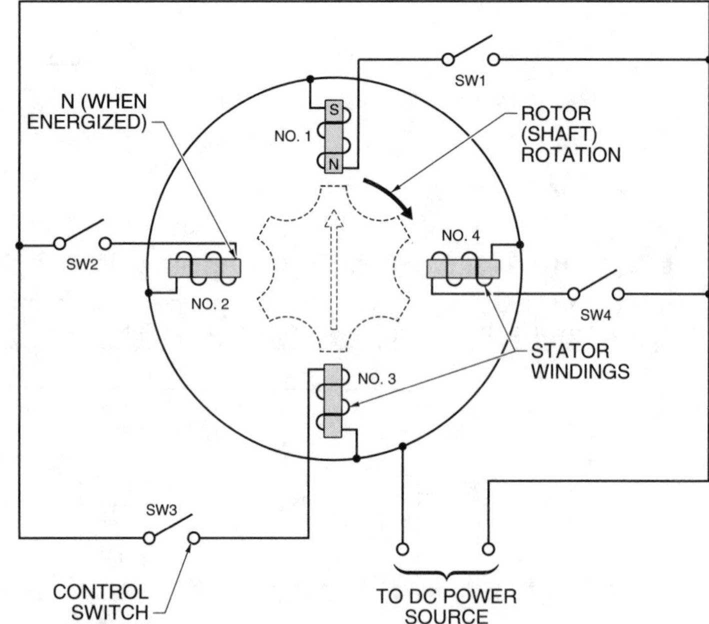

Activity 8-5. Determining Motor Power

Determine the power consumed by each motor. Use an 83% efficiency rating for standard motors and an 89% efficiency rating for energy-efficient motors.

______ **1.** A 1 HP, 3ϕ, standard motor consumes ______ W.

______ **2.** A 2 HP, 3ϕ, energy-efficient motor consumes ______ W.

______ **3.** A 5 HP, 3ϕ, standard motor consumes ______ W.

______ **4.** A 15 HP, 3ϕ, energy-efficient motor consumes ______ W.

______ **5.** A 20 HP, 3ϕ, standard motor consumes ______ W.

______ **6.** A 40 HP, 3ϕ, energy-efficient motor consumes ______ W.

__________ **7.** A 75 HP, 3ϕ, standard motor consumes ________ W.

__________ **8.** A 125 HP, 3ϕ, energy-efficient motor consumes ________ W.

__________ **9.** A 200 HP, 3ϕ, standard motor consumes ________ W.

__________ **10.** A 250 HP, 3ϕ, energy-efficient motor consumes ________ W.

Activity 8-6. Determining Motor Operating Cost

Determine the operating cost for each motor. Calculate years at 52 weeks each.

1. A 1 HP motor has an efficiency rating of 85%. The electrical power rate is $.085/kWh.

__________ **A.** The operating cost per hour is $________.

__________ **B.** The operating cost per 10-hour week is $________.

__________ **C.** The operating cost per 40-hour week is $________.

__________ **D.** The operating cost per year at 10 hours per week is $________.

__________ **E.** The operating cost per year at 40 hours per week is $________.

2. A 10 HP motor has an efficiency rating of 93%. The electrical power rate is $.105/kWh.

__________ **A.** The operating cost per hour is $________.

__________ **B.** The operating cost per 10-hour week is $________.

__________ **C.** The operating cost per 40-hour week is $________.

__________ **D.** The operating cost per year at 10 hours per week is $________.

__________ **E.** The operating cost per year at 40 hours per week is $________.

3. A 20 HP motor has an efficiency rating of 83%. The electrical power rate is $.085/kWh with a 2.5% demand charge.

__________ **A.** The operating cost per hour is $________.

__________ **B.** The operating cost per 10-hour week is $________.

__________ **C.** The operating cost per 40-hour week is $________.

__________ **D.** The operating cost per year at 10 hours per week is $________.

__________ **E.** The operating cost per year at 40 hours per week is $________.

4. A 75 HP motor has an efficiency rating of 96%. The electrical power rate is $.085/kWh.

__________ **A.** The operating cost per hour is $________.

__________ **B.** The operating cost per 10-hour week is $________.

__________ **C.** The operating cost per 40-hour week is $________.

__________ **D.** The operating cost per year at 10 hours per week is $________.

__________ **E.** The operating cost per year at 40 hours per week is $________.

5. A 200 HP motor has an efficiency rating of 87%. The electrical power rate is $.105/kWh.

__________ **A.** The operating cost per hour is $________.

__________ **B.** The operating cost per 10-hour week is $________.

__________ **C.** The operating cost per 40-hour week is $________.

__________ **D.** The operating cost per year at 10 hours per week is $________.

__________ **E.** The operating cost per year at 40 hours per week is $________.

6. A 250 HP motor has an efficiency rating of 90%. The electrical power rate is $.085/kWh with a 2.5% demand charge.

_____________ **A.** The operating cost per hour is $_________.

_____________ **B.** The operating cost per 10-hour week is $_________.

_____________ **C.** The operating cost per 40-hour week is $_________.

_____________ **D.** The operating cost per year at 10 hours per week is $_________.

_____________ **E.** The operating cost per year at 40 hours per week is $_________.

Activity 8-7. Determining Cost Savings and Payback

Determine the cost savings, price premium, and payback period for each motor.

1. The annual operating cost for a standard motor costing $330.00 is $107.00. The annual operating cost of an energy-efficient motor costing $400.00 is $96.30.

_____________ **A.** The savings for operating the energy-efficient motor is $_________ per year.

_____________ **B.** The price premium is $_________ .

_____________ **C.** The payback period is _________ days.

2. The annual operating cost for a standard motor costing $520.00 is $285.00. The annual operating cost of an energy-efficient motor costing $676.00 is $242.50.

_____________ **A.** The savings for operating the energy-efficient motor is $_________ per year.

_____________ **B.** The price premium is $_________ .

_____________ **C.** The payback period is _________ days.

3. The annual operating cost for a standard motor costing $1525.00 is $1680.00. The annual operating cost of an energy-efficient motor costing $1860.50 is $1478.40.

_____________ **A.** The savings for operating the energy-efficient motor is $_________ per year.

_____________ **B.** The price premium is $_________ .

_____________ **C.** The payback period is _________ days.

4. The annual operating cost for a standard motor costing $8900.00 is $4100.00. The annual operating cost of an energy-efficient motor costing $10,591.00 is $3485.00.

_____________ **A.** The savings for operating the energy-efficient motor is $_________ per year.

_____________ **B.** The price premium is $_________ .

_____________ **C.** The payback period is _________ days.

5. The annual operating cost for a standard motor costing $16,175.00 is $30,100.00. The annual operating cost of an energy-efficient motor costing $19,410.00 is $26,187.00.

_____________ **A.** The savings for operating the energy-efficient motor is $_________ per year.

_____________ **B.** The price premium is $_________ .

_____________ **C.** The payback period is _________ days.

6. The annual operating cost for a standard motor costing $17,140.00 is $4450.00. The annual operating cost of an energy-efficient motor costing $20,225.00 is $3782.50.

_____________ **A.** The savings for operating the energy-efficient motor is $_________ per year.

_____________ **B.** The price premium is $_________ .

_____________ **C.** The payback period is _________ days.

Activity 8-8. Control Circuit Modification

1. Redraw the line diagram so that the furnace blower motor is automatically controlled by a temperature switch. Include a red pilot light that turns ON when the furnace is ON.

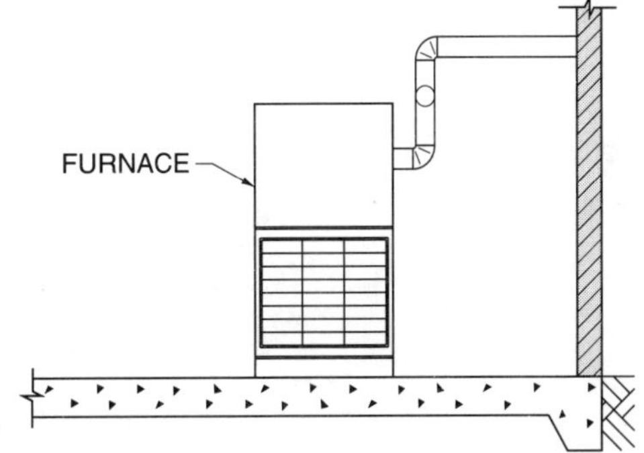

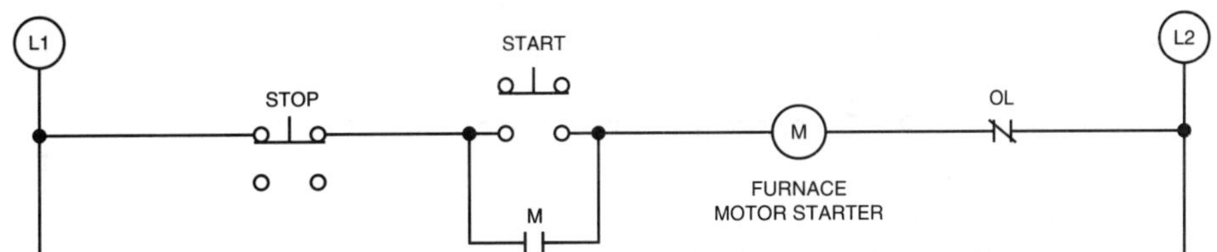

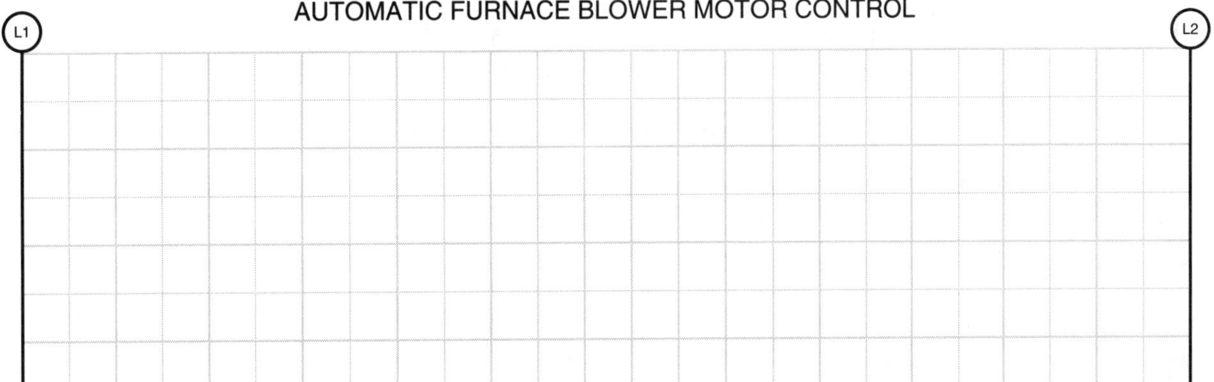

2. Redraw the line diagram by adding a single voltage transformer to reduce the voltage from L1 and L2. Connect the temperature switch and a red pilot light to the secondary side of the transformer so that the control circuit is at a lower voltage.

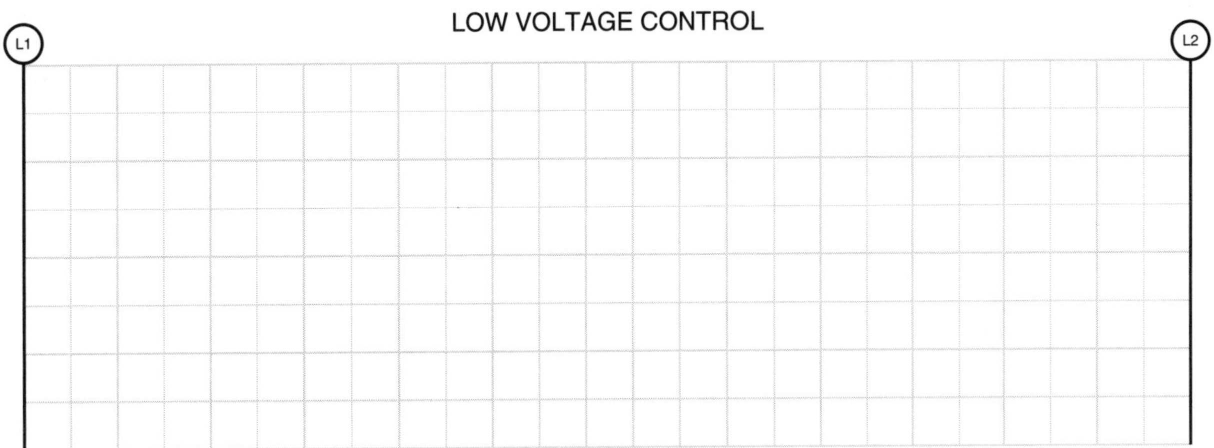

3. Redraw the line diagram so that the circuit includes a second stop/start/jog pushbutton.

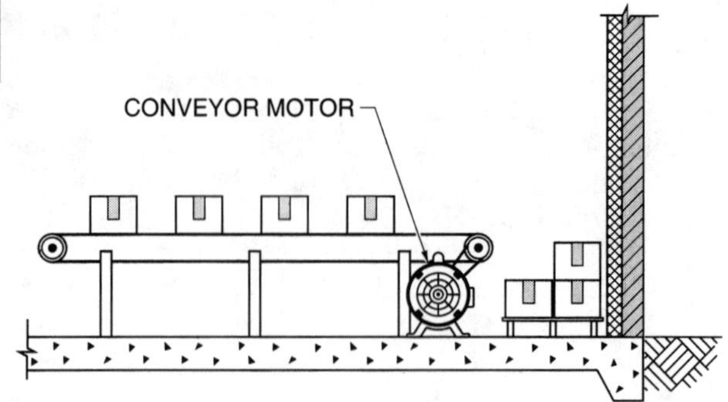

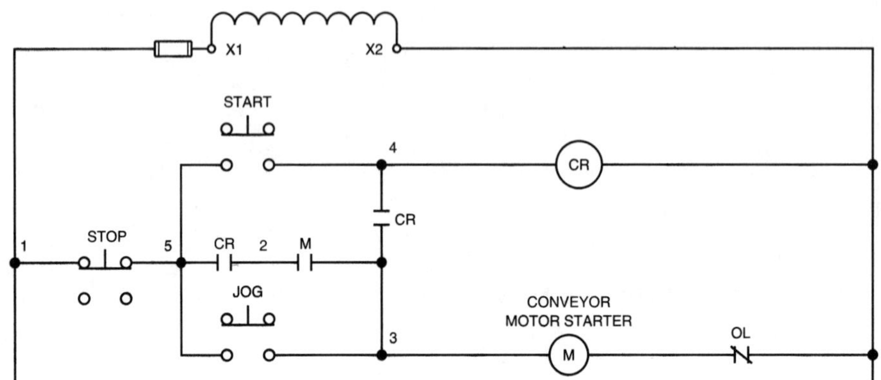

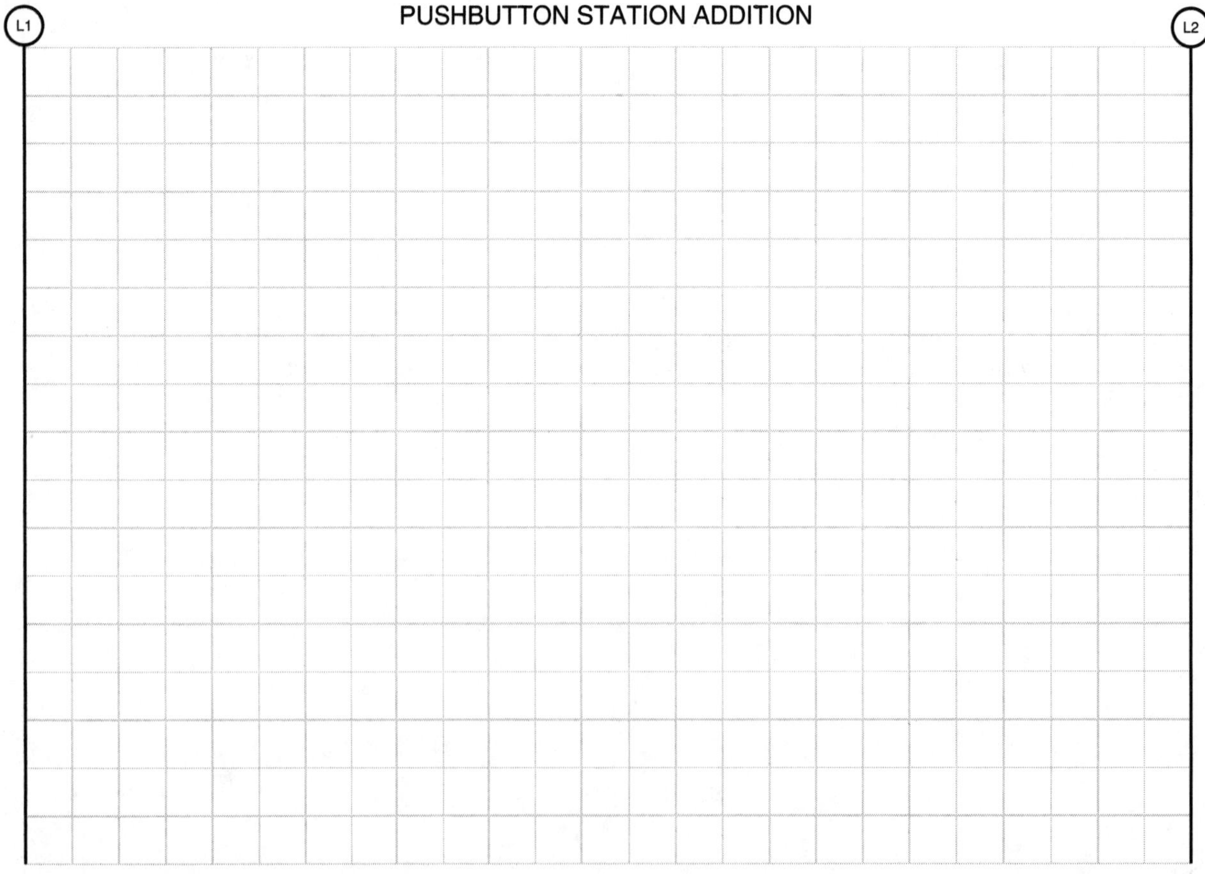

Name ______________________ Date ______________

chapter **8**

SPECIAL MOTORS

TRADE TEST

STOP START M OL

Completion

______ **1.** Mechanical energy is used to produce ________.

______ **2.** One horsepower equals ________ W.

______ **3.** Standard motors have an average efficiency of ________%.

______ **4.** The difference in the purchase price of an energy-efficient motor and a standard motor is the price ________.

______ **5.** The ________ windings of a 3ϕ, wound-rotor motor are marked T1, T2, and T3.

______ **6.** The ________ windings of a 3ϕ, wound-rotor motor are marked M1, M2, and M3.

______ **7.** The starting torque of a 3ϕ, wound-rotor motor is about ________% of the FLT.

______ **8.** A(n) ________ motor is used with loads that require constant speed.

______ **9.** A magnetic field is produced when 3ϕ power is applied to the ________ of a synchronous motor.

______ **10.** Induction motors operate at ________ power factor.

______ **11.** ________ is the most efficient operating condition of a synchronous motor.

______ **12.** A(n) ________ motor divides shaft rotation into discrete distances.

______ **13.** An energy-efficient motor typically costs ________% more than an equivalent standard motor.

______ **14.** Being ________ is the normal operating condition of a synchronous motor.

______ **15.** The step angle of a 20-step stepping motor is ________°.

True-False

T F **1.** A synchronous motor always runs at exactly synchronous speed.

T F **2.** A synchronous motor can operate at unity, lagging, or leading power factor.

T F **3.** Stepping motors are good for applications with varying loads.

T F **4.** If a motor is operated often, an energy-efficient motor is more cost efficient.

T F **5.** A high resistance rotor develops a high starting torque at low starting current.

T F **6.** The motor speed of a synchronous motor remains slightly less than synchronous speed until the DC power is applied to the rotor field.

T F **7.** Synchronous motors may be used for power factor corrections.

T F **8.** Stepping motors are used to operate large loads.

T F **9.** An excitation sequence of SW4, SW3, SW2, and SW1 produces clockwise rotation.

T F **10.** As a wound-rotor motor accelerates, resistance is gradually phased out.

Multiple Choice

_______ **1.** Motors typically convert between _______% and _______% of their electrical power to usable mechanical energy.

A. 40; 60
B. 50; 75
C. 60; 80
D. 75; 95

_______ **2.** Energy-efficient motors have an average efficiency of _______%.

A. 78
B. 83
C. 89
D. 95

_______ **3.** The cost of electrical power is based on the _______.

A. size of the motor
B. efficiency of the motor
C. number of kWh used
D. neither A, B, nor C

_______ **4.** A wound-rotor motor is a 3ϕ motor in which the _______.

A. rotor windings are connected to slip rings
B. rotor windings are connected to stationary brushes
C. slip rings are stationary
D. neither A, B, nor C

_______ **5.** A wound-rotor motor is normally started with _______ resistance in the circuit.

A. no
B. partial
C. full
D. either A, B, or C

_______ **6.** A synchronous motor has a _______-part rotor.

A. one
B. two
C. four
D. eight

_______ **7.** A leading power factor is circuit current leading voltage by some angle between _______° and _______°.

A. 0; 90
B. 0; 180
C. 90; 180
D. 180; 360

_______ **8.** With weak DC power applied to a motor, the power factor is _______.

A. lagging
B. unity
C. leading
D. neither A, B, nor C

_______ **9.** Changing the excitation sequence to the windings of a stepping motor _______ of the motor.

A. increases horsepower
B. decreases torque
C. increases speed
D. reverses direction

_______ **10.** An energy-efficient motor costs _______ than a standard motor.

A. less to purchase and less to operate
B. more to purchase and more to operate
C. less to purchase and more to operate
D. more to purchase and less to operate

Problems

_____ **1.** A motor delivers 39.5 kW of power and draws 42 kW of power from the power lines. What is the efficiency of the motor?

_____ **2.** Is the motor in problem 1 energy efficient?

_____ **3.** A 30 HP motor has a power loss of 2500 W. What is the efficiency of the motor?

_____ **4.** Is the motor in problem 3 energy efficient?

_____ **5.** What is the efficiency of a 50 HP, 460 V, 3ϕ motor with 45 kW from the power source and 41.75 kW delivered to the load?

_____ **6.** Is the motor in problem 5 energy efficient?

For problems 7 through 12, refer to the standard motor.

_____ **7.** What is the efficiency of the motor?

_____ **8.** How much power is consumed by the load?

_____ **9.** What percentage of power is lost when the incoming power is converted to mechanical energy?

_____ **10.** What is the operating cost of the motor at $.125/kWh?

_____ **11.** What is the operating cost of the motor for one 40-hour work week?

_____ **12.** The motor operates 50 weeks per year. What is the annual operating cost of the motor?

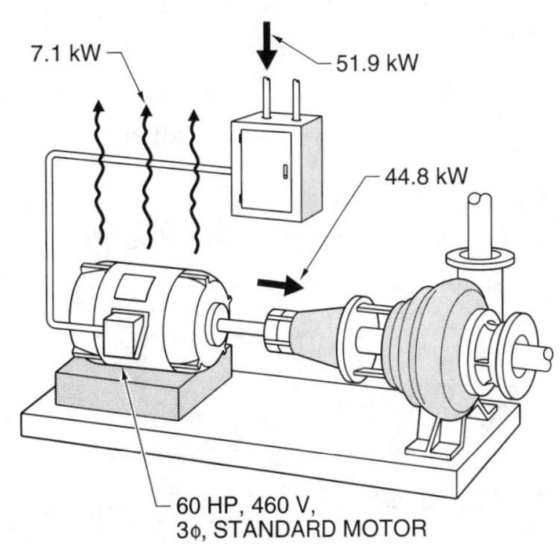

For problems 13 through 18, refer to the energy-efficient motor.

_____ **13.** What is the efficiency of the motor?

_____ **14.** How much power is consumed by the load?

_____ **15.** What percentage of power is lost when the incoming power is converted to mechanical energy?

_____ **16.** What is the operating cost of the motor at $.125 /kWh?

_____ **17.** What is the operating cost of the motor for a 40-hour work week?

_____ **18.** The motor operates 50 weeks per year. What is the annual operating cost of the motor?

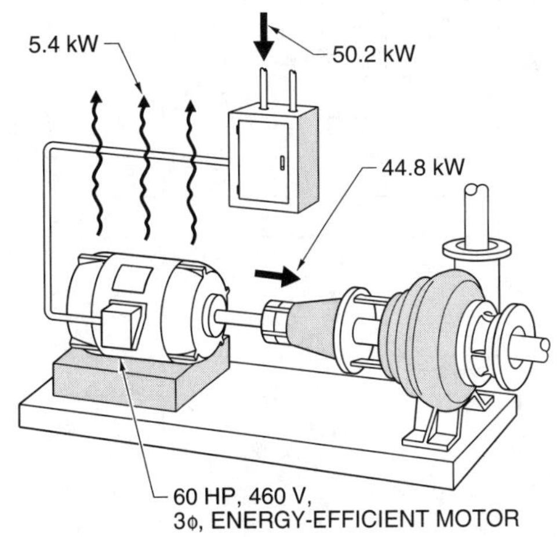

For problems 19 through 22, refer to the standard motor and the energy-efficient motor.

_________ **19.** The energy-efficient motor costs $_________ less per hour to operate than the standard motor.

_________ **20.** The energy-efficient motor costs $_________ less per week to operate than the standard motor.

_________ **21.** The energy-efficient motor has an annual (50-week) savings of $_________ as compared to the standard motor.

_________ **22.** What is the payback period of the energy-efficient motor if the price premium was $322.50?

For problems 23 through 25, refer to Ammeter Readings to identify when the motor is at unity, leading, or lagging power factor.

_________ **23.** The motor is at unity power factor for meter reading _________.

_________ **24.** The motor has a leading power factor for meter reading _________.

_________ **25.** The motor has a lagging power factor for meter reading _________.

AMMETER READINGS

Meter Reading	AC	DC
A	125	17
B	130	10
C	110	14

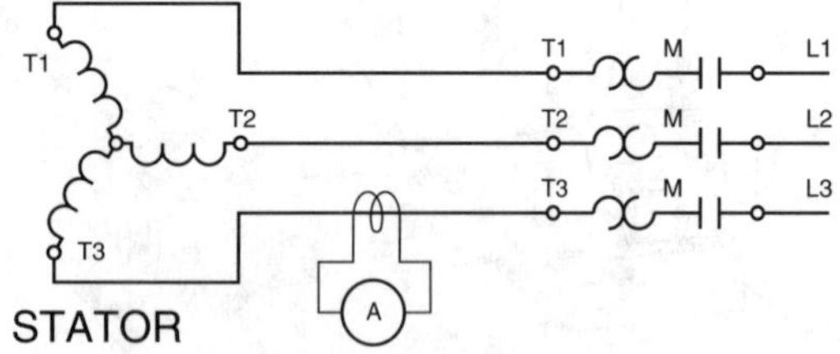

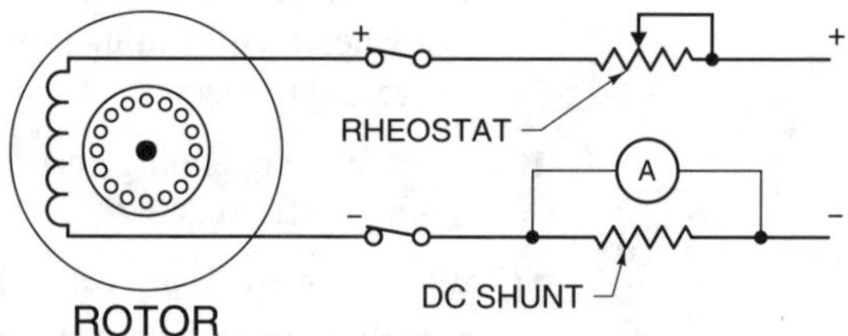

For problem 26, refer to Switch Table.

26. Draw the final position of the rotor.

SWITCH TABLE

SW1	SW2	SW3	SW4
	X		
X			
	X		
		X	
	X		
		X	
			X
		X	
	X		
		X	
	X		
		X	

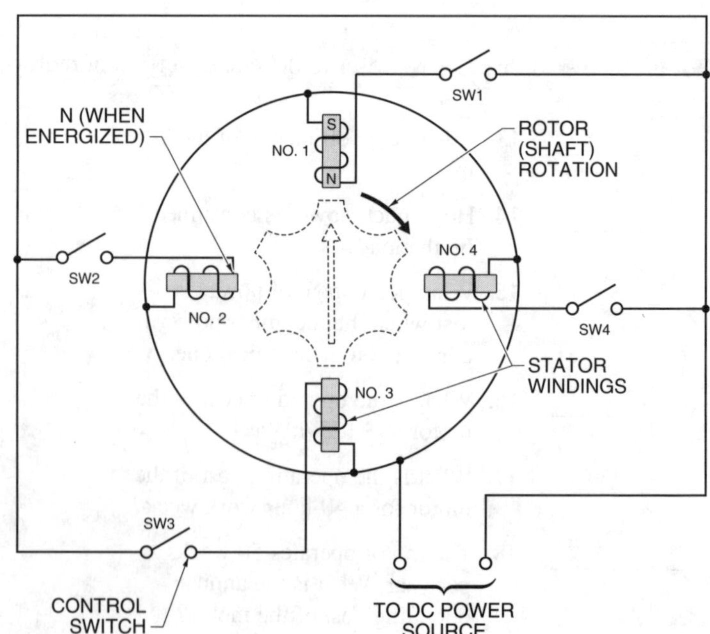

27. Connect the wound-rotor motor to run in forward or reverse directions. Connect the resistors to control the starting torque of the motor.

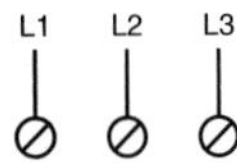

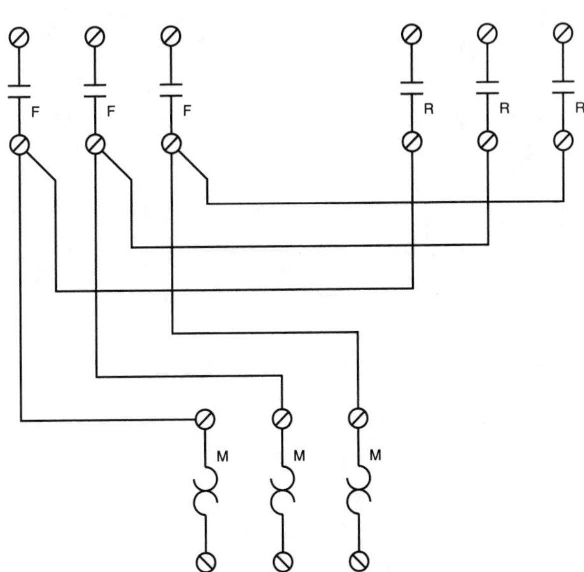

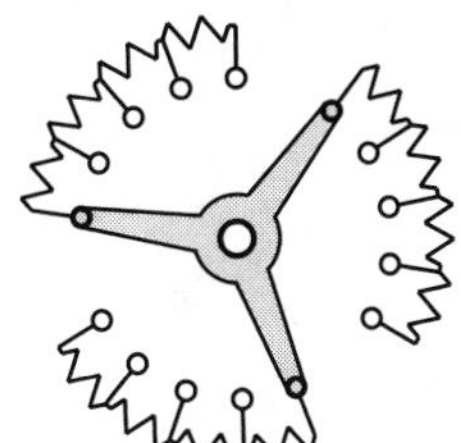

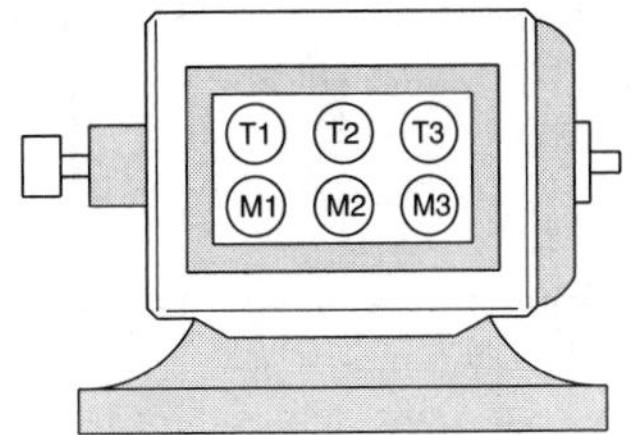

28. Connect the synchronous motor to run in forward or reverse directions. Connect the resistor to control the power factor of the motor.

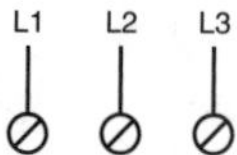

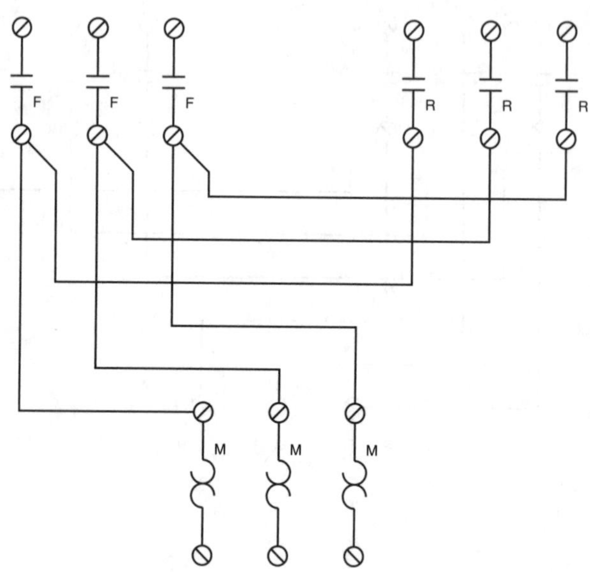

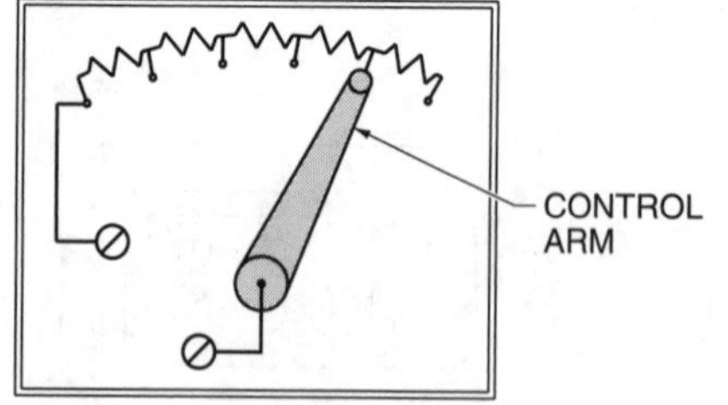

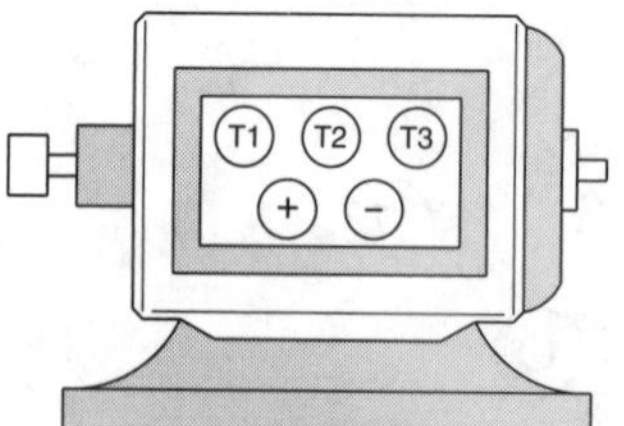

Name ____________ Date ________

chapter 9

ELECTRIC MOTORS

FINAL EXAM

Completion

______ **1.** ______ current is current that reverses its direction of flow twice per cycle.

______ **2.** One horsepower can raise ______ pounds one foot in one second.

______ **3.** The three terminals of a(n) ______ are the anode, cathode, and gate.

______ **4.** Standard motors are designed to operate at an ambient temperature of not more than ______°C.

______ **5.** A(n) ______ motor enclosure allows the passage of air to cool the motor windings.

______ **6.** A(n) ______ circuit is current that leaves the normal current-carrying path by going around the load and back to the power source or ground.

______ **7.** ______ unbalance occurs when lines are out-of-phase.

______ **8.** The stationary part of a 1ϕ motor is the ______.

______ **9.** ______ torque is the maximum torque a motor can provide without an abrupt reduction in motor speed.

______ **10.** Three-phase ______ motors have no brushes.

______ **11.** A(n) ______ diagram shows the control circuit and the power circuit.

______ **12.** A DC series motor has ______ starting torque.

______ **13.** ______ is the amount of electron flow in a circuit.

______ **14.** ______ unbalance occurs when the voltages at the motor terminal are not equal.

______ **15.** The rotating part of a 1ϕ motor is the ______.

______ **16.** ______ current is the current that flows in one direction only.

______ **17.** A(n) ______ method is not required for a 3ϕ motor.

______ **18.** A(n) ______ diagram shows the operational logic of the motor circuit.

______ **19.** The end opposite the shaft is the ______ of a motor.

______ **20.** The ______ is a safety margin for motor overloads.

______ **21.** ______ voltage is any higher-than-normal voltage that temporarily exists on one or more of the power lines.

______ **22.** ______ frequency is the number of cycles of supplied voltage per second.

______ **23.** A(n) ______ is the rotating part of a DC motor.

______ **24.** A six-pole motor has ______ electrical degrees in one revolution.

______ **25.** A(n) ______ converts AC to DC by allowing current to move in only one direction.

______ **26.** The ______ motor is the most simple and least expensive 1ϕ, AC motor.

______ **27.** Temperature ______ is the difference between the winding temperature of a running motor and the ambient temperature.

__________ **28.** _________ wear faster than any other component of a DC motor.

__________ **29.** _________ temperature is the temperature of the air around a piece of equipment.

__________ **30.** A(n) _________ is the stationary windings, or magnets, of a DC motor.

__________ **31.** A(n) _________ motor can operate at more than one voltage level.

__________ **32.** _________ is the force that produces rotation in a motor.

__________ **33.** _________ motors are the most common motors used in industry.

__________ **34.** NEC® _________ lists standard ampere ratings of fuses and fixed-trip CB's.

__________ **35.** Energy-efficient motors have an average efficiency of _________%.

__________ **36.** A(n) _________ is a device that stores an electrical charge.

__________ **37.** A DC _________ motor has the field connected in parallel with the armature.

__________ **38.** The industrial standard for changing the direction of rotation of a 3ϕ motor is to interchange _________ and _________.

__________ **39.** Motor frames are classified by _________.

__________ **40.** A motor operates satisfactorily with a voltage variation of ± _________% from the voltage rating on the nameplate.

__________ **41.** Motors convert electrical energy into _________ energy.

__________ **42.** The cost of electricity is based on the number of _________ used.

__________ **43.** In a constant horsepower motor, torque decreases in the same ratio as the _________ increases.

__________ **44.** A(n) _________ motor can be operated on either DC or 1ϕ, AC.

__________ **45.** A(n) _________ change is a change in which factors increase or decrease at the same rate.

__________ **46.** One HP equals _________ W.

__________ **47.** A motor _________ is a device that connects the motor shaft to the equipment the motor is driving.

__________ **48.** _________ is the leading cause of motor failure.

__________ **49.** _________ is the opposition to electron flow in a circuit.

__________ **50.** _________ torque is produced when the rotor is stationary and full power is applied to the motor.

__________ **51.** When a load is placed on a universal motor, the speed _________.

__________ **52.** A(n) _________ change is a change in which one factor increases at the same rate the other factor decreases.

__________ **53.** A universal motor is usually available in sizes less than _________ HP.

__________ **54.** A(n) _________ is any current over the normal current level.

__________ **55.** _________ is the amount of electrical pressure in a circuit.

__________ **56.** _________ force is the force that moves rotating bodies away from the center of rotation.

__________ **57.** A(n) _________ is a solid-state switching device that switches the current ON by a quick pulse of control current.

__________ **58.** A(n) _________ service condition may contain chemical fumes, lint, dust, explosive gases, etc.

__________ **59.** A(n) _________ power line is any power line that is not grounded.

__________ **60.** A(n) _________ is a conducting medium in which the current flow occurs by ion migration.

Problems

Refer to the motor torque graph to identify the types of motor torque shown.

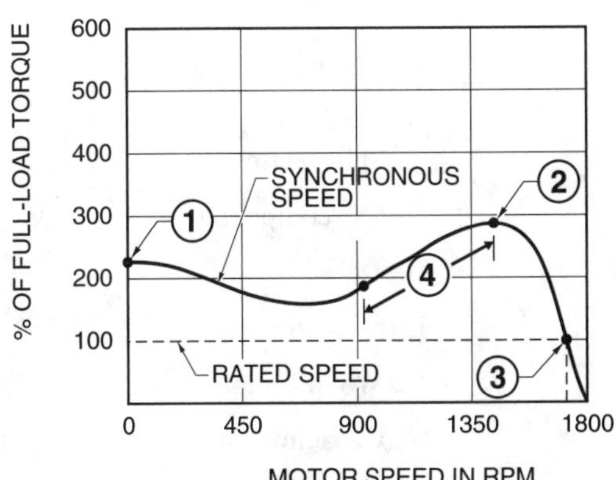

_______ **1.** Point 1 shows _______ torque.

_______ **2.** Point 2 shows _______ torque.

_______ **3.** Point 3 shows _______ torque.

_______ **4.** Point 4 shows _______ torque.

A 460 VAC, 3ϕ motor was placed in service in 1/87. Use the resistance readings to plot the graph and determine when the motor requires service.

_______ **5.** The motor requires service in _______.

INSULATION SPOT TEST			
A	**B**	**A**	**B**
1/87	200	1/90	60
7/87	198	7/90	8
1/88	185	1/91	3
7/88	173	7/91	.1
1/89	171	1/92	.1
7/89	140		

A Test Taken
B Resistance Reading (in MΩ)

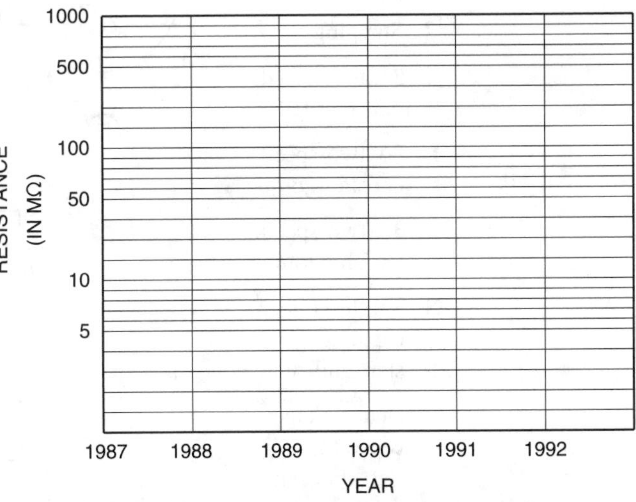

INSULATION SPOT TEST GRAPH

Use the resistance readings to plot the graph and determine the polarization index of the insulation.

_______ **6.** The polarization index of the insulation is _______.

_______ **7.** Is the motor insulation good or bad?

DIELECTRIC ABSORPTION TEST		C	D
		2	95
		3	110
A	**B**	4	98
10	70	5	85
20	71	6	82
30	79	7	78
40	81	8	74
50	83	9	72
60	84	10	70

A Test at _______ Seconds
B Resistance Reading (in MΩ)
C Test at _______ Minutes
D Resistance Reading (in MΩ)

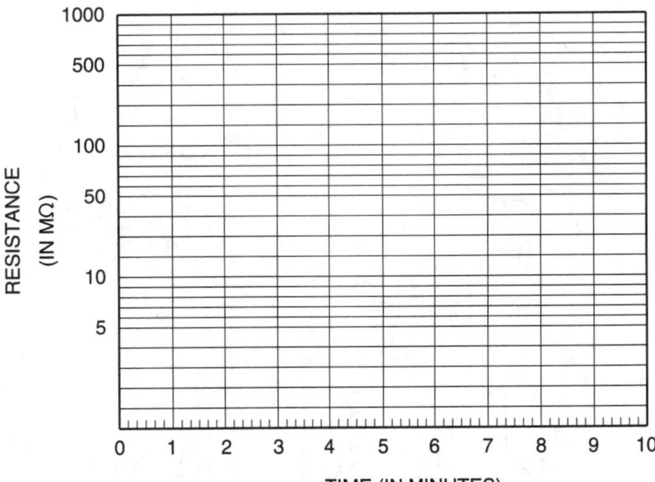

DIELECTRIC ABSORPTION TEST GRAPH

8. Match the motor wiring diagrams to the type of motor.

_____ **A.** 3ϕ, delta
_____ **B.** Dual-voltage, split-phase
_____ **C.** DC compound
_____ **D.** DC series
_____ **E.** Synchronous
_____ **F.** Wound-rotor
_____ **G.** Capacitor-run
_____ **H.** Capacitor-start
_____ **I.** DC shunt
_____ **J.** Stepping
_____ **K.** 3ϕ, two-speed, constant HP
_____ **L.** 3ϕ, two-speed, constant torque
_____ **M.** 3ϕ, two-speed, variable torque
_____ **N.** Single-voltage, capacitor start-and-run
_____ **O.** Dual-voltage, capacitor start-and-run
_____ **P.** Single-voltage, split-phase
_____ **Q.** 3ϕ, wye

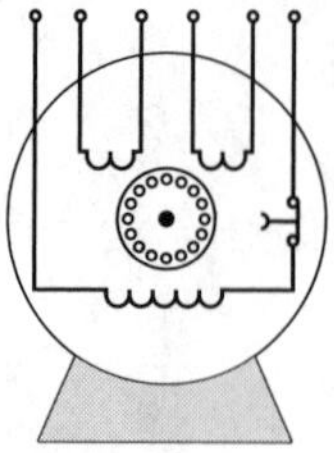

Ⓐ Ⓑ Ⓒ Ⓓ Ⓔ Ⓕ Ⓖ Ⓗ Ⓘ

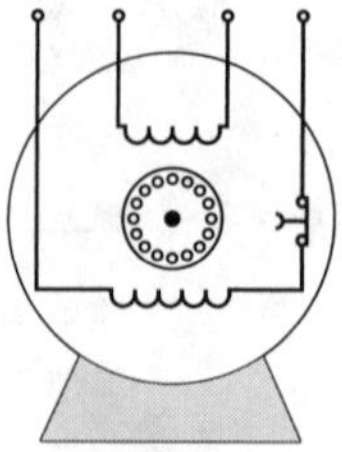

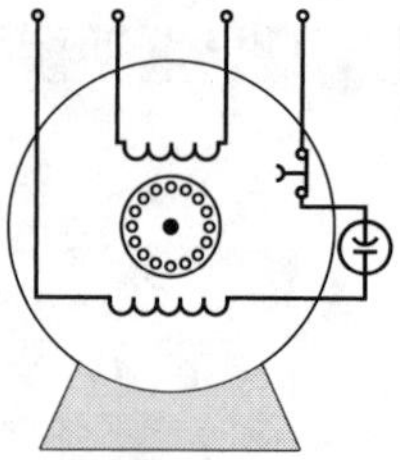

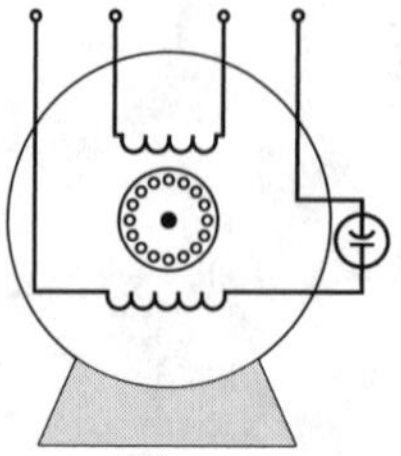

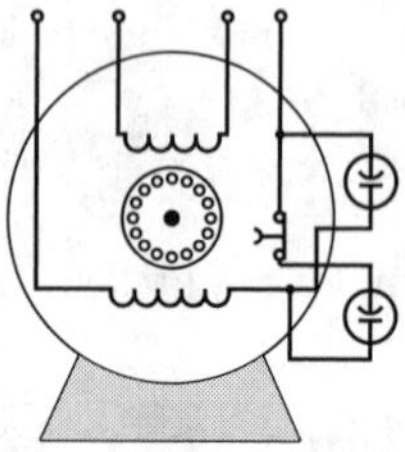

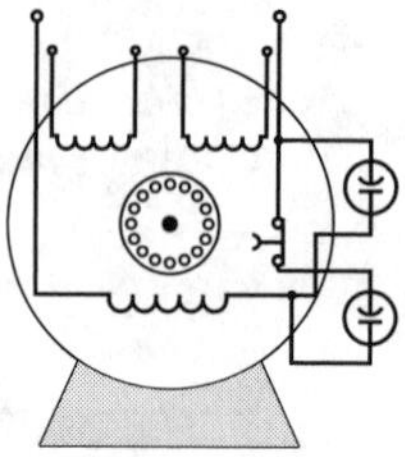

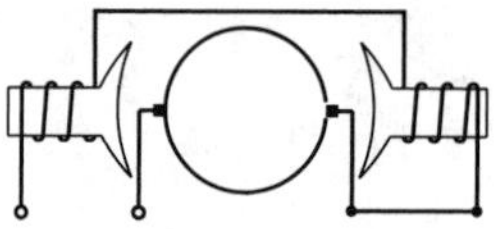

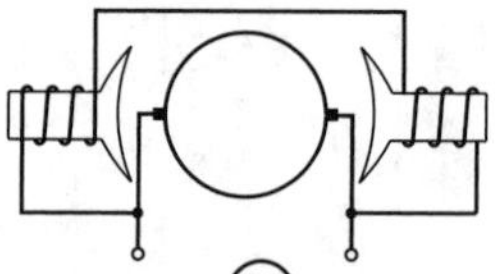

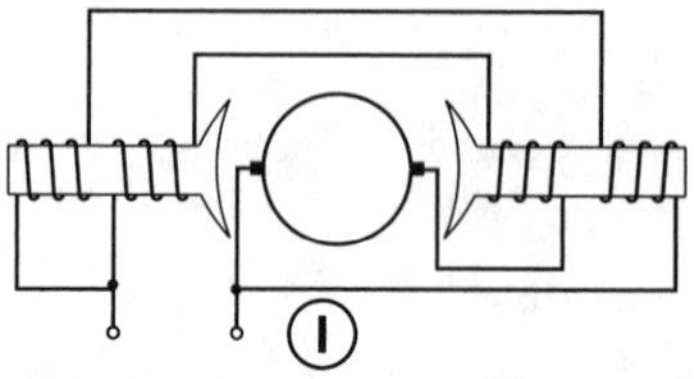

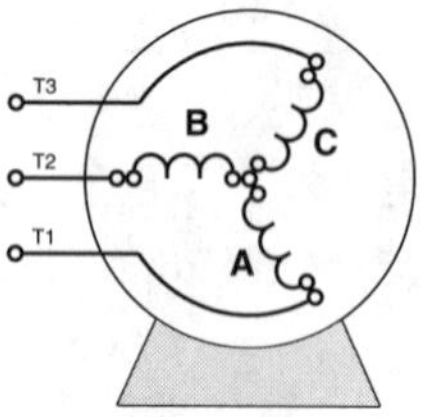

T3 T2 T1 B C A
Ⓙ

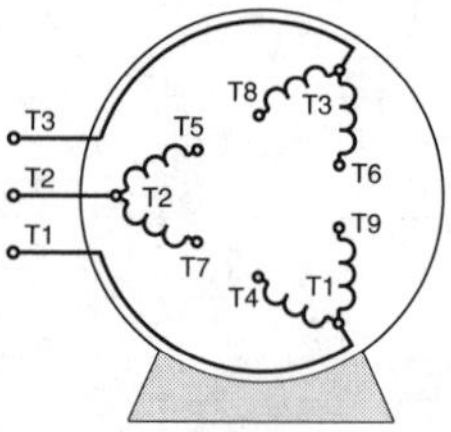

T3 T2 T1 T8 T5 T3 T2 T6 T9 T7 T4 T1
Ⓚ

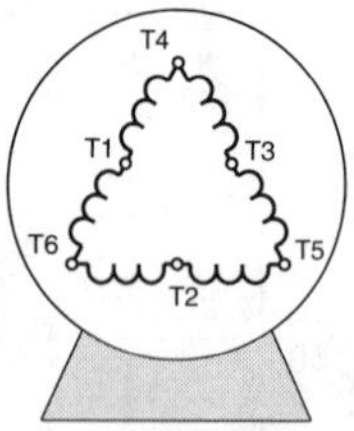

T4 T1 T3 T6 T5 T2
Ⓛ

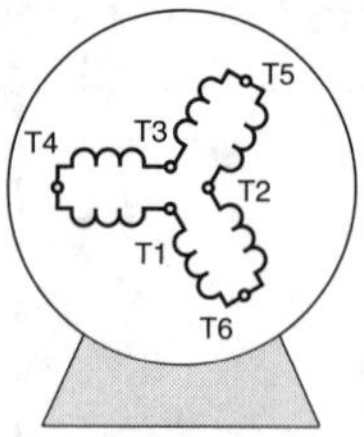

T5 T4 T3 T2 T1 T6
Ⓜ

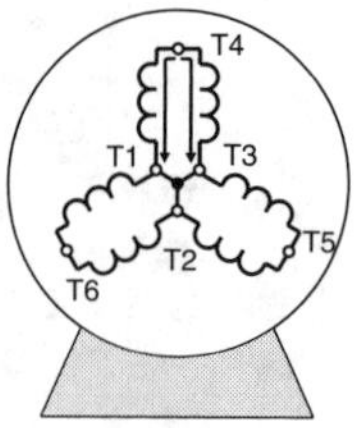

T4 T1 T3 T2 T5 T6
Ⓝ

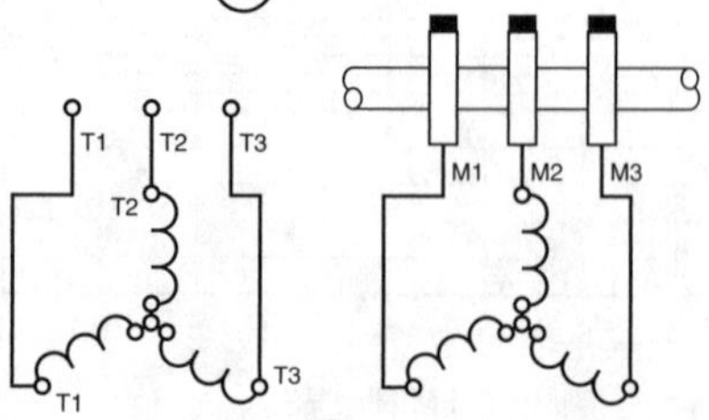

T1 T2 T3 T2 T1 T3 M1 M2 M3
Ⓞ

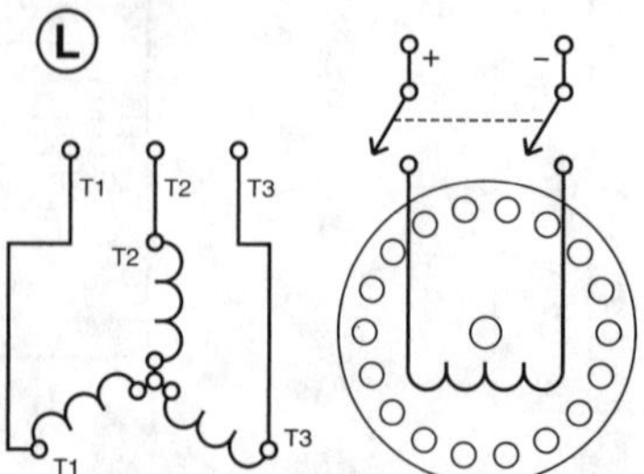

T1 T2 T3 T2 T1 T3 + −
Ⓟ

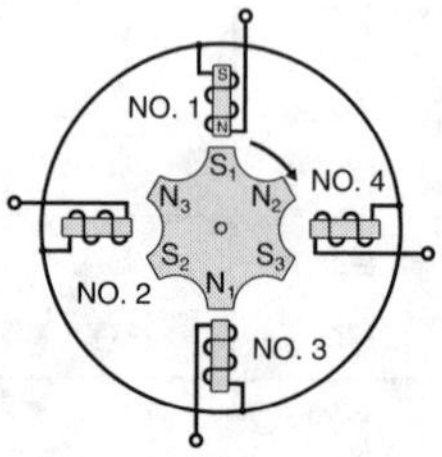

NO. 1 NO. 4 NO. 2 NO. 3 S N S_1 N_3 N_2 S_2 S_3 N_1
Ⓠ

Determine the total voltage and total capacitance of the resistors.

_________ **9.** The total voltage of A is _________ V.

_________ **10.** The total capacitance of A is _________ μF.

_________ **11.** The total voltage of B is _________ V.

_________ **12.** The total capacitance of B is _________ μF.

Ⓐ 220 μF 230 V; 180 μF 230 V

Ⓑ 25 μF 230 V; 25 μF 230 V; 25 μF 230 V

State the value and tolerance of each resistor.

_________ **13.** The resistance value of A is _________ Ω.

_________ **14.** The tolerance of A is ±_________ %.

_________ **15.** The resistance value of B is _________ Ω.

_________ **16.** The tolerance of B is ±_________ %.

_________ **17.** The resistance value of C is _________ Ω.

_________ **18.** The tolerance of C is ±_________ %

Ⓐ	O	O	R	Au
Ⓑ	G	V	BR	Ag
Ⓒ	BR	BK	O	—

Refer to the 25 HP motor for problems 19 through 21. The motor is connected to a gear reducer with a ratio of 15:1 and has an efficiency rating of 88%.

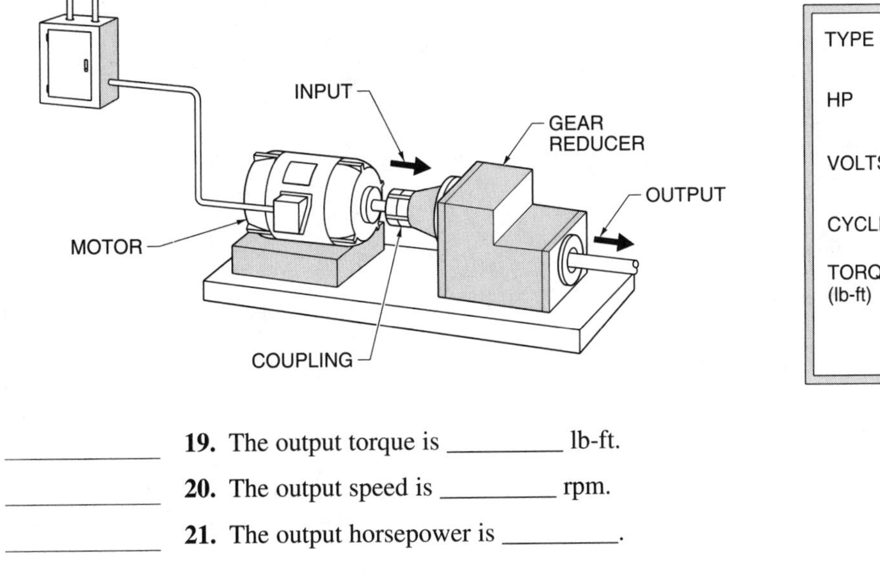

TYPE	AC	PHASE	3
HP	25	RPM	1800
VOLTS	230	AMPS	80
CYCLE	60	DUTY	CONT
TORQUE (lb-ft)	74	TEMP RISE	40° C

_________ **19.** The output torque is _________ lb-ft.

_________ **20.** The output speed is _________ rpm.

_________ **21.** The output horsepower is _________.

Refer to the 1½ HP motor for problems 22 through 24. Refer to the 7½ HP motor for problems 25 through 27. Determine the size of the OCPD for each motor using the motor nameplates. Select a standard size fuse or circuit breaker for the application. *Note:* Select the next smallest size of standard fuse or circuit breaker.

TYPE	AC	PHASE	1
HP	$1\frac{1}{2}$	CYCLE	60
VOLTS	115	AMPS	20
RPM	1725	TEMP RISE	40° C
SF	1.0	CODE	D
TIME RATE	CONT		

__________ **22.** The calculated OCPD size using an NTDF is ________ A.

__________ **23.** The standard size fuse used for the application is ________ A.

__________ **24.** The required number of fuses is ________.

TYPE	AC	PHASE	3
HP	$7\frac{1}{2}$	CYCLE	60
VOLTS	460	AMPS	11
RPM	900	TEMP RISE	50° C
SF	1.35	CODE	F
TIME RATE	CONT		

__________ **25.** The calculated OCPD size using a TDF is ________ A.

__________ **26.** The standard size fuse used for the application is ________ A.

__________ **27.** The required number of fuses is ________.

Refer to the ¼ HP motor for problems 28 and 29. Refer to the 20 HP motor for problems 30 and 31. Determine the current rating of the overload heater and the heater number for each motor.

TYPE	AC	PHASE	1
HP	$\frac{1}{4}$	CYCLE	60
VOLTS	115	AMPS	5.8
RPM	1725	TEMP RISE	40° C
SF	1.0	CODE	D
TIME RATE	CONT		

__________ **28.** The overload heater current rating is ________ A.

__________ **29.** The heater number using a Size 0 starter is ________.

TYPE	AC	PHASE	3
HP	20	CYCLE	60
VOLTS	460	AMPS	27
RPM	1150	TEMP RISE	40° C
SF	1.25	CODE	H
TIME RATE	CONT		

__________ **30.** The overload heater current rating is ________ A.

__________ **31.** The heater number using a Size 2 starter is ________.

Determine the power consumed by each motor in problems 32 through 34. Use an 84% efficiency rating for the standard motors and an 88% efficiency rating for the energy-efficient motor.

____________ **32.** A 5 HP, 3ϕ, standard motor consumes ________ W.

____________ **33.** A 10 HP, 3ϕ, energy-efficient motor consumes ________ W.

____________ **34.** A 30 HP, 3ϕ, standard motor consumes ________ W.

For problems 35 through 39, determine the operating cost of the 5 HP motor. The electrical power rate is $.085/kWh.

____________ **35.** The operating cost per hour is $________.

____________ **36.** The operating cost per 10-hour week is $________.

____________ **37.** The operating cost per 40-hour week is $________.

____________ **38.** The operating cost per year at 10 hours per week is $________.

____________ **39.** The operating cost per year at 40 hours per week is $________.

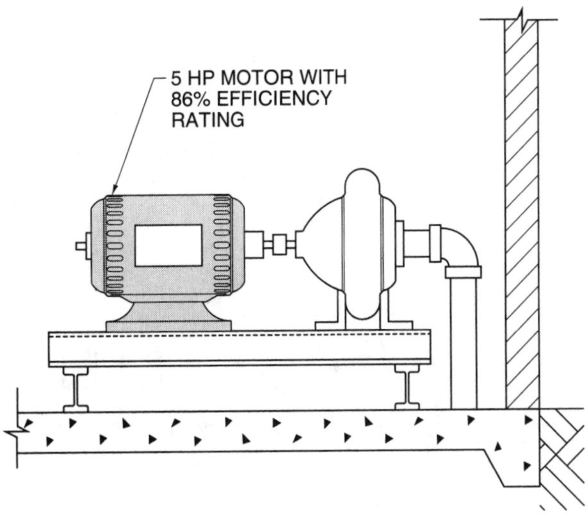

5 HP MOTOR WITH
86% EFFICIENCY
RATING

For problems 40 through 42, determine the cost savings and payback period for each motor. The annual operating cost for a standard motor costing $315.00 is $155.00. The annual operating cost for an energy-efficient motor costing $380.00 is $115.00.

____________ **40.** The savings for operating the energy-efficient motor is $________ per year.

____________ **41.** The price premium is $________.

____________ **42.** The payback period is ________ days.

Refer to Centrifugal Pump for problems 43 through 53.

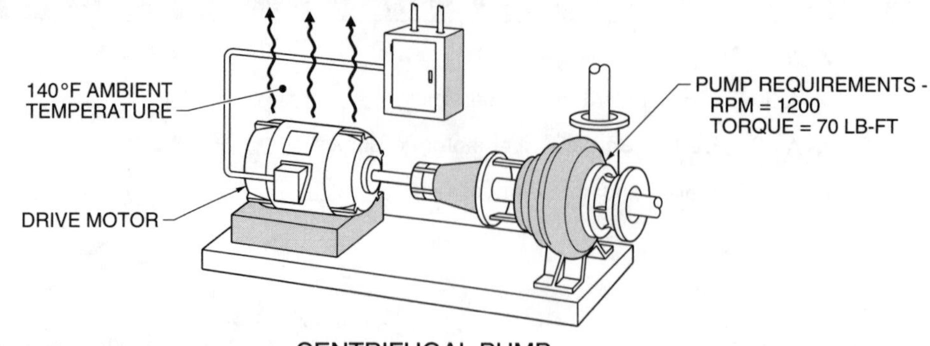

CENTRIFUGAL PUMP

_______ **43.** Assuming 100% efficiency, the drive motor is _______ HP.

_______ **44.** Using standard motor sizes, the smallest size motor that could be used for this application is a(n) _______ HP motor.

_______ **45.** The full-load torque of the smallest size motor that could be used for this application is _______ lb-ft.

_______ **46.** The required coupling torque rating for this application is _______ lb-ft.

_______ **47.** A #_______ coupling is used for this application.

_______ **48.** The standard motor size adjusted for ambient temperature is _______ HP.

_______ **49.** After adjusting for ambient temperature, will the standard motor still deliver enough horsepower to drive the pump?

_______ **50.** After adjusting for ambient temperature, the full-load torque of the standard motor is _______ lb-ft.

_______ **51.** The voltage applied to the motor is within 10% of the motor's rated voltage. The torque of the standard motor when adjusted for voltage variation and ambient temperature is _______ lb-ft.

_______ **52.** After adjusting for voltage variation, will the standard motor still deliver enough torque to drive the pump?

_______ **53.** After adjusting for ambient temperature and voltage variation, a(n) _______ HP motor is required.

54. Connect Meter 1 so that the meter checks Fuse 3. Connect Meter 2 so that the meter checks the voltage at the motor starter coil.

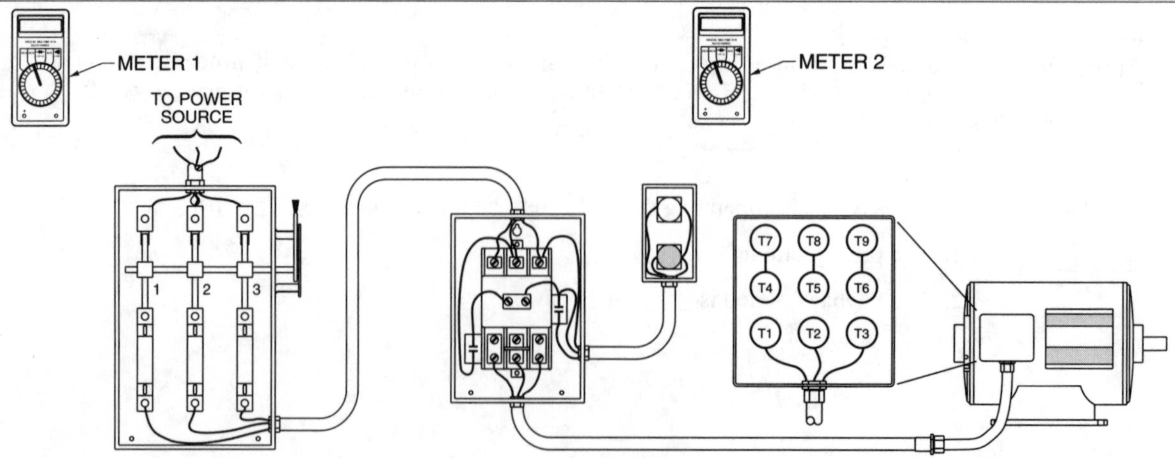

55. Connect Meter 1 to test the output of the circuit breaker. Connect Meter 2 so that the meter checks for phase loss at the motor.

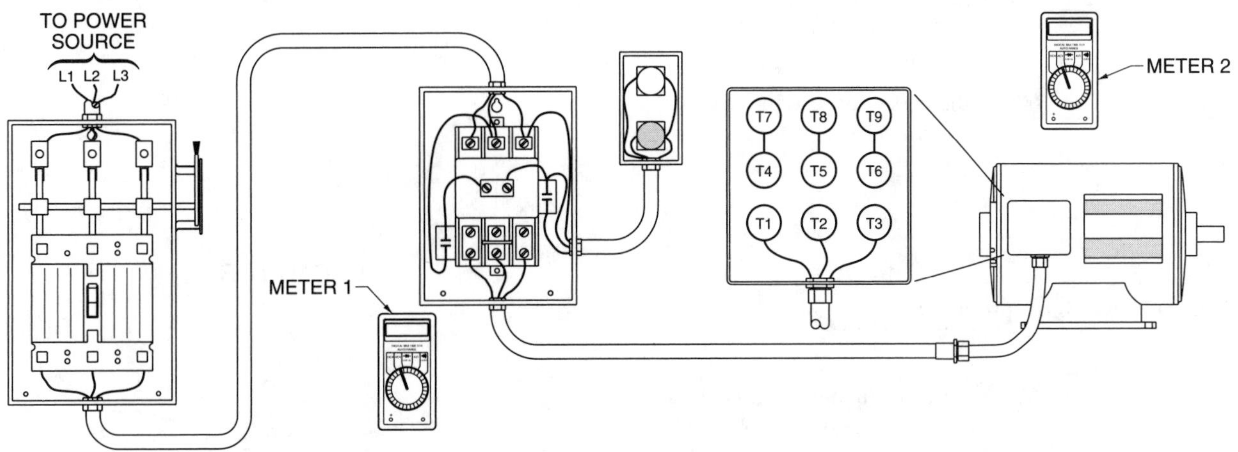

Megohmmeter 1 reads 90 kΩ. Megohmmeter 2 reads 100 MΩ. Megohmmeter 3 reads 80 MΩ.

_____________ **56.** The problem is _________.

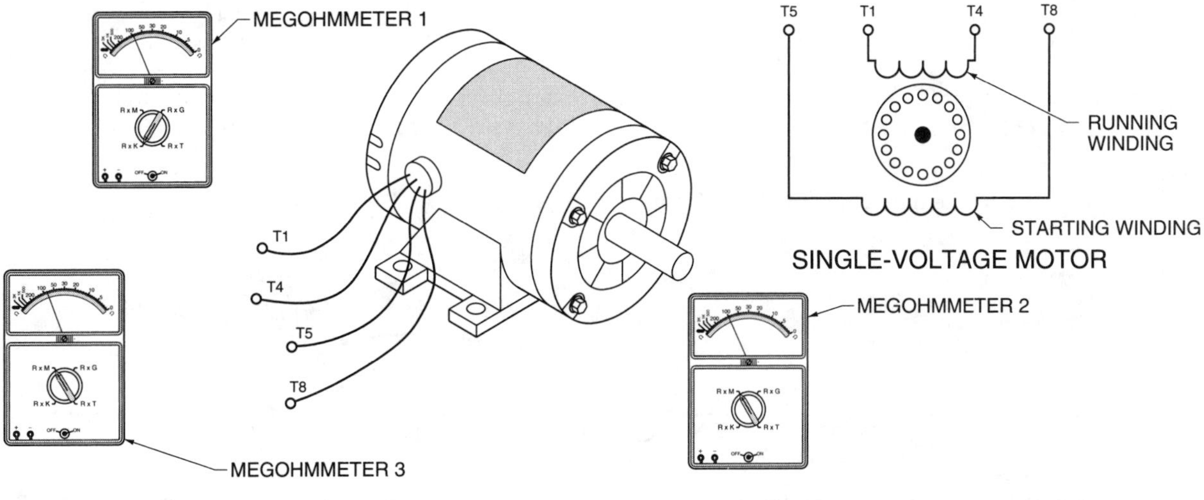

MEGOHMMETER 1
T1
T4
T5
T8
MEGOHMMETER 2
MEGOHMMETER 3
T5 T1 T4 T8
RUNNING WINDING
STARTING WINDING
SINGLE-VOLTAGE MOTOR

Refer to Coils for problems 57 and 58.

_____________ **57.** In Test 1, should the test light be ON or OFF if the armature is good?

_____________ **58.** In Test 2, should the test light be ON or OFF if the armature is good?

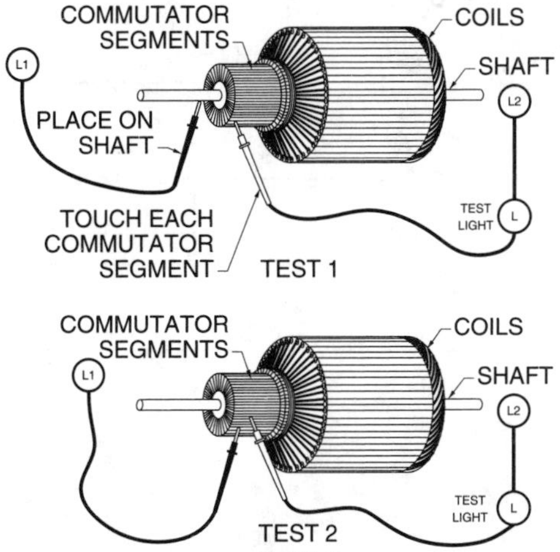

COMMUTATOR SEGMENTS
COILS
SHAFT
L1
L2
PLACE ON SHAFT
TOUCH EACH COMMUTATOR SEGMENT
TEST LIGHT
L
TEST 1
COMMUTATOR SEGMENTS
COILS
SHAFT
L1
L2
TEST LIGHT
L
TEST 2
COILS

Refer to Capacitor for problems 59 and 60.

______ **59.** In the capacitor test, the needle does not move off infinity. The capacitor is ______.

______ **60.** In the capacitor test, the needle moves to zero. The capacitor is ______.

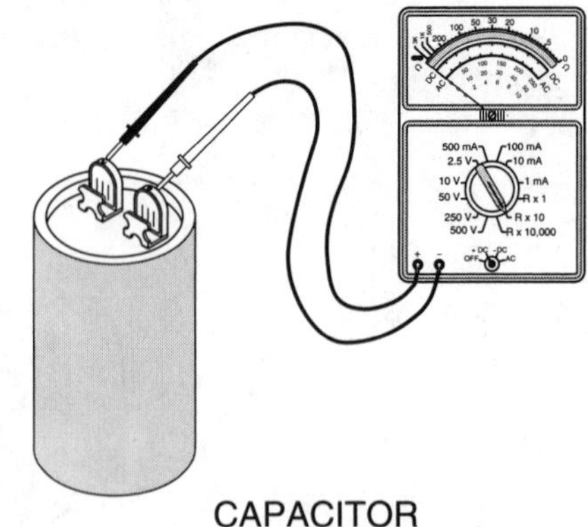

CAPACITOR

Refer to Switch for problems 61 and 62.

______ **61.** If the centrifugal switch is good, the meter in Test 1 should read ______.

______ **62.** If the centrifugal switch is good, the meter in Test 2 should read ______.

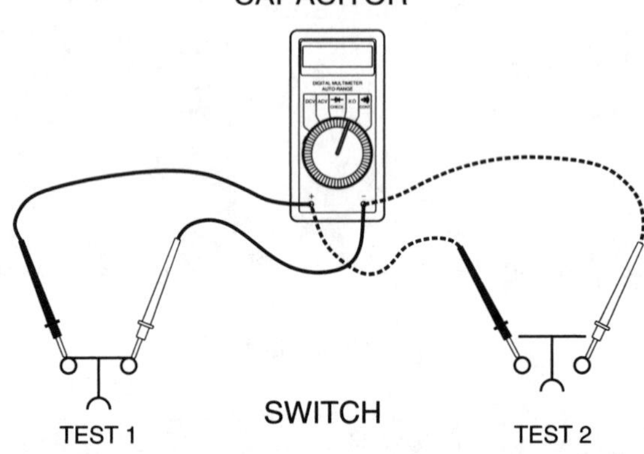

SWITCH

Refer to Start/Stop Station for problem 63. The machine operator reports that Motor 4 does not come ON. Meter 1 reads 115 V at all times. Meter 2 never reads a voltage. Meter 3 reads 115 V when Motors 1, 2, and 3 are ON.

______ **63.** The problem with Motor 4 is a(n) ______.

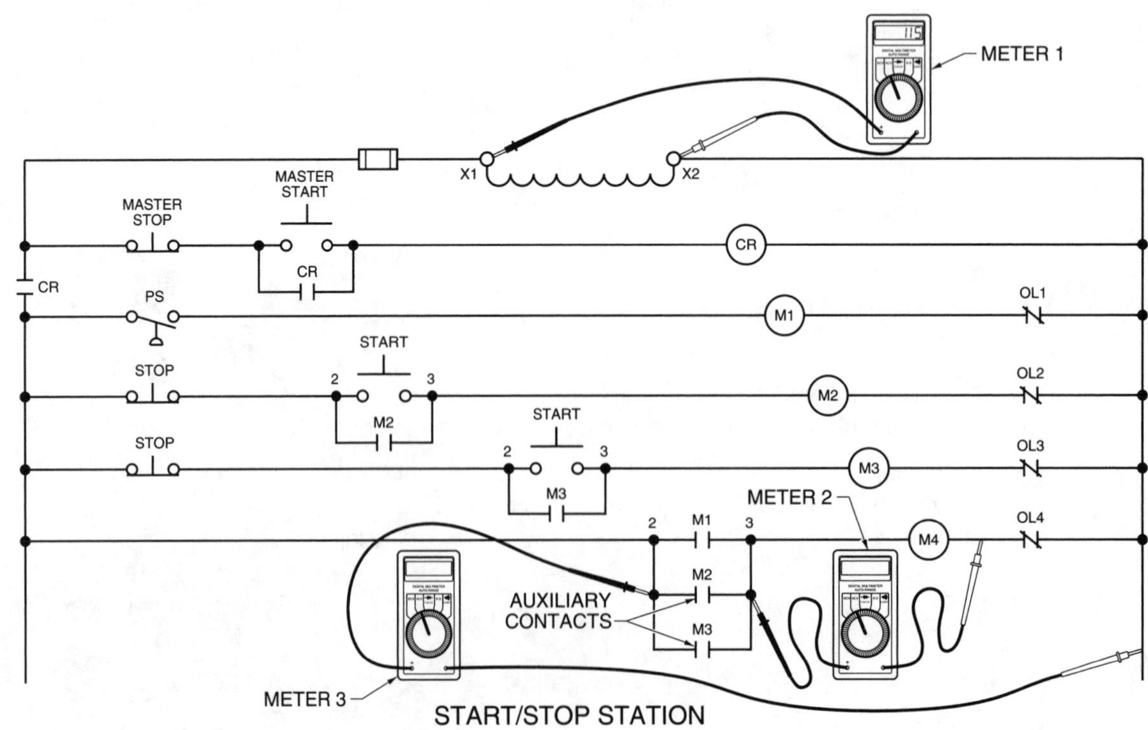

START/STOP STATION

64. Draw the line diagram from the wiring diagram.

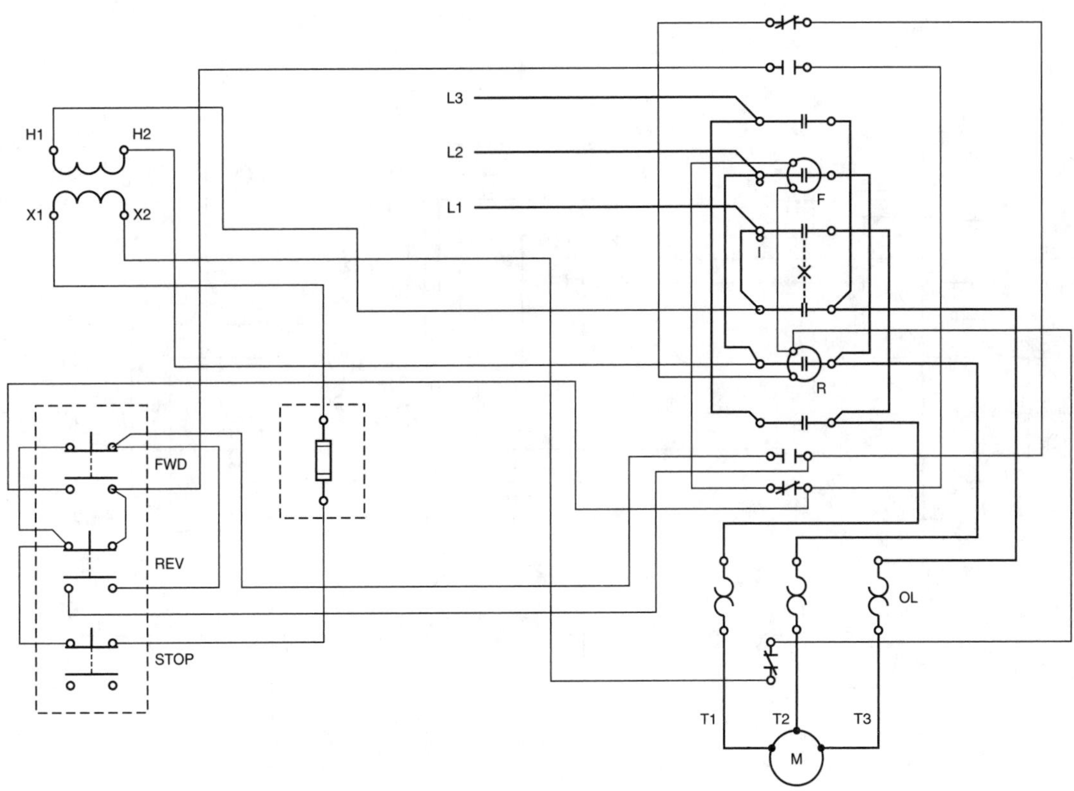

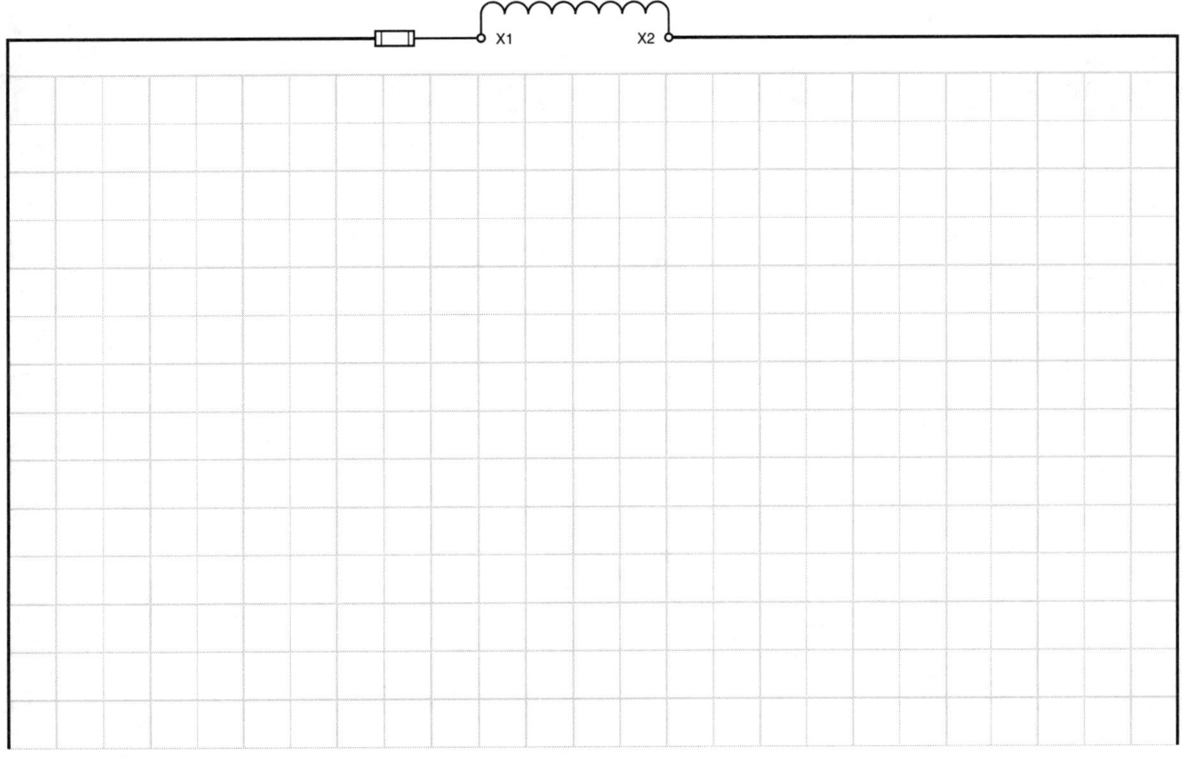

65. Draw the line diagram from the wiring diagram.

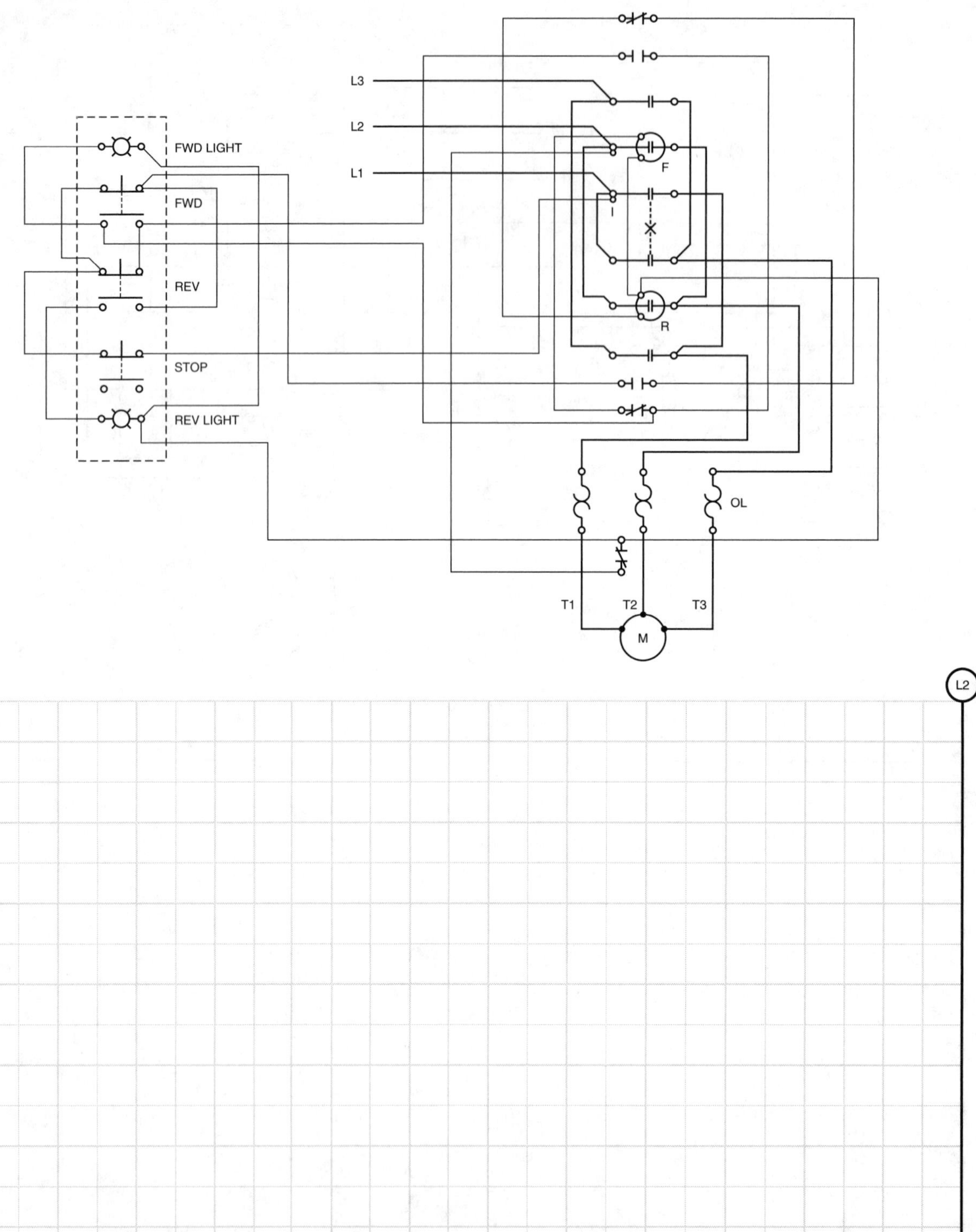

APPENDIX

CHARTS AND TABLES

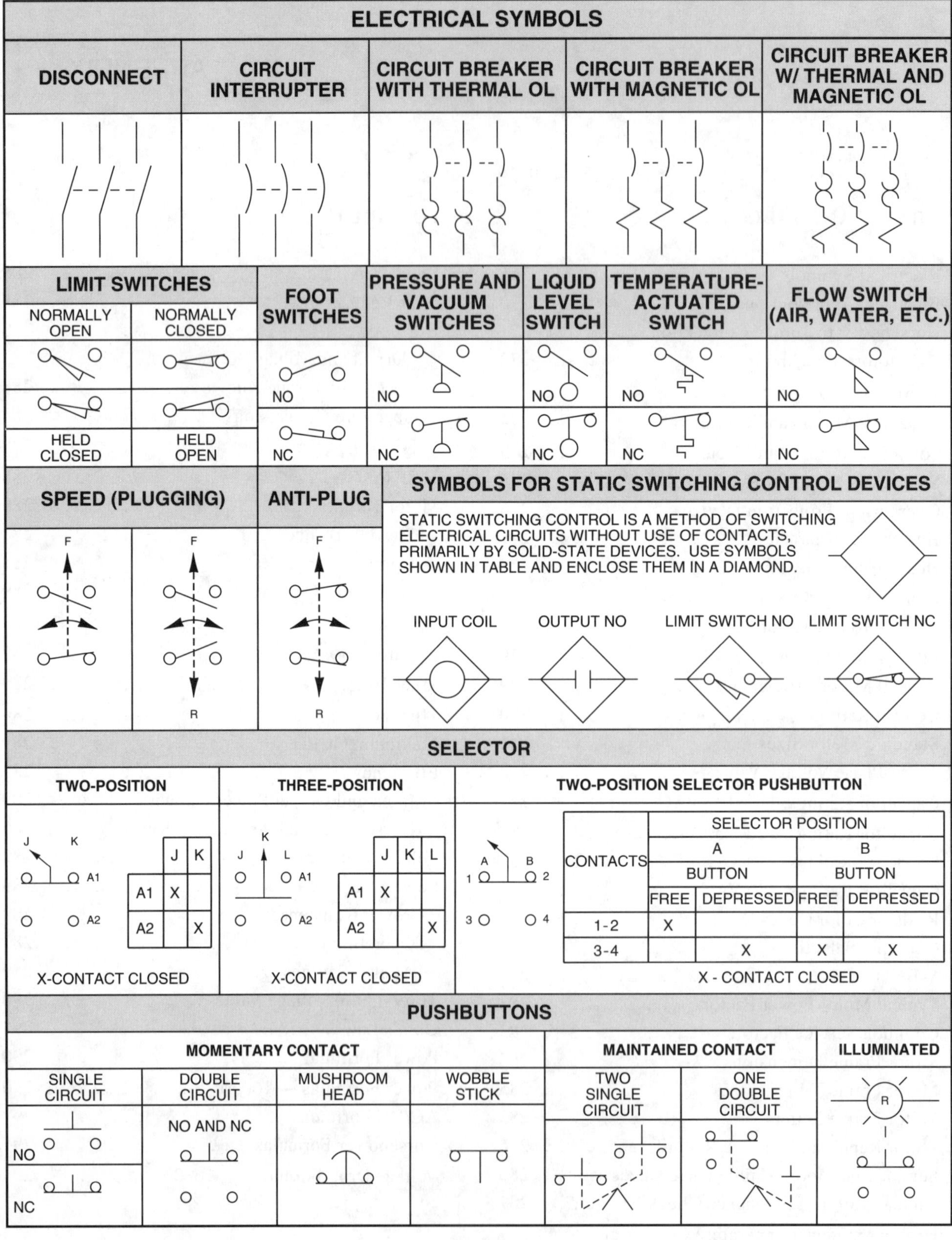

Two-position selector:

	J	K
A1	X	
A2		X

Three-position selector:

	J	K	L
A1	X		
A2			X

Two-position selector pushbutton:

CONTACTS	SELECTOR POSITION			
	A		B	
	BUTTON		BUTTON	
	FREE	DEPRESSED	FREE	DEPRESSED
1-2	X			
3-4		X	X	X

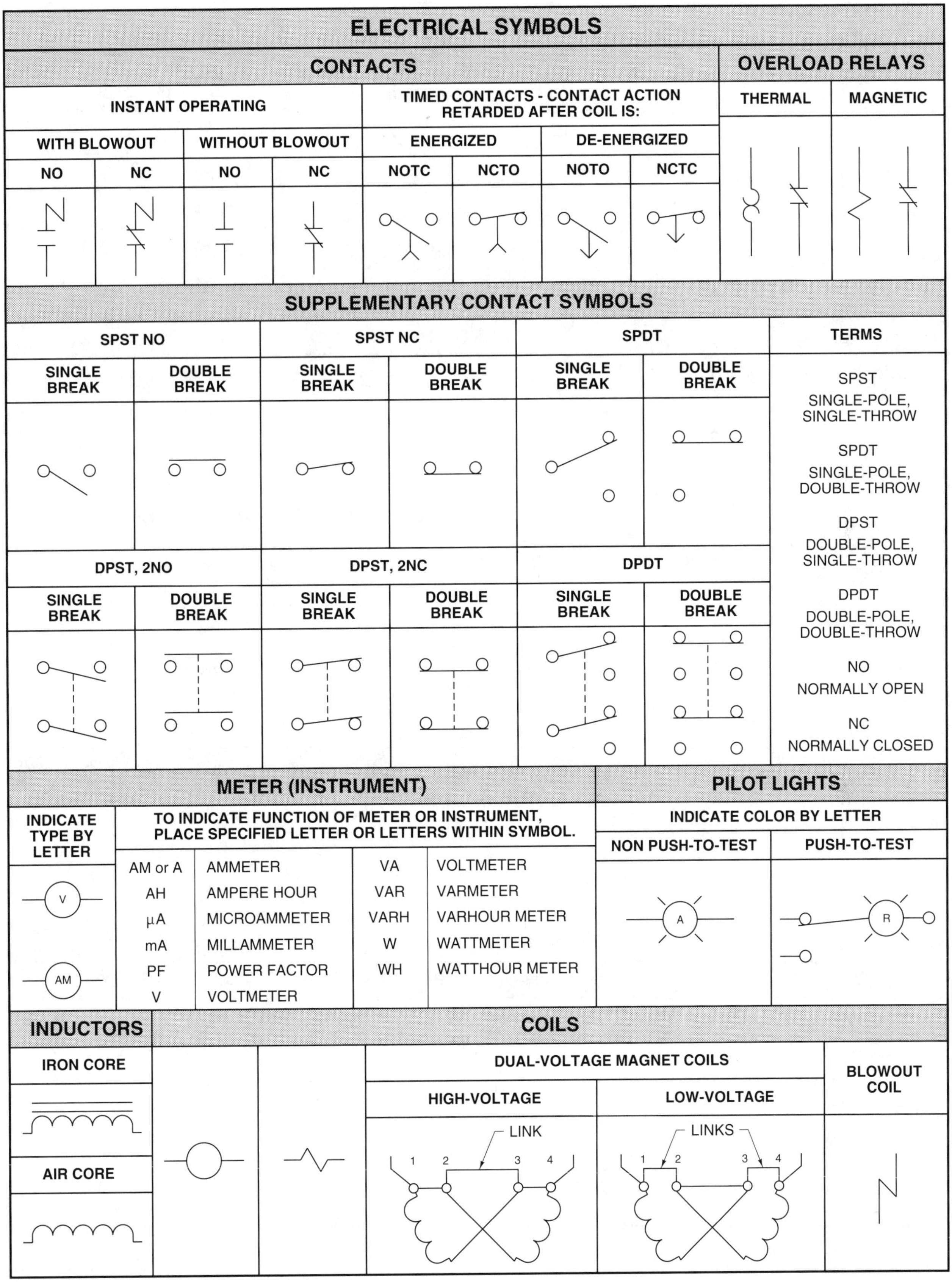

ELECTRICAL SYMBOLS

CONTACTS

INSTANT OPERATING				TIMED CONTACTS - CONTACT ACTION RETARDED AFTER COIL IS:			
WITH BLOWOUT		WITHOUT BLOWOUT		ENERGIZED		DE-ENERGIZED	
NO	NC	NO	NC	NOTC	NCTO	NOTO	NCTC

OVERLOAD RELAYS

THERMAL	MAGNETIC

SUPPLEMENTARY CONTACT SYMBOLS

SPST NO		SPST NC		SPDT	
SINGLE BREAK	DOUBLE BREAK	SINGLE BREAK	DOUBLE BREAK	SINGLE BREAK	DOUBLE BREAK
DPST, 2NO		**DPST, 2NC**		**DPDT**	
SINGLE BREAK	DOUBLE BREAK	SINGLE BREAK	DOUBLE BREAK	SINGLE BREAK	DOUBLE BREAK

TERMS

SPST
SINGLE-POLE, SINGLE-THROW

SPDT
SINGLE-POLE, DOUBLE-THROW

DPST
DOUBLE-POLE, SINGLE-THROW

DPDT
DOUBLE-POLE, DOUBLE-THROW

NO
NORMALLY OPEN

NC
NORMALLY CLOSED

METER (INSTRUMENT)

INDICATE TYPE BY LETTER

V

AM

TO INDICATE FUNCTION OF METER OR INSTRUMENT, PLACE SPECIFIED LETTER OR LETTERS WITHIN SYMBOL.

AM or A	AMMETER	VA	VOLTMETER
AH	AMPERE HOUR	VAR	VARMETER
μA	MICROAMMETER	VARH	VARHOUR METER
mA	MILLAMMETER	W	WATTMETER
PF	POWER FACTOR	WH	WATTHOUR METER
V	VOLTMETER		

PILOT LIGHTS

INDICATE COLOR BY LETTER

NON PUSH-TO-TEST	PUSH-TO-TEST
A	R

INDUCTORS

IRON CORE

AIR CORE

COILS

DUAL-VOLTAGE MAGNET COILS

HIGH-VOLTAGE	LOW-VOLTAGE
LINK 1 2 3 4	LINKS 1 2 3 4

BLOWOUT COIL

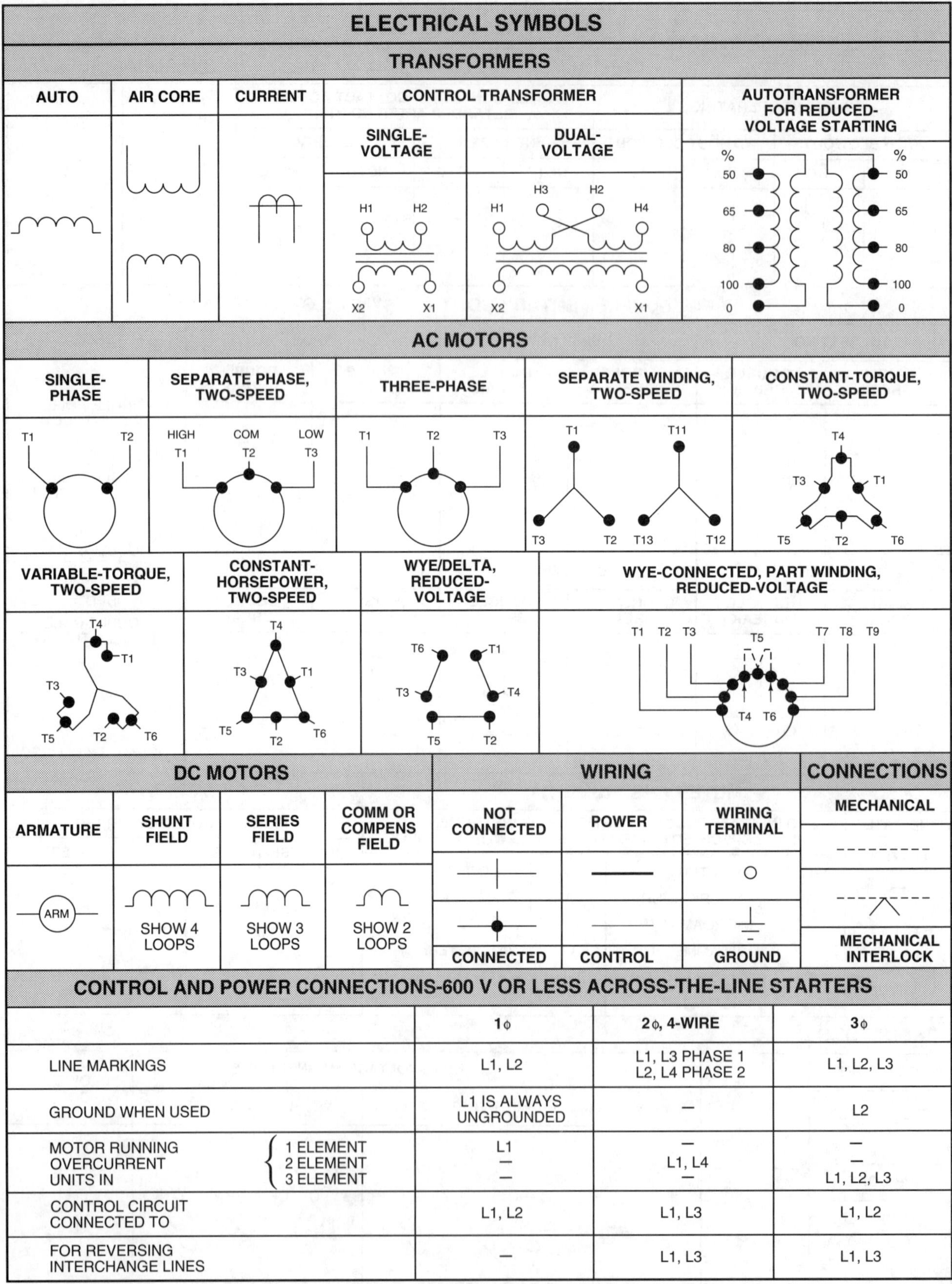

CONTROL AND POWER CONNECTIONS-600 V OR LESS ACROSS-THE-LINE STARTERS

		1ϕ	2ϕ, 4-WIRE	3ϕ
LINE MARKINGS		L1, L2	L1, L3 PHASE 1 L2, L4 PHASE 2	L1, L2, L3
GROUND WHEN USED		L1 IS ALWAYS UNGROUNDED	—	L2
MOTOR RUNNING OVERCURRENT UNITS IN	1 ELEMENT	L1	—	—
	2 ELEMENT	—	L1, L4	—
	3 ELEMENT	—	—	L1, L2, L3
CONTROL CIRCUIT CONNECTED TO		L1, L2	L1, L3	L1, L2
FOR REVERSING INTERCHANGE LINES		—	L1, L3	L1, L3

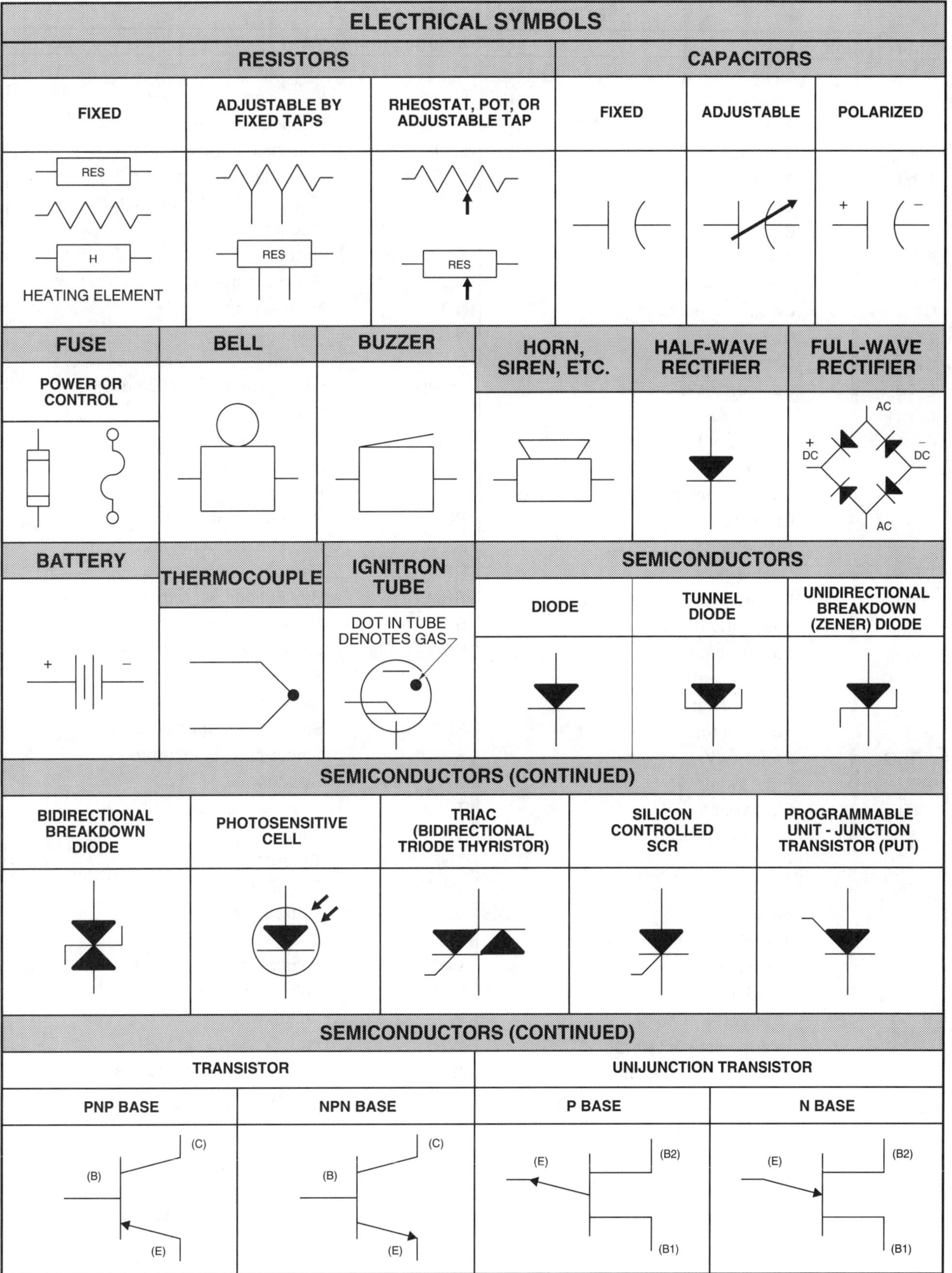
ELECTRICAL SYMBOLS
RESISTORS
CAPACITORS
FIXED
ADJUSTABLE BY FIXED TAPS
RHEOSTAT, POT, OR ADJUSTABLE TAP
FIXED
ADJUSTABLE
POLARIZED
RES
H
HEATING ELEMENT
RES
RES
+
−
FUSE
BELL
BUZZER
HORN, SIREN, ETC.
HALF-WAVE RECTIFIER
FULL-WAVE RECTIFIER
POWER OR CONTROL
AC
+ DC
− DC
AC
BATTERY
THERMOCOUPLE
IGNITRON TUBE
SEMICONDUCTORS
DIODE
TUNNEL DIODE
UNIDIRECTIONAL BREAKDOWN (ZENER) DIODE
DOT IN TUBE DENOTES GAS
+
−
SEMICONDUCTORS (CONTINUED)
BIDIRECTIONAL BREAKDOWN DIODE
PHOTOSENSITIVE CELL
TRIAC (BIDIRECTIONAL TRIODE THYRISTOR)
SILICON CONTROLLED SCR
PROGRAMMABLE UNIT - JUNCTION TRANSISTOR (PUT)
SEMICONDUCTORS (CONTINUED)
TRANSISTOR
UNIJUNCTION TRANSISTOR
PNP BASE
NPN BASE
P BASE
N BASE
(B)
(C)
(E)
(B)
(C)
(E)
(E)
(B2)
(B1)
(E)
(B2)
(B1)

ELECTRICAL ABBREVIATIONS			
Abbreviation	**Term**	**Abbreviation**	**Term**
A	Amps; armature; anode; ammeter	K	Kilo; cathode
Ag	Silver	L	Line; load
ALM	Alarm	LB-FT	Pounds per feet
AM	Ammeter	LB-IN	Pounds per inch
ARM	Armature	LRC	Locked rotor current
Au	Gold	M	Motor; motor starter contacts
BK	Black	MED	Medium
BL	Blue	N	North
BR	Brown	NC	Normally closed
C	Celsius; centigrade	NO	Normally opened
CAP	Capacitor	NTDF	Nontime-delay fuse
CB	Circuit breaker	O	Orange
CCW	Counterclockwise	OCPD	Overcurrent protection device
CONT	Continuous	OL	Overloads
CPS	Cycles per second	OZ/IN	Ounces per inch
CR	Control relay	P	Power consumed
CT	Current transformer	PSI	Pounds per square inch
CW	Clockwise	PUT	Pull-up torque
D	Diameter	R	Resistance; radius; red; reverse
DP	Double-pole	REV	Reverse
DPDT	Double-pole, double-throw	RPM	Revolutions per minute
EMF	Electromotive force	S	Switch; series; slow; south
F	Fahrenheit; forward; fast	SCR	Silicon controlled rectifier
F	Field; forward	SF	Service factor
FLC	Full-load current	SP	Single-pole
FLT	Full-load torque	SPDT	Single-pole, double-throw
FREQ	Frequency	SPST	Single-pole, single-throw
FS	Float switch	SW	Switch
FTS	Foot switch	T	Terminal; torque
FWD	Forward	TD	Time delay
G	Green; gate	TDF	Time-delay fuse
GEN	Generator	TEMP	Temperature
GY	Gray	V	Volts; violet
H	Transformer, primary side	VA	Voltamps
HP	Horsepower	VAC	Volts alternating current
I	Current	VDC	Volts direct current
IC	Intergrated circuit	W	White; watt
INT	Intermediate; interrupt	W/	With
ITB	Inverse time breaker	X	Transformer secondary side
ITCB	Instantaneous trip circuit breaker	Y	Yellow

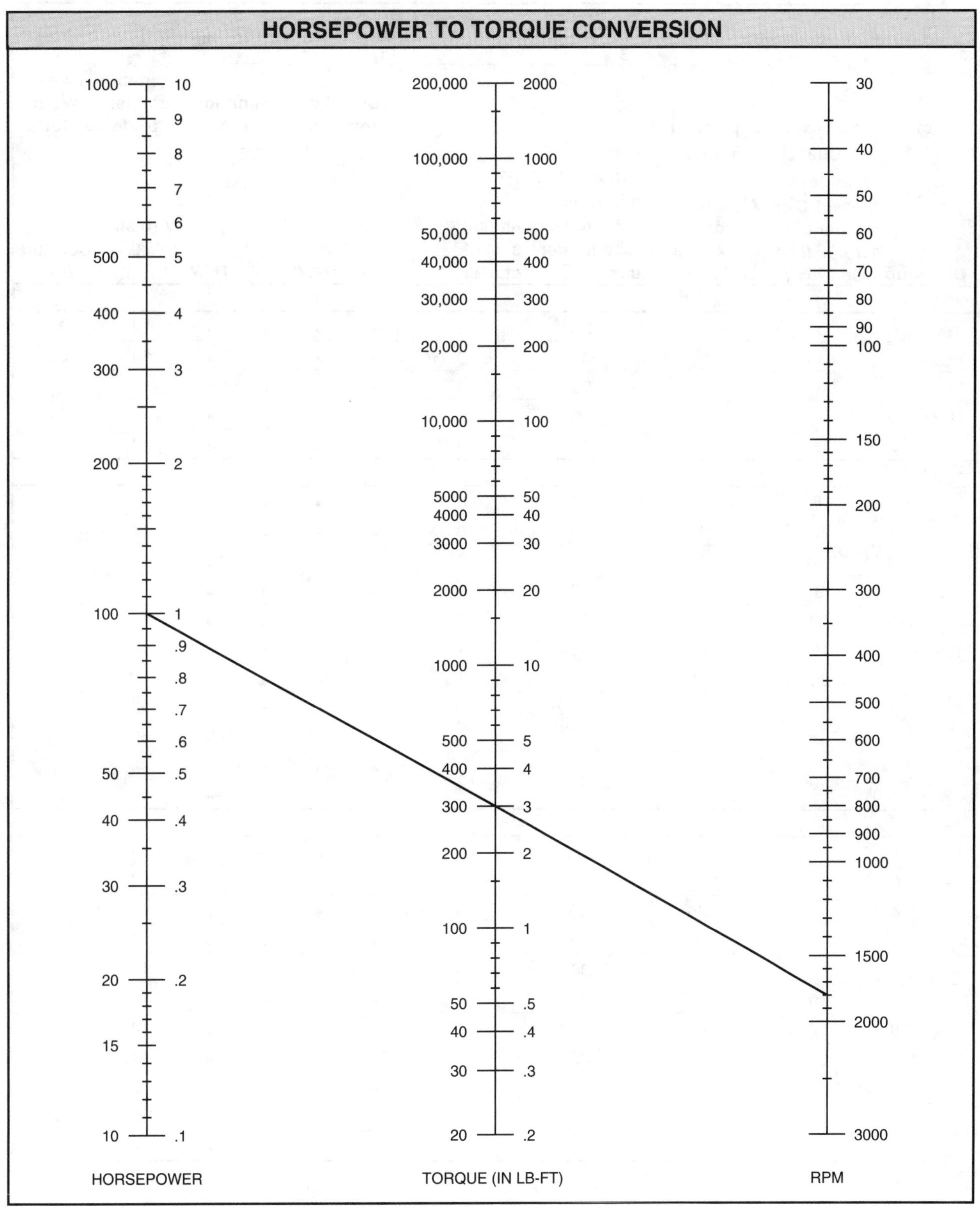
HORSEPOWER TO TORQUE CONVERSION
1000
10
9
8
7
6
500
5
400
4
300
3
200
2
100
1
.9
.8
.7
.6
50
.5
40
.4
30
.3
20
.2
15
10
.1
HORSEPOWER
200,000
2000
100,000
1000
50,000
500
40,000
400
30,000
300
20,000
200
10,000
100
5000
50
4000
40
3000
30
2000
20
1000
10
500
5
400
4
300
3
200
2
100
1
50
.5
40
.4
30
.3
20
.2
TORQUE (IN LB-FT)
30
40
50
60
70
80
90
100
150
200
300
400
500
600
700
800
900
1000
1500
2000
3000
RPM

DC MOTORS AND CIRCUITS											
1		2		3	4	5				6	
Size of motor		Motor overload protection — Dual-element fuse				Controller termination temperature rating				Minimum size of copper wire and trade conduit	
						60°C		75°C			
HP	Amp	Motor less than 40°C or greater than 1.15 SF (Max fuse 125%)	All other motors (Max fuse 115%)	Switch 115% minimum or HP rated or fuse holder size	Minimum size of starter	TW	THW	TW	THW	Wire size (AWG or kcmil)	Conduit (in.)
90 V											
¼	4.0	5	4½	30	0	•	•	•	•	14	½
⅓	5.2	6¼	5 6/10	30	0	•	•	•	•	14	½
½	6.8	8	7½	30	0	•	•	•	•	14	½
¾	9.6	12	10	30	0	•	•	•	•	14	½
1	12.2	15	12	30	0	•	•	•	•	14	½
120 V											
¼	3.1	3½	3½	30	0	•	•	•	•	14	½
⅓	4.1	5	4½	30	0	•	•	•	•	14	½
½	5.4	6¼	6	30	0	•	•	•	•	14	½
¾	7.6	9	8	30	0	•	•	•	•	14	½
1	9.5	10	10	30	0	•	•	•	•	14	½
1½	13.2	15	15	30	1	•	•	•	•	14	½
2	17	20	17½	30	1	•	•	•	•	12	½
5	40	50	45	60	2	•	•	•		6	¾
									•	8	¾
10	76	90	80	100	3	•	•	•		2	1
									•	3	1
180 V											
¼	2	2½	2¼	30	0	•	•	•	•	14	½
⅓	2.6	3 2/10	2 8/10	30	0	•	•	•	•	14	½
½	3.4	4	3½	30	0	•	•	•	•	14	½
¾	4.8	6	5	30	0	•	•	•	•	14	½
1	6.1	7½	7	30	0	•	•	•	•	14	½
1½	8.3	10	9	30	1	•	•	•	•	14	½
2	10.8	12	12	30	1	•	•	•	•	14	½
3	16	20	17½	30	1	•	•	•	•	12	½
5	27	30*	30*	60	1	•		•		8	½
							•			8	¾
									•	10	½

*Fuse reducers required.

1φ MOTORS AND CIRCUITS											
1		2		3	4	5				6	
Size of motor		Motor overload protection — Low-peak or Fusetron®				Controller termination temperature rating				Minimum size of copper wire and trade conduit	
						60°C		75°C			
HP	Amp	Motor less than 40°C or greater than 1.15 SF (Max fuse 125%)	All other motors (Max fuse 115%)	Switch 115% minimum or HP rated or fuse holder size	Minimum size of starter	TW	THW	TW	THW	Wire size (AWG or kcmil)	Conduit (inches)
115 V (120 V system)											
1/6	4.4	5	5	30	00	•	•	•	•	14	1/2
1/4	5.8	7	6 1/4	30	00	•	•	•	•	14	1/2
1/3	7.2	9	8	30	00	•	•	•	•	14	1/2
1/2	9.8	12	10	30	00	•	•	•	•	14	1/2
3/4	13.8	15	15	30	00	•	•	•	•	14	1/2
1	16	20	17 1/2	30	00	•	•	•	•	14	1/2
1 1/2	20	25	20	30	01	•	•	•	•	12	1/2
2	24	30	25	30	01	•	•	•	•	10	1/2
230 V (240 V system)											
1/6	2.2	2 1/2	2 1/2	30	00	•	•	•	•	14	1/2
1/4	2.9	3 1/2	3 2/10	30	00	•	•	•	•	14	1/2
1/3	3.6	4 1/2	4	30	00	•	•	•	•	14	1/2
1/2	4.9	5 6/10	5 6/10	30	00	•	•	•	•	14	1/2
3/4	6.9	8	7 1/2	30	00	•	•	•	•	14	1/2
1	8	10	9	30	00	•	•	•	•	14	1/2
1 1/2	10	12	10	30	0	•	•	•	•	14	1/2
2	12	15	12	30	0	•	•	•	•	14	1/2
3	17	20	17 1/2	30	1	•	•	•	•	12	1/2
5	28	35	30*	60	2		•			8	3/4
						•		•		8	1/2
									•	10	1/2
7 1/2	40	50	45	60	2	•	•	•		6	3/4
									•	8	3/4
10	50	60	50	60	3	•	•	•		4	1
									•	6	3/4

*Fuse reducers required.

3ϕ, 230 V MOTORS AND CIRCUITS — 240 V SYSTEM											
1		2		3	4	5				6	
Size of motor		Motor overload protection Low-peak or Fusetron®				Controller termination temperature rating				Minimum size of copper wire and trade conduit	
						60°C		75°C			
HP	Amp	Motor less than 40°C or greater than 1.15 SF (Max fuse 125%)	All other motors (Max fuse 115%)	Switch 115% minimum or HP rated or fuse holder size	Minimum size of starter	TW	THW	TW	THW	Wire size (AWG or kcmil)	Conduit (inches)
½	2	2½	2¼	30	00	•	•	•	•	14	½
¾	2.8	3½	3 2/10	30	00	•	•	•	•	14	½
1	3.6	4½	4	30	00	•	•	•	•	14	½
1½	5.2	6¼	5 6/10	30	00	•	•	•	•	14	½
2	6.8	8	7½	30	0	•	•	•	•	14	½
3	9.6	12	10	30	0	•	•	•	•	14	½
5	15.2	17½	17½	30	1	•	•	•	•	14	½
7½	22	25	25	30	1	•	•	•	•	10	½
10	28	35	30*	60	2	•	•	•		8	¾
									•	10	½
15	42	50	45	60	2	•	•	•	•	6	1
										6	¾
20	54	60*	60*	100	3	•	•	•	•	4	1
25	68	80	75	100	3	•	•			3	1¼
								•		3	1
									•	4	1
30	80	100	90	100	3	•	•	•		1	1¼
									•	3	1¼
40	104	125	110	200	4	•	•	•		2/0	1½
									•	1	1¼
50	130	150	150	200	4	•	•	•		3/0	2
									•	2/0	1½
75	192	225	200*	400	5	•	•	•		300	2½
									•	250	2½
100	248	300	250	400	5	•	•	•		500	3
									•	350	2½
150	360	450	400*	600	6	•	•	•		300-2ϕ	2-2½
									•	4/0-2ϕ	2-2

*Fuse reducers required.

3ϕ, 460 V MOTORS AND CIRCUITS — 480 V SYSTEM											
1		2		3	4	5				6	
Size of motor		Motor overload protection: Low-peak or Fusetron®				Controller termination temperature rating				Minimum size of copper wire and trade conduit	
						60°C		75°C			
HP	Amp	Motor less than 40°C or greater than 1.15 SF (Max fuse 125%)	All other motors (Max fuse 115%)	Switch 115% minimum or HP rated or fuse holder size	Minimum size of starter	TW	THW	TW	THW	Wire size (AWG or kcmil)	Conduit (inches)
$\frac{1}{2}$	1	$1\frac{1}{4}$	$1\frac{1}{8}$	30	00	•	•	•	•	14	$\frac{1}{2}$
$\frac{3}{4}$	1.4	$1\frac{6}{10}$	$1\frac{6}{10}$	30	00	•	•	•	•	14	$\frac{1}{2}$
1	1.8	$2\frac{1}{4}$	2	30	00	•	•	•	•	14	$\frac{1}{2}$
$1\frac{1}{2}$	2.6	$3\frac{2}{10}$	$2\frac{6}{10}$	30	00	•	•	•	•	14	$\frac{1}{2}$
2	3.4	4	$3\frac{1}{2}$	30	00	•	•	•	•	14	$\frac{1}{2}$
3	4.8	$5\frac{6}{10}$	5	30	0	•	•	•	•	14	$\frac{1}{2}$
5	7.6	9	8	30	0	•	•	•	•	14	$\frac{1}{2}$
$7\frac{1}{2}$	11	12	12	30	1	•	•	•	•	14	$\frac{1}{2}$
10	14	$17\frac{1}{2}$	15	30	1	•	•	•	•	14	$\frac{1}{2}$
15	21	25	20	30	2	•	•	•	•	10	$\frac{1}{2}$
20	27	30*	30*	60	2	•	•	•		8	$\frac{3}{4}$
									•	10	$\frac{1}{2}$
25	34	40	35	60	2	•	•	•		6	1
									•	8	$\frac{3}{4}$
30	40	50	45	60	3	•	•	•		6	1
									•	8	$\frac{3}{4}$
40	52	60*	60*	100	3	•	•	•		4	1
									•	6	1
50	65	80	70	100	3	•	•	•		3	$1\frac{1}{4}$
									•	4	1
60	77	90	80	100	4	•	•	•		1	$1\frac{1}{4}$
									•	3	$1\frac{1}{4}$
75	96	110	110	200	4	•	•	•		1/0	$1\frac{1}{2}$
									•	1	$1\frac{1}{4}$

*Fuse reducers required.

continued

continued

3ϕ, 460 V MOTORS AND CIRCUITS — 480 V SYSTEM											
1	2			3	4	5				6	
Size of motor		Motor overload protection Low-peak or Fusetron®				Controller termination temperature rating				Minimum size of copper wire and trade conduit	
						60°C		75°C			
HP	Amp	Motor less than 40°C or greater than 1.15 SF (Max fuse 125%)	All other motors (Max fuse 115%)	Switch 115% minimum or HP rated or fuse holder size	Minimum size of starter	TW	THW	TW	THW	Wire size (AWG or kcmil)	Conduit (inches)
100	124	150	125	200	4	•	•	•		3/0	2
									•	2/0	1½
125	156	175	175	200	5	•	•	•		4/0	2
									•	3/0	2
150	180	225	200*	400	5	•	•	•		300	2½
									•	4/0	2
200	240	300	250	400	5	•	•	•		500	3
									•	350	2½
250	302	350	325	400	6	•	•	•		4/0-2ϕ	2-2
									•	3/0-2ϕ	2-2
300	361	450	400*	600	6	•	•	•		300-2ϕ	2-1½
									•	4/0-2ϕ	2-2

*Fuse reducers required.

STANDARD SIZES OF FUSES AND CB'S

NEC® 240-6 lists standard ampere ratings of fuses and fixed-trip CB's as follows:
15, 20, 25, 30, 35, 40, 45,
50, 60, 70, 80, 90, 100, 110,
125, 150, 175, 200, 225,
250, 300, 350, 400, 450,
500, 600, 700, 800,
1000, 1200, 1600,
2000, 2500, 3000, 4000, 5000, 6000

OVERCURRENT PROTECTION DEVICES

Motor Type	Code Letter	FLC (%)				
		Motor Size	TDF	NTDF	ITB	ITCB
AC*	—	—	175	300	150	700
AC*	A	—	150	150	150	700
AC*	B–E	—	175	250	200	700
AC*	F–V	—	175	300	250	700
DC	—	⅛ to 50 HP	150	150	150	250
DC	—	Over 50 HP	150	150	150	175

* full-voltage and resistor starting

HEATER TRIP CHARACTERISTICS

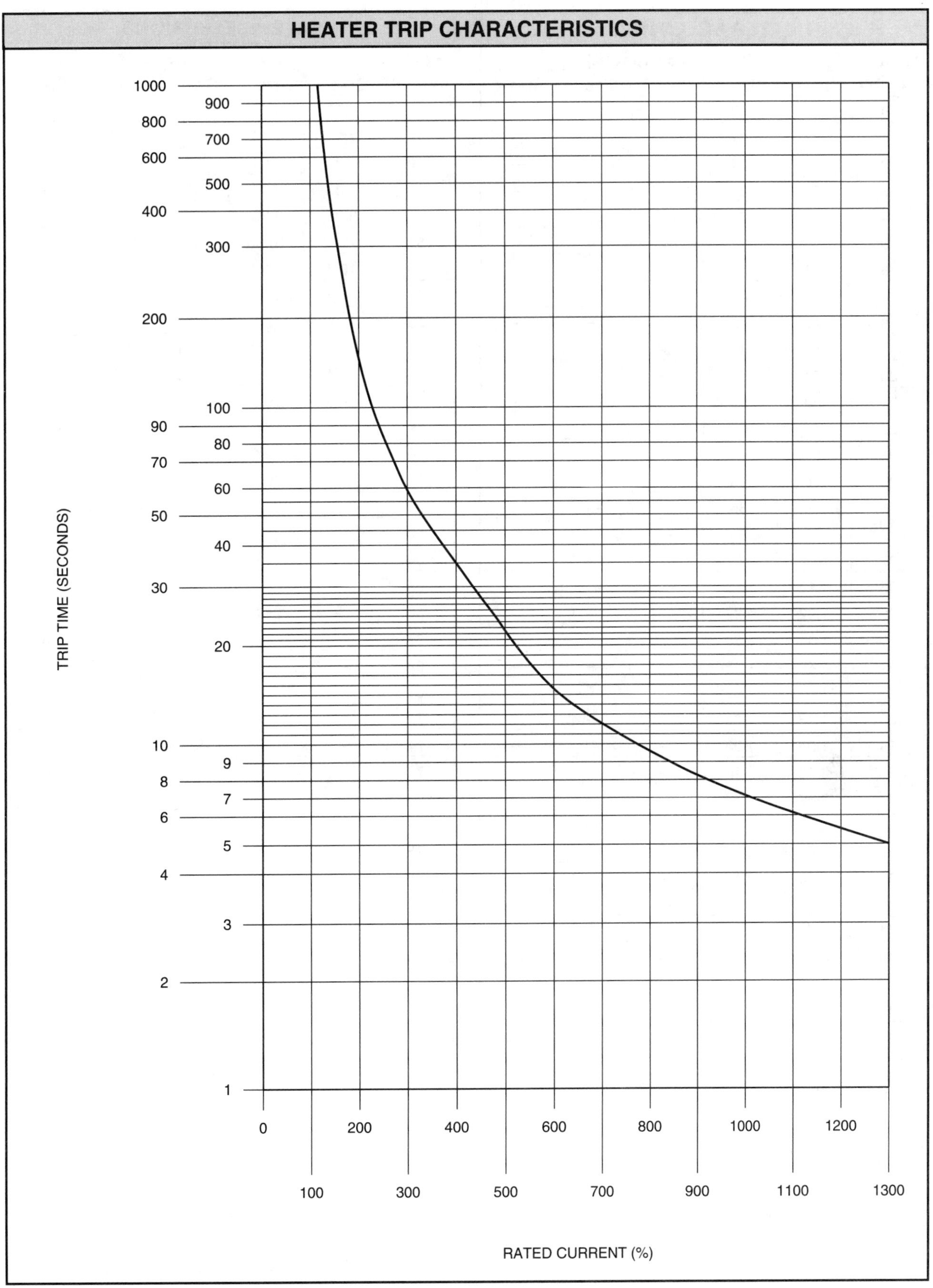

HEATER SELECTIONS					
Heater number	Full-load current (A)*				
	Size 0	Size 1	Size 2	Size 3	Size 4
10	.20	.20	—	—	—
11	.22	.22	—	—	—
12	.24	.24	—	—	—
13	.27	.27	—	—	—
14	.30	.30	—	—	—
15	.34	.34	—	—	—
16	.37	.37	—	—	—
17	.41	.41	—	—	—
18	.45	.45	—	—	—
19	.49	.49	—	—	—
20	.54	.54	—	—	—
21	.59	.59	—	—	—
22	.65	.65	—	—	—
23	.71	.71	—	—	—
24	.78	.78	—	—	—
25	.85	.85	—	—	—
26	.93	.93	—	—	—
27	1.02	1.02	—	—	—
28	1.12	1.12	—	—	—
29	1.22	1.22	—	—	—
30	1.34	1.34	—	—	—
31	1.48	1.48	—	—	—
32	1.62	1.62	—	—	—
33	1.78	1.78	—	—	—
34	1.96	1.96	—	—	—
35	2.15	2.15	—	—	—
36	2.37	2.37	—	—	—
37	2.60	2.60	—	—	—
38	2.86	2.86	—	—	—
39	3.14	3.14	—	—	—
40	3.45	3.45	—	—	—
41	3.79	3.79	—	—	—
42	4.17	4.17	—	—	—
43	4.58	4.58	—	—	—
44	5.03	5.03	—	—	—
45	5.53	5.53	—	—	—
46	6.08	6.08	—	—	—

*Full-load current (A) does not include FLC × 1.15 or 1.25.

HEATER SELECTIONS					
Heater number	Full-load current (A)*				
	Size 0	Size 1	Size 2	Size 3	Size 4
47	6.68	6.68	—	—	—
48	7.21	7.21	—	—	—
49	7.81	7.81	7.89	—	—
50	8.46	8.46	8.57	—	—
51	9.35	9.35	9.32	—	—
52	10.00	10.00	10.1	—	—
53	10.7	10.7	11.0	12.2	—
54	11.7	11.7	12.0	13.3	—
55	12.6	12.6	12.9	14.3	—
56	13.9	13.9	14.1	15.6	—
57	15.1	15.1	15.5	17.2	—
58	16.5	16.5	16.9	18.7	—
59	18.0	18.0	18.5	20.5	—
60	—	19.2	20.3	22.5	23.8
61	—	20.4	21.8	24.3	25.7
62	—	21.7	23.5	26.2	27.8
63	—	23.1	25.3	28.3	30.0
64	—	24.6	27.2	30.5	32.5
65	—	26.2	29.3	33.0	35.0
66	—	27.8	31.5	36.0	38.0
67	—	—	33.5	39.0	41.0
68	—	—	36.0	42.0	44.5
69	—	—	38.5	45.5	48.5
70	—	—	41.0	49.5	52
71	—	—	43.0	53	57
72	—	—	46.0	58	61
73	—	—	—	63	67
74	—	—	—	68	72
75	—	—	—	73	77
76	—	—	—	78	84
77	—	—	—	83	91
78	—	—	—	88	97
79	—	—	—	—	103
80	—	—	—	—	111
81	—	—	—	—	119
82	—	—	—	—	127
83	—	—	—	—	133

FULL-LOAD CURRENTS — DC MOTORS		
Motor rating (HP)	Current (A)	
	120 V	240 V
1/4	3.1	1.6
1/3	4.1	2.0
1/2	5.4	2.7
3/4	7.6	3.8
1	9.5	4.7
1 1/2	13.2	6.6
2	17	8.5
3	25	12.2
5	40	20
7 1/2	48	29

FULL-LOAD CURRENTS — 1φ, AC MOTORS		
Motor rating (HP)	Current (A)	
	115 V	230 V
1/6	4.4	2.2
1/4	5.8	2.9
1/3	7.2	3.6
1/2	9.8	4.9
3/4	13.8	6.9
1	16	8
1 1/2	20	10
2	24	12
3	34	17
5	56	28
7 1/2	80	40
10	100	50

FULL-LOAD CURRENTS — 3φ, AC INDUCTION MOTORS				
Motor rating (HP)	Current (A)			
	208 V	230 V	460 V	575 V
1/4	1.11	.96	.48	.38
1/3	1.34	1.18	.59	.47
1/2	2.2	2.0	1.0	.8
3/4	3.1	2.8	1.4	1.1
1	4.0	3.6	1.8	1.4
1 1/2	5.7	5.2	2.6	2.1
2	7.5	6.8	3.4	2.7
3	10.6	9.6	4.8	3.9
5	16.7	15.2	7.6	6.1
7 1/2	24.0	22.0	11.0	9.0
10	31.0	28.0	14.0	11.0
15	46.0	42.0	21.0	17.0
20	59	54	27	22
25	75	68	34	27
30	88	80	40	32
40	114	104	52	41
50	143	130	65	52
60	169	154	77	62
75	211	192	96	77
100	273	248	124	99
125	343	312	156	125
150	396	360	180	144
200	—	480	240	192
250	—	602	301	242
300	—	—	362	288
350	—	—	413	337
400	—	—	477	382
500	—	—	590	472

TYPICAL MOTOR EFFICIENCIES					
HP	Standard motor (%)	Energy-efficient motor (%)	HP	Standard motor (%)	Energy-efficient motor (%)
1	76.5	84.0	30	88.1	93.1
1.5	78.5	85.5	40	89.3	93.6
2	79.9	86.5	50	90.4	93.7
3	80.8	88.5	75	90.8	95.0
5	83.1	88.6	100	91.6	95.4
7.5	83.8	90.2	125	91.8	95.8
10	85.0	90.3	150	92.3	96.0
15	86.5	91.7	200	93.3	96.1
20	87.5	92.4	250	93.6	96.2
25	88.0	93.0	300	93.8	96.5

CONTROL RATINGS															
		Maximum HP									Transformer switching 50–60 Hz kVA rating inrush peak time Continuous amps				
		Normal duty		Plugging & jogging duty					Resistance heating (kW)		20 times		20-40 times		Capacitor kVA switching rating 3φ kVAR
Size	Load (V)	1φ	3φ	1φ	3φ	Cont amps	Service limit amps	Tungsten & ballast type lamp amps 480 V max	1φ	3φ	1φ	3φ	1φ	3φ	
00	115	½	—	—	—	9	11	—	1.15	2.0	—	—	—	—	—
	200	—	1½	—	—	9	11	—	2.0	3.46	—	—	—	—	—
	230	1	1½	—	—	9	11	—	2.3	4.0	—	—	—	—	—
	380	—	1½	—	—	9	11	—	—	6.5	—	—	—	—	—
	460	—	2	—	—	9	11	—	4.6	8.0	—	—	—	—	—
	575	—	2	—	—	9	11	—	5.8	10.0	—	—	—	—	—
0	115	1	—	½	—	18	21	20	2.3	4.0	0.6	—	0.3	—	—
	200	—	3	—	1½	18	21	20	4.0	6.92	—	1.8	—	0.9	—
	230	2	3	1	1½	18	21	20	4.6	8.0	1.2	2.1	0.6	1.0	—
	380	—	5	—	1½	18	21	20	—	13.1	—	—	—	—	—
	460	—	5	—	2	18	21	20	9.2	15.9	2.4	4.2	1.2	2.1	—
	575	—	5	—	2	18	21	—	11.5	19.9	3.0	5.2	1.5	2.6	—
1	115	2	—	1	—	27	32	30	3.5	6.0	1.2	—	0.6	—	—
	200	—	7½	—	3	27	32	30	6	10.4	—	3.6	—	1.8	—
	230	3	7½	2	3	27	32	30	6.9	11.9	2.4	4.3	1.2	2.1	—
	380	—	10	—	5	27	32	30	—	19.7	—	—	—	—	—
	460	—	10	—	5	27	32	30	13.8	23.9	4.9	8.5	2.5	4.3	—
	575	—	10	—	5	27	32	—	17.3	29.8	6.2	11.0	3.1	5.3	—
1P	115	3	—	1½	—	35	42	45	5.8	—	—	—	—	—	—
	230	5	—	3	—	35	42	45	11.5	—	—	—	—	—	—
1¾	115	—	—	—	—	40	40	45	5.8	9.9	1.6	—	0.8	—	—
	200	—	10	—	5	40	40	45	10	17.3	—	4.9	—	2.4	—
	230	—	10	—	5	40	40	45	11.5	19.9	3.2	5.75	1.6	2.8	—
	380	—	15	—	7½	40	40	45	—	32.9	—	—	—	—	—
	460	—	15	—	7½	40	40	45	23	39.8	6.6	11.2	3.3	5.7	—
	575	—	15	—	7½	40	40	—	28.8	49.7	8.1	14.5	4.1	7.1	—
2	115	3	—	2	—	45	52	60	8.1	13.9	2.1	—	1.0	—	—
	200	—	10	—	7½	45	52	60	14	24.2	—	6.3	—	3.1	—
	230	7½	15	5	10	45	52	60	16.1	27.8	4.1	7.2	2.1	3.6	8
	380	—	25	—	15	45	52	60	—	46.0	—	—	—	—	—
	460	—	25	—	15	45	52	60	32.2	55.7	8.3	14	4.2	7.2	16
	575	—	25	—	15	45	52	—	40.3	69.6	10.0	18	5.2	8.9	20
2½	115	5	—	—	—	60	65	75	10.4	17.9	3.1	—	1.5	—	—
	200	—	15	—	10	60	65	75	18	31.1	—	9.1	—	4.6	—
	230	10	20	—	15	60	65	75	20.7	35.8	6.1	10.6	3.1	5.3	17.5
	380	—	30	—	20	60	65	75	—	59.2	—	—	—	—	—
	460	—	30	—	20	60	65	75	41.4	71.6	12	21	6.1	10.6	34.5
	575	—	30	—	20	60	65	—	51.8	89.5	15	26.5	7.6	13.4	43.5

continued

continued

CONTROL RATINGS

Size	Load (V)	Maximum HP — Normal duty 1φ	Maximum HP — Normal duty 3φ	Maximum HP — Plugging & jogging duty 1φ	Maximum HP — Plugging & jogging duty 3φ	Cont. amps	Service limit amps	Tungsten & ballast type lamp amps 480 V max	Resistance heating (kW) 1φ	Resistance heating (kW) 3φ	Transformer switching 50-60 Hz kVA rating inrush peak time Continuous amps — 20 times 1φ	20 times 3φ	20-40 times 1φ	20-40 times 3φ	Capacitor kVA switching rating 3φ kVAR
3	115	7½	—	—	—	90	104	100	14.4	24.8	4.1	—	2.0	—	—
	200	—	25	—	15	90	104	100	25	43.3	—	12	—	6.1	—
	230	15	30	—	20	90	104	100	28.8	50.0	8.1	14	4.1	7.0	27
	380	—	50	—	30	90	104	100	—	82.2	—	—	—	—	—
	460	—	50	—	30	90	104	100	57.5	99.4	16	28	8.1	14	53
	575	—	50	—	30	90	104	—	71.9	124	20	35	10	18	67
3½	115	—	—	—	—	115	125	150	18.4	31.8	—	—	—	—	—
	200	—	30	—	20	115	125	150	32	55.4	—	16	—	8	—
	230	—	60	—	25	115	125	150	36.8	63.7	11	18.5	5.4	9.5	33.5
	380	—	60	—	30	115	125	150	—	105	—	—	—	—	—
	460	—	75	—	40	115	125	150	73.6	127	21.5	37.5	11.0	18.5	66.5
	575	—	75	—	40	115	125	—	92	159	37	47	13.5	23.5	83.5
4	200	—	40	—	25	135	156	200	39	67.5	—	20	—	10	—
	230	—	50	—	30	135	156	200	44.9	77.6	14	23	6.8	12	40
	380	—	75	—	50	135	156	200	—	128	—	—	—	—	—
	460	—	100	—	60	135	156	200	89.7	155	27	47	14	23	80
	575	—	100	—	60	135	156	—	112	194	34	59	17	29	100
4½	200	—	50	—	30	210	225	250	53	91.7	—	30.5	—	15	—
	230	—	75	—	40	210	225	250	60.9	105	20.5	35	10.4	18	60
	380	—	100	—	75	210	225	250	—	174	—	—	—	—	—
	460	—	150	—	100	210	225	250	122	211	40.5	70.5	20.5	35	120
	575	—	150	—	100	210	225	—	152	264	51	88	25.5	44	150

STANDARD MOTOR SIZES

Classification	Size (HP)
Milli	1, 1.5, 2, 3, 5, 7.5, 10, 15, 25, 35
Fractional	1/20, 1/12, 1/8, 1/6, 1/4, 1/3, 1/2, 3/4
Full	1, 1½, 2, 3, 5, 7½, 10, 15, 20, 25, 30, 40, 50, 60, 75, 100, 125, 150, 200, 250, 300
Full—Special Order	350, 400, 450, 500, 600, 700, 800, 900, 1000, 1250, 1500, 1750, 2000, 2250, 2500, 3000, 3500, 4000, 4500, 5000, 5500, 6000, 7000, 8000, 9000, 10,000, 11,000, 12,000, 13,000, 14,000, 15,000, 16,000, 17,000, 18,000, 19,000, 20,000, 22,500, 30,000, 32,500, 35,000, 37,500, 40,000, 45,000, 50,000

THREE-PHASE VOLTAGE VALUES

For 208 V × 1.732, use 360
For 230 V × 1.732, use 398
For 240 V × 1.732, use 416
For 440 V × 1.732, use 762
For 460 V × 1.732, use 797
For 480 V × 1.732, use 831

CAPACITOR RATINGS

Typical Ratings*	Dimensions**		Model Number***
	Diameter	Length	
110–125 VAC, 50/60 Hz, Starting Capacitors			
88–106	$1\frac{7}{16}$	$2\frac{3}{4}$	EC8815
108–130	$1\frac{7}{16}$	$2\frac{3}{4}$	EC10815
130–156	$1\frac{7}{16}$	$2\frac{3}{4}$	EC13015
145–174	$1\frac{7}{16}$	$2\frac{3}{4}$	EC14515
161–193	$1\frac{7}{16}$	$2\frac{3}{4}$	EC16115
189–227	$1\frac{7}{16}$	$2\frac{3}{4}$	EC18915A
216–259	$1\frac{7}{16}$	$3\frac{3}{8}$	EC21615
233–280	$1\frac{7}{16}$	$3\frac{3}{8}$	EC23315A
243–292	$1\frac{7}{16}$	$3\frac{3}{8}$	EC24315A
270–324	$1\frac{7}{16}$	$3\frac{3}{8}$	EC27015A
324–389	$1\frac{7}{16}$	$3\frac{3}{8}$	EC2R10324N
340–408	$1\frac{13}{16}$	$3\frac{3}{8}$	EC34015
378–454	$1\frac{13}{16}$	$3\frac{3}{8}$	EC37815
400–480	$1\frac{13}{16}$	$3\frac{3}{8}$	EC40015
430–516	$1\frac{13}{16}$	$3\frac{3}{8}$	EC43015A
460–553	$1\frac{13}{16}$	$4\frac{3}{8}$	EC5R10460N
540–648	$1\frac{13}{16}$	$4\frac{3}{8}$	EC54015B
590–708	$1\frac{13}{16}$	$4\frac{3}{8}$	EC59015A
708–850	$1\frac{13}{16}$	$4\frac{3}{8}$	EC70815
815–978	$1\frac{13}{16}$	$4\frac{3}{8}$	EC81515
1000–1200	$2\frac{1}{16}$	$4\frac{3}{8}$	EC100015A
220–250 VAC, 50/60 Hz, Starting Capacitors			
53–64	$1\frac{7}{16}$	$3\frac{3}{8}$	EC5335
64–77	$1\frac{7}{16}$	$3\frac{3}{8}$	EC6435
88–106	$1\frac{13}{16}$	$3\frac{3}{8}$	EC8835
108–130	$1\frac{13}{16}$	$3\frac{3}{8}$	EC10835A
124–149	$1\frac{13}{16}$	$4\frac{3}{8}$	EC12435
130–154	$1\frac{13}{16}$	$4\frac{3}{8}$	EC13035
145–174	$2\frac{1}{16}$	$3\frac{3}{8}$	EC6R22145N
161–193	$2\frac{1}{16}$	$3\frac{3}{8}$	EC6R2216N
216–259	$2\frac{1}{16}$	$4\frac{3}{8}$	EC21635A
233–280	$2\frac{1}{16}$	$4\frac{3}{8}$	EC23335A
270–324	$2\frac{1}{16}$	$4\frac{3}{8}$	EC27035A

* in μF
** in inches
*** Model numbers vary by manufacturer.

CAPACITOR RATINGS

Typical Ratings*	Dimensions**		Model Number***
	Oval	Length	
270 VAC, 50/60 Hz, Running Capacitors			
2		$2\frac{1}{8}$	VH5502
3		$2\frac{1}{8}$	VH5503
4	$1\frac{5}{16} \times 2\frac{5}{32}$	$2\frac{1}{8}$	VH5704
5		$2\frac{1}{8}$	VH5705
6		$2\frac{5}{8}$	VH5706
7.5		$2\frac{7}{8}$	VH9001
10	$1\frac{5}{16} \times 2\frac{5}{32}$	$2\frac{7}{8}$	VH9002
12.5		$3\frac{7}{8}$	VH9003
15	$1\frac{29}{32} \times 2\frac{29}{32}$	$2\frac{1}{8}$	VH9121
17.5		$2\frac{7}{8}$	VH9123
20		$2\frac{7}{8}$	VH5463
25	$1\frac{29}{32} \times 2\frac{29}{32}$	$3\frac{7}{8}$	VH9069
30		$3\frac{7}{8}$	VH5465
35	$1\frac{29}{32} \times 2\frac{29}{32}$	$3\frac{7}{8}$	VH9071
40		$3\frac{7}{8}$	VH9073
45	$1\frac{31}{32} \times 3\frac{21}{32}$	$3\frac{7}{8}$	VH9115
50		$3\frac{7}{8}$	VH9075
440 VAC, 50/60 Hz, Running Capacitors			
10	$1\frac{5}{16} \times 2\frac{5}{32}$	$3\frac{7}{8}$	VH5300
15	$1\frac{29}{32} \times 2\frac{29}{32}$	$2\frac{7}{8}$	VH5304
17.5	$1\frac{29}{32} \times 2\frac{29}{32}$	$3\frac{7}{8}$	VH9141
20	$1\frac{29}{32} \times 2\frac{29}{32}$	$3\frac{7}{8}$	VH9082
25	$1\frac{29}{32} \times 2\frac{29}{32}$	$3\frac{7}{8}$	VH5310
30		$4\frac{3}{4}$	VH9086
35	$1\frac{29}{32} \times 2\frac{29}{32}$	$4\frac{3}{4}$	VH9088
40		$4\frac{3}{4}$	VH9641
45		$3\frac{7}{8}$	VH5351
50	$1\frac{31}{32} \times 3\frac{21}{32}$	$3\frac{7}{8}$	VH5320
55		$4\frac{3}{4}$	VH9084

* in μF
** in inches
*** Model numbers vary by manufacturer.

RESISTOR COLOR CODES

Color	Number		Multiplier	Tolerance (%)
	1st	2nd		
Black (BK)	0	0	1	0
Brown (BR)	1	1	10	—
Red (R)	2	2	100	—
Orange (O)	3	3	1000	—
Yellow (Y)	4	4	10,000	—
Green (G)	5	5	100,000	—
Blue (BL)	6	6	1,000,000	—
Violet (V)	7	7	10,000,000	—
Gray (GY)	8	8	100,000,000	—
White (W)	9	9	1,000,000,000	—
Gold (Au)	—	—	0.1	5
Silver (Ag)	—	—	0.01	10
None	—	—	0	20

COUPLING SELECTIONS		
Coupling number	**Rated torque (lb-in)**	**Maximum shock torque (lb-in)**
10-101-A	16	45
10-102-A	36	100
10-103-A	80	220
10-104-A	132	360
10-105-A	176	480
10-106-A	240	660
10-107-A	325	900
10-108-A	525	1450
10-109-A	875	2450
10-110-A	1250	3500
10-111-A	1800	5040
10-112-A	2200	6160

V-BELTS

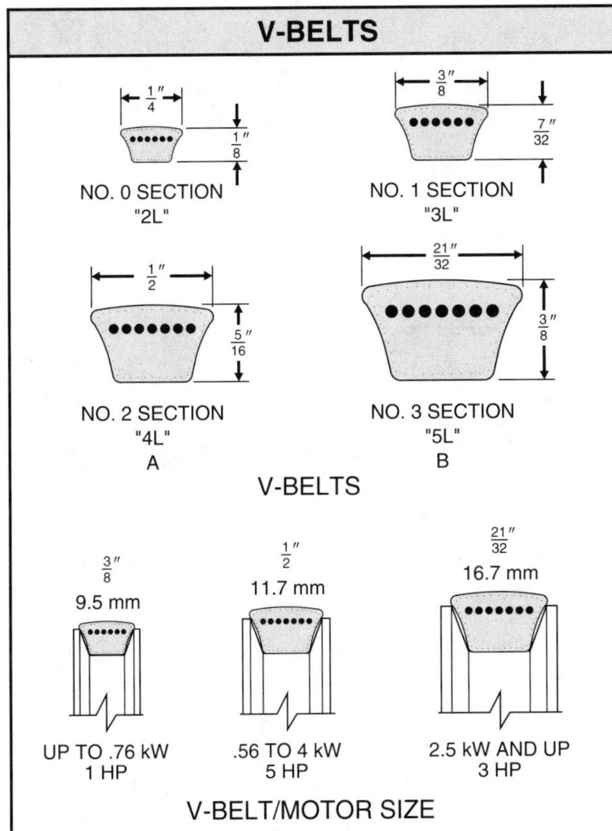

TYPICAL MOTOR POWER FACTORS				
HP	**Speed (rpm)**	**Power Factor at**		
		½ load	**¾ load**	**full load**
0–5	1800	.72	.82	.84
5.01–20	1800	.74	.84	.86
20.1–100	1800	.79	.86	.89
100.1–300	1800	.81	.88	.91

COMMON SERVICE FACTORS	
Equipment	**Service factor**
Blowers	
Centrifugal	1.00
Vane	1.25
Compressors	
Centrifugal	1.25
Vane	1.50
Conveyors	
Uniformly loaded or fed	1.50
Heavy-duty	2.00
Elevators	
Bucket	2.00
Freight	2.25
Extruders	
Plastic	2.00
Metal	2.50
Fans	
Light-duty	1.00
Centrifugal	1.50
Machine tools	
Bending roll	2.00
Punch press	2.25
Tapping machine	3.00
Mixers	
Concrete	2.00
Drum	2.25
Paper mills	
De-barking machines	3.00
Beater and pulper	2.00
Bleacher	1.00
Dryers	2.00
Log haul	2.00
Printing presses	1.50
Pumps	
Centrifugal—general	1.00
Centrifugal—sewage	2.00
Reciprocating	2.00
Rotary	1.50
Textile	
Batchers	1.50
Dryers	1.50
Looms	1.75
Spinners	1.50
Woodworking machines	1.00

MOTOR FRAME DIMENSIONS

Frame No.	Shaft		Key			Dimensions — Inches					
	U	V	W	T	L	A	B	D	E	F	BA
48	1/2	1 1/2*	flat	3/64	—	5 5/8*	3 1/2*	3	2 1/8	1 3/8	2 1/2
56	5/8	1 7/8*	3/16	3/16	1 3/8	6 1/2*	4 1/4*	3 1/2	2 7/16	1 1/2	2 3/4
143T	7/8	2	3/16	3/16	1 3/8	7	6	3 1/2	2 3/4	2	2 1/4
145T	7/8	2	3/16	3/16	1 3/8	7	6	3 1/2	2 3/4	2 1/2	2 1/4
182	7/8	2	3/16	3/16	1 3/8	9	6 1/2	4 1/2	3 3/4	2 1/4	2 3/4
182T	1 1/8	2 1/2	1/4	1/4	1 3/4	9	6 1/2	4 1/2	3 3/4	2 1/4	2 3/4
184	7/8	2	3/16	3/16	1 3/8	9	7 1/2	4 1/2	3 3/4	2 3/4	2 3/4
184T	1 1/8	2 1/2	1/4	1/4	1 3/4	9	7 1/2	4 1/2	3 3/4	2 3/4	2 3/4
203	3/4	2	3/16	3/16	1 3/8	10	7 1/2	5	4	2 3/4	3 1/8
204	3/4	2	3/16	3/16	1 3/8	10	8 1/2	5	4	3 1/4	3 1/8
213	1 1/8	2 3/4	1/4	1/4	2	10 1/2	7 1/2	5 1/4	4 1/4	2 3/4	3 1/2
213T	1 3/8	3 1/8	5/16	5/16	2 3/8	10 1/2	7 1/2	5 1/4	4 1/4	2 3/4	3 1/2
215	1 1/8	2 3/4	1/4	1/4	2	10 1/2	9	5 1/4	4 1/4	3 1/2	3 1/2
215T	1 3/8	3 1/8	5/16	5/16	2 3/8	10 1/2	9	5 1/4	4 1/4	3 1/2	3 1/2
224	1	2 3/4	1/4	1/4	2	11	8 3/4	5 1/2	4 1/2	3 3/8	3 1/2
225	1	2 3/4	1/4	1/4	2	11	9 1/2	5 1/2	4 1/2	3 3/4	3 1/2
254	1 1/8	3 1/8	1/4	1/4	2 3/8	12 1/2	10 3/4	6 1/4	5	4 1/8	4 1/4
254U	1 3/8	3 1/2	5/16	5/16	2 3/4	12 1/2	10 3/4	6 1/4	5	4 1/8	4 1/4
254T	1 5/8	3 3/4	3/8	3/8	2 7/8	12 1/2	10 3/4	6 1/4	5	4 1/8	4 1/4
256U	1 3/8	3 1/2	5/16	5/16	2 3/4	12 1/2	12 1/2	6 1/4	5	5	4 1/4
256T	1 5/8	3 3/4	3/8	3/8	2 7/8	12 1/2	12 1/2	6 1/4	5	5	4 1/4
284	1 1/4	3 1/2	1/4	1/4	2 3/4	14	12 1/2	7	5 1/2	4 3/4	4 3/4
284U	1 5/8	4 5/8	3/8	3/8	3 3/4	14	12 1/2	7	5 1/2	4 3/4	4 3/4
284T	1 7/8	4 3/8	1/2	1/2	3 1/4	14	12 1/2	7	5 1/2	4 3/4	4 3/4
284TS	1 5/8	3	3/8	3/8	1 7/8	14	12 1/2	7	5 1/2	4 3/4	4 3/4
286U	1 5/8	4 5/8	3/8	3/8	3 3/4	14	14	7	5 1/2	5 1/2	4 3/4
286T	1 7/8	4 3/8	1/2	1/2	3 1/4	14	14	7	5 1/2	5 1/2	4 3/4
286TS	1 5/8	3	3/8	3/8	1 7/8	14	14	7	5 1/2	5 1/2	4 3/4
324	1 5/8	4 5/8	3/8	3/8	3 3/4	16	14	8	6 1/4	5 1/4	5 1/4
324U	1 7/8	5 3/8	1/2	1/2	4 1/4	16	14	8	6 1/4	5 1/4	5 1/4
324S	1 5/8	3	3/8	3/8	1 7/8	16	14	8	6 1/4	5 1/4	5 1/4
324T	2 1/8	5	1/2	1/2	3 7/8	16	14	8	6 1/4	5 1/4	5 1/4
324TS	1 7/8	3 1/2	1/2	1/2	2	16	14	8	6 1/4	5 1/4	5 1/4
326	1 5/8	4 5/8	3/8	3/8	3 3/4	16	15 1/2	8	6 1/4	6	5 1/4
326U	1 7/8	5 3/8	1/2	1/2	4 1/4	16	15 1/2	8	6 1/4	6	5 1/4
326S	1 5/8	3	3/8	3/8	1 7/8	16	15 1/2	8	6 1/4	6	5 1/4
326T	2 1/8	5	1/2	1/2	3 7/8	16	15 1/2	8	6 1/4	6	5 1/4
326TS	1 7/8	3 1/2	1/2	1/2	2	16	15 1/2	8	6 1/4	6	5 1/4
364	1 7/8	5 3/8	1/2	1/2	4 1/4	18	15 1/4	9	7	5 5/8	5 7/8
364S	1 5/8	3	3/8	3/8	1 7/8	18	15 1/4	9	7	5 5/8	5 7/8
364U	2 1/8	6 1/8	1/2	1/2	5	18	15 1/4	9	7	5 5/8	5 7/8
364US	1 7/8	3 1/2	1/2	1/2	2	18	15 1/4	9	7	5 5/8	5 7/8

MOTOR FRAME DIMENSIONS

Frame No.	Shaft		Key			Dimensions — Inches					
	U	V	W	T	L	A	B	D	E	F	BA
364T	2 3/8	5 5/8	5/8	5/8	4 1/4	18	15 1/4	9	7	5 5/8	5 7/8
364TS	1 7/8	3 1/2	1/2	1/2	2	18	15 1/4	9	7	5 5/8	5 7/8
365	1 7/8	5 3/8	1/2	1/2	4 1/4	18	16 1/4	9	7	6 1/8	5 7/8
365S	1 5/8	3	3/8	3/8	1 7/8	18	16 1/4	9	7	6 1/8	5 7/8
365U	2 1/8	6 1/8	1/2	1/2	5	18	16 1/4	9	7	6 1/8	5 7/8
365US	1 7/8	3 1/2	1/2	1/2	2	18	16 1/4	9	7	6 1/8	5 7/8
365T	2 3/8	5 5/8	5/8	5/8	4 1/4	18	16 1/4	9	7	6 1/8	5 7/8
365TS	1 7/8	3 1/2	1/2	1/2	2	18	16 1/4	9	7	6 1/8	5 7/8
404	2 1/8	6 1/8	1/2	1/2	5	20	16 1/4	10	8	6 1/8	6 5/8
404S	1 7/8	3 1/2	1/2	1/2	2	20	16 1/4	10	8	6 1/8	6 5/8
404U	2 3/8	6 7/8	5/8	5/8	5 1/2	20	16 1/4	10	8	6 1/8	6 5/8
404US	2 1/8	4	1/2	1/2	2 3/4	20	16 1/4	10	8	6 1/8	6 5/8
404T	2 7/8	7	3/4	3/4	5 5/8	20	16 1/4	10	8	6 1/8	6 5/8
404TS	2 1/8	4	1/2	1/2	2 3/4	20	16 1/4	10	8	6 1/8	6 5/8
405	2 1/8	6 1/8	1/2	1/2	5	20	17 3/4	10	8	6 7/8	6 5/8
405S	1 7/8	3 1/2	1/2	1/2	2	20	17 3/4	10	8	6 7/8	6 5/8
405U	2 3/8	6 7/8	5/8	5/8	5 1/2	20	17 3/4	10	8	6 7/8	6 5/8
405US	2 1/8	4	1/2	1/2	2 3/4	20	17 3/4	10	8	6 7/8	6 5/8
405T	2 7/8	7	3/4	3/4	5 5/8	20	17 3/4	10	8	6 7/8	6 5/8
405TS	2 1/8	4	1/2	1/2	2 3/4	20	17 3/4	10	8	6 7/8	6 5/8
444	2 3/8	6 7/8	5/8	5/8	5 1/2	22	18 1/2	11	9	7 1/4	7 1/2
444S	2 1/8	4	1/2	1/2	2 3/4	22	18 1/2	11	9	7 1/4	7 1/2
444U	2 7/8	8 3/8	3/4	3/4	7	22	18 1/2	11	9	7 1/4	7 1/2
444US	2 1/8	4	1/2	1/2	2 3/4	22	18 1/2	11	9	7 1/4	7 1/2
444T	3 3/8	8 1/4	7/8	7/8	6 7/8	22	18 1/2	11	9	7 1/4	7 1/2
444TS	2 3/8	4 1/2	5/8	5/8	3	22	18 1/2	11	9	7 1/4	7 1/2
445	2 3/8	6 7/8	5/8	5/8	5 1/2	22	20 1/2	11	9	8 1/4	7 1/2
445S	2 1/8	4	1/2	1/2	2 3/4	22	20 1/2	11	9	8 1/4	7 1/2
445U	2 7/8	8 3/8	3/4	3/4	7	22	20 1/2	11	9	8 1/4	7 1/2
445US	2 1/8	4	1/2	1/2	2 3/4	22	20 1/2	11	9	8 1/4	7 1/2
445T	3 3/8	8 1/4	7/8	7/8	6 7/8	22	20 1/2	11	9	8 1/4	7 1/2
445TS	2 3/8	4 1/2	5/8	5/8	3	22	20 1/2	11	9	8 1/4	7 1/2
504U	2 7/8	8 3/8	3/4	3/4	7 1/4	25	21	12 1/2	10	8	8 1/2
504S	2 1/8	4	1/2	1/2	2 3/4	25	21	12 1/2	10	8	8 1/2
505	2 7/8	8 3/8	3/4	3/4	7 1/4	25	23	12 1/2	10	9	8 1/2
505S	2 1/8	4	1/2	1/2	2 3/4	25	23	12 1/2	10	9	8 1/2

* Not NEMA standard dimensions

MOTOR FRAME TABLE								
Frame No. Series	**Third/Fourth Digit of Frame No.**							
	D	**1**	**2**	**3**	**4**	**5**	**6**	**7**
140	3.50	3.00	3.50	4.00	4.50	5.00	5.50	6.25
160	4.00	3.50	4.00	4.50	5.00	5.50	6.25	7.00
180	4.50	4.00	4.50	5.00	5.50	6.25	7.00	8.00
200	5.00	4.50	5.00	5.50	6.50	7.00	8.00	9.00
210	5.25	4.50	5.00	5.50	6.25	7.00	8.00	9.00
220	5.50	5.00	5.50	6.25	6.75	7.50	9.00	10.00
250	6.25	5.50	6.25	7.00	8.25	9.00	10.00	11.00
280	7.00	6.25	7.00	8.00	9.50	10.00	11.00	12.50
320	8.00	7.00	8.00	9.00	10.50	11.00	12.00	14.00
360	9.00	8.00	9.00	10.00	11.25	12.25	14.00	16.00
400	10.00	9.00	10.00	11.00	12.25	13.75	16.00	18.00
440	11.00	10.00	11.00	12.50	14.50	16.50	18.00	20.00
500	12.50	11.00	12.50	14.00	16.00	18.00	20.00	22.00
580	14.50	12.50	14.00	16.00	18.00	20.00	22.00	25.00
680	17.00	16.00	18.00	20.00	22.00	25.00	28.00	32.00

Frame No. Series	**Third/Fourth Digit of Frame No.**								
	D	**8**	**9**	**10**	**11**	**12**	**13**	**14**	**15**
140	3.50	7.00	8.00	9.00	10.00	11.00	12.50	14.00	16.00
160	4.00	8.00	9.00	10.00	11.00	12.50	14.00	16.00	18.00
180	4.50	9.00	10.00	11.00	12.50	14.00	16.00	18.00	20.00
200	5.00	10.00	11.00	—	—	—	—	—	—
210	5.25	10.00	11.00	12.50	14.00	16.00	18.00	20.00	22.00
220	5.50	11.00	12.50	—	—	—	—	—	—
250	6.25	12.50	14.00	16.00	18.00	20.00	22.00	25.00	28.00
280	7.00	14.00	16.00	18.00	20.00	22.00	25.00	28.00	32.00
320	8.00	16.00	18.00	20.00	22.00	25.00	28.00	32.00	36.00
360	9.00	18.00	20.00	22.00	25.00	28.00	32.00	36.00	40.00
400	10.00	20.00	22.00	25.00	28.00	32.00	36.00	40.00	45.00
440	11.00	22.00	25.00	28.00	32.00	36.00	40.00	45.00	50.00
500	12.50	25.00	28.00	32.00	36.00	40.00	45.00	50.00	56.00
580	14.50	28.00	32.00	36.00	40.00	45.00	50.00	56.00	63.00
680	17.00	36.00	40.00	45.00	50.00	56.00	63.00	71.00	80.00

MOTOR FRAME LETTERS	
LETTER	**DESIGNATION**
G	Gasoline pump motor
K	Sump pump motor
M and N	Oil burner motor
S	Standard short shaft for direct connection
T	Standard dimensions established
U	Previously used as frame designation for which standard dimensions are established
Y	Special mounting dimensions required from manufacturer
Z	Standard mounting dimensions except shaft extension

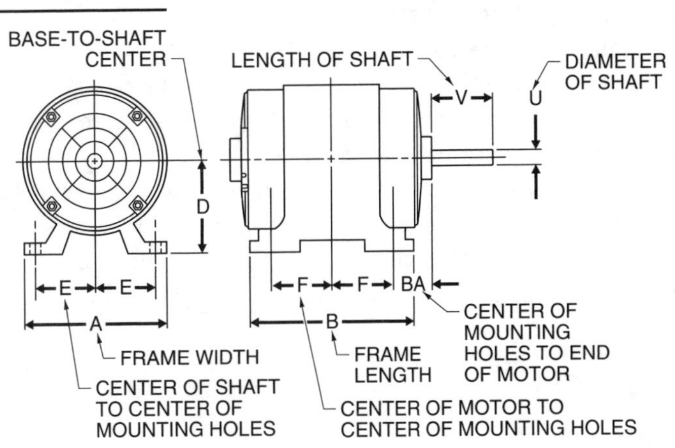

MOTOR REPAIR AND SERVICE RECORD

Motor File #: ______________ Serial #: ______________________________

Date Installed: ____________ Motor Location: ________________________

____

MFR: ______________ Type: ______________ Frame: ______________

HP: ______________ Volts: ______________ Amps: ______________

RPM: ______________ Filter Sizes: ________________________

Date	Operation	Mechanic

SEMIANNUAL MOTOR MAINTENANCE CHECKLIST

Motor File #: ______________ Serial #: ______________________________

Date Installed: ____________ Motor Location: ________________________

____

MFR: ______________ Type: ______________ Frame: ______________

HP: ______________ Volts: ______________ Amps: ______________

RPM: ______________ Date Serviced: ______________

Step	Operation	Mechanic
1	Turn OFF and lock out all power to the motor and its control circuit.	
2	Clean motor exterior and all ventilation ducts.	
3	Check motor's wire raceway.	
4	Check and lubricate bearings as needed.	
5	Check drive mechanism.	
6	Check brushes and commutator.	
7	Check slip rings.	
8	Check motor terminations.	
9	Check capacitors.	
10	Check all mounting bolts.	
11	Check and record line-to-line resistance.	
12	Check and record megohmmeter resistance from L1 to ground.	
13	Check motor controls.	
14	Reconnect motor and control circuit power supplies.	
15	Check line-to-line voltage for balance and level.	
16	Check line current draw against nameplate rating.	
17	Check and record inboard and outboard bearing temperatures.	

ANNUAL MOTOR MAINTENANCE CHECKLIST

Motor File #: ______________ Serial #: ______________________________

Date Installed: ______________ Motor Location: ______________________________

____

MFR: ______________ Type: ______________ Frame: ______________

HP: ______________ Volts: ______________ Amps: ______________

RPM: ______________ Date Serviced: ______________

Step	Operation	Mechanic
1	Turn OFF and lock out all power to the motor and its control circuit.	
2	Clean motor exterior and all ventilation ducts.	
3	Uncouple motor from load and disassemble.	
4	Clean inside of motor.	
5	Check centrifugal switch assemblies.	
6	Check rotors, armatures, and field windings.	
7	Check all peripheral equipment.	
8	Check bearings.	
9	Check brushes and commutator.	
10	Check slip rings.	
11	Reassemble motor and couple to load.	
12	Flush old bearing lubricant and replace.	
13	Check motor's wire raceway.	
14	Check drive mechanism.	
15	Check motor terminations.	
16	Check capacitors.	
17	Check all mounting bolts.	
18	Check and record line-to-line resistance.	
19	Check and record megohmmeter resistance from T1 to ground.	
20	Check and record insulation polarization index.	
21	Check motor controls.	
22	Reconnect motor and control circuit power supplies.	
23	Check line-to-line voltage for balance and level.	
24	Check line current draw against nameplate rating.	
25	Check and record inboard and outboard bearing temperatures.	

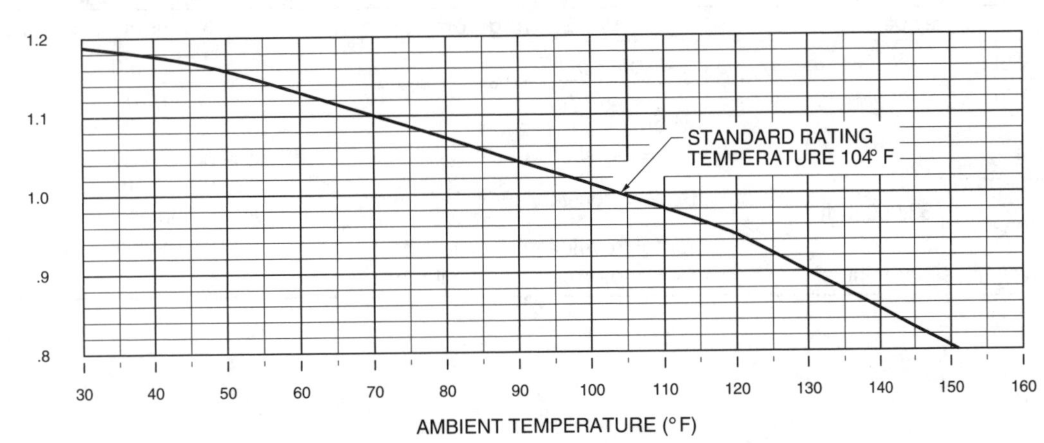

HEATER AMBIENT TEMPERATURE CORRECTION

FORMULAS

CAPACITORS			
Connected in Series		Connected in Parallel	Connected in Series/Parallel
Two Capacitors	Three or More Capacitors		
$C_T = \frac{C_1 \times C_2}{C_1 + C_2}$ where C_T = total capacitance (in μF) C_1 = capacitance of capacitor 1 (in μF) C_2 = capacitance of capacitor 2 (in μF)	$\frac{1}{C_T} = \frac{1}{C_1} + \frac{1}{C_2} + \ldots$	$C_T = C_1 + C_2 + \ldots$	1. Calculate the capacitance of the parallel branch. $C_T = C_1 + C_2 + \ldots$ 2. Calculate the capacitance of the series combination. $C_T = \frac{C_1 \times C_2}{C_1 + C_2}$

GEAR REDUCER		
Output Torque	Output Speed	Output Horsepower
$O_T = I_T \times R_R \times R_E$ where O_T = output torque (in lb-ft) I_T = input torque (in lb-ft) R_R = gear reducer ratio R_E = reducer efficiency (percentage)	$O_S = \frac{I_S}{R_R} \times R_E$ where O_S = output speed (in rpm) I_S = input speed (in rpm) R_R = gear reducer ratio R_E = reducer efficiency (percentage)	$O_{HP} = I_{HP} \times R_E$ where O_{HP} = output horsepower I_{HP} = input horsepower R_E = reducer efficiency (percentage)

HORSEPOWER	
Current and Voltage Known	Speed and Torque Known
$HP = \frac{E \times I \times E_{ff}}{746}$ where HP = horsepower E = voltage (volts) I = current (amps) E_{ff} = efficiency	$HP = \frac{rpm \times T}{5252}$ where HP = horsepower rpm = revolutions per minute T = torque (lb-ft)

TEMPERATURE CONVERSIONS	
Convert °C to °F	Convert °F to °C
$°F = (1.8 \times °C) + 32$	$°C = \frac{(°F - 32)}{1.8}$

MOTOR TORQUE		
Torque	Starting Torque	Nominal Torque Rating
$T = \frac{HP \times 5252}{rpm}$ where T = torque HP = horsepower 5252 = constant $\left(\frac{33{,}000 \text{ lb-ft}}{\pi \times 2} = 5252\right)$ rpm = revolutions per minute	$T = \frac{HP \times 5252}{rpm} \times \%$ where HP = horsepower 5252 = constant $\left(\frac{33{,}000 \text{ lb-ft}}{\pi \times 2} = 5252\right)$ rpm = revolutions per minute % = motor class percentage	$T = \frac{HP \times 63{,}000}{rpm}$ where T = nominal torque rating (in lb-in) 63,000 = constant HP = horsepower rpm = revolutions per minute

LOCKED ROTOR CURRENT

Apparent, 1ϕ

$$LRC = \frac{1000 \times HP \times kVA/HP}{V}$$

where
LRC = locked rotor current (in amps)
1000 = multiplier for kilo
HP = horsepower
kVA/HP = kilovolt amps per horsepower
V = volts

Apparent, 3ϕ

$$LRC = \frac{1000 \times HP \times kVA/HP}{V \times \sqrt{3}}$$

where
LRC = locked rotor current (in amps)
1000 = multiplier for kilo
HP = horsepower
kVA/HP = kilovolt amps per horsepower
V = volts
$\sqrt{3}$ = 1.73

True, 1ϕ

$$LRC = \frac{1000 \times HP \times kVA/HP}{V \times PF \times E_{ff}}$$

where
LRC = locked rotor current (in amps)
1000 = multiplier for kilo
HP = horsepower
kVA/HP = kilovolt amps per horsepower
V = volts
PF = power factor
E_{ff} = motor efficiency

True, 3ϕ

$$LRC = \frac{1000 \times HP \times kVA/HP}{V \times \sqrt{3} \times PF \times E_{ff}}$$

where
LRC = locked rotor current (in amps)
1000 = multiplier for kilo
HP = horsepower
kVA/HP = kilovolt amps per horsepower
V = volts
$\sqrt{3}$ = 1.73

MAXIMUM OCPD

$$OCPD = FLC \times R_M$$

where
FLC = full-load current (from motor nameplate or NEC® Table 430-150)
R_M = maximum rating of OCPD

Motor Type	Code Letter	FLC (%)				
		Motor Size	TDF	NTDF	ITB	ITCB
AC*	—	—	175	300	150	700
AC*	A	—	150	150	150	700
AC*	B–E	—	175	250	200	700
AC*	F–V	—	175	300	250	700
DC	—	⅛ to 50 HP	150	150	150	250
DC	—	Over 50 HP	150	150	150	175

* full-voltage and resistor starting

EFFICIENCY

Input and Output Power Known

$$E_{ff} = \frac{P_{out}}{P_{in}}$$

where
E_{ff} = efficiency (%)
P_{out} = output power (W)
P_{in} = input power (W)

Horsepower and Power Loss Known

$$E_{ff} = \frac{746 \times HP}{746 \times HP + W_l}$$

where
E_{ff} = efficiency (%)
746 = constant
HP = horsepower
W_l = watts lost

VOLTAGE UNBALANCE

$$V_u = \frac{V_d}{V_a} \times 100$$

where
V_u = voltage unbalance (%)
V_d = voltage deviation (V)
V_a = voltage average (V)
100 = constant

POWER

Power Consumed

$$P = \frac{HP \times 746}{E_{ff}}$$

where
P = power consumed (W)
HP = horsepower
746 = constant
E_{ff} = efficiency (%)

Operating Cost

$$C_{/hr} = \frac{P_{/hr} \times C_{/kWh}}{1000}$$

where
$C_{/hr}$ = operating cost per hour
$P_{/hr}$ = power consumed per hour
$C_{/kWh}$ = cost per kilowatt hour
1000 = constant to remove kilo

Annual Savings

$$S_{Ann} = C_{Ann\ Std} - C_{Ann\ Eff}$$

S_{Ann} = annual cost savings
$C_{Ann\ Std}$ = annual operating cost for standard motor
$C_{Ann\ Eff}$ = annual operating cost for energy-efficient motor

THREE-PHASE VOLTAGE VALUES
For 208 V × 1.732, use 360
For 230 V × 1.732, use 398
For 240 V × 1.732, use 416
For 440 V × 1.732, use 762
For 460 V × 1.732, use 797
For 480 V × 1.732, use 831

Ohm's Law

Ohm's law is the relationship between the voltage, current, and resistance in an electrical circuit. Ohm's law states that current in a circuit is proportional to the voltage and inversely proportional to the resistance. It is written $I = E/R$, $R = E/I$, and $E = R \times I$.

Power Formula

The *power formula* is the relationship between the voltage, current, and power in an electrical circuit. The power formula states that the power in a circuit is equal to the voltage times the current. It is written $P = E \times I$, $E = P/I$, and $I = P/E$. Any value in these relationships is found using Ohm's Law and Power Formula.

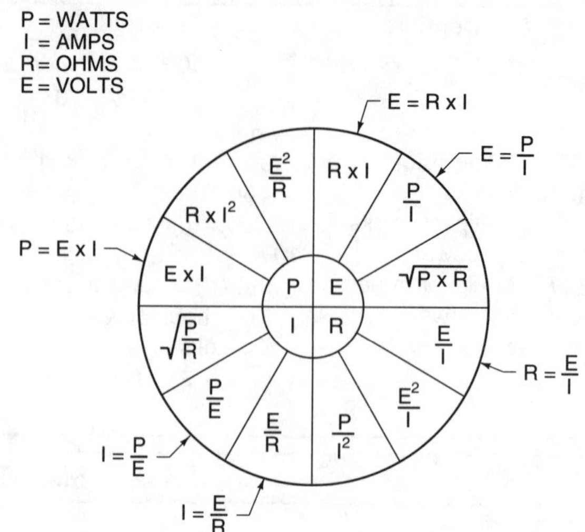

OHM'S LAW AND POWER FORMULA

POWER FORMULAS —1φ, 3φ

Phase	To Find	Use Formula	Example		
			Given	Find	Solution
1φ	I	$I = \frac{VA}{V}$	32,000 VA, 240 V	I	$I = \frac{VA}{V}$ $I = \frac{32,000\ VA}{240\ V}$ $I =$ **133 A**
1φ	VA	$VA = I \times V$	100 A, 240 V	VA	$VA = I \times V$ $VA = 100\ A \times 240\ V$ $VA =$ **24,000 VA**
1φ	V	$V = \frac{VA}{I}$	42,000 VA, 350 A	V	$V = \frac{VA}{I}$ $V = \frac{42,000\ VA}{350\ A}$ $V =$ **120 V**
3φ	I	$I = \frac{VA}{V \times \sqrt{3}}$	72,000 VA, 208 V	I	$I = \frac{VA}{V \times \sqrt{3}}$ $I = \frac{72,000\ VA}{360\ V}$ $I =$ **200 A**
3φ	VA	$VA = I \times V \times \sqrt{3}$	2 A, 240 V	VA	$VA = I \times V \times \sqrt{3}$ $VA = 2 \times 416$ $VA =$ **832 VA**

AC/DC FORMULAS				
To Find	**DC**	**AC**		
		1ϕ, 115 or 220 V	**1ϕ, 208, 230, or 240 V**	**3ϕ—All Voltages**
I, HP known	$\frac{HP \times 746}{E \times E_{ff}}$	$\frac{HP \times 746}{E \times E_{ff} \times PF}$	$\frac{HP \times 746}{E \times E_{ff} \times PF}$	$\frac{HP \times 746}{1.73 \times E \times E_{ff} \times PF}$
I, kW known	$\frac{kW \times 1000}{E}$	$\frac{kW \times 1000}{E \times PF}$	$\frac{kW \times 1000}{E \times PF}$	$\frac{kW \times 1000}{1.73 \times E \times PF}$
I, kVA known		$\frac{kVA \times 1000}{E}$	$\frac{kVA \times 1000}{E}$	$\frac{kVA \times 1000}{1.763 \times E}$
kW	$\frac{I \times E}{1000}$	$\frac{I \times E \times PF}{1000}$	$\frac{I \times E \times PF}{1000}$	$\frac{I \times E \times 1.73 \times PF}{1000}$
kVA		$\frac{I \times E}{1000}$	$\frac{I \times E}{1000}$	$\frac{I \times E \times 1.73}{1000}$
HP (output)	$\frac{I \times E \times E_{ff}}{746}$	$\frac{I \times E \times E_{ff} \times PF}{746}$	$\frac{I \times E \times E_{ff} \times PF}{746}$	$\frac{I \times E \times 1.73 \times E_{ff} \times PF}{746}$

E_{ff} = efficiency

HORSEPOWER FORMULAS				
To Find	**Use Formula**	**Example**		
		Given	**Find**	**Solution**
HP	$HP = \frac{I \times E \times E_{ff}}{746}$	240 V, 20 A, 85% E_{ff}	HP	$HP = \frac{I \times E \times E_{ff}}{746}$ $HP = \frac{240\ V \times 20\ A \times 85\%}{746}$ $HP = \mathbf{5.5}$
I	$I = \frac{HP \times 746}{E \times E_{ff} \times PF}$	10 HP, 240 V, 90% E_{ff}, 88% PF	I	$I = \frac{HP \times 746}{E \times E_{ff} \times PF}$ $I = \frac{10\ HP \times 746}{240\ V \times 90\% \times 88\%}$ $I = \mathbf{39\ A}$

VOLTAGE DROP FORMULAS —1ϕ, 3ϕ					
Phase	**To Find**	**Use Formula**	**Example**		
			Given	**Find**	**Solution**
1ϕ	VD	$VD = \frac{2 \times R \times L \times I}{CM}$	240 V, 40 A, 60′ L, 16,510 CM, 12 R	VD	$VD = \frac{2 \times R \times L \times I}{CM}$ $VD = \frac{2 \times 12 \times 40 \times 60}{16,510}$ $VD = \mathbf{3.5}$
3ϕ	VD	$VD = \frac{2 \times R \times L \times I}{CM}$	208 V, 110 A, 75′ L, 66,360 CM, 12 R, .866 multiplier	VD	$VD = \frac{2 \times R \times L \times I}{CM}$ $VD = \frac{2 \times 12 \times 75 \times 110}{66,360}$ $VD = 2.98 \times .866$ $VD = \mathbf{2.58}$

* $\frac{\sqrt{3}}{2} = .866$

Terms in this glossary are defined as they relate to electric motors.

A

AC motor: Motor that uses alternating current. May be 1ϕ or 3ϕ. See *alternating current.*

alternating current (AC): Current that reverses its direction of flow twice per cycle. Usually generated and distributed as 3ϕ power. See *current.*

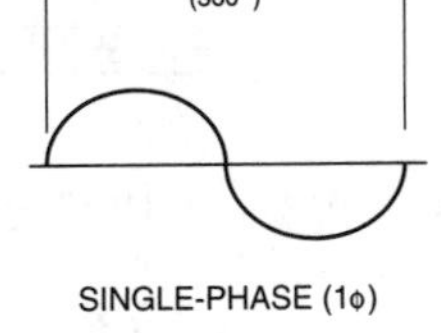

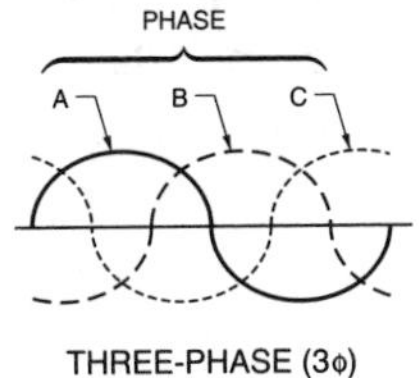

alternating current

ambient temperature: Temperature of air surrounding a piece of equipment.

ampacity: Amount of current for which a conductor or device is rated. See *current.*

angular misalignment: Misalignment that occurs when two shafts are not parallel. See *parallel.*

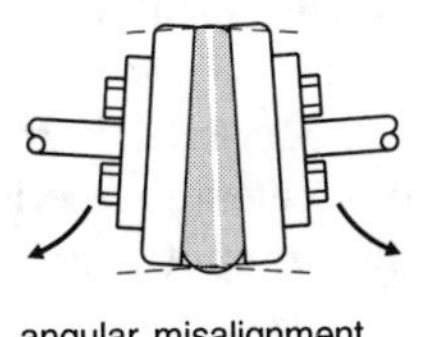

angular misalignment

apparent LRC: Locked rotor current of a motor without considering power factor or efficiency. See *locked rotor current* and *power factor.*

application service factor: Multiplier that corrects for the operating conditions of the motor coupling. See *motor coupling.*

armature: Rotating part of a DC motor. See *DC motor.*

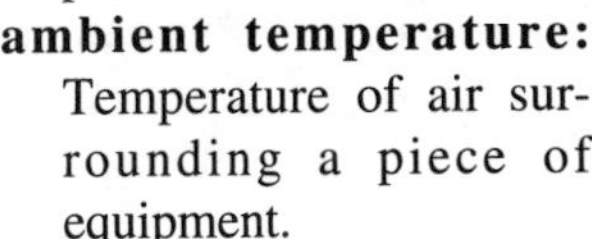

armature

B

breakdown torque: Maximum torque a motor can provide without an abrupt reduction in motor speed. See *torque.*

brushes: Sliding contacts that make the connection between the rotating armature and the stationary part of the DC motor. See *armature* and *DC motor.*

C

capacitor: Device that stores an electric charge.

capacitor motor: Single-phase motor with a capacitor connected in series with the stator windings to produce phase displacement in the starting winding. See *single-phase motor, capacitor,* and *series.*

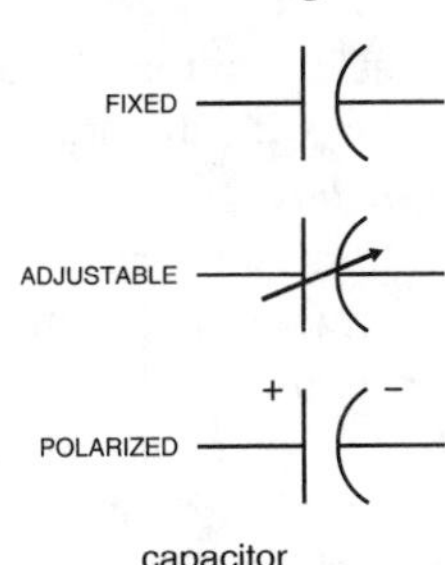

capacitor

centrifugal force: Force that moves rotating bodies away from the center of rotation.

centrifugal switch: Switch that opens to disconnect the starting winding when the rotor reaches a certain preset speed and reconnects the starting winding when the speed falls below a preset value. See *rotor.*

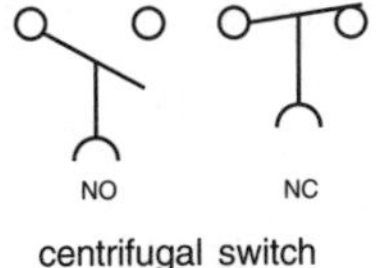

centrifugal switch

clockwise rotation: Direction of rotation is forward when motor is viewed from front. End opposite the shaft is the front of the motor.

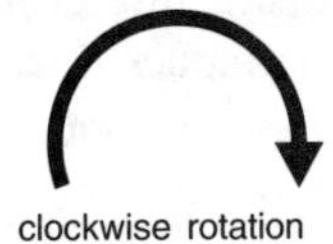

clockwise rotation

commutator: Part of an armature that connects each armature winding to insulated copper bars on which the brushes ride. See *armature.*

compensated universal motor: Universal motor with extra windings added to the field poles. See *universal motor.*

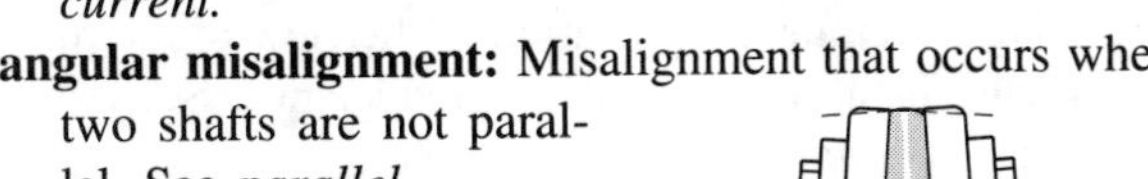

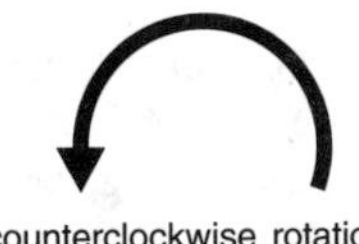

counterclockwise rotation

counterclockwise rotation: Direction of rotation is reverse when motor is viewed from front. End opposite the shaft is the front of the motor.

counterelectromotive force (counter EMF): Voltage generated by a motor that is opposite to the supply voltage. See *voltage.*

current: Amount of electron flow in a circuit. Current equals voltage divided by resistance ($I = E/R$). See *voltage* and *resistance.*

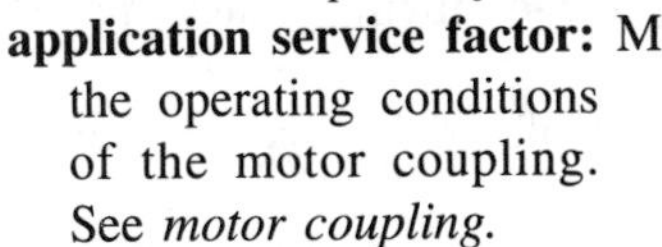

$$I = \frac{E}{R}$$

current

D

DC compound motor: Motor with a field connected in both series and shunt with the armature. See *DC motor, series,* and *resistance.*

DC motor: Motor that uses direct current connected to the field and armature to produce rotation. See *direct current, field,* and *armature.*

DC permanent-magnet motor: Motor that uses magnets, not the coils of wire, for the field winding. See *DC motor.*

DC series motor: Motor with the field connected in series with the armature. See *DC motor, series,* and *armature.*

DC shunt motor: Motor with the field connected in shunt (parallel) with the armature. See *DC motor* and *armature.*

dielectric absorption test: Test that checks the absorption characteristics of humid or contaminated insulation.

dielectric material: Medium in which an electric field is maintained with little or no outside energy supply.

direct current (DC): Current that flows in one direction only. See *current.*

dual-voltage motor: Motor that operates at more than one voltage level. See *voltage.*

E

eddy current: Unwanted current induced in the metal field structure of the motor due to the rate of change in the induced magnetic flux. See *current.*

electrolyte: Conducting medium in which the current flow occurs by ion migration.

environmental conditions: Conditions that surround a motor.

F

field: Stationary windings, or magnets, of a DC motor. See *DC motor.*

frequency: Number of complete electric cycles per second.

full-load current (FLC): Current level required to produce full-load torque on the motor shaft at rated speed. See *full-load torque.*

full-load torque: Torque required to produce the rated power at full speed of the motor. See *torque.*

G

grounded circuit: Circuit in which current leaves its normal path and travels to the frame of the motor. See *current.*

H

horsepower (HP): Unit of power equal to 746 W, or 33,000 lb-ft per minute (550 lb-ft per second).

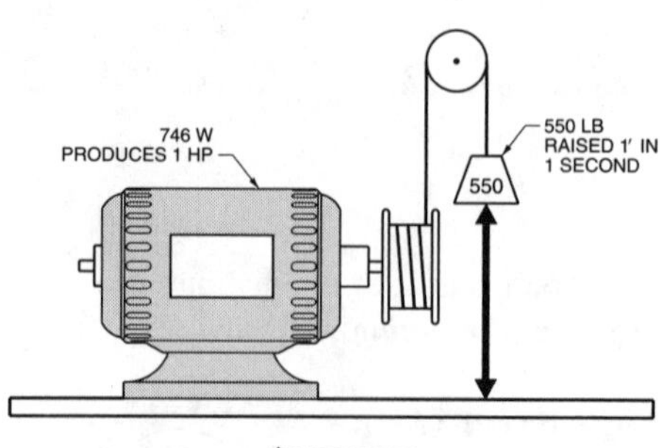

horsepower

hot power line (ungrounded power line): Any power line that is not grounded.

hysteresis: Power loss due to molecular friction because of the inability of individual molecules to instantly change their direction when current changes direction. See *current.*

I

induction motor: Motor that has no physical, electrical connection to the rotor. See *rotor.*

inductive reactance: Opposition to the flow of alternating current in a circuit due to inductance. See *alternating current.*

inrush current: High current drawn by a motor during its acceleration period. See *current.*

insulation spot test: Test that checks motor insulation over the life of the motor.

insulation step voltage test: Test that creates electrical stress on internal insulation cracks to reveal aging or damage not found during other motor insulation tests.

interpoles: Auxiliary poles placed between the main field poles of the motor.

inverse change: Change in which one factor increases at the same rate that the other factor decreases.

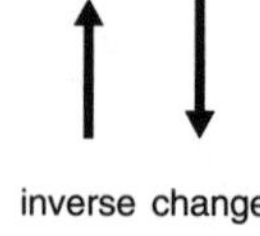
inverse change

L

lagging power factor: Circuit current lagging behind voltage by some angle between 0° and 90°. See *current* and *voltage.*

leading power factor: Circuit current leading voltage by some angle between 0° and 90°. See *current* and *voltage.*

line frequency: Number of cycles of supplied voltage per second. See *voltage.*

locked in step: Lack of rotation when the stator's field and the rotor's field are parallel to one another. See *stator, field, rotor,* and *parallel.*

locked rotor current (LRC): Highest level of inrush current that occurs the moment the motor is turned ON. See *inrush current.*

locked rotor torque: Torque a motor produces when the rotor is stationary and full power is applied to the motor. See *torque.*

M

megohmmeter: Ohmmeter capable of measuring very high resistances by using high voltages. See *resistance* and *voltage.*

motor coupling: Device that connects the motor shaft to the equipment the motor is driving.

motor damage: Damage that occurs to a properly manufactured motor.

motor defect: Imperfection created during the manufacture of the motor that impairs its use.

motor efficiency: Measure of the effectiveness with which a motor converts electrical energy to mechanical energy.

motor FLC: Current level required to produce full-load torque on the motor shaft at rated speed. See *full-load current* and *full-load torque.*

motor service factor: Safety margin for motor overloads. See *overload.*

N

noncompensated universal motor: Universal motor without extra windings added to the field poles. See *universal motor.*

O

open circuit: Circuit that no longer provides a path for current to flow. See *current.*

open motor enclosure: Motor enclosure with openings to allow passage of air to cool the windings.

overcurrent: Any current over the normal current level. See *current.*

over cycling: Process of turning a motor ON and OFF repeatedly.

overload: 1. Condition that occurs when the load connected to the motor exceeds the full-load torque rating of the motor. See *full-load torque.* **2.** Application of too much load to a motor.

P

parallel: Side-by-side connection of components that provides more than one path for current to flow. See *current.*

parallel misalignment: Misalignment that occurs when two shafts are parallel but not on the same line. See *parallel.*

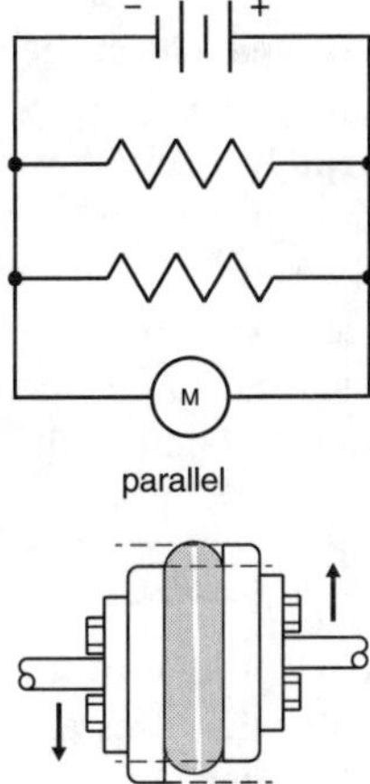

parallel

parallel misalignment

permissible temperature rise: Difference between ambient temperature and motor's listed maximum ambient temperature. See *ambient temperature.*

phase unbalance: Unbalance that occurs when lines are out-of-phase.

pigtail: Extended, flexible connection.

polarity: Particular state of an object, either positive or negative, which refers to the two electrical poles, north and south.

power factor: Ratio of the power used by a motor to the power not used.

proportional change: Change in which factors increase or decrease at the same rate.

pull-up torque (accelerating torque): Torque required to bring a load up to the correct speed. See *torque.*

pure DC power: Power obtained from a battery or DC generator.

R

rectifier: Component that converts AC to DC by allowing the current to move in only one direction. See *alternating current* and *direct current.*

repulsion motor: Motor with the rotor connected to the power supply through brushes that ride on a commutator. See *rotor* and *commutator.*

resistance: Opposition to electron flow in a circuit. Resistance equals current times volts ($R = I \times E$). See *current* and *voltage.*

$$R = I \times E$$

resistance

rotor: Rotating part of an AC motor. See *AC motor.*

S

SCR: Three-terminal semiconductor thyristor that is normally an open circuit until a signal applied to the gate switches it to the conducting state in one direction. See *thyristor.*

self-excited shunt field: Shunt field connected to the same power supply as the armature. See *armature.*

separately excited shunt field: Shunt field connected to a different power supply than the armature. See *armature.*

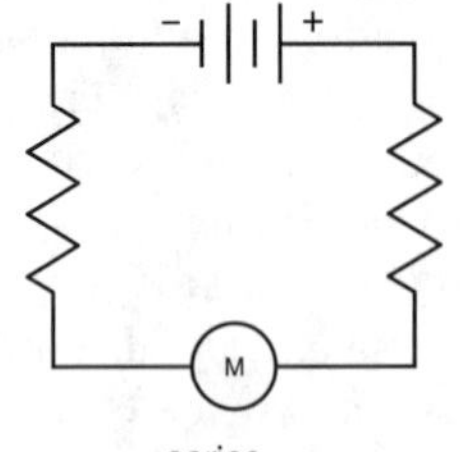

series

series: End-to-end connection of components that provides only one path for current to flow. See *current.*

shaded-pole motor: AC motor that uses a shaded stator pole for starting. See *AC motor* and *stator.*

short circuit: Circuit in which current takes a shortcut around the normal path of current flow. See *current.*

single-phase motor: AC motor that operates on 1ϕ electricity. See *AC motor.*

single-phase power: One of the three alternating currents in a circuit. See *alternating current.*

single phasing: Operation of a motor designed to operate on three phases operating on only two phases because one phase is lost. See *three-phase motor.*

single-voltage motor: Motor that operates at only one voltage level. See *voltage.*

slip: Difference between the synchronous speed and actual speed of a motor. See *synchronous speed.*

split-phase motor: AC motor that can run on one or more phases. See *AC motor.*

starting torque: Torque required to start a motor. See *torque.*

stator: Stationary part of an AC motor to which the power lines are directly connected. See *AC motor.*

stepping motor: Motor that divides shaft rotation into discrete distances (steps).

surge voltage: Any higher-than-normal voltage that temporarily exists on one or more of the power lines. See *voltage.*

synchronous speed: Theoretical speed of a motor based on the motor's number of poles and the line frequency.

T

temperature rise: Difference between the winding temperature of a running motor and the ambient temperature. See *ambient temperature.*

thermal overloads: Heat sensing devices that provide a means of monitoring the current drawn by a motor.

thermal switch: Switch that operates its contacts when a preset temperature is reached.

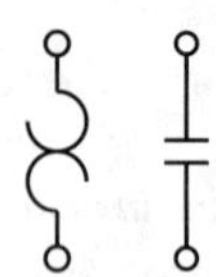
thermal switch

three-phase motor: AC motor that operates on 3ϕ electricity. See *AC motor.*

three-phase power: Combination of three alternating currents in a circuit with their voltages displaced 120 electrical degrees or one-third of a cycle. See *alternating current.*

thyristor: Solid-state switching device that switches current ON by a quick pulse of control current.

torque: Force that produces rotation in a motor.

totally enclosed motor enclosure: Motor enclosure that prevents air entering the enclosure.

triac: Three-terminal thyristor that is triggered into conduction in either direction by a small current to its gate. See *thyristor.*

true LRC: Locked rotor current of a motor with the power factor and efficiency considered. See *locked rotor current.*

U

universal motor: Motor that can be operated on either DC or 1ϕ, AC.

V

voltage: Amount of electrical pressure in a circuit. Voltage equals current times resistance ($E = I \times R$). See *current* and *resistance.*

$$E = I \times R$$

voltage

voltage unbalance: Unbalance that occurs when the voltages at the motor terminals are not equal. See *voltage.*

INDEX